MATHPOWER 9

ONTARIO EDITION

MATHPOWER™ 9

ONTARIO EDITION

MATHPOWER™ 9, *Ontario Edition*, Authors

George Knill, B.Sc., M.S.Ed.
Hamilton, Ontario

Rene Baxter, B.A., B.Ed., M.Ed.
Saskatoon, Saskatchewan

Dino Dottori, B.Sc., M.S.Ed.
North Bay, Ontario

George Fawcett, B.A.
Hamilton, Ontario

Mary Lou Forest, B.Ed.
Edmonton, Alberta

Michael Hamilton, B.Sc., M.Sc.
St. Catharines, Ontario

Stan Pasko, B.A., B.Ed., M.Ed., Ph.D.
Callander, Ontario

Harry Traini, B.Sc.
Hamilton, Ontario

Michael Webb, B.Sc., M.Sc., Ph.D.
Toronto, Ontario

MATHPOWER™ 9, *Ontario Edition*, Technology Consultant

Fred Ferneyhough
Brampton, Ontario

MATHPOWER™ 9, *Ontario Edition*, Reviewers

Patricia Angel
Etobicoke, Ontario

Shirley Dalrymple
Newmarket, Ontario

Gerry Doersken
Toronto, Ontario

Fred Ferneyhough
Brampton, Ontario

Mary Howe
London, Ontario

Louis Lim
Belleville, Ontario

Dean Murray
Milton, Ontario

Elizabeth Pattison
Niagara Falls, Ontario

Jamie Pyper
London, Ontario

Jim Sparks
Bradford, Ontario

McGraw-Hill Ryerson

Toronto Montréal New York Burr Ridge Bangkok Bogotá Caracas
Lisbon London Madrid Mexico City Milan New Delhi
Seoul Singapore Sydney Taipei

McGraw-Hill
Ryerson Limited
A Subsidiary of The **McGraw-Hill** Companies

MATHPOWER™ 9
Ontario Edition

ISBN 0-07-560796-4

http://www.mcgrawhill.ca

1 2 3 4 5 6 7 8 9 0 TRI 99

Printed and bound in Canada

Care has been taken to trace ownership of copyright material contained in this text. The publishers will gladly take any information that will enable them to rectify any reference or credit in subsequent printings.

Claris and ClarisWorks are registered trademarks of Claris Corporation.
Microsoft® is a registered trademark of Microsoft Corporation.
Corel® Paradox® are registered trademarks of Corel Corporation and Corel Corporation Limited.
CBL™ and CBR™ are trademarks of Texas Instruments Incorporated.

Canadian Cataloguing in Publication Data

Main entry under title:

Mathpower 9

Ontario ed.
Includes index.
ISBN 0-07-560796-4

1. Mathematics. 2. Mathematics – Problems, exercises, etc.
I. Knill, George, date. II. Title: Mathpower nine.

QA107.M37642 1999   510   C99-931122-0

PUBLISHER: Diane Wyman
EDITORIAL CONSULTING: Michael J. Webb Consulting Inc.
ASSOCIATE EDITORS: Jean Ford, Sheila Bassett, Mary Agnes Challoner, Maggie Cheverie, Janice Nixon
SENIOR SUPERVISING EDITOR: Carol Altilia
PERMISSIONS EDITOR: Jacqueline Donovan
SENIOR PRODUCTION COORDINATOR: Yolanda Pigden
ART DIRECTION: Wycliffe Smith Design Inc.
COVER DESIGN: Dianna Little
INTERIOR DESIGN: Wycliffe Smith Design Inc.
ELECTRONIC PAGE MAKE-UP: Tom Dart/First Folio Resource Group, Inc.
COVER ILLUSTRATIONS: Citrus Media
COVER IMAGE: ©Chris Amarol/Nonstock/PNI; ©Roy Bishop/Stock, Boston/PNI

CONTENTS

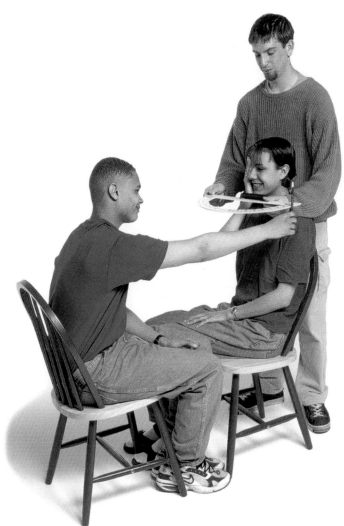

CHAPTER TOUR

CHAPTER OPENER

MODELLING MATH

The chapter opening pages pose a real-world problem that can be investigated using a mathematical model. Some examples of mathematical models are graphs, diagrams, formulas, equations, computer models, or actual physical models. The lessons in the chapter will prepare you to solve the real-world problem in the Modelling Math section, which is the last numbered section in each chapter.

GETTING STARTED

A Getting Started section begins each chapter. This section reviews the mathematics that you will need to use in the chapter.

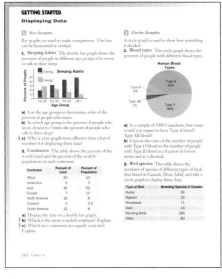

LOGOS

Four logos are used throughout the textbook to indicate special kinds of problems or opportunities for research.

✏ When you see this logo, you will be asked to demonstrate an understanding of what you have learned by communicating it in a meaningful way.

🧩 This logo signals that you will need to think critically when you answer a question.

🤝 This logo indicates an opportunity to work with a classmate or in a larger group to solve a problem.

🛰 For a problem with this logo, you will need to use your research skills to find information from the Internet, a print data bank, or some other source.

NUMBERED SECTIONS

MODELLING MATH

In this section you will apply what you have learned in the chapter. You will use this knowledge, and a mathematical model, to investigate and solve the real-world problem posed in the opening pages of the chapter.

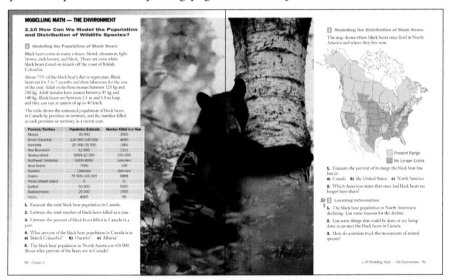

PROBLEM SOLVING: STRATEGIES

In these sections, found in the first four chapters, you will use 12 problem solving strategies. The questions allow you to practise your new skills immediately. See pages xviii–xix for a more complete description of how problem solving is integrated throughout the textbook.

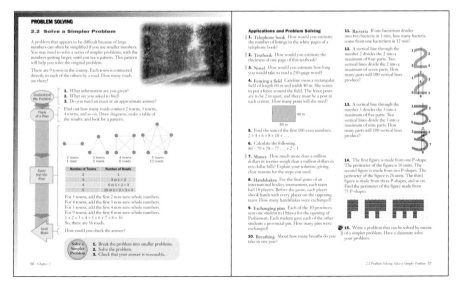

CONSISTENT LESSON STRATEGY

Each core section of *MATHPOWER*™ 9, *Ontario Edition*, provides you with an opportunity to learn mathematics in a variety of ways. You will use the process of inquiry, where you will develop methods for exploring new problems or procedures.

Explore/Inquire

An important part of learning mathematics is to discover new concepts for yourself. Each section begins with an exploration in a rich problem solving situation. Many of these situations provide you with the opportunity to explore through hands-on experiences. The exploration is followed by a set of inquire questions. The explorations and inquire questions allow you to construct your own learning. The explorations will also show you how mathematics is applied to the real world.

Examples

The examples show you how to use what you have learned. They provide model solutions to problems.

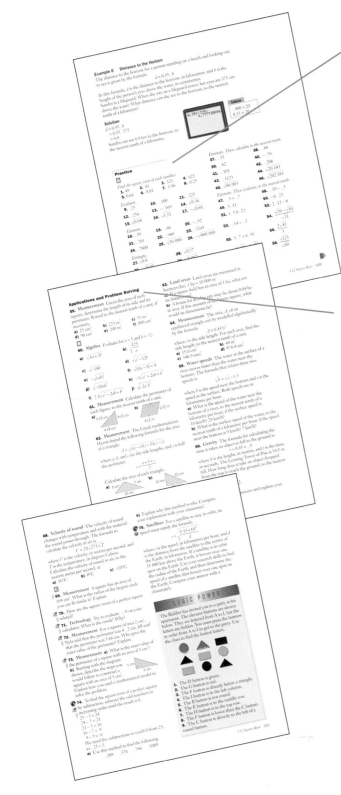

Practice

It is important that you master essential mathematics skills. For this reason, the examples are followed by practice questions. By completing these questions, you practise what you have learned so that you can stabilize your learning.

Applications and Problem Solving

Mathematics is powerful when it is applied. The questions in this section allow you to use what you have learned to solve problems, and to apply and extend what you have learned. Some problems provide the opportunity for you to work with classmates, to describe the method you used to solve the problem, and to communicate your findings. The descriptors on many of the problems show connections to other disciplines, to other topics in mathematics, and to people's daily experiences.

The questions in the Practice and Applications and Problem Solving are separated into A, B, and C sections. The questions in the A and B sections can all be completed using what you have learned in the lesson and what is modelled in the Examples. Section C provides challenging and thought-provoking questions.

SPECIAL FEATURES

INVESTIGATING MATH

The explorations in the Investigating Math sections will actively involve you in learning mathematics, either individually or with your classmates.

TECHNOLOGY

These sections allow you to explore the use of graphing and scientific calculators, scientific probes, geometry software, the Internet, and graphics software. See pages xx–xxi for a more complete description of how Technology is integrated throughout the book.

COMPUTER DATA BANK

The Computer Data Bank sections are to be used in conjunction with the *MATHPOWER*™ 9, *Ontario Edition*, *Computer Data Bank*. In these sections, you will explore the power of a computer database program in solving problems and will learn more about data analysis. The explorations in these sections use ClarisWorks 4.0 and 5.0, Corel Paradox 8, Microsoft Works 4.0 and Microsoft Access 97 for Windows 95, and ClarisWorks 4.0 and 5.0 for Macintosh OS 7.0.

MATH STANDARDS

There are 10 Math Standard pages before Chapter 1. By working through these pages, you will explore the mathematical concepts that citizens of the twenty-first century will need to understand.

CAREER CONNECTIONS

The explorations on the Career Connection pages will provide you with some applications of mathematics to the world of work.

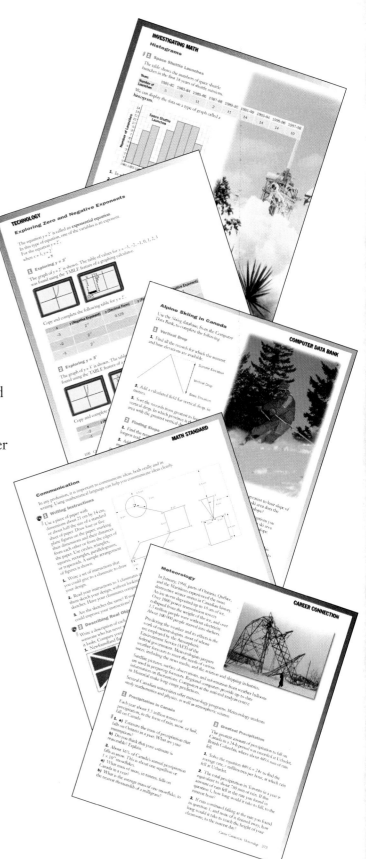

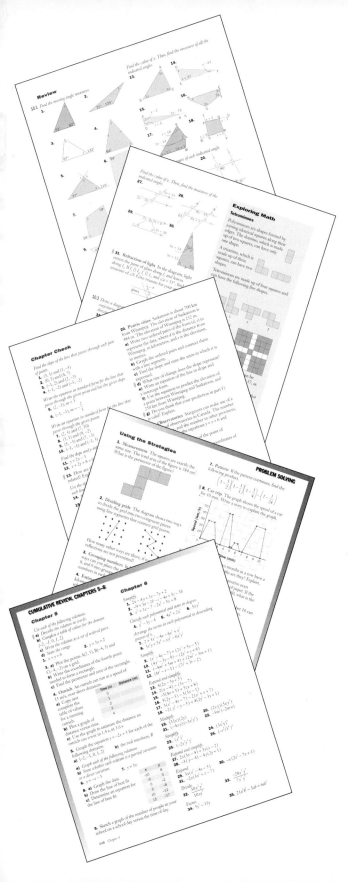

END-OF-CHAPTER FEATURES

REVIEW

The Review section allows you to review your progress. The questions in each Review are keyed to section numbers in the chapter, so you can identify any sections that require further study.

EXPLORING MATH

At the end of the Review section in each chapter, the Exploring Math column contains a Rich Learning Task.

CHAPTER CHECK

At the end of the chapter, the Chapter Check allows you to test your progress.

PROBLEM SOLVING: USING THE STRATEGIES

Each of these sections includes a variety of problems that can be solved using different strategies. See pages xviii–xix for a more complete description of how problem solving is integrated throughout the textbook.

CUMULATIVE REVIEW

Chapter 4, Chapter 8, and Chapter 10 end with cumulative reviews. The cumulative review at the end of Chapter 4 covers the work you did in Chapters 1–4. The cumulative review at the end of Chapter 8 covers Chapters 5–8. The cumulative review at the end of Chapter 10 covers Chapters 9–10, and the final cumulative review covers Chapters 1–10.

END-OF-TEXTBOOK FEATURES

ANSWERS

Answers are found on pages 566–607.

GLOSSARY

The illustrated glossary, on pages 608–619, explains mathematical terms.

INDEXES

The book includes three indexes — an applications index, a technology index, and a general index, on pages 620–642.

In whatever career you choose, and in other parts of your daily life, you will be required to solve problems. An important goal of mathematics education is to help you become a good problem solver.

George Polya was one of the world's best teachers of problem solving. The problem solving model he developed has been adapted for use in this book. The model is a guide. It will help you decide what to do when you "don't know what to do."

The problem solving model has the following four steps.

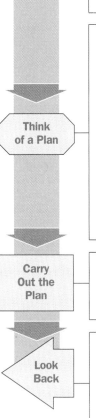

Understand the Problem

Read the problem and ask yourself these questions.
• What am I asked to find?
• Do I need an exact or approximate answer?
• What information am I given?
• What are the conditions or requirements?
• Is enough information given?
• Is there too much information?
• Have I solved a similar problem?

Think of a Plan

The main challenge in solving a problem is to devise a plan, or an outline of how to proceed. Organize the information and plan how to use it by deciding on a problem solving strategy. The following list of strategies, some of which you have used in previous grades, may help.

• Act out the problem.
• Look for a pattern.
• Work backward.
• Use a formula.
• Use logic.
• Draw and read graphs.
• Make an assumption.
• Guess and check.

• Use manipulatives.
• Solve a simpler problem.
• Use a diagram or flowchart.
• Sequence the operations.
• Use a data bank.
• Change your point of view.
• Use a table or spreadsheet.
• Identify extra information.

Carry Out the Plan

Estimate the answer to the problem. Choose the calculation method you will use to solve the problem. Then, carry out your plan, using paper and pencil, a calculator, a computer, or manipulatives. After solving the problem, write a final statement that gives the solution.

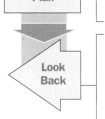

Look Back

Check your calculations in each step of the solution. Then, ask yourself these questions:
• Have I solved the problem I was asked to solve?
• How can I judge that the answer is reasonable?
• Does the answer agree with my estimate?
• Is there another way to solve the problem?

Opportunities for you to develop your problem solving skills appear throughout this textbook.

In the first four chapters, there are 12 numbered problem solving sections. Each section focusses on one strategy. The section provides an example of how the strategy can be used and includes problems that can be solved using the strategy.

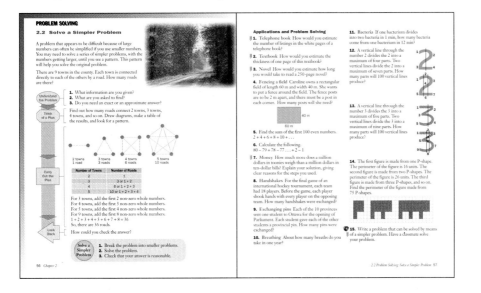

At the end of each chapter, you will find a section headed Problem Solving: Using the Strategies. Each of these sections includes a variety of problems that can be solved using different strategies.

Every numbered section of the book includes the subheading Applications and Problem Solving. The problems under this subheading are related to that section and provide you with many opportunities to apply problem solving strategies.

Many numbered sections include Power Problems, which have been grouped into four types — Logic Power, Pattern Power, Number Power, and Word Power. These problems are challenging and fun.

Rich Learning Tasks can be found in the Applications and Problem Solving questions. They are also found in the Using the Strategies pages, the Exploring Math column, Computer Data Bank pages, and Career Connection pages.

As described on pages xvi–xvii, many special features in the book involve explorations. These features — including Math Standard, Technology, Investigating Math, Modelling Math, Computer Data Bank, and Career Connection sections — are filled with opportunities for you to refine your problem solving skills.

TECHNOLOGY

Technology can help you learn and do mathematics and improve your problem solving skills. The ability to use technology effectively is a skill that will help you be successful in today's high-technology society and workplace.

GRAPHING CALCULATOR

The graphing calculator is a powerful tool that is integrated into regular sections, where appropriate. Graphing calculator investigations can also be found in some Technology sections. There are many graphing calculator displays in the texbook. Most were generated using the TI-83, but the TI-92 was used for algebraic displays.

GEOMETRY SOFTWARE

Dynamic geometry software allows you to construct, visualize, and change the characteristics of a geometric figure quickly. This feature allows you to analyze the many possibilities of a geometric problem and make a conjecture about the solution to the problem. Chapter 10, Geometry, includes investigations that provide the opportunity to explore and discover geometric relationships, using dynamic geometry software.

COMPUTER DATA BANK

In the Computer Data Bank sections, you will use the power of the computer and a database program to process information and solve a variety of problems.

There are six Computer Data Bank sections. They appear in Chapters 1, 3, 4, 5, 7, and 8. In chapter 1, the section titled Using the Databases, will introduce you to databases and how they are used. The databases in Chapters 3, 4, 5, 7, and 8 are titled:
Box Office Hits
Nations of the World
Summer Olympics
Healthy Eating
Alpine Skiing in Canada

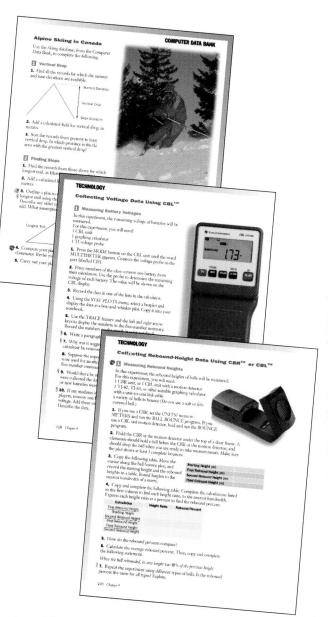

SCIENTIFIC PROBES

In the Statistics chapter you will have the opportunity to analyze data that you collect using scientific probes.

The activities use the Texas Instruments TI-82 or TI-83 graphing calculator with the Texas Instruments Calcualtor-Based Laboratory™ (CBL™) or the Calculaotr-Based Ranger™ (CBR™) Systems. The CBL™ can collect data such as motion, force, sound, light, voltage, and temperature. The CBR™ collects motion data only. Data are retrieved and analyzed on the graphing calculator.

SPREADSHEETS

Spreadsheet investigations can be found in Technology sections. You are also encouraged to use spreadsheets to organize and analyze data.

SCIENTIFIC CALCULATORS

The use of scientific calculators is shown throughout the course. Remember to check the result shown on the calculator by estimating.

THE INTERNET

There are many opportunities throughout the course to gather data and solve problems using the Internet.

MATH STANDARD

Number and Operation

Mathematics is based on number operations and how numbers relate to each other.

1 Numbers of Possibilities

1. If you follow the arrows, how many different paths spell COUGAR?

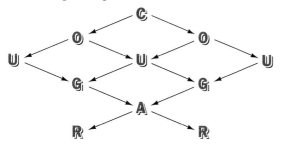

2. There are 2 roads from Hart to Adams. There are 4 roads from Adams to Young. How many different routes are there from Hart to Young?

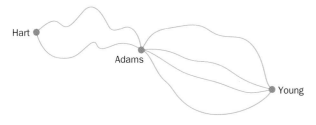

3. Four people, Lisa, Ben, Ona, and Dino, are going on a trip in a car. The car will seat 2 in the front and 2 in the back. Only Lisa and Dino can drive. In how many different ways can the 4 people sit in the car?

4. How many different, even, 4-digit house numbers can you make with the digits 2, 3, 4, and 5, if you can use each digit more than once?

2 Working With Numbers

1. One way to find the sum of the numbers from 1 to 10 is to use pairs of numbers. There are five pairs of numbers that add to 11. Since $11 \times 5 = 55$, the sum of the numbers is 55.

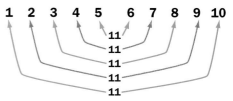

Use this method to find the sum of
a) the whole numbers from 1 to 200
b) the whole numbers from 1 to 1000
c) the whole numbers from 1 to 1 000 000
d) the first twenty odd numbers

3 Sequences

Copy each sequence and predict the next 3 terms.
1. 2, 6, 10, 14, ■, ■, ■
2. 3, 7, 15, 31, ■, ■, ■
3. 486, 162, 54, 18, ■, ■, ■
4. 3, 4, 7, 11, 18, ■, ■, ■

Patterns, Functions, and Algebra

Algebra is the language of mathematics.
Patterns can often be modelled using algebra.

1 Patterns in Polygons

1. a) Draw the next figure in the sequence.

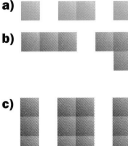

| 1 | 2 | 3 |

b) Copy and complete the table for the sequence.

Figure	Perimeter
1	4
2	8
3	12
4	
5	

c) Describe the pattern in words.
d) Write an expression for finding the perimeter from the figure number, n.
e) Use the expression from part d) to find the perimeter of the 20th figure; the 55th figure.

2. Repeat question 1 for these sequences.

a)

b)

c)

2 Solving Equations

Solve.

1. $x + 4 = 12$ **2.** $x - 5 = 7$

3. $2x = 16$ **4.** $\dfrac{x}{3} = 2$

5. $x + 6 = 11$ **6.** $x - 7 = 2$

7. $4x = 12$ **8.** $\dfrac{x}{2} = 1$

3 Finding Values

1. $s + u = 15$
$r + s + t = 15$
If $r = 6$ and $t = 4$, find u.

2. $y + z = 5$
$w + x = 7$
$x + y = 6$
If $w = 3$, find z.

3. $a = b$
$x = a + b + c + d$
$c = d$
If $x = 10$ and $b = 2$, find d.

4. $w = y$
$x = w + z$
$z = y + m$
If $w = 3$ and $x = 10$, find m.

5. $y + w = u$
$x = y - z$
If $x = 8$, $z = 3$, and $u = 11$, find w.

4 Patterns in Tables

Copy each table. Describe the rule that lets you find y if you know x, or find x if you know y. Use the rule to complete each table.

1.

x	y
9	1
15	7
22	
8.1	
	11
	3.3

2.

x	y
8	4
36	18
40	
6.4	
	8.1
	9.7

3.

x	y
3	17
9	11
13	7
4	
18	
	6.2
	15.5

4.

x	y
1	3
5	11
9	19
6	
12	
2.5	
	9

MATH STANDARD

Geometry and Spatial Sense

Geometry is the study of shapes and their properties. Geometry is found in science, in recreation, and in practical tasks, such as painting a room or constructing a building.

1 Cubes

1. The box is in the shape of a cube and has no top. Sixty-four small, identical cubes fill the box completely. 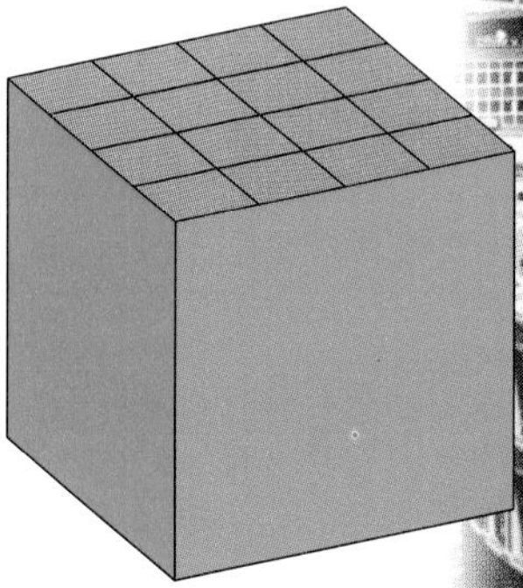
a) How many small cubes touch the bottom of the box?
b) How many small cubes touch the sides of the box?
c) How many small cubes do not touch the sides or the bottom of the box, and are not visible from above the box?

2. Compare the problem solving strategies you used in question 1, parts b) and c), with your classmates' strategies.

2 A Geometric Spiral

1. Mark a 16-by-16 square on a grid, and draw four 4-by-4 squares on the grid, as shown.

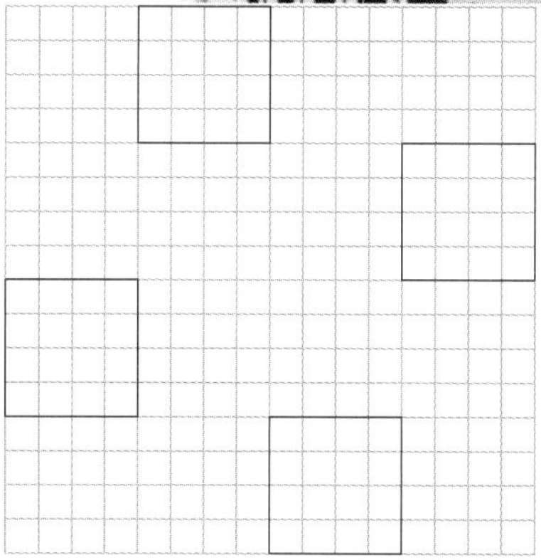

Make spirals by adding isosceles right triangles to each square, with the hypotenuse as a side of the square.

Continue by adding squares to the sides of the triangles, triangles to the sides of the squares, and so on.

The diagram shows one spiral and the start of the other three. Complete all the spirals in your own drawing.

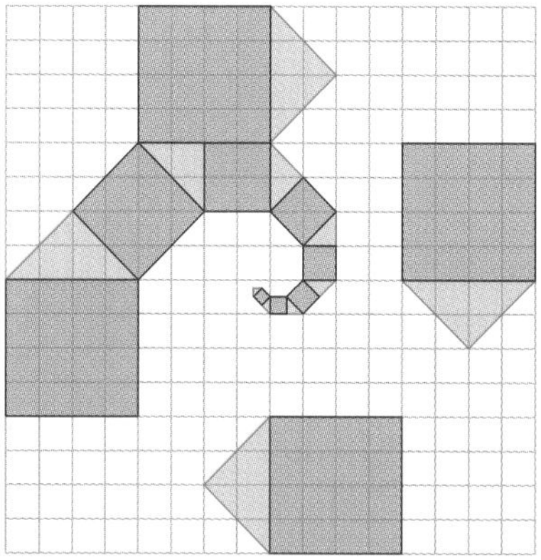

2. Colour the figures in the spirals to make a pleasing design.

Measurement

Measurement is the process of using numbers to describe such properties as mass, speed, and dimensions. Measurements are involved in many applications of mathematics, in such fields as transportation and weather forecasting.

1 Flying Times

The table shows the approximate average flying speeds for some aircraft.

Aircraft	Average Flying Speed (km/h)
B747-300	850
L-1011-200	800
MD-80	700
DC-9-50	600
DASH 8-100	500

1. Calculate the travelling time for each of the following flights. Allow an extra 15 min for each takeoff and 15 min for each landing.
a) 800 km from Halifax to Montréal on an L-1011-200
b) 2125 km from Toronto to St. John's on a B747-300
c) 300 km from Windsor to Toronto on a DASH 8-100

2. How many minutes would you save if you flew 700 km from Edmonton to Regina on an MD-80 instead of a DC-9-50?

3. The flying time for a direct flight from Vancouver to Montréal on a B747-300 can be as much as 45 min shorter than the return flight on the same aircraft. Explain why.

2 Blizzard Hours

The graph shows the average numbers of blizzard hours in a year for 15 cities in Canada.

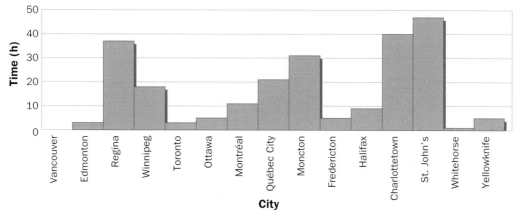

1. For which city is the number of blizzard hours about twice the number for Québec City?

2. Which city has about one fifth of the number of blizzard hours in St. John's?

3. Which city has about two thirds of the number of blizzard hours in Winnipeg?

4. For which two cities in the same province is the ratio of blizzard hours about 6:1?

5. Do you think that Vancouver has never had a blizzard? Explain.

MATH STANDARD

Data Analysis, Statistics, and Probability

1 Comparing Climates

Environment Canada has been collecting data on temperature and precipitation for many years. The bar graphs show the average temperature and amount of precipitation for each month of the year in several cities across Canada.

1. Which city has the greatest difference in average monthly temperatures? the least difference?

2. Which city has the greatest difference in average monthly precipitation? the least difference?

3. In which city might a golfer choose to live? Why?

4. In which city might a skier choose to live? Why?

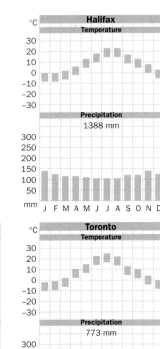

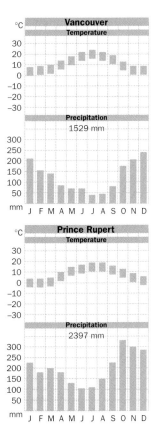

2 Selecting Marbles

Suppose there are 2 blue marbles, 3 red marbles, and 5 white marbles in a bag. You select 1 marble, look at the colour, and return it to the bag.

1. a) The probability of picking a red marble is $\frac{3}{10}$. Why?

b) What is the probability of picking a blue marble? a white marble?

2. What percent of the time should you pick a white marble?

3. If you selected a marble 100 times, how many times should you pick a white marble?

Problem Solving

In any career you pursue, you will need to solve problems. This book will help you to develop your problem solving skills.

1 Solving Problems

Solve each problem.

1. How many different bracelets can be made using 5 identical blue beads and 2 identical yellow beads?

2. The diagram shows how to shade 4 of the 9 squares to give just one line of symmetry. In how many other ways can you shade 4 of the 9 squares to give one line of symmetry?

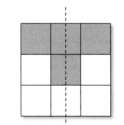

3. The diagram shows how to make 2 non-overlapping triangles with 4 straight lines. How many non-overlapping triangles can you make with 5 straight lines?

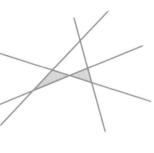

2 Describing Methods

Solve each problem. In each case, describe the method you used.

1. A basketball team is standing in a circle. The team members are evenly spaced and numbered in order, clockwise, from 1 up. Player number 5 is directly opposite player number 12. How many players are in the circle?

2. The number that represents the area of a square is twice the number that represents the sum of its sides. What is the side length of the square?

3. What is the smallest number of colours needed to paint a cube so that no two adjacent faces are painted the same colour?

MATH STANDARD

Reasoning and Proof

The ability to reason logically, to think your way through a problem, is a skill you can develop.

1 Number Expressions

For each card, use all the numbers only once. Use as many of the operations +, −, ×, ÷, and brackets ( ) as you wish. Write an expression with the value 24 for each card.

1.   **2.**   **3.**

2 Logic Problems

1. There are three books on the counter, a math book, a science book, and a geography book. The books are blue, green, and black. The books belong to Sari, Terri, and Dmitri. Using the following clues, copy and complete the tables to reason who owns which book.

- Sari's book is not about geography.
- Dmitri's book is not blue or green.
- The science book is not green.
- The math book is blue.

	Colour of Book		
	Blue	Green	Black
Sari			
Terri			
Dmitri			

	Colour of Book		
	Blue	Green	Black
Math			
Science			
Geography			

	Colour of Book	Subject of Book
Sari		
Terri		
Dmitri		

 **2.** Use the table to make up the clues to a problem that can be solved by reasoning.

Bicycles		
Jim	green	3-speed
Ali	blue	5-speed
Sue	red	10-speed

Communication

In any profession, it is important to communicate ideas, both orally and in writing. Using mathematical language can help you communicate ideas clearly.

 1 **Writing Instructions**

 Use a piece of paper with dimensions about 21 cm by 14 cm, or about half the size of a standard sheet of paper. Draw four or five plane figures on the paper, marking their dimensions and their distances from each other or from the edges of the paper. Use circles, triangles, squares, rectangles, parallelograms, or trapezoids. A sample arrangement of figures is shown.

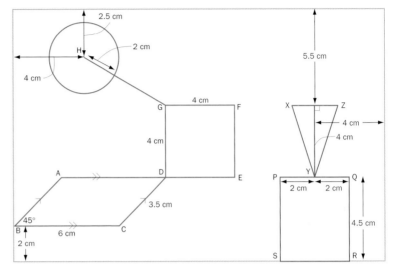

1. Write a set of instructions that you could give to a classmate to draw your design.

2. Read your instructions to 3 classmates and have each of them sketch your design, without looking at each other's sketches. Have your classmates compare their sketches with yours.

3. Are the sketches the same? If not, are there ways you could improve your instructions?

2 **Describing Real Objects**

Write a description of each of the following objects, so that someone who has never seen it will have a clear idea of how it looks. Compare your descriptions with a classmate's.

1. Newfoundland flag

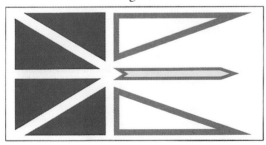

2. Canada Post mailbox

Connections

There are connections between mathematics and other disciplines, including the arts, the sciences, business, and many others.

 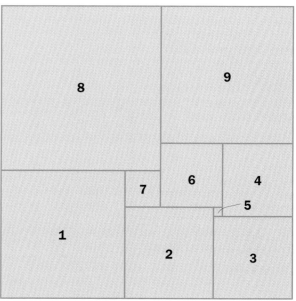

1 Mathematics and Art

The above painting was done by Mary Russel. There are 9 different small squares contained inside the large figure.

1. In the schematic diagram, the squares have been numbered from 1 to 9. If the area of square 2 is 100 square units, and the area of square 3 is 81 square units, find the area of each of the other 7 squares.

2. Which two squares have the same total area as squares 2 and 9?

3. Identify 3 pairs of squares in which the area of the larger square is 4 times the area of the smaller square.

4. Which 4 squares have a total area that equals half the area of square 8?

5. Is the large figure a square? Explain.

2 Mathematics and the Media

1. People who broadcast music at radio stations use mathematics every day. List some of the ways in which mathematics is used at a radio station.

2. List some of the ways in which mathematics is used in publishing a newspaper or magazine.

3 Mathematics and Sports

1. Select a sport and list 5 ways in which mathematics is used in this sport.

2. Describe how the sport would be different if it did not include any mathematics.

Representation

Representations, such as drawings, charts, and graphs, are some of the ways of modelling ideas in mathematics.

1 Using a Tree Diagram

The map shows a one-way road system connecting 5 towns. The arrows indicate the direction you must travel. The numbers give the approximate travel time, in minutes, between towns.

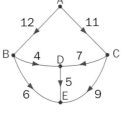

The tree diagram shows the possible routes you can take to get from A to E.
a) What is the travelling time for each route?
b) Which route takes the least time?
c) What is the minimum travelling time if you must go through C?

2 Drawing a Tree Diagram

The map shows a one-way road system and the approximate travel time, in minutes, between towns. The arrows indicate the direction you must travel.

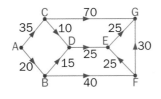

1. Draw a tree diagram to show the possible routes from A to G.

2. Which route takes the least time?

3. Which route takes the most time?

4. Which route takes the least time if you must go through F?

CHAPTER 1

Connecting Numbers and Variables

How Can We Model Distances in the Solar System?

stronomers define an astronomical unit (AU) as the average distance of the Earth from the sun. This distance is about 150 000 000 km.

1. Neptune is about 30 AU from the sun. How far is that in kilometres?

2. Jupiter is about 5.2 AU from the sun. How far is that in kilometres?

3. The circumference of the Earth at the Equator is about 40 000 km. How many times as great is 1 AU?

4. Explain why we do not use the astronomical unit to measure distances on Earth.

5. a) Why do astronomers not use the astronomical unit to measure distances to the stars?
b) What unit do astronomers use for these distances?

In Modelling Math — Astronomy on pages 42 and 43, mathematical models will be used to represent distances in the solar system.

Math Magic

1 The Stubborn Coin Trick

1. a) Place a coin on any red card. Move the coin horizontally, to the left or right, onto the nearest black card.
b) Move the coin vertically, up or down, onto the nearest red card.
c) Move the coin diagonally onto the nearest black card.
d) Move the coin down or to the right onto the nearest red card.

2. Try the trick a few times to find out how it works. Do you always end up on the same card?

3. Explain how the trick works. To do this, you might try working backward.

2 Repeat, Repeat, Repeat

1. Pick a number from 2 to 9. Multiply it by 41. Multiply your answer by 271. What is the result?

2. Pick another number from 2 to 9 and repeat the process. What is the result?

3. Explain how the trick works.

3 Lucky Number

1. a) Mark 20 lines in a row. Cross out any number of lines, up to 9.
b) Count the number of lines you have left. Find the sum of the two digits of this number.
c) Cross out a number of lines equal to the sum you found in part b).
d) Cross out two more lines. How many are left?

2. Repeat the process several times, but vary the number of lines you cross out in part a).

3. Explain how the trick works.

4 The Stubborn Card Trick

1. a) Pick a number greater than 4.
b) Place your finger on the card marked A. Then, use your finger to count your chosen number of steps along the card trail.
c) Count the same number of steps backward, but go around the circle instead of returning to A.

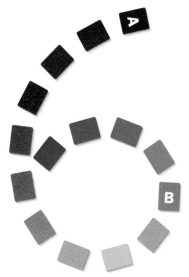

2. Repeat the process several times, starting with different numbers greater than 4. Where do you always land?

3. Explain how the trick works.

Warm Up

Integers

Add.
  1. $(+4) + (+5)$ 2. $(+3) + (-2)$
  3. $(-3) + (-3)$ 4. $(-1) + (+6)$
  5. $(-7) + (+2)$ 6. $(+3) + (-4)$
  7. $(-7) + (-2)$ 8. $(-5) + (+5)$

Simplify.
  9. $(+4) + (+3) + (+5)$
 10. $(+7) + (+6) + (-3)$
 11. $(-5) + (+4) + (+2)$
 12. $(-7) + (-3) + (+1)$
 13. $(-6) + (+8) + (-2)$
 14. $(-4) + (-3) + (-6)$

Subtract.
 15. $(+11) - (+6)$ 16. $(-9) - (-12)$
 17. $(-10) - (+5)$ 18. $(+14) - (+4)$
 19. $(+9) - (-11)$ 20. $(-14) - (-7)$
 21. $(-16) - (-14)$ 22. $(+18) - (-4)$

Simplify.
 23. $(+5) - (+2) + (+6)$
 24. $(+8) + (+4) - (-2)$
 25. $(-4) - (+1) - (+3)$
 26. $(-6) + (-4) - (+1)$
 27. $(-3) - (+9) + (-1)$
 28. $(-2) - (-3) - (-5)$

Multiply.
 29. $(+4)(+7)$ 30. $(-4)(+6)$
 31. $(-3)(-6)$ 32. $(+9)(-9)$

Simplify.
 33. $(-2)(-3)(+4)$ 34. $(+3)(+2)(-1)$
 35. $(+4)(-5)(+2)$ 36. $(-3)(-2)(-3)$
 37. $(+6)(-2)(-1)$ 38. $(+5)(+5)(+2)$
 39. $(0)(-3)(+4)$ 40. $(-4)(+4)(-2)$

Divide.
 41. $(+12) \div (+4)$ 42. $(-15) \div (+3)$
 43. $(-10) \div (-5)$ 44. $(+20) \div (-4)$

Mental Math

Operations

Calculate.
  1. $566 + 121$ 2. $545 + 232$
  3. $616 + 303$ 4. $876 + 123$
  5. $656 - 234$ 6. $285 - 164$
  7. $742 - 141$ 8. $567 - 456$
  9. 2002×4 10. 1010×6
 11. 3434×2 12. 1212×3
 13. $606 \div 3$ 14. $8080 \div 4$
 15. $8642 \div 2$ 16. $515 \div 5$

Multiplying by Multiples of 5

To multiply 38×5, first multiply 38 by 10.
$38 \times 10 = 380$
Then, divide by 2.

Estimate
$$40 \times 5 = 200$$

$380 \div 2 = 190$
So, $38 \times 5 = 190$.

Calculate.
  1. 26×5 2. 54×5 3. 73×5
  4. 102×5 5. 898×5 6. 435×5
  7. 5.2×5 8. 12.8×5 9. 36.4×5

To multiply 19×50, first multiply 19 by 100.
$19 \times 100 = 1900$
Then, divide by 2.

Estimate
$$20 \times 50 = 1000$$

$1900 \div 2 = 950$
So, $19 \times 50 = 950$.

Calculate.
 10. 56×50 11. 61×50 12. 134×50
 13. 256×50 14. 3.1×50 15. 10.2×50

 16. Using a similar method, multiplying 58 by 0.5 is easier than multiplying 58 by 5. Explain why.

Calculate.
 17. 88×0.5 18. 57×0.5 19. 132×0.5
 20. 450×0.5 21. 9.6×0.5 22. 14.4×0.5

 23. Explain why the rule for multiplying by 5 works.

1.1 Strategies for Estimation

Explore: Make a Comparison

The table shows the cost of souvenirs at a Beatles' music and souvenir store.

Item	Price ($)
Cavern poster	14.45
Beatles history book	37.95
Lennon glasses	13.75
T-shirt	28.25
Album cover	13.60
London Palladium picture	14.95

a) Estimate the total cost of a poster, book, and glasses by rounding each price to the nearest dollar.

b) Estimate the total cost of the three items by rounding each price to the nearest ten dollars.

c) Calculate the exact total cost of the three items.

Inquire

1. For the above estimates, what is the advantage of rounding

  a) to the nearest dollar?

  b) to the nearest ten dollars?

2. Estimate the total cost of an album cover, London Palladium picture, and T-shirt by rounding to

  a) the nearest dollar

  b) the nearest ten dollars

As well as rounding, there are other ways to estimate sums and differences.

Example 1   Clustering

Estimate $15.35 + $14.85 + $12.95 by clustering.

Solution

The prices cluster around $14, so a good estimate is $3 \times \$14$ or $42.

Compatible numbers are numbers that can be computed mentally.

Example 2 Using Compatible Numbers
Use compatible numbers to estimate $13.25 + $38.05 + $11.75.

Solution
$13.25 + $11.75 is about $13 + $12 or $25.
$25 + $38.05 is about $25 + $40 or $65.
The estimate is about $65.

Example 3 Using Front-End Estimation
Estimate $345 + 513 + 263 + 836$ by front-end estimation.

Solution
Add the front digits, in this case, the hundreds.
$300 + 500 + 200 + 800 = 1800$
Look for compatible numbers in the parts that are left.
$45 + 63 \doteq 100$ $\doteq$ means approximately equals.
$13 + 36 \doteq 50$
Adjust the estimate.
$1800 + 100 + 50 = 1950$
So, $345 + 513 + 263 + 836$ is about 1950.

Example 4 Bird Migration
The Arctic tern is the long-distance migratory champion of the animal world. It flies from the far north to winter along the shores of Antarctica. The trip is about 17 500 km long and takes about 16 weeks. Estimate how far the tern flies each week.

Solution
Divide to estimate the distance.

Method 1
Round both numbers to the highest place value.
$$\frac{17\ 500}{16} \doteq \frac{20\ 000}{20}$$
$$= 1000$$
The tern flies about 1000 km each week.

Method 2
Round 16 to the highest place value, 20.
Substitute for 17 500 to obtain compatible numbers.
$$\frac{17\ 500}{16} \doteq \frac{18\ 000}{20}$$
$$= 900$$
The tern flies about 900 km each week.

To estimate products and quotients with decimals less than 1, we substitute 1 or multiples of 0.1 or 0.5.

Example 5   Products and Quotients of Decimals
Estimate.
a) 0.85×5.6 **b)** $0.533 \div 10.2$ **c)** 0.261×3.1

Solution
a) $0.85 \times 5.6 \doteq 1 \times 6$ **b)** $0.533 \div 10.2 \doteq 0.5 \div 10$ **c)** $0.261 \times 3.1 \doteq 0.3 \times 3$
$\qquad\qquad = 6$ $\qquad\qquad\qquad = 0.05$ $\qquad\qquad\qquad = 0.9$

Practice

A

In questions 1–26, compare your estimated and calculated answers to check that your calculated answers are reasonable.

Estimate by rounding, and then calculate.
1. $346 + 221 + 147$
2. $678 - 431$
3. $\$34.79 + \$12.56 + \$29.89 + \$15.21$
4. $\$385.78 - \$115.60$

Estimate by clustering, and then calculate.
5. $56 + 44 + 61 + 51$
6. $\$18.45 + \$20.56 + \$22.99$
7. $\$387 + \$415 + \$390 + \$410$

Estimate by finding compatible numbers, and then calculate.
8. $13 + 38 + 61 + 48$
9. $\$23.56 + \$78.31 + \$101.45$
10. $\$6.35 + \$4.12 + \$58.23$
11. $\$124.55 - \$99.81$

Estimate by front-end estimation, and then calculate.
12. $623 + 555 + 201 + 777$
13. $\$4.56 + \$3.78 + \$2.56$
14. $\$23.70 + \$11.34 + \$23.80 + \$56.24$

Estimate, and then calculate.
15. 34.5×21.9 **16.** $\$23.87 \times 19$
17. $\$130 \div 12$ **18.** $\$650 \div 20$
19. $\$45.67 \times 12$ **20.** $\$5613.42 \div 52$
21. 59×0.86 **22.** 212×0.43
23. $334 \div 0.91$ **24.** $67 \div 0.52$
25. 139×1.678 **26.** $47.89 \div 2.22$

Applications and Problem Solving

In questions 27–41, estimate by the method of your choice, and then calculate the answer. Use your estimate to check that your calculated answer is reasonable.

27. Monthly earnings Last month, Carl earned $147.67 working part-time at a restaurant. Maya earned $217.89. What was the difference in their earnings?

28. Hourly pay Colleen worked for 12.5 h and was paid $191.25. How much did she earn per hour?

29. Online costs It costs $0.37/min to access a database through your computer. What is the cost if you are online for 17 min?

30. Long-distance call A long-distance telephone call costs $0.27/min. What is the cost for a 43-min call?

B

31. Shopping Chen bought three items for $2.45, $3.56, and $11.18. How much change did he get from a $20 bill?

32. Butterfly A monarch butterfly can fly 1000 km without stopping to feed.
a) How many hours does it take the monarch to fly this distance at 16 km/h?
b) How many hours would it take you to walk this distance?

33. Theme park Adult tickets to a theme park cost $48.50. Children's tickets cost $31.75. What is the cost for 3 adults and 2 children?

34. Bank account Copy and complete the following table to show Leolo's account balance on each date.

Date	Withdrawal	Deposit	Balance
April 27			$567.81
April 28	$23.85		
April 30		$85.00	
May 1	$123.45		
May 6	$67.60		
May 13		$160.00	

35. Shopping Samantha received $14.63 change from a $50 bill. Her cash register receipt showed the total of her purchases as $34.37. Samantha claimed that the sales clerk had made an error. Was Samantha right? If so, how great was the sales clerk's error?

36. Car rally During the car rally, Caroline averaged 78 km/h for 4.5 h. How far did she drive?

37. Keyboarding Carlos can keyboard 43 words/min. How many minutes will it take him to input his 7500-word essay?

38. Canadian islands The table shows the areas of the six largest islands in Canada. Find their total area.

Island	Area (km²)
Baffin	504 751
Victoria	217 290
Ellesmere	196 236
Newfoundland	108 860
Banks	70 028
Devon	55 247

39. Supersonic flight A Concorde jet cruises at a speed of 2300 km/h. At this speed, how long would it take to fly the following distances?
a) across Canada, a distance of 5514 km
b) to the moon, a distance of 384 365 km
c) to the sun when it is closest to the Earth, 147 000 000 km away

40. Blue whale A blue whale has a mass of about 138 000 kg. If the students in your school had an average mass of 58 kg, would their total mass be greater than a blue whale's?

C

41. Population research The **population density** of a country is the average number of people per square kilometre. Canada has an area of 9 976 000 km². Use your research skills to find the current population of Canada. Then, determine Canada's population density, to the nearest tenth.

42. Estimate the following. Explain why you chose your estimation method. Compare your method with your classmates'.
a) $149 \div 23$ **b)** 12.1×0.43
c) 27.5×0.83 **d)** $4869 \div 24$

43. Sports research Use your research skills to estimate the following. Then, compare your estimates with your classmates'.
a) the total number of fans who attended the last 10 Grey Cup games
b) the total number of fans who attended Toronto Blue Jays home games in the last 10 years

WORD POWER

In an anagram, the letters can be in any order except the right one. The word TEN has 5 anagrams.

NET   NTE   ETN   ENT   TNE

1. How many anagrams are there for

a) FOUR?   **b)** NINE?

2. Why are your answers different, even though *four* and *nine* both contain 4 letters?

INVESTIGATING MATH

Words to Symbols

1 Icebergs

The longest parade in the world runs from March to July. The "floats" have masses between 500 000 t and 10 000 000 t. They are up to 10 000 years old. The parade consists of hundreds of icebergs that pass Newfoundland's east coast.

The part of an iceberg above the water is called the tip. The height, t, of the tip is $\frac{1}{7}$ of the total height of an iceberg. So, an expression for the total height of an iceberg is $7t$. Write an expression in terms of t for the height of the part of an iceberg that is underwater.

2 Numbers

Match the words with the symbols.

1.	a number increased by five	$5n$
2.	a number decreased by one	$n + 3$
3.	a number divided by nine	$n - 1$
4.	two less than a number	$n + 5$
5.	three more than a number	$6 - n$
6.	five times a number	$n - 2$
7.	six decreased by a number	$2 + n$
8.	two increased by a number	$n \div 9$

If n represents a number, write an algebraic expression using numbers and symbols for each of the following statements.

9. three times a number
10. a number increased by one
11. a number decreased by five
12. the product of six and a number
13. a number divided by five
14. three more than twice a number
15. ten decreased by a number
16. seven divided by a number

In each case, let the number be x. Write an expression for each statement.

17. a number increased by four
18. seven times a number
19. a number multiplied by nine
20. three divided by a number
21. seven more than a number
22. half of a number
23. a number diminished by eight
24. the product of a number and two
25. Write 3 new statements. Have a classmate write an algebraic expression for each.

3 Tables

Copy and complete the tables.

1. The second number is 9 less than the first.

First Number	15	24	31	x	$3y$	$m + 10$
Second Number						

2. There are 4 times as many red cubes as blue cubes.

Number of Blue Cubes	11	23	40	x	$2d$
Number of Red Cubes					

3. The first number is 8 more than the second.

First Number	45	56		x		$3m$	$t + 11$	
Second Number			18		y			$y + 5$

4. Francine is 4 years younger than Terry.

Francine's Age		19		m		$4t$	
Terry's Age	16		x		$5y$		$3w + 8$

5. There are 6 times as many cars as motorcycles.

Number of Cars		72		y		
Number of Motorcycles	13		x		$4m$	$\frac{1}{2}n$

4 Rectangles

1. The length of a rectangle is 5 cm more than its width.
a) Which dimension is smaller?
b) Let the smaller dimension be x. Then, write the larger dimension in terms of x.
c) Draw and label a diagram of the rectangle.
d) Write an expression for the perimeter of the rectangle in terms of x.

2. The side length of a square is x metres. What is its perimeter?

3. a) Copy and complete the table for the dimensions of a rectangle. Its length is 3 m more than its width.

Width (m)	10	15	x	$10x$	$4x + 1$
Length (m)					

b) Write an expression for the perimeter of each rectangle. Compare your expressions with a classmate's.

4. Repeat question 3 for the following table. The length of the rectangle is now 7 m more than the width.

Width (m)	10		x		$3t$		$5z + 4$
Length (m)		24		y		$4n$	

1.2 Variables in Expressions

Explore: Use a Table

Authors of books are paid a set amount for every book sold. This amount is called a **royalty.** Sarah Barker wrote a book on sailboat racing. Copy and complete the table to show Sarah's royalties.

Number of Books Sold	10	20	30	100	352
Sarah's Royalties ($)	30	60			

Inquire

1. How much would Sarah make if the following numbers of books were sold?

a) 1   **b)** 1000   **c)** 5000   **d)** 20 000   **e)** n

2. If the letter n represents the number of books sold, n is called a **variable.** Why?

3. In your own words, define a variable.

Sarah's publisher pays expenses of 35¢/km when Sarah drives to bookstores to promote her book. We can use the letter d to represent the distance driven, in kilometres.

Sarah's expenses, in cents, can be expressed as $35d$. This is an example of an **algebraic expression**. In the expression $35d$, the multiplication symbol is understood, so $35d$ means $35 \times d$. The expression $35d$ represents many different amounts of money, since its value depends on the value of d.

When $d = 80$, $35d$ is 35×80 or 2800, which is $28.00.
When $d = 200$, $35d$ is 35×200 or 7000, which is $70.00.

Expressions such as $5t$, $x + 7$, and $2(l + w)$ are also algebraic expressions. The letters t, x, l, and w are variables.

Example   Racing Lessons

André gives sailboat racing lessons. The cost, in dollars, is given by the expression $30t + 25$, where t represents the time, in hours.
Calculate the cost of lessons that last

a) 7 h   **b)** 20.5 h

Solution

a) When $t = 7$,
$$30t + 25 = 30(7) + 25 \qquad \text{Multiply first.}$$
$$= 210 + 25$$
$$= 235$$
The lessons cost $235.

b) When $t = 20.5$,
$$30t + 25 = 30(20.5) + 25$$
$$= 615 + 25$$
$$= 640$$
The lessons cost $640.

Estimate

$30 \times 20 = 600$
$600 + 25 = 625$

Practice

A

Write an expression for each of the following.
1. the product of 7 and 11
2. the product of x and 3
3. the sum of 5 and 8
4. the sum of 9 and y
5. the product of x and y
6. 7 more than m
7. 8 less than y
8. the quotient y divided by x
9. 4 times t

10. Find the value of $4n$ when n has each value.
a) 2   **b)** 3   **c)** 4   **d)** 1
e) 0   **f)** 9   **g)** 10   **h)** 35

11. Find the value of $3t + 1$ when t has each value.
a) 2   **b)** 3   **c)** 0   **d)** 10
e) 3.5   **f)** 1.1   **g)** 6.2   **h)** 8.8

12. Find the value of $2x - 1$ when x has each value.
a) 2   **b)** 1   **c)** 5   **d)** 10
e) 1.5   **f)** 3.1   **g)** 8.2   **h)** 9.5

13. Evaluate for $c = 3$ and $d = 2$.
a) $c + d$ **b)** $3c + 4d$ **c)** $5d + 6c$
d) $3c + d + 7$ **e)** $6c - d$ **f)** $4cd + 8$
g) $2c + 4d$ **h)** $8d - 3c$ **i)** $7 - c - 2d$

14. Evaluate each expression for the given value of the variable.
a) $2m + 4, m = 5.3$
b) $6t - 7, t = 4.6$
c) $5s + 13, s = 9.1$
d) $25 - 2x, x = 3.5$

15. Evaluate for $r = 4.1$, $s = 3.2$, and $t = 5.6$.
a) $r + s + t$
b) $3r + 4s + 5t$
c) $4t - s + 5r$
d) $4st + 3rs + rt$
e) $5rst - 9$
f) $8.5 + 2rst$

Applications and Problem Solving

B

16. **Earnings** Sophia earns \$13/h installing swimming pools.
a) Write an expression for her earnings if she works n hours.
b) Use the expression to calculate her earnings if she works 41 h; 53.5 h.

17. **Graduation banquet** For a banquet, the manager of the Purple Onion restaurant charges \$300 for the room plus \$35/person.
a) Write an expression for the cost of a graduation banquet for n people.
b) Use the expression to find the cost of a graduation banquet for 250 people.

18. **Driving distances a)** Write an expression for the distance a car travels in t hours at a speed of s kilometres per hour.
b) Use the expression to calculate the distance travelled at 75 km/h for 3.5 h.

19. Let $2x$ represent an even number. Write an expression for each statement.
a) the next even number after $2x$
b) the next odd number after $2x$
c) the last even number before $2x$

20. **Van rental** When he moved to a new apartment, Jamal rented a van for \$60 for the day, plus \$0.40 per kilometre driven. He drove 38 km altogether. Calculate the cost of renting the van for the day.

C

21. For what whole-number values of the variable is the second expression greater than the first? Explain and justify your reasoning.
a) $4x, x^2$
b) $9n, n^3$

PROBLEM SOLVING

1.3 Sequence the Operations

The solutions to some problems have several steps that must be performed in the proper sequence.

Bob Robertson is a gold miner in the Klondike. He has 400 claims and pays the Canadian government $10 per year to operate each one. Bob employs 14 people during the season, which runs from April to freeze-up in October. Each employee works 12 h a day for $19.75/h. One year, 9 people worked 143 days, and the other 5 worked 131 days. If gold was worth $12 000/kg, how many kilograms of gold did Bob's claims have to produce to cover the salaries and government costs? Round your answer to the nearest kilogram.

Understand the Problem

1. What information are you given?
2. What are you asked to find?
3. What is the proper sequence of steps?

Think of a Plan

Calculate the wages of the 14 employees. Add the amount paid to the government. Divide the total expenses by $12 000 to find out how many kilograms of gold were needed. Use a calculator to find the exact answer.

Carry Out the Plan

Wages of 9 employees
= 9 × 143 × 12 × $19.75
= $305 019

Estimate

| 10 × 140 × 10 × 20 |
| = 280 000 |

Wages of 5 employees
= 5 × 131 × 12 × $19.75
= $155 235

Estimate

| 5 × 130 × 10 × 20 |
| = 130 000 |

Payment to government
= 400 × $10
= $4000

Total expenses
= $305 019 + $155 235 + $4000
= $464 254

Estimate

| 300 000 + 160 000 + 4000 |
| = 464 000 |

Kilograms of gold needed
$$= \frac{\$464\ 254}{\$12\ 000}$$
$$\doteq 39$$

```
464254/12000
         38.68783333
```

Estimate

| 480 000 ÷ 12 000 = 40 |

Bob's claims had to produce 39 kg of gold to cover salaries and government costs.

Look Back

How can you work backward to check your answer?

Applications and Problem Solving

1. Learning words At ages 3, 4, and 5, a child learns about 3 new words each day. About how many words does a child learn in these 3 years?

2. Speaking The average person normally speaks about 125 words/min. In 2.5 h of speaking, how many words does the average person speak?

3. Track meet A sports arena has 17 624 seats. Tickets for a track meet cost $22.50 each. If 1057 tickets remain unsold, what is the value of the tickets sold? Explain how you know that your answer is reasonable.

4. Highway driving Tamar and Ken left the highway service centre at the same time and travelled in the same direction. Tamar drove at 90 km/h, and Ken drove at 70 km/h.
a) How far did Tamar drive in 3.5 h?
b) How far did Ken drive in 4 h?
c) How far apart were they after 4.5 h?

5. Parking costs The parking garage charges $5.50 for the first hour or part of an hour. The charge is $2.00 for each additional half hour or part of a half hour. Eileen arrived at 08:17 and left at 11:45. How much was she charged?

6. Summer job Mohammed works on a highway survey crew during the summer. He earns $16.70/h for up to 35 h/week. He earns time-and-a-half for hours over 35 h/week. If he works 41 h in one week, how much does he earn?

7. Speed of light Light travels through space at a speed of 298 000 km/s. A **light-year** is the distance light travels through space in one year. How far is a light-year?

8. Time What time will it be 213 000 h from now?

9. Theatre festival Twenty-four students are going to a theatre festival. The total cost is $12 866. The school will pay $1100 towards the total cost. The students will share the rest of the cost equally. Each student will pay in 5 equal monthly instalments. How much is each instalment?

10. Passenger pigeons The passenger pigeon was a North American migratory bird. At one time, there were huge numbers of these pigeons, but they became extinct in 1914. A flock of passenger pigeons was once described as follows.

The column was 500 m wide and flew overhead at 500 m/min. It took three hours to fly by. Each square metre was occupied by ten pigeons.

How many pigeons were in the flock?

LOGIC POWER

There are 14 cubes in the structure, which sits on a table. Each face of each cube has an area of 1 m^2. If you paint the exposed surface, how many square metres do you paint?

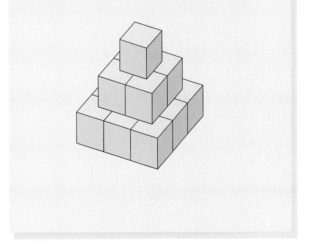

1.4 Exponents, Powers, and Variables

Bloodhounds are widely used as tracking dogs. A bloodhound's sense of smell is 1 000 000 times more powerful than a human's.

The number 1 000 000 can be rewritten as a repeated multiplication. Exponents are used as a short way to write repeated multiplication.

$$1\ 000\ 000 = 10 \times 10 \times 10 \times 10 \times 10 \times 10 = 10^6$$

standard form   repeated multiplication   exponential form

$$1\ 000\ 000 = 10^6$$ — exponent

base   power

Explore: Do an Experiment

When you repeatedly fold a piece of paper in half, the number of layers increases with the number of folds. Fold a standard piece of paper, and copy and complete the table.

Number of Folds	Number of Layers
1	2 or 2^1
2	$2 \times 2 = 4$ or 2^2
3	
4	
5	
6	

Inquire

1. If you were to fold the piece of paper the following numbers of times, how many layers would you have?
a) 5   **b)** 7   **c)** 50

2. Explain how you found your answers to question 1.

3. If 10 layers of paper are about 1 mm thick, how thick is a piece of paper after 10 folds?

4. What is the maximum number of times you can fold a piece of paper?

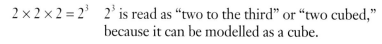

$3 \times 3 = 3^2$ 3^2 is read as "three to the second," or more commonly "three squared," because it can be modelled as a square.

$2 \times 2 \times 2 = 2^3$ 2^3 is read as "two to the third" or "two cubed," because it can be modelled as a cube.

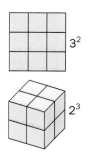

Exponents are also used with variables.

$3y^4$ means $3 \times y \times y \times y \times y$ $3y^4$ is read as "three y to the fourth."

When an exponent is outside a pair of brackets, the exponent is applied to everything inside the brackets.

$(3y)^4$ means $(3y) \times (3y) \times (3y) \times (3y)$
$= 3 \times 3 \times 3 \times 3 \times y \times y \times y \times y$
$= 81y^4$

Example   Evaluating Expressions

If $x = 2$ and $y = 3$, evaluate $5x^4 + 6xy$.

Solution

$5x^4 + 6xy = 5(2)^4 + 6(2)(3)$
$ = 5(16) + 36$
$ = 80 + 36$
$ = 116$

Graphing calculator

5(2)^4+6(2)(3)
                116

Scientific calculator

5 ⊠ 2 ⓨˣ 4 ⊞ 6 ⊠ 2
⊠ 3 ⊟ ▢ 116.

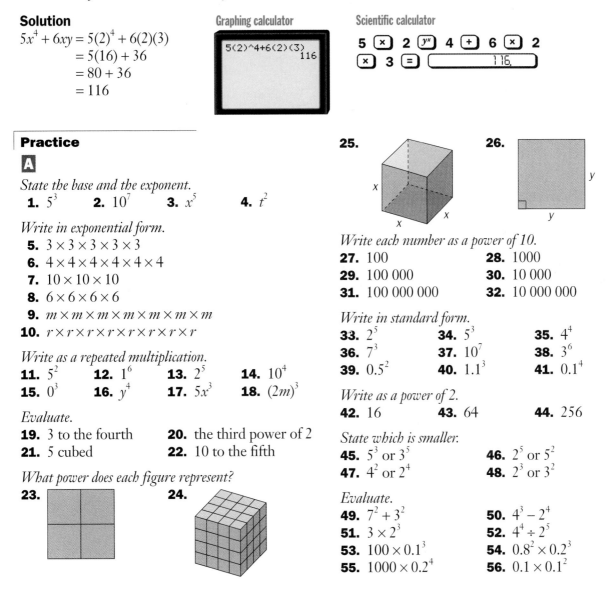

Practice

A

State the base and the exponent.
  1. 5^3 **2.** 10^7 **3.** x^5 **4.** t^2

Write in exponential form.
  5. $3 \times 3 \times 3 \times 3 \times 3$
  6. $4 \times 4 \times 4 \times 4 \times 4 \times 4$
  7. $10 \times 10 \times 10$
  8. $6 \times 6 \times 6 \times 6$
  9. $m \times m \times m \times m \times m \times m \times m$
  10. $r \times r \times r \times r \times r \times r \times r \times r$

Write as a repeated multiplication.
  11. 5^2 **12.** 1^6 **13.** 2^5 **14.** 10^4
  15. 0^3 **16.** y^4 **17.** $5x^3$ **18.** $(2m)^3$

Evaluate.
  19. 3 to the fourth   **20.** the third power of 2
  21. 5 cubed   **22.** 10 to the fifth

What power does each figure represent?
  23.   **24.**

25.   **26.**

Write each number as a power of 10.
  27. 100   **28.** 1000
  29. 100 000   **30.** 10 000
  31. 100 000 000   **32.** 10 000 000

Write in standard form.
  33. 2^5 **34.** 5^3 **35.** 4^4
  36. 7^3 **37.** 10^7 **38.** 3^6
  39. 0.5^2 **40.** 1.1^3 **41.** 0.1^4

Write as a power of 2.
  42. 16   **43.** 64   **44.** 256

State which is smaller.
  45. 5^3 or 3^5 **46.** 2^5 or 5^2
  47. 4^2 or 2^4 **48.** 2^3 or 3^2

Evaluate.
  49. $7^2 + 3^2$ **50.** $4^3 - 2^4$
  51. 3×2^3 **52.** $4^4 \div 2^5$
  53. 100×0.1^3 **54.** $0.8^2 \times 0.2^3$
  55. 1000×0.2^4 **56.** 0.1×0.1^2

Evaluate.
57. $7^2 + 3^3$ **58.** $4^3 - 2^2$
59. $2^2 \times 2^3$ **60.** $4^2 \div 2^2$

61. Evaluate for $x = 4$.
a) x^3 **b)** $x^2 - 5$ **c)** $5x^2 - 7$ **d)** $(2x)^2$

62. Evaluate for $t = 3$ and $s = 2$.
a) $t^2 + s^2$ **b)** $(t + s)^3$
c) $t^3 - s^3$ **d)** $2t^2 - s^2$
e) $6s^3 - 2st$ **f)** $(3t)^2 - 4st$

Applications and Problem Solving

63. **Bacteria** A scientist found that the number of bacteria in a culture doubled every hour. If there were 1000 bacteria at 08:00, how many were there at the following times?
a) 09:00   **b)** 11:00   **c)** 14:00

B

64. **Giant pandas** The ancestors of Ling Ling, the giant panda, included 2 parents and 4 grandparents. Her grandparents were 2 generations before her.
a) How many ancestors were in the seventh generation before Ling Ling? Express your answer in exponential form.
b) How many ancestors were in the tenth generation before Ling Ling? Express your answer in exponential form.

65. **Baseball** If a ball is hit straight up at a speed of 30 m/s, its height, h metres, after t seconds is given by the formula $h = 30t - 5t^2$.
a) What is the height of the ball after 1 s? 3 s? 4 s?
b) After how many seconds will the ball hit the ground, if no one catches it?

66. **Pattern a)** Describe the pattern in this sequence.
$$1, 4, 27, 256, \dots$$
b) Write the fifth and sixth numbers in the sequence in exponential form.

67. **Technology** Use a calculator to evaluate each of the following.
a) 2^6 **b)** 3^7 **c)** 4^8 **d)** 0.3^3

68. If $f(x) = 3x^2 + 1$
then $f(2) = 3(2)^2 + 1$
$$= 3 \times 4 + 1$$
$$= 13$$
Find the following.
a) $f(4)$ **b)** $f(10)$ **c)** $f(0)$

C

69. **Quadruplets** The product of the ages of a set of quadruplets is 16 times the sum of their ages. How old are they? Explain your solution, giving clear reasons for the steps you used.

70. **Triplets** The product of the ages of a set of triplets is 12 times the sum of their ages. How old are they?

71. Decide whether each statement is always true, sometimes true, or never true for whole numbers greater than 1. Explain your reasoning.
a) Twice a number is smaller than the number squared.
b) The cube of a number is greater than the square of the number.
c) Powers with the same base but different exponents are equal.

72. **Chess** A story says that the inventor of chess asked his ruler to give him 1 grain of wheat on the first square of the chessboard, 2 on the second, 4 on the third, 8 on the fourth, and so on for all 64 squares.

Suppose you could stack loonies on a chessboard in the same manner.
a) How many loonies would you stack on the fourth square? the fifth square? the sixth square? the seventh square?
b) About how high would the stack be on the sixty-fourth square? Compare your result with your classmates'.

1.5 The Exponent Rules

The mass of a polar bear is 4 times the mass of a mountain lion. The mass of a mountain lion is 8 times the mass of a raccoon. Therefore, the mass of a polar bear is 4×8 or 32 times the mass of a raccoon.

The multiplication 4×8 can be written as the multiplication of two powers with the same base, $2^2 \times 2^3$, to give 32 or 2^5. The exponent rules are shortcuts for multiplying and dividing powers with the *same base*.

Explore: Discover the Relationship

Copy and complete the table.

Exponential Form	Standard Form	Result in Standard Form	Result in Exponential Form
$2^2 \times 2^3$	4×8	32	2^5
$3^2 \times 3^2$			
$2^3 \times 2^4$			
$10^3 \times 10^3$			
$2^5 \div 2^2$			
$3^4 \div 3^2$			
$10^5 \div 10^3$			

Inquire

1. For the multiplications, how are the exponents in the first column related to the exponents in the last column?

2. Write a rule for multiplying powers with the same base.

3. For the divisions, how are the exponents in the first column related to the exponents in the last column?

4. Write a rule for dividing powers with the same base.

Example 1   Multiplying Powers
Simplify $2^5 \times 2^3$.

Solution 1

$2^5 \times 2^3 = 2 \times 2 \times 2 \times 2 \times 2 \times 2 \times 2 \times 2$
$= 2^8$

Solution 2

To multiply powers with the same base, add the exponents.
$x^m \times x^n = x^{m+n}$
$2^5 \times 2^3 = 2^{5+3}$
$= 2^8$

Example 2   Dividing Powers

Simplify $y^7 \div y^2$.

Solution 1

$$y^7 \div y^2 = \frac{y \times y \times y \times y \times y \times y \times y}{y \times y}$$
$$= y \times y \times y \times y \times y$$
$$= y^5$$

Solution 2

To divide powers with the same base, subtract the exponents.
$$x^m \div x^n = x^{m-n}$$
$$y^7 \div y^2 = y^{7-2}$$
$$= y^5$$

Example 3   Power of a Power

Simplify.   **a)** $(2^4)^3$ **b)** $(y^2)^4$

Solution

a) $(2^4)^3 = 2^4 \times 2^4 \times 2^4$
$\qquad = 2^{4+4+4}$
$\qquad = 2^{12}$

b) $(y^2)^4 = y^2 \times y^2 \times y^2 \times y^2$
$\qquad = y^{2+2+2+2}$
$\qquad = y^8$

To raise a power to a power, multiply the exponents.
$$(x^m)^n = x^{m \times n}$$

Practice

A

Simplify.

1. $5^3 \times 5^4$ **2.** $2^3 \times 2^7$ **3.** $7^5 \times 7^5$
4. $10^6 \times 10$ **5.** $4^2 \times 4^9$ **6.** 3×3^6
7. $y^2 \times y^4$ **8.** $x^3 \times x^6$ **9.** $a \times a^6$

Simplify.

10. $4^5 \div 4^3$ **11.** $3^7 \div 3^6$
12. $9^2 \div 9^2$ **13.** $10^6 \div 10^5$
14. $4^7 \div 4$ **15.** $5^8 \div 5^8$
16. $m^5 \div m^4$ **17.** $x^3 \div x$

Simplify.

18. $(2^3)^4$ **19.** $(3^5)^2$ **20.** $(4^2)^7$
21. $(10^5)^3$ **22.** $(5^4)^4$ **23.** $(x^5)^4$
24. $(y^3)^3$ **25.** $(t^6)^7$ **26.** $(m^2)^5$

Applications and Problem Solving

B

Find the value of x.

27. $5^3 \times 5^x = 5^7$ **28.** $3^4 \times 3^x = 3^6$
29. $8^x \times 8^2 = 8^8$ **30.** $6^x \times 6^5 = 6^6$
31. $4^3 \times 4^x = 4^6$ **32.** $m^7 \times m^x = m^9$
33. $t^x \times t^3 = t^6$ **34.** $y^x \times y^4 = y^5$

Find the value of x.

35. $3^6 \div 3^x = 3^2$ **36.** $6^7 \div 6^x = 6^5$
37. $7^x \div 7^4 = 7^3$ **38.** $2^x \div 2^2 = 2^8$
39. $9^5 \div 9^x = 9^4$ **40.** $m^x \div m^2 = m^7$
41. $m^x \div m = m^3$ **42.** $y^6 \div y^x = y$

Find the value of x.

43. $(2^3)^x = 2^6$ **44.** $(3^x)^4 = 3^{12}$
45. $(5^x)^2 = 5^8$ **46.** $(7^5)^x = 7^{10}$
47. $(x^3)^x = x^9$ **48.** $(m^x)^5 = m^{15}$
49. $(t^4)^x = t^{20}$ **50.** $(z^x)^5 = z^5$

51. Solar system An **order of magnitude** is the approximate size of a quantity, expressed as a power of 10. To the nearest orders of magnitude, the mass of the Earth is 10^{25} kg, and the mass of the sun is 10^{30} kg. About how many times the mass of the Earth is the mass of the sun?

C

52. On a test, a student wrote that $2^3 \times 3^2 = 6^5$.
a) What mistake did the student make?
b) What is the value of $2^3 \times 3^2$?

53. A student said that $6^3 \div 2^2 = 3^1$.
a) What mistake did the student make?
b) What is the value of $6^3 \div 2^2$?

1.6 Reviewing Integers

Explore: Use a Table

The table shows the temperatures in cities across Canada at 17:00 on one day in winter. List the temperatures in order from highest to lowest.

City	Temperature (°C)
Vancouver	5
Calgary	−7
Regina	−5
Winnipeg	−3
Toronto	0
Ottawa	2
Montréal	3
Québec City	−1
Halifax	1
St. John's	−4

Inquire

1. In what way are the temperatures in Winnipeg and Montréal
a) alike?   **b)** different?
2. Which temperature is higher, Calgary's or Ottawa's? by how many degrees?
3. Which temperature is lower, Regina's or Québec City's? by how many degrees?

Numbers like +5, −7, and −10 are called **integers**. These numbers are used to show direction *above* or *below* some zero point. For temperature, the zero point is 0°C.
The integer +5 represents 5°C above zero.
The integer −7 represents 7°C below zero.

Integers can be shown on a number line.

$$\xleftarrow{\hspace{1cm}} \quad -5 \quad -4 \quad -3 \quad -2 \quad -1 \quad 0 \quad +1 \quad +2 \quad +3 \quad +4 \quad +5 \quad \xrightarrow{\hspace{1cm}}$$

negative integers   **The integer 0 is neither positive nor negative.**   **positive integers**

Every integer, except 0, has an **opposite**.

$$\xleftarrow{\hspace{1cm}} \quad -6 \quad -5 \quad -4 \quad -3 \quad -2 \quad -1 \quad 0 \quad +1 \quad +2 \quad +3 \quad +4 \quad +5 \quad +6 \quad \xrightarrow{\hspace{1cm}}$$

−4 ◄───── **These are opposite integers.** ─────► +4

When two integers are compared on a number line, the integer to the right is the greater.

$$-4 \quad -3 \quad -2 \quad -1 \quad 0 \quad +1 \quad +2 \quad +3$$

Since +3 is to the right of −4, we say "+3 is greater than −4," and we write $+3 > -4$. We can also say "−4 is less than +3," and write $-4 < +3$.

A positive integer can be written without the + sign. So, +3 becomes 3, and +15 becomes 15. A negative integer must always be written with the − sign.

We can list the integers, I, as follows.
$$I = \ldots, -3, -2, -1, 0, 1, 2, 3, \ldots$$

Example 1   Graphing Integers
Graph the following integers on a number line.
a) $x > -3$ **b)** $x \leq 2$

Solution
a) $x > -3$ means the integers greater than −3.

$$-4 \quad -3 \quad -2 \quad -1 \quad 0 \quad +1 \quad +2$$

The red arrow means that the integers continue without end.

b) $x \leq 2$ means the integers less than or equal to 2.

$$-2 \quad -1 \quad 0 \quad +1 \quad +2 \quad +3 \quad +4$$

Integer addition can be related to a number line. Think of positive integers as trips to the right and negative integers as trips to the left.

To show $(+3) + (-7)$, start at 0 and go 3 units to the right. Then, go 7 units to the left. The single trip that gives the same result as $(+3) + (-7)$ is (-4).

$$+3$$
$$-4 \quad -3 \quad -2 \quad -1 \quad 0 \quad +1 \quad +2 \quad +3$$
$$-7$$

$$(+3) + (-7) = (-4) \quad \text{or} \quad 3 + (-7) = -4$$

Example 2   Adding on a Number Line
Use a number line to add $(+4) + (-3) + (-5)$.

Solution

$$+4$$
$$-4 \quad -3 \quad -2 \quad -1 \quad 0 \quad +1 \quad +2 \quad +3 \quad +4$$
$$-5 \qquad \qquad -3$$

$$(+4) + (-3) + (-5) = -4 \quad \text{or} \quad 4 + (-3) + (-5) = -4$$

Example 3   Adding Integers
Add $7 + (-4) + (-6) + 8 + (-1)$.

Solution

$$7 + (-4) + (-6) + 8 + (-1)$$
$$= \underbrace{3} + (-6) + 8 + (-1)$$
$$= \underbrace{-3} + 8 + (-1)$$
$$= \underbrace{5} + (-1)$$
$$= 4$$

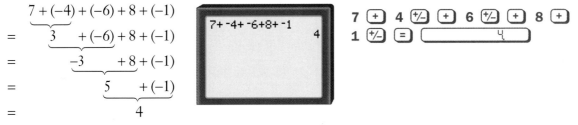

Recall that, to subtract an integer, you add its opposite.

Example 4   Subtracting Integers
Evaluate.   **a)** $(+9) - (-6)$ **b)** $-5 - (+2)$ **c)** $14 + (-4) - 2$

Solution

a) $(+9) - (-6)$
$= (+9) + (+6)$
$= 15$

b) $-5 - (+2)$
$= -5 + (-2)$
$= -7$

c) $14 + (-4) - 2$
$= \underbrace{14 + (-4)} + (-2)$
$= \underbrace{10 \quad + (-2)}$
$= 8$

Example 5   Subtracting Integers
Evaluate.
a) $-3 + 4 - 2$ **b)** $5 - 6 + 7 - 8$

Solution

A calculator will subtract integers directly.

a) $-3 + 4 - 2$
$= \underbrace{1} - 2$
$= \underbrace{-1}$

b) $5 - 6 + 7 - 8$
$= \underbrace{-1} + 7 - 8$
$= \underbrace{6} - 8$
$= -2$

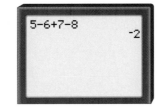

The multiplication and division rules for integers are as follows.
• The product or quotient of two positive integers is a positive integer.
$$4 \times 5 = 20 \qquad \frac{20}{4} = 5$$

• The product or quotient of two negative integers is a positive integer.
$$-4 \times (-5) = 20 \qquad \frac{-20}{-4} = 5$$

• The product or quotient of a positive integer and a negative integer is a negative integer.
$$-4 \times 5 = -20 \qquad 4 \times (-5) = -20$$
$$\frac{-20}{5} = -4 \qquad \frac{20}{-5} = -4$$

Example 6   Multiplying Integers

Multiply.   **a)** $(-2)(-5)$ **b)** $4(-3)$ **c)** $-3(-4)$

Solution

a) $(-2)(-5) = 10$ **b)** $4(-3) = (+4)(-3)$ **c)** $-3(-4) = (-3)(-4)$
$\qquad\qquad\qquad\qquad\quad = -12 \qquad\qquad\qquad\qquad\quad = 12$

Example 7   Dividing Integers

Divide.   **a)** $36 \div (-9)$ **b)** $(-48) \div (-6)$

Solution

a) $36 \div (-9) = -4$ **b)** $(-48) \div (-6) = 8$

Example 8   Dividing Integers

Simplify.   **a)** $-15 \div 3$ **b)** $\dfrac{(-8)(-6)}{4(-3)}$

Solution

a) $-15 \div 3 = -5$ **b)** $\dfrac{(-8)(-6)}{4(-3)} = \dfrac{+48}{-12}$
$\qquad\qquad\qquad\qquad\qquad\qquad\qquad\quad = -4$

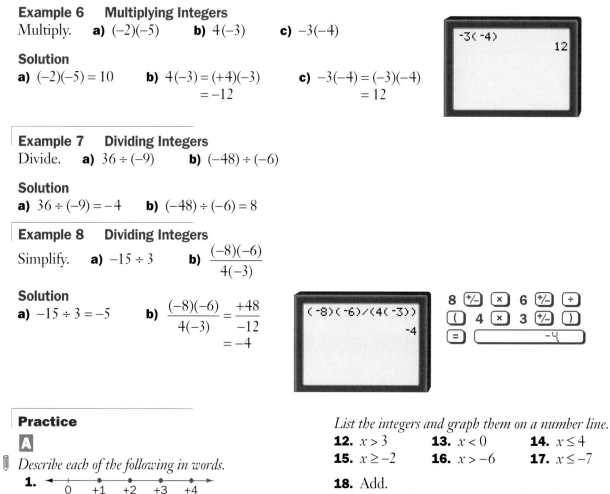

Practice

Describe each of the following in words.

1.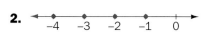

2. (number line from −4 to 0)

3. (number line from −5 to 0)

Write the integers in order from least to greatest.

4. $-2, 0, -3, 5$ **5.** $-4, -1, -3, -2$
6. $-15, 18, -11, 14$ **7.** $-1, 1, -2, 2$

Graph the integers on a number line.

8. integers less than 5
9. integers greater than −2
10. the positive even integers
11. integers less than or equal to 0

List the integers and graph them on a number line.

12. $x > 3$ **13.** $x < 0$ **14.** $x \le 4$
15. $x \ge -2$ **16.** $x > -6$ **17.** $x \le -7$

18. Add.
a) $(+3) + (+2)$ **b)** $(+4) + (-8)$
c) $(-3) + (-4)$ **d)** $(-8) + (+8)$
e) $(-4) + (+6)$ **f)** $(+9) + (-5)$

19. Add.
a) $-11 + 4$ **b)** $14 + 3$
c) $8 + (-10)$ **d)** $-12 + (-11)$
e) $16 + (-5)$ **f)** $-15 + 15$

20. Evaluate.
a) $4 + 7 + (-4)$ **b)** $-6 + (-2) + 5$
c) $-7 + 6 + (-8)$ **d)** $9 + (-3) + (-6)$
e) $7 + (-1) + 0$ **f)** $-2 + (-2) + (-2)$

21. Estimate, then add.
a) $123 + (-78)$ **b)** $-237 + (-324)$
c) $-762 + 456$ **d)** $678 + (-821)$
e) $-405 + (-306)$ **f)** $-777 + 888$

22. Subtract.
a) $(+4) - (+1)$ **b)** $(+9) - (-4)$
c) $(-2) - (+6)$ **d)** $(+7) - (-8)$
e) $(-7) - (-7)$ **f)** $(-4) - (-3)$

23. Subtract.
a) $7 - (-3)$ **b)** $-6 - (-5)$
c) $4 - 9$ **d)** $0 - (-2)$
e) $-3 - 7$ **f)** $-2 - (-2)$
g) $13 - 18$ **h)** $-21 - 37$

24. Evaluate.
a) $7 - (-2) + 5$ **b)** $-3 - (-4) - (-1)$
c) $-5 + (-2) - 9$ **d)** $7 - (-6) + (-8)$
e) $2 - 5 - 3$ **f)** $-4 - 6 + 8$

25. Evaluate.
a) $4 - 2 - 3 + 5$ **b)** $-3 + 7 + 6 - 7$
c) $8 - 1 - 5 - 6$ **d)** $4 - 9 + 3 - 1$
e) $-4 + 6 - 1 + 3 - 6$ **f)** $-2 - 3 - 1 + 5 + 7$
g) $5 - 7 + 2 - 3 + 6$ **h)** $2 - 3 - 5 + 1 + 3$

26. Multiply.
a) $(+10)(-3)$ **b)** $(-11)(-3)$
c) $(+12)(+2)$ **d)** $(-3)(+10)$

27. Multiply.
a) $5 \times (-7)$ **b)** $-6 \times (-5)$
c) $(-7) \times 8$ **d)** 8×7
e) -6×0 **f)** $9(-5)$
g) $-5(6)$ **h)** $-11(-5)$

28. Evaluate.
a) $-3(-4)(+5)$ **b)** $-4 \times 2 \times 6$
c) $-2 \times 3 \times (-5)$ **d)** $3 \times 7 \times (-2)$
e) $6(-1) \times 8$ **f)** $4 \times (-3) \times 5$
g) $0(-5)(-7)$ **h)** $-3 \times 2 \times 2$
i) $-1 \times 0 \times 3$ **j)** $8(-2)(-2)$

29. Divide.
a) $(+18) \div (-2)$ **b)** $(-36) \div (-9)$
c) $(+10) \div (+5)$ **d)** $(-40) \div (+5)$

30. Divide.
a) $\dfrac{-27}{-9}$ **b)** $\dfrac{-45}{5}$ **c)** $\dfrac{0}{-2}$

31. Divide.
a) $49 \div (-7)$ **b)** $25 \div 5$
c) $-60 \div 12$ **d)** $-28 \div (-4)$

32. Evaluate.
a) $\dfrac{(-2)(+8)}{(-4)}$ **b)** $\dfrac{-40}{(-5)(-2)}$

c) $\dfrac{8(-5)}{(-2)(-2)}$ **d)** $\dfrac{(-4)(+9)}{(-2)(+3)}$

e) $\dfrac{-10(-6)}{4(-5)}$ **f)** $\dfrac{(-10)(+6)}{(-3)(-2)}$

Applications and Problem Solving

B

33. Expressions like $-2 < x \le 3$ are read from the middle in both directions. This expression means that x is less than or equal to 3 and greater than -2. The following integers satisfy these conditions.

$$-1, 0, 1, 2, 3$$

List the integers that satisfy the following.
a) $1 < x < 4$ **b)** $-2 < x \le 5$
c) $-2 \le x < 7$ **d)** $-4 \le x \le 1$
e) $-6 < x \le 0$ **f)** $-8 \le x < 1$

34. Copy and complete the tables.

a)

x	x + 4
3	
2	
1	
0	
−1	
−2	
−3	

b)

y	y − 5
3	
2	
1	
0	
−1	
−2	
−3	

c)

m	−6 + m
2	
1	
0	
−1	
−2	

d)

t	−2t
2	
1	
0	
−1	
−2	

35. Temperature changes The temperature in Sudbury was 4°C. What was the temperature after a rise of 5°C followed by a fall of 10°C?

36. Boiling points The boiling point of liquid nitrogen is –196°C. The boiling point of liquid hydrogen is –253°C. What is the difference between these boiling points?

37. Elevations a) Mount Everest has an elevation of 8863 m. Death Valley has an elevation of –86 m. What is the difference between these elevations?
b) The surface of the Dead Sea has an elevation of –400 m. Which is higher, the Dead Sea or Death Valley, and by how much?

38. Evaluate for $x = -3$.
a) $5x$ **b)** $-4x$ **c)** $5x - 4$
d) $x - 2$ **e)** $2x + 1$ **f)** $x + 3$

39. Evaluate for $x = -2$ and $y = -3$.
a) xy **b)** $3xy$ **c)** $-5xy$
d) $(4x)(6y)$ **e)** $-2xy - 3$ **f)** $5xy + 3y$

40. Falling temperatures The temperature in Québec City was 3°C at midnight. The average temperature drop was 2°C/h until 05:00.
a) What was the total temperature change?
b) What was the temperature at 05:00?

41. Average temperature The nightly low temperatures in Calgary one week were +1°C, –5°C, –12°C, –3°C, +4°C, +6°C, and –5°C. What was the average low temperature?

42. Descending aircraft An aircraft has an altitude of 10 200 m. It descends to 8450 m in 5 min. Calculate its rate of change in altitude, in metres per minute.

43. Technology Use your calculator to evaluate each of the following. Use estimation to check that each answer is reasonable.
a) $-34 + (-76) + (-56) + 98$
b) $45 + (-47) + (-22) + 88$
c) $-85 - 129$
d) $58 - (-87)$
e) $(-71)(+14)$
f) $(-56)(-21)$
g) $246 \div (-41)$
h) $-406 \div (-29)$

44. Here are 3 ways to write the integer –15 as the sum of consecutive integers.
$(-1) + (-2) + (-3) + (-4) + (-5) = -15$
$(-4) + (-5) + (-6) = -15$
$(-7) + (-8) = -15$
Here are 2 ways to write the integer –5 as the sum of consecutive integers.
$(-2) + (-3) = -5$
$1 + 0 + (-1) + (-2) + (-3) = -5$
a) Write each of the following integers as the sum of consecutive integers. Compare your answers with a classmate's.
    –9   26   –22   18
b) Write each of the following integers as the sum of consecutive integers in 3 ways. Compare your answers with a classmate's.
    –21   9   –27

PATTERN POWER

Aziza and Efra are twin babies.
1. Determine the sum and product of their ages when they reach 1, 2, 3, 4, and 5 years of age.

2. Determine the quotient of the product over the sum at each of the ages in question 1.

3. Describe the pattern in the quotients.

4. Use the pattern to predict the quotient of the product over the sum when the twins' ages reach
a) 25   **b)** 50   **c)** 70

5. Check your answers to question 4 by calculating the sum and product of their ages and finding the quotient in each case.

6. How old will the twins be when the quotient has these values?
a) 15   **b)** 24.5   **c)** 40

Sorting Networks

One of the most time-consuming tasks a computer does is sort information, especially numbers.

Consider the following representation of a sorting network. The numbers to be sorted start at the square nodes on the left and move along the lines until they reach the triangular nodes, where they are compared. The larger number comes out of the top of the triangle, and the smaller number comes out of the bottom. This process is repeated until the numbers reach the square nodes at the right.

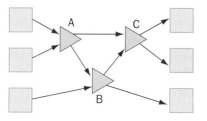

If the sorting network is designed properly, the numbers are sorted, with the largest number at the top and the smallest number at the bottom.

1 Sorting Integers

Use the sorting network above. Suppose the integers –2, –8, and 5 are in the three squares at the left, with –2 at the top, –8 in the middle, and 5 at the bottom.

1. a) Which two integers are being compared at node A?

b) Which two integers are being compared at node B?

c) Which two integers are being compared at node C?

d) Are the integers sorted properly?

2. Repeat question 1, with the three integers to be sorted being –12, 14, and 0. At the start, –12 is in the top node, 14 is in the middle node, and 0 is in the bottom node.

2 Other Sorting Networks

Use the following two networks.

Network 1

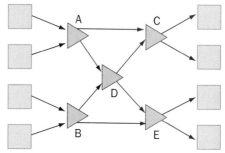

Network 2

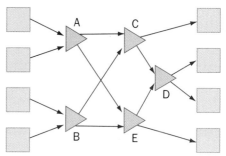

Suppose the integers to be sorted, from top to bottom, are –6, –9, –1, and 10.

1. Does Network 1 sort the integers correctly?

2. Does Network 2 sort the integers correctly?

3. Design a different network to sort four integers. Test your network using four different integers.

3 Sorting With a Graphing Calculator

1. Describe how a graphing calculator can be used to sort numbers.

2. Use a graphing calculator to generate 20 random integers from –50 to 50 and sort them in

a) descending order (from greatest to least)

b) ascending order (from least to greatest)

1.7 Powers With Integral Bases

The leg span of the giant spider from South America is 25 cm. Like all spiders, it has 8 legs.

We can write the number 8 as the power 2^3. In this power, the exponent is 3 and the base is 2.

2^3 — exponent; base; power

The base of a power can also be a negative number. We can extend the exponent rules to simplify powers with integers as bases.

Explore: Look for a Pattern

Copy and complete the table.

Exponential Form	Result as a Repeated Multiplication	Result in Exponential Form	Result in Standard Form
$(-2)^2 \times (-2)^3$	$(-2) \times (-2) \times (-2) \times (-2) \times (-2)$	$(-2)^{2+3}$ or $(-2)^5$	-32
$(-2)^3 \times (-2)^4$			
$(+3)^2 \times (+3)^3$			
$(-2)^8 \div (-2)^3$			
$(-3)^4 \div (-3)^2$			
$(+5)^3 \div (+5)$			

Inquire

1. Write the exponent rule for multiplying powers with the same integral base.

2. Write the exponent rule for dividing powers with the same integral base.

3. Describe the difference between
a) $(1+3)^2$ and $1^2 + 3^2$ **b)** $(1-3)^2$ and $1^2 - 3^2$ **c)** $(-3)^2$ and -3^2

Example 1 Simplifying Powers
Simplify $(-2)^3$.

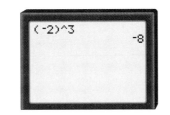

(-2)^3
-8

Solution
$(-2)^3 = (-2) \times (-2) \times (-2)$
$= -8$

Example 2 Simplifying the Product of Powers
Simplify.
a) $(-4)^3 \times (-4)^5$ **b)** $(-y)^2 \times (-y)^3$

Solution
To multiply powers with the same integral base, add the exponents.
$x^m \times x^n = x^{m+n}$
a) $(-4)^3 \times (-4)^5 = (-4)^{3+5}$
$= (-4)^8$
b) $(-y)^2 \times (-y)^3 = (-y)^{2+3}$
$= (-y)^5$

Example 3 Simplifying the Quotient of Powers

Simplify.

a) $(-6)^5 \div (-6)^2$ **b)** $(-t)^3 \div (-t)$

Solution

To divide powers with the same integral base, subtract the exponents.

$x^m \div x^n = x^{m-n}$

a) $(-6)^5 \div (-6)^2 = (-6)^{5-2}$ **b)** $(-t)^3 \div (-t) = (-t)^{3-1}$

$\quad\quad\quad\quad\quad\quad = (-6)^3$ $\quad\quad\quad\quad\quad\quad = (-t)^2$

Example 4 Simplifying a Power of a Power

Simplify.

a) $((-2)^2)^3$ **b)** $((-m)^4)^2$

Solution

a) $((-2)^2)^3 = (-2)^2 \times (-2)^2 \times (-2)^2$ **b)** $((-m)^4)^2 = (-m)^4 \times (-m)^4$

$\quad\quad\quad\quad = (-2)^{2+2+2}$ $\quad\quad\quad\quad\quad = (-m)^{4+4}$

$\quad\quad\quad\quad = (-2)^6$ $\quad\quad\quad\quad\quad = (-m)^8$

Example 3 suggests the following rule.

To raise a power with an integral base to a power, multiply the exponents.

$(x^m)^n = x^{m \times n}$

Example 5 Evaluating the Product of Powers

Evaluate $(-5)^4(-5)^3$.

Solution

$(-5)^4(-5)^3 = (-5)^{4+3}$

$\quad\quad\quad\quad = (-5)^7$

$\quad\quad\quad\quad = -78\ 125$

5 $\boxed{+/-}$ $\boxed{y^x}$ 4 $\boxed{\times}$ 5 $\boxed{+/-}$ $\boxed{y^x}$ 3

$\boxed{=}$ $\boxed{\quad -78\ 125.\quad}$

Example 6 Product of Powers With Different Bases

Evaluate $(-4)^2 \times (-3)^3$.

Solution

Because the bases are not the same, evaluate each power before multiplying.

$(-4)^2 \times (-3)^3 = 16 \times (-27)$

$\quad\quad\quad\quad\quad = -432$

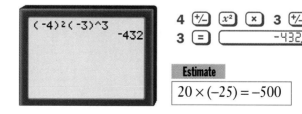

4 $\boxed{+/-}$ $\boxed{x^2}$ $\boxed{\times}$ 3 $\boxed{+/-}$ $\boxed{y^x}$

3 $\boxed{=}$ $\boxed{\quad -432.\quad}$

Estimate

$20 \times (-25) = -500$

Example 7   Evaluating Expressions

Evaluate for $x = -2$ and $y = -1$.

a) $x^2 + y^3$ **b)** $3x^3 - 2y^2$

Solution

a) $x^2 + y^3 = (-2)^2 + (-1)^3$
$$= 4 - 1$$
$$= 3$$

b) $3x^3 - 2y^2 = 3(-2)^3 - 2(-1)^2$
$$= 3(-8) - 2(+1)$$
$$= -24 - 2$$
$$= -26$$

```
3(-2)^3-2(-1)²
                    -26
```

Practice

A

Simplify.

1. 7^2 **2.** $(-2)^2$ **3.** $(-3)^3$

4. $(+2)^3$ **5.** $(-2)^4$ **6.** $(+2)^4$

7. $(-1)^5$ **8.** $(+1)^9$ **9.** $(-1)^8$

State the base.

10. 2^6 **11.** $(-5)^2$ **12.** -1^4 **13.** $(-9)^3$

State the exponent.

14. -2^5 **15.** 4^2 **16.** $(-4)^0$ **17.** -5

Write in exponential form.

18. $(-4) \times (-4) \times (-4)$

19. $(-3)(-3)(-3)(-3)(-3)$

20. $p \times p \times p \times p \times p \times p$

21. $(-n)(-n)(-n)(-n)$

22. $3 \times 3 \times 3 \times (-2) \times (-2) \times 3 \times (-2)$

Write as a repeated multiplication.

23. $(-2)^5$ **24.** -2^5 **25.** $(-x)^3$

Write in standard form.

26. 3^2 **27.** $(-3)^2$ **28.** $(-1)^4$

29. -1^5 **30.** $(-5)^3$ **31.** -5^3

32. $(-0.5)^3$ **33.** 1.1^4 **34.** $(-2.5)^2$

Simplify.

35. $5^3 \times 5^6$ **36.** $(-8)^2 \times (-8)^3$

37. $(-2)^3(-2)^4$ **38.** $2^2 \times 2^3 \times 2$

39. $(-2.1)^5(-2.1)^3$ **40.** $(-0.2)^3(-0.2)^2$

Simplify.

41. $5^4 \div 5^3$ **42.** $6^8 \div 6^2$

43. $\dfrac{(-4)^5}{(-4)^3}$ **44.** $\dfrac{(-9)^7}{(-9)^2}$

Simplify.

45. $(2^3)^2$ **46.** $((-3)^7)^4$

47. $((-5)^2)^3$ **48.** $((-6)^5)^3$

49. $((-4)^6)^7$ **50.** $((-2.3)^3)^4$

Simplify.

51. $x^4 \times x^2$ **52.** $y^{12} \div y^5$

53. $z^8 \div z$ **54.** $(-m)^6(-m)^4$

55. $(s^2)^4$ **56.** $((-r)^3)^2$

Simplify, then calculate.

57. $(-5)^2 \times (-5)^3$ **58.** $6^2 \times 6^5$

59. $(-2)^3(-2)^5(-2)^2$ **60.** $(-1)^5(-1)^7$

61. $(-3.1)^5(-3.1)^3$ **62.** $(-3)^6 \div (-3)^4$

63. $(-10)^5 \div (-10)$ **64.** $(-4)^6 \div (-4)^5$

Calculate.

65. $2^8 \div 2^4$ **66.** $(-3)^7 \div (-3)$

67. $(-3)^2 \times (-3)^3$ **68.** $(3^2)^3$

69. $\dfrac{(-4)^3 \times (-4)^5}{(-4)^5}$ **70.** $\dfrac{4^9}{4^3 \times 4^2}$

71. $(-2)^3(-2)^5$ **72.** $(-3)^1(-3)^3$

73. $((-2)^3)^2$ **74.** $(6^2)^3 \div (6^2)^2$

Evaluate.

75. $(-8)^2$ **76.** $6(-4)^3$

77. $(-3)^2(6)^2$ **78.** $(-1)^5 + 3^3$

79. $4^5 - 3^5$ **80.** $(-2)^5 \times (-3)^4$

81. $9^2 \div (-2)^3$ **82.** $(-5)^2(-4)^4$

83. $(1.3)^2(-2)^4$ **84.** $(1.5)^2 \div (-5)^3$

85. Evaluate for $n = 3$.
a) $5n^2$ **b)** $-6n^3$
c) $1 + 7n^5$ **d)** $n^3 - 6n$

86. Evaluate for $x = -2$ and $y = 3$.
a) x^3 **b)** $5y^4$
c) $x^2 + y^2$ **d)** $3x^3y^3$
e) $(x - y)^3$ **f)** $(y - x)^2$
g) $-6xy$ **h)** $-4x^2y^3$
i) $4x^3 - 5y$ **j)** $(3x^2)(-2y^2)$

Applications and Problem Solving

B

87. Find the value of x.
a) $3^x = 81$ **b)** $(-2)^x = -512$
c) $x^5 = 1024$ **d)** $(-x)^3 = -1000$
e) $-5^x = -625$ **f)** $-x^2 = -1.69$
g) $(0.2)^x = 0.0016$ **h)** $x^3 = -0.216$

88. Bacteria There are 10 bacteria in a culture at the beginning of an experiment. The number of bacteria doubles every 24 h. The table shows the number of bacteria present over the first few days.

Elapsed Time (days)	Number of Bacteria
1	10×2 $= 10 \times 2^1$ $= 20$
2	$10 \times 2 \times 2$ $= 10 \times 2^2$ $= 40$
3	$10 \times 2 \times 2 \times 2$ $= 10 \times 2^3$ $= 80$

a) Complete the table up to the end of day 5. How many bacteria are there after 5 days?
b) Use the pattern to calculate the number of bacteria after 1 week.

89. a) Write -8 as a power with base -2.
b) Can you write -16 as a power with base -2? Explain and justify your reasoning.

90. Measurement The formula for the volume, V, of a cube is
$$V = x^3$$
where x is the edge length. Copy the chart and use the formula to complete it.

Edge Length (cm)	Volume (cm³)
5	
7	
4.2	
	1000
	512

91. The exponent rules can be applied to powers with fractional bases.

$$\left(\frac{1}{2}\right)^3 = \left(\frac{1}{2}\right)\left(\frac{1}{2}\right)\left(\frac{1}{2}\right) \qquad \left(\frac{-1}{2}\right)^3 = \left(\frac{-1}{2}\right)\left(\frac{-1}{2}\right)\left(\frac{-1}{2}\right)$$
$$= \left(\frac{1}{8}\right) \qquad\qquad\qquad = \left(\frac{-1}{8}\right)$$

Use the rules to evaluate the following.

a) $\left(\frac{1}{2}\right)^4$ **b)** $\left(\frac{-3}{2}\right)^3$ **c)** $\left(\frac{-2}{3}\right)^5$

d) $4\left(\frac{-1}{2}\right)^2$ **e)** $\left(\frac{1}{2}\right)^2\left(\frac{-1}{2}\right)^3$ **f)** $\left(\frac{-1}{4}\right)^5 - 1$

C

92. If the base of a power is negative, and the exponent is even, is the standard form of the number positive or negative? Explain.

93. If the base of a power is negative, and the exponent is odd, is the standard form of the number positive or negative? Explain.

94. a) Are the products $(-4)^3 \times (-4)^2$ and $(-4)^2 \times (-4)^3$ the same? Explain.
b) Are the quotients $(-4)^3 \div (-4)^2$ and $(-4)^2 \div (-4)^3$ the same? Explain.
c) Are the powers $((-4)^3)^2$ and $((-4)^2)^3$ the same? Explain.

95. A new student in your class does not know how to evaluate such powers as $(-2)^4$ and -2^4. Write an explanation and compare it with your classmates'.

PROBLEM SOLVING

1.8 Look for a Pattern

Patterns are everywhere, and people often use them in their work. Scientists look for patterns in their research findings. Air traffic controllers use traffic patterns.

Using patterns to predict results is a very useful problem solving tool. Store managers and hotel managers use patterns to predict and plan for their busy times. Meteorologists use patterns to help predict the weather.

A group of towns has a phone network to call volunteer firefighters in the event of a forest fire. The fire chief phones 2 firefighters and gives them information about the fire. In the second round of calls, these 2 firefighters each phone 2 more. In the third round of calls, each person called in the second round phones 2 more people. How many firefighters are called in the ninth round of calls?

Understand the Problem

1. What information are you given?
2. What are you asked to find?
3. Do you need an exact or an approximate answer?

Think of a Plan

Make a table. Write the numbers of people called in the first few rounds of calls and look for a pattern.

Round of Calls	1	2	3	4	5	6	7	8	9
Number of People Called	2 or 2^1	4 or 2^2	8 or 2^3	16 or 2^4					

Carry Out the Plan

The number of calls in a round equals 2 raised to an exponent that equals the round number.

From this pattern, we predict that 2^5 people are called in the fifth round, 2^6 people in the sixth round, and so on.

In the ninth round of calls, 2^9 or 512 people are called.

Look Back

Does the answer seem reasonable?

Can you think of another way to solve the problem?

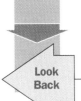

Look for a Pattern

1. Use the given information to find a pattern.
2. Use the pattern to solve the problem.
3. Check that the answer is reasonable.

Applications and Problem Solving

In questions 1–5, determine the pattern in each set of numbers. Then, write the next two numbers.

1. 5, 8, 11, 14, ■, ■

2. 14, 12, 10, 8, ■, ■

3. 10, 12, 9, 11, 8, 10, 7, ■, ■

4. 5, 10, 20, 40, ■, ■

5. 256, 128, 64, 32, ■, ■

6. Toothpicks The diagrams show figures made from toothpicks.

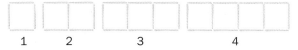

1   2   3   4

If the pattern continues, how many toothpicks are needed for
a) the 5th diagram?   **b)** the 6th diagram?
c) the 50th diagram?

7. Sums of cubes The numbers 1, 8, 27, and 64 are the first 4 cubes.
a) Find the sum of the first 2 cubes.
b) Find the sum of the first 3 cubes.
c) Find the sum of the first 4 cubes.
d) Describe the pattern in the sums.
e) Use the pattern to find the sum of the first 9 cubes.

8. Find the pattern and complete the chart.

$$1 \times 1 = ■$$
$$11 \times 11 = ■$$
$$111 \times 111 = ■$$
$$1111 \times 1111 = ■$$
$$11\,111 \times 11\,111 = ■$$
$$111\,111 \times 111\,111 = ■$$

9. Scholarship fund A computer company donated money to a university scholarship fund for 10 years. In the first year, the company gave $1 000 000. In every year after that, it gave $100 000 more than in the previous year. How much did the university receive in the tenth year?

10. Chess tournament Sixteen people entered a chess tournament. Each player played until losing a game. If there were no draws, how many games were played?

11. Hotel rooms There are 10 rooms on each floor of a hotel. There are 9 floors. The rooms are numbered from 10 to 19 on the first floor, from 20 to 29 on the second floor, and so on. You have been hired to put new brass numbers on each room door. For example, you will put one brass "1" and one brass "0" on the door of the first room. To have enough brass numbers, how many will you need to buy for each digit from 0 to 9?

12. Cubic blocks If you place a cubic block on a table, 5 faces are showing. If you add another block, as shown, 8 faces are showing. How many faces are showing when there are 21 blocks in a row?

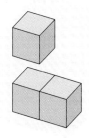

13. Pile of logs How many logs will be in a pile with 7 logs in the bottom row?

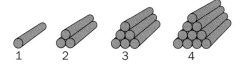

1   2   3   4

14. Staircase The staircase has 4 steps and is made up of 20 cubes. How many cubes are needed for a staircase with 12 steps?

15. Write a problem you can solve by finding a pattern. Have a classmate solve your problem.

1.9 Order of Operations: Whole Numbers, Decimals, and Integers

In 1962, astronaut John Glenn became the first American to orbit the Earth. He volunteered to return to space in 1998 to conduct space-based research on aging. He was then 77 years old.

The space-shuttle launch schedule is a detailed list of events that must occur at specific times and in a specific order for a launch to be successful. In the following partial list, T represents the launch time.

Time	Event
T – 04 h 45 min	Wake flight crew.
T – 03 h 15 min	Astronauts suit up.
T – 02 h 55 min	Flight crew leaves for launch pad.
T – 02 h 30 min	Flight crew enters shuttle.
⋮	⋮
T – 00 h 09 min	Flight director gives GO for launch.
T – 00 h 07 min	Orbiter arm retracts.
T – 00 h 02 min	Flight crew starts suit oxygen supply.
T – 00 h 00 min	Ignition

Mathematical operations must also be done in order.

Explore: Examine the Solutions

Maria, Indira, and David gave different solutions to the same problem.

Maria's Solution

$(-24) \div (-4) + (-2) \div 2$
$= +6 + (-2) \div 2$
$= +4 \div 2$
$= 2$

Indira's Solution

$(-24) \div (-4) + (-2) \div 2$
$= +6 + (-1)$
$= +5$

David's Solution

$(-24) \div (-4) + (-2) \div 2$
$= (-24) \div (-6) \div 2$
$= (-24) \div (-3)$
$= 8$

In what order were the operations performed by
a) Maria?   **b)** Indira?   **c)** David?

Inquire

1. Is there an error in Maria's solution? If so, what is it?
2. Is there an error in Indira's solution? If so, what is it?
3. Is there an error in David's solution? If so, what is it?

To avoid confusion, mathematicians have agreed on the following **order of operations**. Remember it with the acronym **BEDMAS.**
- Do all calculations in **b**rackets first.   **B**
- Simplify numbers with **e**xponents.   **E**
- **D**ivide and **m**ultiply in order from left to right   **DM**
- **A**dd and **s**ubtract in order from left to right.   **AS**

Example 1   Fraction Bar

Evaluate $\dfrac{9+3}{4} + 7$.

Solution

The fraction bar is a division and grouping symbol.

$$\dfrac{9+3}{4} + 7 = \dfrac{(9+3)}{4} + 7 \quad \text{brackets}$$
$$= \dfrac{12}{4} + 7 \qquad \text{divide}$$
$$= 3 + 7 \qquad \text{add}$$
$$= 10$$

Example 2   Exponents

Evaluate $5(9 - 7)^3 + 4$.

Solution

$$5(9 - 7)^3 + 4 \quad \text{brackets}$$
$$= 5(2)^3 + 4 \qquad \text{exponents}$$
$$= 5(8) + 4 \qquad \text{multiply}$$
$$= 40 + 4 \qquad \text{add}$$
$$= 44$$

Example 3   Decimals

Evaluate $8.6^2 - 2(7.2 - 1.3)$.

Solution

$$8.6^2 - 2(7.2 - 1.3) \quad \text{brackets}$$
$$= 8.6^2 - 2(5.9) \qquad \text{exponents}$$
$$= 73.96 - 2(5.9) \qquad \text{multiply}$$
$$= 73.96 - 11.8 \qquad \text{subtract}$$
$$= 62.16$$

```
8.6²-2(7.2-1.3)
           62.16
```

8 [.] 6 [x²] [−] 2 [×] [( ] 7 [.] 2
[−] 1 [.] 3 [ )] [=] [62.16]

Estimate

$$9^2 - 2(6) = 81 - 12$$
$$= 69$$

Example 4   Integers

Evaluate $4(-3) \div (-2) - (-5)$.

Solution

$$4(-3) \div (-2) - (-5) \quad \text{multiply}$$
$$= (-12) \div (-2) - (-5) \quad \text{divide}$$
$$= 6 - (-5) \qquad \text{subtract}$$
$$= 6 + 5$$
$$= 11$$

Example 5   Powers of Integers

Evaluate $2(5-8)^2 + 15$.

Solution

$$
\begin{aligned}
2(5-8)^2 + 15 && \text{brackets} \\
= 2(-3)^2 + 15 && \text{exponents} \\
= 2(9) + 15 && \text{multiply} \\
= 18 + 15 && \text{add} \\
= 33
\end{aligned}
$$

Example 6   Dividing Integers

Evaluate $\dfrac{-3 \times 2 + 16}{20 \div (-4)}$.

Solution

The fraction bar is a division and grouping symbol.

$$
\begin{aligned}
\frac{-3 \times 2 + 16}{20 \div (-4)} = \frac{(-3 \times 2 + 16)}{(20 \div (-4))} && \text{brackets} \\
= \frac{10}{-5} && \text{divide} \\
= -2
\end{aligned}
$$

Practice

A

Evaluate.

1. $12 + 7 - 6$

2. $12 \times 5 - 6$

3. $14 - 10 \div 5$

4. $20 \div 5 \times 3$

5. $2^3 + 5 \times 6$

6. $3(8-2) + 6^2$

7. $(18-6) \div 4$

8. $4^3 - (5-3)^3$

9. $\dfrac{10}{5-3}$

10. $\dfrac{6 \times 2}{4+2}$

11. $3^2 - 4 \times 2$

12. $2^3 + 3^2 - 2^4$

13. $\dfrac{3 + 4 \times 3}{5}$

14. $\dfrac{9 \times 4 - 6}{7 - 1}$

15. $\dfrac{20 \div 5}{2 \times 2}$

16. $5^2 + \dfrac{19 - 11}{18 \div 9}$

Evaluate.

17. $3.4 \times 2 - 1.6 \div 2^2$

18. $24.5 + 13 \times 0.6$

19. $\dfrac{9.8 + 7.8}{4}$

20. $23.5 - 1.2(3.6 + 4.4)$

21. $(5.6 - 4.3)(8.1 + 2.2)$

Evaluate.

22. $3.2^3 - (4.6 + 2.1)$

23. $5.2 \times 3 - 2.4^2$

24. $6.3 \div 9 + 11.2$

25. $(14 + 5.6) \div 2$

26. $34.6 - 15.5 \div 5$

27. $1.2 \times 100 + 15$

Evaluate.

28. $15 \div (-3) + 8$

29. $3 \times 4 - 2$

30. $10 - (-5) + 7$

31. $-6 + (-7) - 3$

32. $-3(-6) + (-5)$

33. $-6 \times 7 - 15$

34. $9 + 4 - 2 - 1$

35. $11 + (-8) \div (-4)$

Evaluate.

36. $15 \times 6 \div 3$

37. $-7(-6) \div (-3)$

38. $-2(-9) \div 6$

39. $5(-2)(-3) + 7$

40. $10 - (-4)(+2)$

41. $-3(+6) + 3(-4)$

42. $-20 \div 4 \times 3 + 2$

43. $9 \times (-8) \div (-2)$

Evaluate.
44. $5(8-7)+6$
45. $-6+4(3-9)$
46. $-2(9-4)-3$
47. $-(6-3)-(2-6)$
48. $4(2-5)+5(2+1)$

Evaluate.
49. $-2+(-3)^2$ **50.** $(-4)^2+5$
51. -4^2+5 **52.** $(-2)^3-(-3)$
53. $-4+(-2)^2+5$ **54.** $(5-2)^2+6$
55. $-3(-7)-(-1)^3$
56. $2(3-7)^2-(-2)(-3)$

Evaluate.
57. $\dfrac{-3\times8}{4}$ **58.** $\dfrac{5\times(-8)}{-10}$

59. $\dfrac{-8\div4}{-2\div(-1)}$ **60.** $\dfrac{4-12}{3-(-5)}$

61. $\dfrac{-6\times8}{-7+(-5)}$ **62.** $\dfrac{-21\div(-3)}{-7\times(-1)}$

Applications and Problem Solving
B

63. Use brackets to make each statement true.
a) $7+1\div2=4$
b) $5\times8-6=10$
c) $15\div3+2+1=4$
d) $6+4\div2\times2=2.5$
e) $4.8+1.6-1.2\times5=6.8$
f) $3\times1.7+5.7\div3=7.4$
g) $15+2^2\div7+12=1$

64. Restaurant meals A group of 10 skiers ate dinner at the Mountaintop Restaurant. The meal had a set price of $29.95, including the tax and tip. Four of the group had discount coupons and paid only half price. What was the total cost of dinner?

65. Use brackets to make each statement true.
a) $-1-3-8\div4=-3$
b) $3^2+4\times2-5=-3$
c) $6^2-20\div2+6=2$

66. Birthday gift For your next birthday, a relative offers you a choice of two amounts of money, both in dollars. The amounts are given by
$$(2x-20)^2 \text{ and } \frac{1}{2}(x-9)^3$$
where x is your age on your next birthday. Which amount is larger?

67. Technology Use a calculator to evaluate each of the following. Use estimation to check that each answer is reasonable.
a) $34\times(-12)\div51$
b) $-504\div(-56)+77$
c) $75-85\times(-9)+57$
d) $(79.6-56.1)^2-64.25$
e) $-78+(23+16)\times(32-49)$

C

68. English There are two meanings of "5 less than −3 squared."
a) Use symbols to model the meanings.
b) What value results from each meaning?
c) Rewrite the phrase in words to make the two meanings clear. Compare your wording with a classmate's.

69. Here is a way to make the number 1 using five 2s and the order of operations.
$$2^2-\frac{2}{2}-2=1$$
Write the numbers from 2 to 9 using five 2s and the order of operations. Compare your expression for each number with a classmate's.

WORD POWER

Lewis Carroll invented a word game called doublets. The object is to go from one word to another by changing one letter at a time. You must form a real word each time you change a letter. Change the word FOOT to the word BALL by changing one letter at a time. Compare your list of words with your classmates'. The best solution has the fewest steps.

1.10 Expressions With Integers

Explore: Use a Formula

To raise money for charity, a company held a paper airplane contest. The planes were flown from the roof of a skyscraper. The formula for the height of the winning plane at any given time was

$$h = \frac{700 + 15t - t^2}{4}$$

where h was the height of the plane, in metres, and t was the flight time, in seconds.

Substitute 1 for t to find the height after 1 s. Compare your answer with a classmate's.

Inquire

1. What was the height after 2 s? 3 s?
2. What was the height after 10 s? 15 s? 20 s?
3. Describe the plane's motion so far.
4. What was the height after 35 s? 40 s?
5. After how many seconds did the plane hit the ground? Explain.

Many formulas and expressions are evaluated when variables are replaced by integers.

Example 1   Expressions With One Variable
Evaluate the expressions for $x = -2$.
a) $-7x$ **b)** $8 - 5x$ **c)** $-x^2 + 3x - 5$

Solution

a) $-7x$
$= -7(-2)$
$= 14$

b) $8 - 5x$
$= 8 - 5(-2)$
$= 8 + 10$
$= 18$

c) $-x^2 + 3x - 5$
$= -(-2)^2 + 3(-2) - 5$
$= -4 - 6 - 5$
$= -15$

Example 2   Expressions With Two Variables
Evaluate for $s = -3$ and $t = 4$.
a) $-6st$ **b)** $5s - 2t$ **c)** $4s^2 - 2st - t$

Solution

a) $-6st$
$= -6(-3)(4)$
$= 72$

b) $5s - 2t$
$= 5(-3) - 2(4)$
$= -15 - 8$
$= -23$

c) $4s^2 - 2st - t$
$= 4(-3)^2 - 2(-3)(4) - 4$
$= 4(9) - 2(-3)(4) - 4$
$= 36 + 24 - 4$
$= 56$

Practice

1. Evaluate for $x = 2$.

a) $4x$ **b)** $x + 2$ **c)** $x - 2$
d) $-2x$ **e)** $7 - x$ **f)** $2x + 4$

2. Evaluate for $x = -3$.

a) $2x$ **b)** $x + 5$ **c)** $-4x$
d) $x - 1$ **e)** $5 - x$ **f)** $2x + 3$

3. Evaluate for $s = -2$ and $t = 3$.

a) $5s$ **b)** $4st$ **c)** $s + t$
d) $t - s$ **e)** $-3st$ **f)** $-s - t$

4. Evaluate for $r = -6$.

a) $-4r$ **b)** $3(r + 1)$ **c)** $7 - 3r$
d) $-2 + 3r$ **e)** $-(r - 4)$ **f)** $-r - 4$
g) $2r + 1$ **h)** $-7r - 2$ **i)** $5r - 8$

5. Evaluate for $m = -2$.

a) $m^2 + 1$ **b)** $6 + m^3$
c) $-4m^3$ **d)** $m^2 + 3m - 1$
e) $-m^3 - 4m^2$ **f)** $m^2 - 2m - 3$
g) $(7 - m)^2$ **h)** $2m^2 + 5m + 6$

6. Evaluate for $x = -4$ and $y = -1$.

a) $3x + 2y$ **b)** $7 - 3xy$
c) $x^2 + y^2$ **d)** $4x + 3y - 6$
e) $2x^2 - y^2$ **f)** $5(x + y)^2$
g) $-3(x - y)^3$ **h)** $x^2 - 3xy + y^2$
i) $2x^2 - xy - y^2$ **j)** $(x + 2)(y - 4)$

Applications and Problem Solving

7. Copy and complete the tables.

a)

x	2x − 1
2	
1	
0	
−1	
−2	

b)

t	t² + 3
2	
1	
0	
−1	
−2	

c)

y	y + 1
2	
1	
0	
−1	
−2	

b)

m	m − 2
2	
1	
0	
−1	
−2	

8. Falling object The highest dam in Canada is the Mica Dam on the Columbia River. The height of the dam is about 245 m. The height of an object dropped from the top of the dam is given by the formula
$$h = -5t^2 + 245$$
where h is the height, in metres, and t is the time, in seconds, since the object was dropped.

a) What is the height of the object after 2 s? 6 s?
b) Find the height of the object after 7 s. Explain your answer.

9. Gravity Suppose a rock is thrown upward at a speed of 20 m/s from the edge of a 60-m cliff beside the ocean. The height of the rock above the edge of the cliff is given by the formula
$$h = 20t - 5t^2$$
where h is the height, in metres, and t is the time, in seconds, since the rock was thrown upward.

a) What is the height of the rock after 1 s? 2 s? 3 s?
b) What is the height of the rock after 4 s? Explain.
c) What is the height of the rock after 5 s? Explain.
d) After how many seconds does the rock hit the water?

10. Weather data A weather station in Kingston records the temperature at noon every day. The formula
$$\frac{a + b + c + d}{4}$$
calculates the average of four readings. Find the average of the following.

a) $a = -2°C, b = -6°C, c = -5°C, d = +1°C$
b) $a = -1°C, b = +2°C, c = -3°C, d = -6°C$

PROBLEM SOLVING

1.11 Use a Data Bank

You must locate information to solve some problems. There are many sources of information, including the Internet, libraries, newspapers, magazines, atlases, experts, and print data banks.

A grade 9 history class is going from Saint John to Ottawa, and then to Montreal, and back to Saint John. The students will spend 3 days in Ottawa and 2 days in Montreal. Their bus can average 70 km/h. The students plan to leave Saint John on a Monday morning. Draw up a schedule for the trip.

Understand the Problem

1. What information are you given?
2. What are you asked to find?
3. What information do you need to locate?
4. Do you need an exact or an approximate answer?

Think of a Plan

You need the driving distances between the cities. You could use the Internet, an atlas, an almanac, or a road map, or you could ask at a tourist information centre. To calculate the time required for each part of the trip, divide the distance by the average speed.

Carry Out the Plan

Saint John to Ottawa   1130 km
Ottawa to Montreal   190 km
Montreal to Saint John   940 km

Saint John to Ottawa takes $1130 \div 70 \doteq 16$ h. Allow 2 days.

Ottawa to Montreal takes $190 \div 70 \doteq 3$ h. Allow $\frac{1}{2}$ a day.

Montreal to Saint John takes $940 \div 70 \doteq 13$ h. Allow $1\frac{1}{2}$ days.

Schedule: Leave Saint John Monday morning. Arrive in Ottawa Tuesday evening. Spend Wednesday, Thursday, and Friday in Ottawa. Leave Saturday morning for Montreal. Arrive in Montreal at noon on Saturday. Spend the rest of Saturday and Sunday in Montreal. Leave Montreal for Saint John on Monday morning. Arrive in Saint John on Tuesday around noon.

Look Back

Does the schedule seem reasonable?

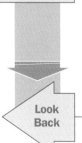

Use a Data Bank

1. Locate the information you need.
2. Solve the problem.
3. Check that the answer is reasonable.

Applications and Problem Solving

Use the Internet or another source to find the data you need to solve the following problems.

1. Distances **a)** What is the flying distance between Thunder Bay and Toronto?
b) What is the driving distance between Thunder Bay and Toronto?
c) How much longer is the driving distance than the flying distance?

2. Tour schedule A high school band is planning a tour. The band will leave from Halifax and stop in Saint John, Québec City, Toronto, and Montréal, in that order. The band will play one concert at a high school in each city and will then return to Halifax. The band will travel on a bus that can average 80 km/h. The band will leave Halifax on Monday morning. Draw up a schedule for the trip.

3. Flying times Sandra flew from Vancouver to Halifax to compete in a gymnastics competition. She left Vancouver at 11:00. The flight to Toronto took 4 h. She took 1 h and 15 min to change planes in Toronto. The flight to Halifax took 1 h and 30 min. What time was it in Halifax when she landed?

4. Wind chill What is the wind chill temperature if the thermometer reading is −23°C and the wind speed is 32 km/h?

5. Bridges The world's longest covered bridge is at Hartland, New Brunswick. The world's longest cantilevered bridge is the Pont de Québec across the St. Lawrence River. How many times longer is the Pont de Québec?

6. Territories Which of Canada's three territories has about the same area as the other two territories combined?

7. Time difference If it is 09:00 on July 1 in Paris, France, what is the time and the date in Sydney, Australia?

8. Population density The population density of a country, city, or region is the average number of people living on each square kilometre of land. Use the area and the population of each Canadian province to work out the population density of each. Rank the population densities from greatest to least.

9. Promotional tour **a)** You are the manager of a music group that wants to tour 10 cities in Ontario and Québec for two weeks to promote its new CD. Make up a travel schedule for the group.
b) Compare your schedule with your classmates'. Decide the best features of each schedule.

LOGIC POWER

Draw the grid and place three pennies, one nickel, and one dime on it as shown. By sliding one coin at a time into a neighbouring empty square, make the nickel and the dime change places. You can move horizontally or diagonally. Make the switch in as few moves as possible.

Forestry

Almost half of the land in Canada is covered in forests. About one tenth of all the forested land in the world is in Canada.

Canada's forests are valuable in many ways. As an essential part of the environment, they recycle oxygen into the atmosphere and provide a habitat for many types of animals. Humans use forests for many recreational activities and as an important economic resource. Because Canada's forests are so vast, they form an important part of the economy.

The hundreds of thousands of Canadians who depend on the forests for their careers include loggers, forest rangers, newspaper workers, and furniture makers. Exported forest products earn more revenue for Canada than any other type of export.

1 Forest Fires

Canada spends hundreds of millions of dollars a year to fight the fires that consume large areas of forest. The table includes data describing forest fires started in different ways in Canada for one year.

1. Copy and complete the table. The first line has been completed for you.

2. Estimate and then calculate the total number of forest fires with each cause in Canada for the year shown.

3. What was the main cause of forest fires in Canada that year?

4. On the average, a fire caused by humans burned an area of about 80 ha of forest, whereas a fire caused by lightning burned about 1800 ha of forest.

a) Give possible reasons why a fire caused by lightning might burn more forest than a fire caused by humans.

b) Estimate the total area of Canadian forest burned in one year in fires caused by humans; in fires caused by lightning.

2 Locating Information

Use your research skills to complete the following.

1. Choose a career that depends on Canada's forests in some way.

2. Describe how you could train for this career.

3. List some employers for people with this career.

| | Number of Forest Fires | | | |
Location	Caused by Humans	Caused by Lightning	Unknown Cause	Total
British Columbia	1132	342	0	1474
Alberta	419	358	27	
Saskatchewan	295	355	0	
Manitoba		396	0	660
Ontario	975	1115		2122
Québec	662		0	1145
New Brunswick	395		71	547
Nova Scotia		4	50	408
Prince Edward Island		0	15	29
Newfoundland	86	17		103
The Territories	143		4	363
National Parks	33	28		62

Using the Databases

Answer the following to familiarize yourself with the *MATHPOWER*™ *9, Ontario Edition, Computer Data Bank.* Use the *Movies, Olympics, Nutrition, Nations,* and *Skiing* databases included in the Computer Data Bank.

1 Movie Costs

1. Find all the records for which the cost and length are available.

 **2. a)** How could you calculate cost per minute, in dollars?
b) Add a calculated field for cost per minute, in dollars, rounding to the nearest dollar per minute.

3. Sort the records from greatest to least cost per minute. Which movie cost the most per minute? the least?

2 Winning Times

1. Find all the records for *100-m Dash, Women*.

2. Sort those records from fastest to slowest winning time.

3. What is the median winning time? Explain how you know.

4. What is the mode winning time? How frequently does it occur?

5. Determine the mean winning time, to the nearest hundredth of a second.

3 Food Graphs

1. Find and display the records for the following foods.
Cheese, cheddar   Banana, raw
Muffin, blueberry   Cheesecake
Display the following fields together.
Food   Water, %   Protein, g
Carbohydrates, g   Fat, g

2. a) How could you calculate the percent, by mass, of each component in a food?
b) Add three calculated fields for the percent of protein, the percent of carbohydrates, and the percent of fat, rounding the percents to the nearest tenth. Display the following fields together.
Food   Water, %   Protein, %
Carbohydrates, %   Fat, %

3. Copy and paste these data onto a spreadsheet, and create a graph for each food to show the percents. Compare your graphs with a classmate's.

4. What type of graph did you use? Explain why.

4 Ski Trails

1. Find all the records for which the percents of novice, intermediate, and expert trails are available. How many records are displayed?

2. For how many records is the percent of intermediate trails greater than the percent of expert trails? What fraction is this of the records displayed in question 1? Would you have predicted the fraction? Explain.

5 Nations Around the World

1. What is the mean inflation rate for the nations in Europe?

2. Gross domestic product (GDP) measures the value of all goods and services produced in a nation. What is the mean GDP for the nations in Africa?

3. Which continent has the greatest difference in literacy rates between the nations with the highest and the lowest literacy rates? What is the difference?

MODELLING MATH — ASTRONOMY

1.12 How Can We Model Distances in the Solar System?

1 Modelling Diameters in the Solar System

The table shows the diameters of the sun and the planets in the solar system relative to Earth's diameter.

Planet or Star	Diameter (Earth = 1)
Sun	109
Mercury	0.38
Venus	0.95
Earth	1.00
Mars	0.53
Jupiter	11.2
Saturn	9.4
Uranus	4.0
Neptune	3.8
Pluto	0.2

1. Explain what is meant by the heading "Earth = 1" in the diameter column of the table.

2. How were the diameters of the other planets and the sun calculated? Compare your answer with a classmate's.

3. a) Estimate how many times the smallest planet could fit across the diameter of the sun.
b) Check your estimate with a calculator. How close was your estimate?

4. Which planets are approximately the same size?

5. Earth's diameter is approximately 12 760 km. What are the approximate diameters of the other planets and the sun?

6. Using circles, or parts of circles, make a scale drawing to model how the sizes of the planets and the sun compare.

7. Write three English words that are derived from *sol*, the Latin word for sun.

2 Modelling Distances From the Sun

The table shows how far from the sun each planet is, relative to the Earth.

Planet	Average Distance From Sun (Earth = 1)
Mercury	0.39
Venus	0.72
Earth	1.00
Mars	1.52
Jupiter	5.2
Saturn	9.5
Uranus	19.2
Neptune	30.1
Pluto	39.6

1. Explain why the numbers increase from the top to the bottom of the table.

2. Compare the meaning of the heading "Earth = 1" in this table to its meaning in the previous table.

3. The average distance of the Earth from the sun is about 150 million kilometres. Calculate the average distance from the sun for the other planets.

4. Make a scale drawing to model how the distances of the planets from the sun compare.

5. Explain why the heading of the second column of the table could be written as "Average Distance From Sun (AU)," where AU represents astronomical units.

3 Extending the Model

1. Draw a circle about 2 cm in diameter to model the apparent size of the sun observed from the Earth.

2. Draw a circle that models the apparent size of the sun if it was observed from
a) Mercury   **b)** Venus   **c)** Mars

3. What would be the apparent diameter of the sun if it was observed from Pluto, to the nearest hundredth of a centimetre?

4 Researching Space Probes and Shuttle Missions

1. Use your research skills to collect data on the most recent space probe or shuttle mission. Then, write a press release to describe what was supposed to happen.

2. List 3 points supporting the view that the money spent on space probes and shuttle missions is well worth it.

3. List 3 points supporting the view that the money spent on space probes and shuttle missions is not worth it.

Review

1.1 Estimate by rounding, and then calculate.
1. $46.51 + $93.60 + $15.35
2. $513.40 − $480.29
3. $7.60 + $8.35 + $9.74 + $11.33

Estimate by clustering, and then calculate.
4. $37.40 + $43.80 + $41.40
5. $15.85 + $17.70 + $12.10 + $14.14

Estimate by finding compatible numbers, and then calculate.
6. $14.60 + $85.70 + $260.20
7. $25.10 + $115.20 + $74.18 + $182.20

Estimate by front-end estimation, and then calculate.
8. $122 + 351 + 275$
9. $8.63 + $4.38 + $7.99

Estimate, and then calculate.
10. $569 - 292$ **11.** $4521 - 2888$
12. $4.56 - 3.87$ **13.** $1.008 - 0.76$
14. 345×54 **15.** 7401×83
16. 4.23×0.72 **17.** 5.67×1.9
18. $966 \div 42$ **19.** $16\,002 \div 63$
20. $18.72 \div 3.6$ **21.** $4.704 \div 0.84$

1.2
22. Evaluate for $c = 5$ and $d = 6$.
a) $5c + 4d$ **b)** $3d + 4cd$
c) $14 - c - d$ **d)** $6c - 2d + 8$

23. Find the value of $4t - 2$ when t equals
a) 8.6   **b)** 7.2   **c)** 9.9

24. Riverboat rental To rent a riverboat for a banquet costs $675, plus $35 per person.
a) Write an expression for the cost of a banquet for n people.
b) How much would it cost for a banquet for 150 people?
c) If the 150 people shared the cost equally, how much would each have to pay?

1.4 Write as a power of 3.
25. 27   **26.** 243

Evaluate.
27. $5^3 + 3^2$ **28.** 5×2^4
29. $4^3 - 2^2$ **30.** $9^2 \div 3^3$

44   *Chapter 1*

31. Evaluate for $c = 2$ and $d = 3$.
a) $c^2 + d^2$ **b)** $(c + d)^3$
c) $4d^2 - c^3$ **d)** $4d^3 - 5cd$

32. Baton twirling A baton is thrown straight up at 15 m/s. The expression $h = 15t - 5t^2$ gives the baton's height, h metres, after t seconds.
a) What is the height of the baton after 1 s? 2 s?
b) After how many seconds will the thrower catch the baton? State your assumptions.

1.5 Simplify. Express each answer in exponential form.
33. $2^3 \times 2^5$ **34.** $5^7 \div 5^3$ **35.** $(2^4)^2$
36. $7^8 \times 7^4$ **37.** $(3^3)^3$ **38.** $6^5 \div 6$
39. $n^4 \times n^3$ **40.** $g^9 \div g^5$ **41.** $(r^2)^3$

Find the value of x.
42. $2^x \times 2^3 = 2^5$ **43.** $3^5 \div 3^x = 3^2$
44. $(5^x)^2 = 5^8$ **45.** $(t^2)^x = t^6$

1.6 Evaluate.
46. $-3 + 4 - 6 + 2$ **47.** $-2 - 3 - 5 - 7$
48. $7 - 6 + 4 - (-2)$ **49.** $-3 + 7 - (-9) - 1$

Evaluate.
50. -11×9 **51.** $9 \times (-4)$
52. $-6 \times (-7)$ **53.** $-2(-6)$
54. $-3 \times 4 \times (-2)$ **55.** $(-4)^2$
56. -4^2 **57.** $(-2)^2 \times 3$

58. Evaluate for $t = -2$.
a) $3t + 7$ **b)** $t^2 + 2t - 1$
c) $t(5t - 4)$ **d)** $2t^2 - t + 8$
e) $t^3 - t^2 - t$ **f)** $-t^3 + t^2 + t$

59. Descending aircraft A plane is flying at 30 000 m. The temperature outside the plane is −27°C. As the plane descends, the temperature increases by 1°C for every 1000-m drop in altitude. What is the temperature on the ground?

1.7 Evaluate.
60. $(-9)^2$ **61.** $5(-3)^3$
62. $(-3)^2(2^3)$ **63.** $(-1)^2 + 5^2$
64. $(-3)^5 \div (-3)^3$ **65.** $(1.2)^2(-3)^2$
66. $8^2 \div (-2)^3$ **67.** $\dfrac{2^8}{2^3 \times 2^4}$
68. $\dfrac{(-5)^2(-5)^4}{(-5)^3}$ **69.** $6^2 - (-4)^3$

70. Evaluate for $x = -2$ and $y = -3$.
a) y^3 **b)** $4x^2$
c) $-2x^3y^2$ **d)** $(y-x)^2$

1.9 *Evaluate.*
71. $7 \times 5 - (3 \times 2)$
72. $8 \times 7 - 3 + 6^2$
73. $(8-3) \times (9-7)^3$
74. $6(12.6 - 9.3) + 9.1$
75. $2.1^2 + 8.9 - 3.1$

Evaluate.
76. $5 + (-3) + (-2)$
77. $-6 \times 2 + 8$
78. $10 - 3(-4)$
79. $15 \div (-5) + 6 - (-1)^3$
80. $3 \times (-2)^2 + 4 \times (-3)$

Evaluate.
81. $\dfrac{10 \times (-2)}{5}$ **82.** $\dfrac{8-12}{1-2}$

83. $\dfrac{-14 \times (-3)}{12 \div (-2)}$ **84.** $\dfrac{18-42}{-6 \times (-2)}$

1.10 **85.** Evaluate for $x = -2$ and $y = -3$.
a) $3x + 2y$ **b)** $6xy$
c) $x^3 + y^2$ **d)** $7(x+y)^2 - 1$
e) $-3(x-y)$ **f)** $x - 2xy + y$
g) $2x^2 - y^2$ **h)** $4xy - x^2 - y^2$

86. Falling object The Century Twenty-One Building in Hamilton, Ontario, is about 125 m tall. If an object is dropped from this height, its height above the ground, h metres, is given by the formula
$$h = 125 - 5t^2$$
where t seconds is the time since the object was dropped. Find the height of the object at these times after it is dropped.
a) 1 s   **b)** 2 s
c) 4 s   **d)** 5 s

Exploring Math

Designing With Panels

A rectangular wall is to be built from panels of wood that are each 1 m wide and 2 m long. The height of the wall must be 2 m. A 2 m high wall built from 1 panel has only 1 possible design.

A 2 m high wall built from 2 panels has 2 possible designs.

If there are 5 panels, the length of the wall is 5 m. One way to assemble the 5 panels is as shown.

Designs that are reflections of each other are considered different, so this design with 5 panels is different from the one above.

1. Copy and complete the table by finding the number of designs for 2 m high walls with each number of panels.

Number of Panels	Number of Designs
1	1
2	2
3	
4	
5	
6	
7	

2. Use the pattern to describe how the number of designs can be predicted for a given number of panels.

3. Predict the number of designs for
a) 10 panels   **b)** 15 panels

Chapter Check

Estimate, and then calculate.

1. $234 + 561 + 88$ **2.** $4.37 + 0.98 + 17.69$
3. $303 - 187$ **4.** $42.03 - 6.75$
5. 45×56 **6.** 3.81×8.6
7. $2025 \div 25$ **8.** $0.364 \div 5.6$

9. Evaluate for $r = 4$ and $t = 5$.
a) $5r + 4t$ **b)** $3rt + t^2$

10. Evaluate for $x = 0.5$ and $y = 1.2$.
a) $3x + 5y$ **b)** $10xy - 2x$

11. Evaluate for $x = 3$ and $y = 5$.
a) $x^2 + y^2$ **b)** $(y - x)^4$
c) $4y^2 - 3x^3$ **d)** $2y^3 - 7xy$

Write as a power of 2.
12. 8 **13.** 32 **14.** 128

Write each answer in exponential form.
15. $3^4 \times 3^5$ **16.** $2^7 \div 2^3$ **17.** $(5^2)^4$
18. $x^4 \times x^2$ **19.** $y^5 \div y^2$ **20.** $(a^2)^5$

Evaluate.
21. $-4 - 7$ **22.** $-3 - (-6)$
23. $6 \times (-2)$ **24.** $(-5)(-3)$
25. $-3 \times (-4)$ **26.** $-21 \div (-7)$
27. $-9 \div 3$ **28.** $16 \div (-2)$

Evaluate.
29. $\dfrac{-8}{2(-2)}$ **30.** $\dfrac{14 + 8}{3 - 1}$

31. $\dfrac{(-2)(-10)}{-8 \div 4}$ **32.** $\dfrac{15(-6)}{-3(10)}$

33. Evaluate for $x = -2$ and $y = -4$.
a) x^3 **b)** $3y^2$
c) $-x^2y^3$ **d)** $(x - y)^3$

Evaluate.
34. $40 \div 5 - 2 \times 3$
35. $(7 - 5)^3 + 28 \div 7$
36. $2^3 + 4^2 - 3$
37. $5(11 - 8) - 2^2$
38. $10(4.8 - 2.5) + 7.8$
39. $0.6^2 + 7.2 \div 0.1$

Evaluate.
40. $(-5)^2 - 4 + 5$
41. $(-3)(-8) \div (-6)$
42. $-7 + 10 \div (-5)$
43. $5 \times (-2) - 8 \times 2$

44. Internet service Athena paid an initial $40 fee for connection to the Internet and $25/month for her Internet service.
a) Write an expression to represent the total cost for the first n months of service.
b) What was the total cost of Athena's Internet service over the first 2 years?

45. Gravity A ball is thrown upward at a speed of 20 m/s. The expression $h = 20t - 5t^2$ gives the ball's height, h metres, after t seconds. Find the height after each of the following lengths of time.
a) 1 s
b) 2 s
c) 3 s

Vet School.

Reprinted with special permission of King Features Syndicate.

Using the Strategies

1. Perfect squares If you take two of each of the numbers from 1 to 13, you now have 26 numbers. Write these numbers in pairs so that the sum of every pair of numbers is a perfect square.

2. Toothpicks There are 20 toothpicks in a pile. In how many ways can they be organized into 3 groups, with an even number of toothpicks in each group?

3. Triangular numbers The first 4 triangular numbers are shown.

| 1 | 3 | 6 | 10 |

What are the next 3 triangular numbers?

4. Driving distances A delivery van and a bus left a highway garage at the same time and travelled in opposite directions. The van travelled at 80 km/h, and the bus travelled at 75 km/h. How far apart were the two vehicles after 3.5 h?

5. Difference of squares The whole number 5 can be written as the difference of the squares of two whole numbers.
$$5 = 3^2 - 2^2$$
What other whole numbers between 1 and 10 can be written as the difference of the squares of two whole numbers?

6. Power boat The front seat of a power boat can hold 3 people. In how many ways can Jose, Alicia, and Jennifer be seated in the front seat if only Jose and Alicia can drive the boat?

7. Products Determine the pattern and predict the next two lines.
$$101 \times 101 = \blacksquare$$
$$202 \times 202 = \blacksquare$$
$$303 \times 303 = \blacksquare$$

8. Consecutive numbers The number 63 can be written as the sum of consecutive whole numbers as follows.
$$63 = 20 + 21 + 22$$
a) Find another way to write 63 as the sum of consecutive whole numbers.
b) Find four consecutive whole numbers that add to 138.

9. Birthday Two days ago, Robert was 16 years old. Next year, Robert will be 19 years old. What is today's date and when is Robert's birthday?

10. Perfect squares When you add the digits of the number 45, you create a perfect square.
$$4 + 5 = 9 \text{ or } 3^2$$
How many other numbers between 1 and 100 have digits that add to give perfect squares?

11. Ages The number 72 can be factored as follows.
$$72 = 36 \times 2$$
$$= 18 \times 2 \times 2$$
$$= 9 \times 2 \times 2 \times 2$$
$$= 3 \times 3 \times 2 \times 2 \times 2$$
Use this technique to find the age of each person in a group of teenagers, if the product of their ages is 661 500.

12. Bean toss In a bean toss game, each person throws two bags.
Scoring A and B gives 18 points.
Scoring A and C gives 15 points.
Scoring B and C gives 13 points.
What will you score if you toss both bags in B?

13. Elevations How much higher above sea level is Mexico City than Calgary?

14. Nunavut On average, how many square kilometres of Nunavut Territory are there per resident of the territory?

15. Longest street The world's longest street is Yonge Street, which runs from Toronto to Rainy River. If you drove the length of Yonge Street at 80 km/h, how long would the trip take, to the nearest hour?

Right Whales in the Gulf of Maine

New Brunswick

Eastport

Bay of Fundy

Maine

GRAND
MANAN
ISLAND

Digby

Nova Scotia

Yarmouth

Portland

New Hampshire

Gulf of Maine

Browns
Bank

Massachusetts

Georges
Bank

CANADA

U.S.A.

Proposed Santuary

Concentration of
Right Whales

0   40   80 km

Ratio, Rate, and Percent

How Can We Model the Population and Distribution of Wildlife Species?

One reason for monitoring the population and distribution of a wildlife species is to determine if the species is at risk of becoming extinct. If the species is at risk, scientists can determine why and make plans for its recovery.

The most endangered of all whale species is the northern right whale. There were once an estimated 200 000 northern right whales, and they were found in every ocean. Now there are about 2500. Of these, about 325 spend from July to November in the Gulf of Maine. They have been catalogued using photographs.

Since northern right whales move much more slowly than other whales, the main threat to their safety is shipping. Therefore, marine biologists have designated an area of the ocean off the coast of Nova Scotia as a northern right whale sanctuary. In this area, from July to November, ships avoid whales by reducing their speed to 8 km/h, about one quarter of the normal speed, and by having someone constantly watching for whales.

1. What fraction of the 200 000 right whales remain today?

2. What fraction of the 200 000 right whales have been lost?

3. What fraction of the remaining right whales inhabit the Gulf of Maine?

4. What human activities may cause a species to become extinct?

On pages 90 and 91, mathematical models will be used to study the population and distribution of black bears.

Exploring Patterns

1 Patterns in Pictures

Find each pattern and draw the missing diagram in your notebook.

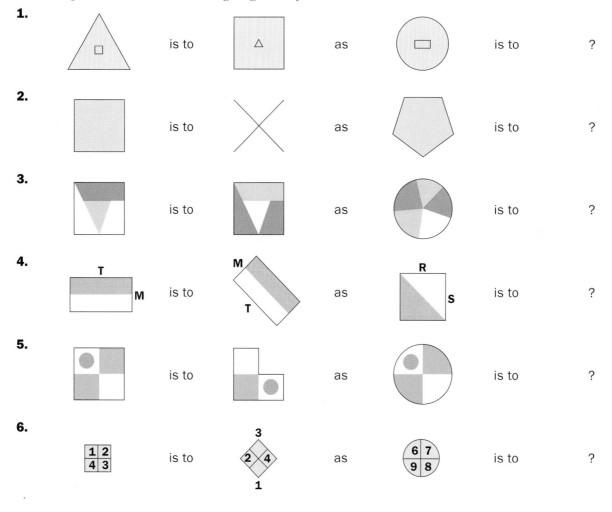

2 Patterns in Letters

Find each pattern and determine the missing letters.
1. ABC is to XYZ as DEF is to ▰▰▰.
2. BUS is to SUB as TIP is to ▰▰▰.
3. A is to F as G is to ▰▰▰.
4. STEM is to MET as FARE is to ▰▰▰.
5. E is to B as L is to ▰▰▰.
6. D is to K as M is to ▰▰▰.

3 Patterns in Numbers

Find each pattern and write the next 3 numbers.
1. 1, 4, 7, 10, ▰, ▰, ▰
2. 21, 17, 13, ▰, ▰, ▰
3. 2, 4, 8, ▰, ▰, ▰
4. 1, 2, 4, 7, 11, 16, ▰, ▰, ▰
5. 1, 5, 4, 8, 7, 11, 10, ▰, ▰, ▰
6. 20, 17, 18, 15, 16, 13, ▰, ▰, ▰
7. 1, 1, 2, 3, 5, 8, ▰, ▰, ▰

Warm Up

1. Copy and complete the table.

	Fraction	Decimal	Fraction (denominator of 100)
a)	$\frac{1}{5}$	0.2	$\frac{20}{100}$
b)	?	0.54	?
c)	?	0.6	?
d)	$\frac{1}{10}$	?	?
e)	$\frac{3}{4}$	?	?
f)	$\frac{7}{25}$	?	?
g)	?	0.5	?
h)	?	0.25	?
i)	?	0.76	?
j)	$\frac{7}{20}$	?	?

2. For the following diagram, write the fraction in simplest form, and the decimal, for each comparison.

a) the white squares to all squares
b) the red squares to all squares
c) the grey squares to all squares
d) the combined red and grey squares to all squares
e) the combined red and white squares to all squares
f) the combined grey and white squares to all squares
g) the grey squares to the red squares
h) the white squares to the red squares

Mental Math

Equivalent Fractions

State two fractions that are equivalent to each of the following.

1. $\frac{1}{2}$ **2.** $\frac{1}{5}$ **3.** $\frac{1}{3}$ **4.** $\frac{1}{4}$

5. $\frac{3}{4}$ **6.** $\frac{3}{2}$ **7.** $\frac{4}{7}$ **8.** 2

Express each fraction in simplest form.

9. $\frac{15}{30}$ **10.** $\frac{9}{21}$ **11.** $\frac{6}{14}$ **12.** $\frac{25}{40}$

13. $\frac{10}{4}$ **14.** $\frac{16}{6}$ **15.** $\frac{36}{8}$ **16.** $\frac{35}{10}$

Dividing by Multiples of 5

To divide $95 \div 5$, first divide 95 by 10.
$95 \div 10 = 9.5$
Then, multiply by 2.
$9.5 \times 2 = 19$
So, $95 \div 5 = 19$

> **Estimate**
> $100 \div 5 = 20$

Calculate.
1. $85 \div 5$ **2.** $105 \div 5$ **3.** $135 \div 5$
4. $14 \div 5$ **5.** $39 \div 5$ **6.** $42 \div 5$
7. $61 \div 5$ **8.** $123 \div 5$ **9.** $101 \div 5$

To divide $120 \div 50$, first divide 120 by 100.
$120 \div 100 = 1.2$
Then, multiply by 2.
$1.2 \times 2 = 2.4$
So, $120 \div 50 = 2.4$

> **Estimate**
> $100 \div 50 = 2$

Calculate.
10. $160 \div 50$ **11.** $210 \div 50$ **12.** $370 \div 50$
13. $980 \div 50$ **14.** $135 \div 50$ **15.** $285 \div 50$
16. $1150 \div 50$ **17.** $45 \div 50$ **18.** $65 \div 50$

19. Using a similar method, dividing 24 by 0.5 is easier than dividing 24 by 5. Explain why.

Calculate.
20. $26 \div 0.5$ **21.** $53 \div 0.5$ **22.** $118 \div 0.5$
23. $650 \div 0.5$ **24.** $9.5 \div 0.5$ **25.** $3.2 \div 0.5$

26. Explain why the rule for dividing by 5 works.

2.1 Ratios

The word "Toronto" is made up of 4 consonants and 3 vowels. A **ratio** is a comparison of two numbers with the same units. The ratio of consonants to vowels in the word "Toronto" is "four to three."

We can write a ratio in different ways. The ratio of consonants to vowels is written in ratio form as 4:3, in fraction form as $\frac{4}{3}$, or in words as "four to three." The ratio 4:3 has 2 **terms**. The **first term** is 4, and the **second term** is 3.

Explore: Complete the Table

Copy the table. Complete it by finding the ratio of consonants to vowels for the capital city of each of Canada's other provinces and territories.

City	Ratio of Consonants to Vowels		
	In Words	In Ratio Form	In Fraction Form
Charlottetown			
Edmonton			
Fredericton			
Halifax			
Iqaluit			
Québec			
Regina			
St. John's			
Toronto	four to three	4:3	$\frac{4}{3}$
Victoria			
Whitehorse			
Winnipeg			
Yellowknife			

Inquire

1. List the capitals that have the same ratios of consonants to vowels. Explain your reasoning.

2. Which capital has the greatest ratio of consonants to vowels?

A ratio is in lowest terms or simplest form when the greatest common factor of the terms is 1.

Example 1   Members of Parliament

Of the Members of Parliament (MPs) in Ottawa, 14 are elected from Manitoba, and 10 are elected from New Brunswick. Write the ratio of the number of MPs elected from Manitoba to the number elected from New Brunswick. Express the ratio in lowest terms.

Solution

The ratio of MPs elected from Manitoba to MPs elected from New Brunswick is 14:10.

$$14{:}10 = \frac{14}{10}$$
$$= \frac{14 \div 2}{10 \div 2} \qquad \text{Divide the numerator and the denominator by the greatest common factor.}$$
$$= \frac{7}{5}$$

The ratio is $\frac{7}{5}$, or 7:5, or 7 to 5.

To write a ratio of 2 quantities with different units, first make the units the same. For example, the ratio of 1 week to 1 day is not 1:1. The correct ratio is 7 days to 1 day or 7:1.

Example 2   Comparing Quantities

Write each ratio in simplest form in 3 ways.

a) 1 min to 30 s   **b)** 2 years to 15 months

Solution

The units of the quantities being compared must be the same.

a) 1 min = 60 s

$$60{:}30 = \frac{60}{30}$$
$$= \frac{60 \div 30}{30 \div 30} \qquad \text{The greatest common factor is 30.}$$
$$= \frac{2}{1}$$

The ratio is $\frac{2}{1}$, or 2:1, or 2 to 1.

b) 2 years = 24 months

$$24{:}15 = \frac{24}{15}$$
$$= \frac{24 \div 3}{15 \div 3}$$ The greatest common factor is 3.
$$= \frac{8}{5}$$

The ratio is $\frac{8}{5}$, or 8:5, or 8 to 5.

Practice

A

1. Use the diagram to write each ratio in 3 ways.
a) red squares to blue squares
b) red squares to green squares

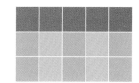

c) green squares to blue squares
d) red squares to all squares
e) all squares to blue squares
f) blue squares to all squares
g) green squares to red squares

2. Draw four 5-by-5 squares on grid paper. Use a different diagram to model each ratio.
a) 17:8   **b)** 3:2   **c)** 4:21   **d)** 16:9

3. Write each ratio in 3 ways.
a) 3 cups of sugar to 5 cups of fruit
b) 3 cans of water to 1 can of concentrate
c) 50 L of gasoline to 1 L of oil
d) 25 drops of paint to 4 drops of solvent
e) $2 saved to $3 spent

4. Write each ratio in simplest form.
a) $\frac{6}{15}$ **b)** 4:12
c) 8:16   **d)** 3 to 18
e) 6:10   **f)** 14:7
g) 12 to 2   **h)** 8:18
i) $\frac{24}{10}$ **j)** 18:4
k) 10:25   **l)** 56:28

5. Write as a ratio in simplest form.
a) 1 min to 45 s
b) 2 kg to 250 g
c) 73 days to 1 year
d) 1.5 L to 750 mL
e) 35¢ to $1.05
f) 1 m to 175 cm

Applications and Problem Solving

6. Home appliances One year, 48% of Canadian households owned dishwashers and 30% owned air conditioners. Write the ratio of households with dishwashers to households with air conditioners in lowest terms.

7. Countries For the name of each country, express the ratio of the number of consonants to the number of vowels in lowest terms.
a) Canada
b) Australia
c) France
d) Germany
e) Iceland
f) Bolivia
g) Afghanistan
h) Mozambique
i) Cuba
j) Madagascar

8. Comparison shopping The same ballpoint pen cost 90¢ in one store and $1.20 in another store. Write the ratio of the lower cost to the higher cost in lowest terms.

9. Nutrition A food guide reported that half a cup of orange juice contained 49 mg of Vitamin C, and half a cup of grapefruit juice contained 42 mg of Vitamin C. Write the ratio of the mass of Vitamin C in orange juice to the mass of Vitamin C in grapefruit juice. Express your answer in simplest form.

10. Light bulbs The power used by a light bulb is indicated by the power rating in watts (W). Express the following power ratings as ratios in lowest terms.
a) 100 W to 60 W **b)** 40 W to 60 W
c) 40 W to 150 W **d)** 150 W to 100 W

B

11. Photography Naji took 15 pictures on a 36-exposure roll of film. Express each of the following ratios in lowest terms.
a) the number of pictures he took to the number of exposures remaining
b) the total number of exposures on the roll to the number of pictures he took
c) the number of exposures remaining to the total number of exposures on the roll

12. Hockey One season, the Pittsburgh Penguins won 40 games, lost 24 games, and tied 18 games. Write a ratio in simplest form to compare
a) games won to games lost
b) games tied to games won
c) games lost to games tied

C

13. One term of a two-term ratio is a prime number. What can you state about the other term, if it is possible to write the ratio in simpler form?

14. Newspaper research a) Without looking at a newspaper, as a group estimate the ratio of advertising space to non-advertising space in a local newspaper.
b) Get a copy of the local paper and determine the ratio of advertising space to non-advertising space. You need to estimate and add fractions of pages to get this ratio.

c) Decribe your solution and include the reason why you completed each step. Compare your solution and your strategy with those of other groups.
d) Is the ratio different for a magazine?

15. Radio research Estimate, and then determine, the ratio of "DJ talk minutes" to "music minutes" on your favourite radio station.

16. TV advertising research Estimate, and then determine, the ratio of "advertising minutes" to "non-advertising minutes" for a 1-h TV show of your choice.

17. TV research a) Estimate the ratio of the height to the width of a TV screen. Is the ratio constant for all TV screens? Compare your findings with a classmate's.
b) Repeat part a) for a desktop instead of a TV screen.

18. School research Find these ratios for your school. Write them in lowest terms.
a) grade 9 girls to grade 9 boys
b) grade 9 students to all students
c) all students to all teachers

NUMBER POWER

Find the missing sum.

L	M	M	M	?
N	L	L	N	40
N	P	N	N	21
P	P	P	P	48
35	47	38	24	

PROBLEM SOLVING

2.2 Solve a Simpler Problem

A problem that appears to be difficult because of large numbers can often be simplified if you use smaller numbers. You may need to solve a series of simpler problems, with the numbers getting larger, until you see a pattern. This pattern will help you solve the original problem.

There are 9 towns in the county. Each town is connected directly to each of the others by a road. How many roads are there?

Understand the Problem

1. What information are you given?
2. What are you asked to find?
3. Do you need an exact or an approximate answer?

Think of a Plan

Find out how many roads connect 2 towns, 3 towns, 4 towns, and so on. Draw diagrams, make a table of the results, and look for a pattern.

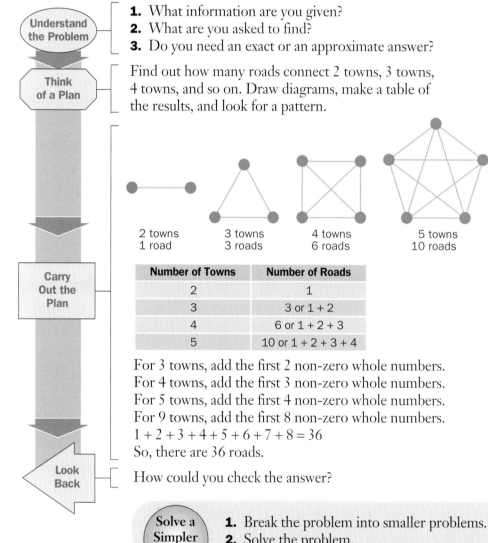

2 towns	3 towns	4 towns	5 towns
1 road	3 roads	6 roads	10 roads

Carry Out the Plan

Number of Towns	Number of Roads
2	1
3	3 or 1 + 2
4	6 or 1 + 2 + 3
5	10 or 1 + 2 + 3 + 4

For 3 towns, add the first 2 non-zero whole numbers.
For 4 towns, add the first 3 non-zero whole numbers.
For 5 towns, add the first 4 non-zero whole numbers.
For 9 towns, add the first 8 non-zero whole numbers.
$1 + 2 + 3 + 4 + 5 + 6 + 7 + 8 = 36$
So, there are 36 roads.

Look Back

How could you check the answer?

Solve a Simpler Problem

1. Break the problem into smaller problems.
2. Solve the problem.
3. Check that your answer is reasonable.

Applications and Problem Solving

1. Telephone book How would you estimate the number of listings in the white pages of a telephone book?

2. Textbook How would you estimate the thickness of one page of this textbook?

3. Novel How would you estimate how long you would take to read a 250-page novel?

4. Fencing a field Caroline owns a rectangular field of length 60 m and width 40 m. She wants to put a fence around the field. The fence posts are to be 2 m apart, and there must be a post in each corner. How many posts will she need?

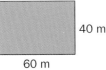

5. Find the sum of the first 100 even numbers.
$2 + 4 + 6 + 8 + 10 + \ldots$

6. Calculate the following.
$80 - 79 + 78 - 77 \ldots + 2 - 1$

7. Money How much more does a million dollars in toonies weigh than a million dollars in ten-dollar bills? Explain your solution, giving clear reasons for the steps you used.

8. Handshakes For the final game of an international hockey tournament, each team had 18 players. Before the game, each player shook hands with every player on the opposing team. How many handshakes were exchanged?

9. Exchanging pins Each of the 10 provinces sent one student to Ottawa for the opening of Parliament. Each student gave each of the other students a provincial pin. How many pins were exchanged?

10. Breathing About how many breaths do you take in one year?

11. Bacteria If one bacterium divides into two bacteria in 1 min, how many bacteria come from one bacterium in 12 min?

12. A vertical line through the number 2 divides the 2 into a maximum of four parts. Two vertical lines divide the 2 into a maximum of seven parts. How many parts will 100 vertical lines produce?

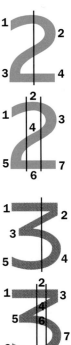

13. A vertical line through the number 3 divides the 3 into a maximum of five parts. Two vertical lines divide the 3 into a maximum of nine parts. How many parts will 100 vertical lines produce?

14. The first figure is made from one P-shape. The perimeter of the figure is 16 units. The second figure is made from two P-shapes. The perimeter of the figure is 26 units. The third figure is made from three P-shapes, and so on. Find the perimeter of the figure made from 75 P-shapes.

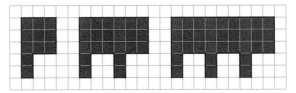

15. Write a problem that can be solved by means of a simpler problem. Have a classmate solve your problem.

INVESTIGATING MATH

Equations

Recall the steps for solving equations.

Solving by addition		Solving by subtraction	

Solving by addition

$$x - 3 = 7$$

Add 3 to both sides: $\quad x - 3 \;\boxed{+3}\; = 7 \;\boxed{+3}$

$$x = 10$$

Solving by subtraction

$$x + 4 = 10$$

Subtract 4 from both sides: $\quad x + 4 \;\boxed{-4}\; = 10 \;\boxed{-4}$

$$x = 6$$

Solving by division

$$3x = 15$$

Divide both sides by 3: $\quad \dfrac{3x}{3} = \dfrac{15}{3}$

$$x = 5$$

Solving by multiplication

$$\frac{x}{2} = 7$$

Multiply both sides by 2: $\quad \boxed{2\times}\dfrac{x}{2} = \boxed{2\times}7$

$$x = 14$$

1 Famous Canadians

The letters shown in the table each represent a different number.

Letter	A	B	C	D	E	F	G	H	I	J	L
Number											
Letter	M	N	O	R	S	T	U	W	X	Y	
Number											

1. Solve the following equations to find the value of each letter. Copy and complete the table.

$A + 3 = 7$ $\qquad$ $B - 5 = 11$ $\qquad$ $4C = 20$ $\qquad$ $\dfrac{D}{3} = 9$

$E - 8 = 16$ $\qquad$ $10F = 120$ $\qquad$ $G - 17 = 8$ $\qquad$ $H + 12 = 19$

$\dfrac{I}{9} = 5$ $\qquad$ $13J = 39$ $\qquad$ $L + 18 = 24$ $\qquad$ $5M = 130$

$N - 19 = 1$ $\qquad$ $\dfrac{O}{6} = 14$ $\qquad$ $14R = 112$ $\qquad$ $S - 18 = 3$

$T + 22 = 23$ $\qquad$ $26U = 286$ $\qquad$ $\dfrac{W}{5} = 8$ $\qquad$ $X + 25 = 39$

$7Y = 105$

2. Replace each of the following numbers with its corresponding letter to find the names of six famous Canadians. State what each of them became famous for.

a) 21 7 4 20 45 4 1 40 4 45 20

b) 26 45 5 7 4 24 6 3 12 84 14

c) 6 11 5 15 26 4 11 27 26 84 20 1 25 84 26 24 8 15

d) 6 45 20 5 84 6 20 4 6 24 14 4 20 27 24 8

e) 6 4 11 8 4 21 24 5 84 8 27

f) 8 84 16 24 8 1 16 4 1 24 26 4 20

3. Describe how the photograph shown is related to one of the famous Canadians from question 2.

2 Sets of Equations

Each of the following questions includes a set of four equations. The solution to each equation is shown in the brackets. Copy each set of equations and use each of the numbers from 0 to 9 only once to complete each set. Some of the numbers have been placed for you.

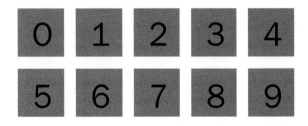

1.

$x - \blacksquare = \boxed{2}$ $(x = 5)$

$x - \blacksquare = \blacksquare - 3$ $(x = 5)$

$x - \blacksquare = \blacksquare + 1$ $(x = 10)$

$x + \blacksquare - \boxed{8} = \boxed{9} + \blacksquare$ $(x = 11)$

2.

$x + \blacksquare = 7$ $(x = 4)$

$x + \blacksquare = \blacksquare + 2$ $(x = 3)$

$\blacksquare + x + \boxed{6} = \blacksquare + 3$ $(x = 5)$

$x - \boxed{2} + \blacksquare = \blacksquare - \boxed{0}$ $(x = 3)$

3.

$\blacksquare x = 8$ $(x = 2)$

$\blacksquare x + \blacksquare = 8$ $(x = 1)$

$\blacksquare + \boxed{2} x = \blacksquare$ $(x = 3)$

$\boxed{0} + \blacksquare x = \blacksquare + \boxed{9} + 1$ $(x = 3)$

4.

$\dfrac{x}{\blacksquare} = 2$ $(x = 12)$

$\dfrac{x}{\blacksquare} + \blacksquare = 5$ $(x = 5)$

$\blacksquare + \dfrac{x}{2} = \blacksquare + 2$ $(x = 6)$

$\dfrac{x}{\blacksquare} + \blacksquare = \boxed{7} - \blacksquare$ $(x = 18)$

2.3 Equivalent Ratios and Proportions

Canadian movie director James Cameron won an Oscar for Best Director for the movie *Titanic*. Céline Dion, who sang the song "My Heart Will Go On" for the movie soundtrack, has won several Grammy awards for her music.

The statement "Movie is to Oscar as Music is to Grammy" is an analogy. In Canada, the top award for movies is the Genie, and for music is the Juno. Therefore, the statement "Movie is to Genie as music is to Juno" is also an analogy.

The above analogies are usually written as follows.
Movie:Oscar as Music:Grammy
Movie:Genie as Music:Juno

The colon symbol means "is to."

The word "analogy" comes from the Greek word *analogous*, which means "in due ratio." Analogy questions are very common on aptitude tests. These questions ask you to find a relationship between two words, and then find a similar relationship in a different pair of words.

Explore: Complete the Analogies

Copy and complete the analogies. Compare your solutions with a classmate's.
a) Dog:Bark as Cow:▨
b) Letter:Alphabet as Toe:▨
c) Bear:Cub as Sheep:▨
d) Up:Down as Hot:▨
e) Train:Track as Car:▨
f) Ruler:Length as Thermometer:▨
g) Elephants:Herd as Geese:▨

Inquire

1. Copy and complete these number analogies.
a) 1:3 as 2:▨ **b)** 4:16 as 5:▨ **c)** 12:6 as 30:▨

2. How do word analogies and number analogies compare?

3. Find the value of x in each of the following.
a) $10:x$ as $20:4$ **b)** $7:3$ as $42:x$ **c)** $x:30$ as $3:15$

Such ratios as $1:2$, $2:4$, $3:6$, and $4:8$ make the same comparison. They are known as **equivalent ratios** or **equal ratios**.

The table shows the number of cans of water and concentrated lime juice needed to make limeade.

Cans of Water	4	8	12	16	20
Cans of Concentrate	1	2	3	4	5

The ratios of cans of water to cans of concentrate are $4:1$, $8:2$, $12:3$, $16:4$, and $20:5$, or $\dfrac{4}{1}, \dfrac{8}{2}, \dfrac{12}{3}, \dfrac{16}{4}$, and $\dfrac{20}{5}$.

These are all examples of equivalent ratios.

> We can find equivalent ratios by dividing or multiplying by the same whole number, except 0.

Example 1 Finding Equivalent Ratios

Find an equivalent ratio.

a) $3:4$ **b)** $24:18$

Solution

a)
$$3:4 = \frac{3}{4}$$
$$= \frac{3 \times 2}{4 \times 2}$$
$$= \frac{6}{8}$$

b)
$$24:18 = \frac{24}{18}$$
$$= \frac{24 \div 6}{18 \div 6}$$
$$= \frac{4}{3}$$

Example 2 Identifying Equivalent Ratios

Are the ratios in each pair equivalent?

a) $12:8$, $3:2$ **b)** $3:5$, $50:75$

Solution

a)
$$\frac{12}{8} = \frac{12 \div 4}{8 \div 4}$$
$$= \frac{3}{2}$$
$$\frac{3}{2} = \frac{3}{2}$$

So, $12:8$ and $3:2$ are equivalent ratios.

b)
$$\frac{50}{70} = \frac{50 \div 25}{75 \div 25}$$
$$= \frac{2}{3}$$

To compare $\dfrac{3}{5}$ and $\dfrac{2}{3}$, use the lowest common denominator, 15.

$$\frac{3}{5} = \frac{3 \times 3}{5 \times 3} \qquad \frac{2}{3} = \frac{2 \times 5}{3 \times 5}$$
$$= \frac{9}{15} \qquad\qquad = \frac{10}{15}$$

$$\frac{9}{15} \neq \frac{10}{15} \qquad \neq \text{ means "does not equal"}$$

So, $3:5$ and $50:75$ are not equivalent ratios.

A statement that ratios are equal is called a **proportion**.

$\frac{1}{3} = \frac{2}{6}$ and $1:3 = 2:6$ are two ways of writing the same proportion.

Both forms are read as "one is to three as two is to six."

Notice that, if $\frac{1}{3} = \frac{2}{6}$, then $1 \times 6 = 3 \times 2$. Multiply the numerator of one ratio by the denominator of the other ratio.

In general, if $\frac{a}{b} = \frac{c}{d}$ Multiply both sides by bd.

$$(bd) \times \frac{a}{b} = (bd) \times \frac{c}{d}$$
$$\text{then } ab = bc$$

This is known as the **cross-product rule**.

Example 3   Pottery Soldiers

There was a fantastic archeological find in Shensi Province, China, in 1974. A life-sized army made of pottery was found buried near the tomb of the Emperor Ch'in Shih Huang Ti, who died about 210 B.C. The tomb and the army were built by about 1 000 000 workers. To estimate the number of soldiers in the army, archeologists excavated a 10-m strip of the 200-m long rectangle. They found 270 of the pottery soldiers. How many soldiers did they estimate to be in the 200-m long rectangle?

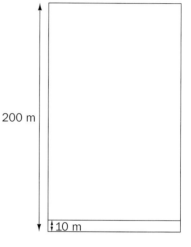

200 m

10 m

Solution

Estimate the number of soldiers by solving a proportion.
Let x represent the total number of soldiers.

$$\frac{\text{Total number of soldiers}}{\text{Length of rectangle}} = \frac{\text{Number of soldiers found}}{\text{Number of metres excavated}}$$

$$\frac{x}{200} = \frac{270}{10}$$

Method 1: Using equivalent ratios

$$\frac{x}{200} = \frac{270 \times 20}{10 \times 20}$$
$$\frac{x}{200} = \frac{5400}{200}$$
$$x = 5400$$

Method 2: Using the cross-product rule

$$\frac{x}{200} = \frac{270}{10}$$
$$10x = 200 \times 270$$
$$10x = 54\ 000$$
$$x = 5400$$

Estimate

$$200 \times 250 = 50\ 000$$
$$50\ 000 \div 10 = 5000$$

About 5400 soldiers were in the rectangle.

Example 4   Solving Proportions

Find the unknown terms.

a) $30:24 = x:8$ **b)** $\frac{4}{1.5} = \frac{10}{n}$

Solution

a) Use equivalent ratios.

$$\frac{30}{24} = \frac{x}{8}$$

$$\frac{30 \div 3}{24 \div 3} = \frac{x}{8}$$

$$\frac{10}{8} = \frac{x}{8}$$

$$10 = x$$

b) Use the cross-product rule.

$$\frac{4}{1.5} = \frac{10}{n}$$

$$4n = 10 \times 1.5$$

$$4n = 15 \qquad \text{Divide both sides by 4.}$$

$$\frac{4n}{4} = \frac{15}{4}$$

$$n = 3.75$$

To solve some problems with proportions, consider the number of equal parts a ratio represents.

Example 5   Motor Bike Fuel

For a new motor bike, the recommended ratio of gas to oil is $25:1$, by volume. How much gas and how much oil are needed to fill a 13-L tank on a new motor bike?

Solution

The total number of parts in the mixture is $25 + 1$ or 26.

Gas makes up $\frac{25}{26}$ of the mixture.

Oil makes up $\frac{1}{26}$ of the mixture.

The mixture has a volume of 13 L.

Let the volume of gas in the mixture be x.

$$\frac{x}{13} = \frac{25}{26}$$

Method 1: Using equivalent ratios

$$\frac{x}{13} = \frac{25 \div 2}{26 \div 2}$$

$$\frac{x}{13} = \frac{12.5}{13}$$

$$x = 12.5$$

Method 2: Using the cross-product rule

$$\frac{x}{13} = \frac{25}{26}$$

$$26x = 13 \times 25$$

$$26x = 325 \qquad \text{Divide both sides by 26.}$$

$$x = 325 \div 26$$

$$= 12.5$$

Estimate

$$10 \times 30 = 300$$
$$300 \div 30 = 10$$

$13 - 12.5 = 0.5$

So, 12.5 L of gas and 0.5 L of oil are needed.

Practice

A

For each ratio, write two equivalent ratios.

1. $6:5$ **2.** $3:1$ **3.** $1:5$

4. $25:40$ **5.** $\frac{2}{8}$ **6.** $\frac{18}{10}$

7. $9:6$ **8.** $\frac{16}{2}$ **9.** $\frac{4}{7}$

State whether the ratios in each pair are equivalent.

10. $\frac{2}{3}, \frac{4}{6}$ **11.** $\frac{4}{5}, \frac{8}{10}$

12. $\frac{5}{15}, \frac{1}{4}$ **13.** $\frac{6}{15}, \frac{3}{10}$

14. $9:5, 18:15$ **15.** $5:10, 6:12$

16. $8:6, 4:3$ **17.** $16:12, 12:9$

Solve for x.

18. $\dfrac{x}{15} = \dfrac{3}{5}$ **19.** $\dfrac{5}{1} = \dfrac{x}{3}$

20. $\dfrac{3}{x} = \dfrac{18}{24}$ **21.** $\dfrac{4}{3} = \dfrac{8}{x}$

22. $x:2 = 10:5$ **23.** $6:x = 10:25$

24. $8:x = 6:3$ **25.** $5:3 = 45:x$

Solve for x.

26. $2.5:x = 2:7$ **27.** $10:6.5 = x:2.6$

28. $\dfrac{4.9}{1.75} = \dfrac{3.36}{x}$ **29.** $\dfrac{x}{12.5} = \dfrac{0.8}{4}$

Applications and Problem Solving

B

30. Neptune and Pluto Neptune orbits the sun 3 times in the time it takes Pluto to orbit the sun twice.
a) How many orbits does Neptune complete while Pluto orbits 8 times?
b) How many orbits does Pluto complete while Neptune orbits 15 times?

31. Camera cost A camera costs $175. Tai and his brother share the cost in the ratio $2:3$. What is Tai's share?

32. Orange juice To make orange juice from frozen concentrate, you use concentrate and water in the ratio $1:3$, by volume. How much concentrate and how much water do you need to make 1 L of orange juice? Give your answers in millilitres.

33. Environment To make an environmentally-safe furniture polish, you can combine lemon oil and mineral oil in the ratio $3:200$, by volume. How much lemon oil do you need to make 10.15 L of polish?

34. Measurement The dimensions of a rectangle are in the ratio $5:3$. If the longer side is 18 cm, what is the length of the shorter side?

35. Measurement Two squares have side lengths in the ratio $3:2$.
a) What is the ratio of the areas of the squares?
b) If the smaller square has an area of 24 cm^2, what is the area of the larger square?

36. Measurement Two squares have areas in the ratio $49:25$.
a) What is the ratio of the side lengths of the squares? Explain and justify your reasoning.
b) If the larger square has a side length of 17.5 m, what is the side length of the smaller square?

37. Metallurgy Bronze is an alloy that contains the metals copper and tin in the ratio $23:2$, by mass.
a) What mass of each metal is present in 100 g of the alloy?
b) How many grams of copper are there for 100 g of tin?
c) How many grams of tin are there for 100 g of copper? Round your answer to the nearest tenth of a gram.

C

38. Work with a partner to try to make two equivalent ratios from four different prime numbers. Describe and explain your findings.

LOGIC POWER

The 2 squares intersect at 2 points.

Draw diagrams to show 2 squares intersecting at 3, 4, 5, and 6 points.

2.4 Rates and Unit Pricing

Ten weeks before the Barcelona Olympics, Canadian rower Silken Laumann broke her right leg in a rowing accident. Doctors told her that she would not row for at least 6 months. However, Silken competed in the games and won a bronze medal in the women's single skulls. The race was 2 km long, and Silken rowed at an average rate, or average speed, of about 16 km/h.

A **rate** is a comparison of two numbers expressed in different units. A rate is usually written as a **unit rate**, in which the second term is 1. Silken's average speed is an example of a unit rate. It could be written as 16 km : 1 h.

Explore: Solve the Problem

A Greek cycling champion named Kanellos Kanellopoulos set a world distance record for human-powered flight when he repeated the mythical flight of Daedalus. Kanellos pedalled an ultralight aircraft 5 m above the sea for 120 km, from the island of Crete to the island of Santorini. The trip took about 3 h.

a) Express the speed of the aircraft as a unit rate, in kilometres per hour.
b) Who travelled faster, Silken or Kanellos? How many times as fast?

Inquire

1. When Canada's Percy Williams won the gold medal in the 100-m run at the Amsterdam Olympics, his time was 10.8 s. What was his speed, to the nearest tenth of a metre per second?

2. When Canada's Donovan Bailey won the gold medal in the 100-m run at the Atlanta Olympics, his time was 9.84 s. What was his speed, to the nearest tenth of a metre per second?

3. How many minutes did Silken Laumann take to complete a 2-km race at 16 km/h? Explain and justify your reasoning.

Example 1   Pay Rate
Tania earned $67.50 for working for 6 h at a recreation centre. What was her rate of pay?

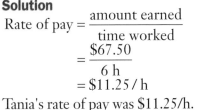

Solution

$$\text{Rate of pay} = \frac{\text{amount earned}}{\text{time worked}}$$
$$= \frac{\$67.50}{6 \text{ h}}$$
$$= \$11.25 / \text{h}$$

Tania's rate of pay was $11.25/h.

Estimate
$66 \div 6 = 11$

Example 2　Running Speed

A white-tailed deer can run at 13 m/s. How far can it run in 1 min?

Solution

Let the distance the deer can run in 1 min be x.

Write a proportion, making sure that the units agree.

The rate is $\dfrac{13 \text{ m}}{1 \text{ s}}$.

$$\frac{13}{1} = \frac{x}{60}$$

$$\frac{13 \times 60}{1 \times 60} = \frac{x}{60}$$

$$\frac{780}{60} = \frac{x}{60}$$

$$780 = x$$

$1 \text{ min} = 60 \text{ s}$

Estimate

$\boxed{10 \times 60 = 600}$

The deer can run 780 m in 1 min.

To compare prices of various goods that come in different sizes, we use unit rates, known as **unit prices**.

Example 3　Comparing Unit Prices

At a fall fair, a 200-g bag of popcorn costs $1.00. A 750-g bag of the same popcorn costs $2.70. Which size is the better value?

Solution

Let the unit price be the cost per gram or $\dfrac{\text{cost}}{1 \text{ g}}$.

Let the $\dfrac{\text{cost}}{1 \text{ g}}$ be $\dfrac{x}{1}$. Convert dollars to cents.

For the 200-g bag,

$$\frac{100}{200} = \frac{x}{1}$$

$$\frac{100 \div 200}{200 \div 200} = \frac{x}{1}$$

$$\frac{0.5}{1} = \frac{x}{1}$$

$$0.5 = x$$

For the 750-g bag,

$$\frac{270}{750} = \frac{x}{1}$$

$$\frac{270 \div 750}{750 \div 750} = \frac{x}{1}$$

$$\frac{0.36}{1} = \frac{x}{1}$$

$$0.36 = x$$

Estimate

$\boxed{300 \div 1000 = 0.3}$

The unit price is 0.5¢/g.　　　The unit price is 0.36¢/g.

Since $0.36 < 0.5$, the 750-g size is the better value.

Since the price per unit of mass or volume is often very small, we may express the unit price as the price per 100 units.

Example 4   Prices Per Hundred Units

The price of a 1-L bottle of natural spring water is $2.19. A 750-mL bottle of the same water costs $1.79.

a) Express each unit price as the cost per 100 mL.
b) Which size is the better value?

Solution

Let the $\dfrac{\text{cost}}{100 \text{ mL}}$ be $\dfrac{x}{100}$.

Recall that 1 L = 1000 mL.

For the 1-L bottle,

$$\frac{x}{100} = \frac{2.19}{1000}$$
$$1000x = 2.19 \times 100$$
$$1000x = 219$$
$$\frac{1000x}{1000} = \frac{219}{1000}$$
$$x = 0.219$$

For the 750-mL bottle,

$$\frac{x}{100} = \frac{1.79}{750}$$
$$750x = 1.79 \times 100$$
$$750x = 179$$
$$\frac{750x}{750} = \frac{179}{750}$$
$$x \doteq 0.239$$

Estimate
$$200 \div 800 = 0.25$$

179/750
.2386666667

The unit price is about
$0.22/100 mL.

The unit price is about
$0.24/100 mL.

Since $0.22/100 mL < $0.24/100 mL, the 1-L bottle is the better value.

Practice

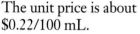

Write as a unit rate.
 1. 48 hot dogs for 16 people
 2. 150 words typed in 3 min
 3. driving 240 km in 3 h
 4. $31.80 for 3 h of work
 5. $9.48 for 3 cans of juice
 6. $186 for a 6-day car rental
 7. 432 heartbeats in 6 min
 8. jogging 1.8 km in 12 min

Express the unit rate in the units shown in brackets.
 9. 66 h of sunshine in 12 days (h/day)
 10. $98 tax on 14 barrels of oil ($/barrel)
 11. $99 for 16.5 m of fabric ($/m)
 12. 120 km : 1 h (km/min)
 13. 9 km in 6 h (m/min)

Express as a unit rate.
 14. 68 students for 2 buses
 15. 120 hamburgers for 60 people
 16. driving 165 km in 3 h
 17. 750 mL of juice for 6 people
 18. skiing 14 km in 4 h
 19. $129 for 12 h of work
 20. 900 g of batter for 4 cakes

Find the unit price. Round to the nearest tenth of a cent if necessary.
 21. $15.30 for 3 small pizzas
 22. $4.20 for 10 coloured markers
 23. $3.29 for 10 pens
 24. $48.00 for 15 party hats
 25. $28.50 for 6 sandwiches
 26. $0.70 for 40 g of potato chips
 27. $100.00 for 2.5 h of golf lessons

Applications and Problem Solving

28. Insects The wing beat of a tiny insect is the fastest action of any animal. The common midge can beat its wings at about 132 000 times per minute. Express this rate in beats per second.

29. Newspaper carriers Copy and complete the table to show the earnings of four newspaper carriers.

Carrier	Wages for 4 Weeks	Wages per Week
Bob	$78.00	▬
Terry	▬	$23.50
Susan	▬	$21.75
Yurko	$83.40	▬

30. Pay rate Paolo earned $500/week by working 8 h/day, 5 days/week. What was his hourly rate of pay?

B

31. Roberta Bondar The space shuttle *Discovery* carried Dr. Roberta Bondar to an altitude of 300 km in about 8.5 min after liftoff. At what speed did the shuttle climb
a) to the nearest kilometre per minute?
b) to the nearest hundred kilometres per hour?

32. Buffalo populations The table shows the buffalo populations of four national parks and the areas of the parks, in hectares.

National Park	Place	Area (ha)	Number of Buffalo
Elk Island	Alberta	19 400	750
Wind Cave	S. Dakota	11 450	325
Wood Buffalo	Alberta – NWT	4 480 400	3375
Yellowstone	Idaho – Montana – Wyoming	898 300	2850

a) Find the area per buffalo in each park, to the nearest tenth of a hectare.
b) Rank the parks from greatest to least area per buffalo.

33. Advertising An advertisement stated that 4 L of paint would cover 40 m^2. How much paint is needed to paint 70 m^2?

34. Pay rate **a)** Write a pay rate of $20/h as a ratio with units hours per dollar.
b) How are the two ways of writing the ratio related?
c) What is the product of the two ways of writing the ratio?

35. Earth's rotation The Earth spins 360° about its axis in 24 h. How many degrees does it spin in 10 h?

36. Nutrition Eating 2 fresh peaches gives you about 294 kJ of energy. How much energy would 3 fresh peaches give you?

37. Pay rates Nicole earned $78.00 for 8 h of house painting. Leon earned $115.20 for 12 h of house painting. Who had the higher rate of pay and by how much?

38. City populations In Stratford, Ontario, there are about 30 000 people in an area of 20 km^2. In Kingston, Ontario, there are about 60 000 people in an area of 30 km^2. In which city are there more people per square kilometre?

39. Physiology Each of your fingernails grows at about 0.05 cm/week. Each of your toenails grows at about 0.65 cm/year. Do your toenails or your fingernails grow faster?

40. Olympic Games Great Britain's Linford Christie won the men's 100-m run at the Barcelona Olympics in 9.96 s. That year, the Canadian women's team won the 3000-m speed skating relay at the Winter Olympics in 4 min 36.62 s. Who travelled faster, the sprinter or the speed skaters?

41. Densities The density of a material is defined as its mass per unit volume. A 15-cm^3 lump of uranium has a mass of 285.75 g. A 25-cm^3 lump of gold has a mass of 472 g.
a) Express the density of each of these metals in grams per cubic centimetre.
b) State which metal has the higher density.

42. Comparison shopping Decide which is the better value.

a) $340.00 for a bus for 35 people or $432.00 for a bus for 40 people

b) $4.30 for 4 L of milk or $2.40 for 2 L of milk

c) 28 g of mixed nuts for $0.98 or 35 g of mixed nuts for $1.40

d) ski rentals at $72.00 for 5 h or $52.50 for 3 h

e) 1.5 L of juice for $2.40 or 2.5 L of juice for $3.50

f) 500 sheets of computer paper for $9.50 or 2000 sheets of computer paper for $36.00

g) 18 L of gas for $10.98 or 8 L of gas for $4.72

43. Comparison shopping Calculate the rate per 100 units to find the better value.

a) 450 g of peanuts for $3.00 or 250 g of peanuts for $2.00

b) 700 g of cheese for $5.60 or 0.5 kg of cheese for $4.50

c) 90 mL of hand lotion for $4.05 or 0.6 L of hand lotion for $21.00

d) 50 drinking straws for $0.69 or 110 drinking straws for $1.49

44. Paper costs Loose-leaf paper costs $1.49 for 200 sheets or $3.49 for 500 sheets. Find

a) the least you can pay for 1000 sheets

b) the least you can pay for 1600 sheets

45. Keeping time The world's most accurate mechanical clock is in Copenhagen Town Hall in Denmark. The clock will lose or gain no more than 0.5 s in 300 years. How long would the clock take to lose or gain 1 min? What assumptions have you made?

46. List reasons why the unit price is often lower for a larger size of a product than for a smaller size of the same product.

C

47. Fuel efficiency research The fuel consumption of a car is reported in litres per 100 km (L/100 km) by Transport Canada. The smaller the value, the more fuel efficient the car is.

a) Copy the table. Complete it by calculating the fuel consumption of each car, to the nearest tenth of a litre per hundred kilometres.

Car	Distance Travelled (km)	Fuel Used (L)	Fuel Consumption (L/100 km)
A	500	26.5	
B	700	40.5	
C	600	33	
D	1000	74	
E	1500	99	

b) Rank the cars from highest to lowest fuel consumption.

c) Another way to determine fuel efficiency is to find the number of kilometres travelled per litre of fuel (km/L). Convert the fuel consumption in L/100 km to the units km/L. Round each answer to the nearest tenth of a kilometre per litre.

d) Use your research skills to investigate the fuel consumptions of cars. List five cars that could be called "gas guzzlers" and five cars you regard as fuel efficient. Compare your lists with your classmates'.

48. With a classmate, list the advantages and disadvantages of buying 1 L of milk for $2.00 or 2 L of milk for $3.69.

49. Advertising research Collect store flyers that advertise food products. With a classmate, compare prices of 10 products in different stores. When product sizes differ, calculate the best value.

50. Heart rate research a) Measure your heart beat for 10 s. At this rate, how many times does your heart beat in 1 min? 1 day? 1 year? Compare your results with a classmate's.

b) List some factors you must take into account when comparing heart rates.

c) Use your research skills to investigate how doctors and nurses measure heart rates.

51. Write a problem that involves two unit rates. Have a classmate solve your problem.

PROBLEM SOLVING

2.5 Make Assumptions

To solve some problems, you must make assumptions.

The Alaska Highway runs from Dawson Creek, B.C., to Fairbanks, Alaska. It is 2400 km long. The speed limit is 80 km/h. The De Marco family is leaving Dawson Creek at 09:00 on a Wednesday to drive to Fairbanks. They plan to stop for 10 h to eat and sleep on Wednesday night and on Thursday night. At what time on what day should they arrive in Fairbanks?

Understand the Problem

1. What information are you given?
2. What are you asked to find?
3. What assumptions should you make?

Think of a Plan

Assume that the De Marco family will drive at the speed limit. Calculate the time they will spend driving. Add 20 h to this time for eating and sleeping.

Carry Out the Plan

If the De Marco family drives at the 80 km/h speed limit, the time needed to drive 2400 km is found by dividing 2400 km by 80 km/h.

$$\frac{2400}{80} = 30$$

Thirty hours from 09:00 on Wednesday is 15:00 on Thursday.

Add 20 h for eating and sleeping.

The De Marco family should arrive in Fairbanks at 11:00 on Friday.

Look Back

How could you use subtraction and multiplication to check your answer?

> **Make Assumptions**
> 1. Decide what assumption(s) to make.
> 2. Use your assumption(s) to solve the problem.
> 3. Check that your answer is reasonable.

Applications and Problem Solving

Solve the following problems and state each assumption that you make.

1. Part-time job Imran earned $215.75 in the first month at his part-time job. How much can he expect to earn in one year?

2. Charity fund-raising The drama club sells oranges to raise money for charity. Last year, each member of the club sold 20 cases. How many cases can the 43 members of the club expect to sell this year?

3. School dance Clara surveyed 40 students in the school. Ten of them said they would attend the dance. If the school has 800 students, how many can Clara expect to attend the dance?

4. Patrol boat A patrol boat travels at a speed of 15 km/h. How far can the boat travel in 5 h?

5. Sprint training John trained for 5 weeks and reduced his time in the 100-m dash from 12.0 s to 11.5 s. He reasoned that, with 20 more weeks of training, he would be able to run 100 m in 9.5 s and break the world record. What assumption did he make? Is he necessarily correct? Explain.

6. Bike trails Soo Lin surveyed 100 people who bought new bikes. Of those surveyed, 80 said the town needed new bike trails. There are 10 000 people in the town, so Soo Lin reported that 8000 people wanted new bike trails. What assumption did she make? Explain.

7. Camping Six tents are placed 5.2 m apart in a straight line. What is the distance from the first tent to the last tent?

8. Car trip The distance from Eagle's Nest to Brewsterville is 425 km. For the first 150 km, the trip is along a highway, where the speed limit is 100 km/h. The rest of the trip is along a country road, where the speed limit is 50 km/h.
a) How long will it take Paulina to drive from Eagle's Nest to Brewsterville?
b) If she leaves Eagle's Nest at 16:45, at what time will she arrive in Brewsterville?

9. Cutting rope How many cuts must you make in a rope to make the following number of pieces?
a) 3   **b)** 4

10. Time How many seconds are there in February?

11. Sequences Identify the next three terms in each of the following.
a) 200, 100, 50, 25, . . .
b) 14, 17, 21, 26, . . .
c) 3, 7, 15, 31, . . .

12. Bus tour A tour bus is leaving Ottawa for Miami, Florida, at 08:00 on a Thursday. The driver can drive for a maximum of 10 h/day. The bus must stop for at least a 1-h break after about every 4 h of driving. At about what time and on what day will the bus arrive in Miami?

13. Write a problem in which the solution requires at least one assumption. Have a classmate solve your problem and state the assumption(s).

NUMBER POWER

Copy the diagram and place the numbers from 1 to 9 in the circles so that the consecutive sums of each side differ by 4.

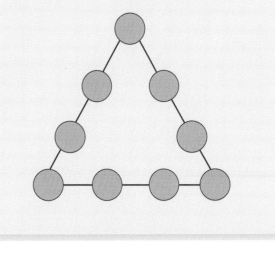

2.6 Percent

Recall that a **percent** is a fraction with a denominator of 100.
For example, 5% means $\frac{5}{100}$.

Explore: Complete the Table

The card section for a college football team uses 100 seats in the shape of a square for each letter. Each card is orange on one side and white on the other to represent the school colours. The card holders spell out the team's nickname, LIONS, using the orange cards. Copy and complete the table.

Card Section					
Number of Orange Cards	36				
Fraction of All Cards	$\frac{36}{100}$				
Decimal					
Percent of All Cards					

Inquire

1. What percent of the square does each letter use?

2. How are the last 3 entries in each column of the table related?

3. What percent of the square would each of your initials use?

4. The card section puts a "period" at the end of L-I-O-N-S by using 4 orange cards. What percent of all the cards is the period?

Example 1 Radio Listeners

At any given time, 3 out of every 5 radio listeners in Canada are in their cars. What percent of the radio listeners are in cars?

Solution

3 out of 5 can be written as the fraction $\frac{3}{5}$.

Write an equivalent fraction with a denominator of 100.

$$\frac{3 \times 20}{5 \times 20} = \frac{60}{100}$$
$$= 60\%$$

So, 60% of the radio listeners are in cars.

Practice

A

What percent of each card section is orange?

1. **2.**

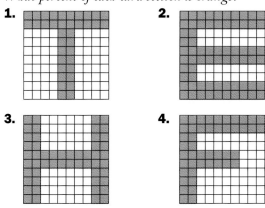

3. **4.**

What percent of each figure is shaded?

5. **6.**

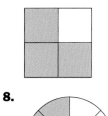

7. **8.**

9. **10.**

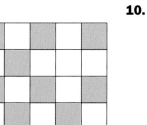

In your notebook, draw each of the following.

11. a square with 50% shaded
12. a circle with 75% shaded
13. a triangle with 50% shaded
14. a rectangle with 20% shaded
15. a square with 10% shaded
16. a rectangle with $33\frac{1}{3}$% shaded

Write as percents.

17. $\frac{17}{100}$ **18.** $\frac{61}{100}$ **19.** $\frac{90}{100}$

20. $\frac{30}{100}$ **21.** $\frac{5}{100}$ **22.** $\frac{8}{100}$

Write as percents.

23. 0.29 **24.** 0.65 **25.** 0.58
26. 0.6 **27.** 0.05 **28.** 0.02

Write as percents.

29. $\frac{1}{2}$ **30.** $\frac{7}{10}$ **31.** $\frac{4}{5}$

32. $\frac{17}{20}$ **33.** $\frac{13}{25}$ **34.** $\frac{29}{50}$

Applications and Problem Solving

35. Population About 40 out of every 100 people in Canada live in Ontario. What percent of the people in Canada live in Ontario?

36. Canadian penny A penny is 0.98 pure copper. Write the amount of copper in a penny as a percent.

37. Forested land About $\frac{9}{10}$ of the land in Ontario is forested. What percent of the land is forested?

38. Fabric The label on a T-shirt stated that 60% of the fabric was cotton, and the remainder was polyester. What percent of the fabric was polyester? Explain and justify your reasoning.

B

39. Weather A weather forecaster stated that the probability of precipitation was 70%. Explain what this means.

40. Fresh water Quebec and Ontario each have about 24% of the fresh water in Canada. What percent of Canada's fresh water is found outside these two provinces?

41. a) Why is the symbol % used for percent?
b) State the origin of the word "percent."

2.7 Ratios, Fractions, and Decimals as Percents

Pure gold is too soft for most uses, so it is often mixed with other metals to make it harder. The purity of the mixture of the metals, called an alloy, is expressed in a unit called a karat.

For an 18-karat ring, $\frac{18}{24}$ of the ring is gold, or the ratio of the mass of the gold to the mass of the ring is $18:24$.

$18:24$ is $\frac{18}{24}$ or $\frac{3}{4}$, so $\frac{3}{4}$ or 75% of the ring is gold.

Explore: Complete the Table

Copy and complete the following table.

Purity of Gold (in karats)	Ratio of Mass of Gold to Mass of Alloy	Fraction Form	Decimal Form	Percent Gold
18	18:24	$\frac{18}{24}$	0.75	75%
6				
12				
24				
15				

Inquire

1. What is the mass of gold in a 12-karat bracelet with a mass of 500 g?
2. What percent of a 9-karat ring is gold?
3. What percent of a 10-karat ring is gold?
4. Write a rule for changing a decimal to a percent.
5. Write a rule for changing a fraction to a percent.
6. Write a rule for changing a ratio to a percent.
7. Is it possible to have a ring that is 25-karat gold? Explain.

Example 1   Writing Decimals as Percents
Write as percents.
a) 0.45   **b)** 0.875   **c)** 0.006

Solution
To change a decimal to a percent, multiply the decimal by 100%.

a) $0.45 = 0.45 \times 100\%$
$= 45\%$

b) $0.875 = 0.875 \times 100\%$
$= 87.5\%$

c) $0.006 = 0.006 \times 100\%$
$= 0.6\%$

Example 2 Larry Walker

One year, while playing for the Colorado Rockies, Canadian Larry Walker won the National League batting championship with a batting average of .363. About what percent of the time did he get a hit?

Solution 1

$$0.363 = 0.363 \times 100\%$$
$$= 36.3\%$$

Larry got a hit about 36% of the time.

Solution 2

$$0.363 = \frac{363}{1000}$$
$$= \frac{363 \div 10}{1000 \div 10}$$
$$= \frac{36.3}{100}$$
$$= 36.3\%$$

Larry got a hit about 36% of the time.

Example 3 Writing Fractions as Percents

Write $\frac{7}{20}$ as a percent.

Solution

Method 1: Multiplying by 100%

$$\frac{7}{20} = \frac{7}{20} \times 100\%$$
$$= 35\%$$

Method 2: Writing the fraction as a decimal

$$\frac{7}{20} = 7 \div 20$$
$$= 0.35$$
$$0.35 \times 100\% = 35\%$$

Method 3: Using equivalent fractions

$$\frac{7}{20} = \frac{7 \times 5}{20 \times 5}$$
$$= \frac{35}{100}$$
$$= 35\%$$

Method 4: Using the cross-product rule

Let x be the percent.

$$\frac{7}{20} = \frac{x}{100}$$
$$700 = 20x$$
$$\frac{700}{20} = \frac{20x}{20}$$
$$35 = x$$

So, $\frac{7}{20} = 35\%$

Example 4 Store Sale

A store advertised a sale of $\frac{2}{3}$ off. What percent is $\frac{2}{3}$? Round your answer to the nearest tenth of a percent.

Solution

$$\frac{2}{3} = 2 \div 3$$
$$= 0.666\,666\,\ldots$$
$$\doteq 0.667$$
$$0.667 \times 100\% = 66.7\%$$

```
2/3*100
        66.66666667
```

2 ⊕ 3 ⊞ ⊜ `66.66666667`

Example 5   Endangered Species

The ratio of endangered species of birds to all bird species is $1:40$. What percent of bird species are endangered?

Solution

Write the ratio as a decimal and multiply by 100%.

$$1:40 = \frac{1}{40}$$
$$= 0.025$$
$$0.025 \times 100\% = 2.5\%$$

About 2.5% of bird species are endangered.

Example 6   Writing Percents as Decimals

Write as decimals.

a) 9%   **b)** 12.5%   **c)** 0.9%

Solution

Write the percent as a fraction and divide the numerator by the denominator.

a) $9\% = \dfrac{9}{100}$ **b)** $12.5\% = \dfrac{12.5}{100}$ **c)** $0.9\% = \dfrac{0.9}{100}$

$\quad\quad\quad = 0.09$ $\quad\quad\quad = 0.125$ $\quad\quad\quad = 0.009$

Example 7   Percents Greater Than 100%

Write as decimals.

a) 200%   **b)** 150%   **c)** 325%

Solution

a) $200\% = \dfrac{200}{100}$ **b)** $150\% = \dfrac{150}{100}$ **c)** $325\% = \dfrac{325}{100}$

$\quad\quad\quad = 2$ $\quad\quad\quad = 1.5$ $\quad\quad\quad = 3.25$

Example 8   Gravity

If you can jump 2 m on Earth, you can jump 12 m on the moon. What percent of the height of a jump on Earth is the height of a jump on the moon?

Solution

$$\frac{12}{2} \times 100\% = 6 \times 100\%$$
$$= 600\%$$

The height of a jump on the moon is 600% of the height of a jump on Earth.

Practice

A

Write as percents.
1. 0.65   2. 0.83   3. 0.98
4. 0.02   5. 0.08   6. 0.6
7. 0.7   8. 0.752   9. 0.863
10. 0.005   11. 0.15   12. 0.49

Write as percents.
13. $\frac{1}{10}$ 14. $\frac{3}{5}$ 15. $\frac{3}{8}$
16. $\frac{1}{2}$ 17. $\frac{9}{10}$ 18. $\frac{7}{20}$
19. $\frac{13}{16}$ 20. $\frac{11}{25}$ 21. $\frac{36}{45}$

Write as percents, to the nearest tenth of a percent.
22. $\frac{1}{3}$ 23. $\frac{5}{11}$ 24. $\frac{7}{9}$ 25. $\frac{7}{24}$

Write the ratios as percents.
26. 1:2   27. 4:5   28. 9:20
29. 1:8   30. 9:16   31. 2:25

Write the percents as decimals.
32. 19%   33. 35%   34. 90%
35. 1%   36. 66.6%   37. 37.5%
38. 4.5%   39. 0.8%   40. 0.55%

Write each percent as a fraction in lowest terms.
41. 30%   42. 24%   43. 52%
44. 75%   45. 88%   46. 5%
47. 2%   48. 64%   49. 38%

Write as decimals.
50. 300%   51. 400%   52. 350%
53. 500%   54. 110%   55. 115%
56. 125%   57. 101%   58. 250%

Write as percents.
59. $\frac{6}{5}$ 60. $\frac{7}{4}$ 61. $\frac{5}{2}$
62. 3   63. 1.5   64. 2.6

Calculate.
65. What percent is 25 of 125?
66. What percent is 90 of 200?

67. What percent is 10 of 40?
68. What percent is 45 of 50?
69. What percent is 16 of 10?
70. What percent is 36 of 24?

Applications and Problem Solving

71. **Reading books** Two out of every five Canadians read at least 10 books a year. What percent of Canadians read at least 10 books a year?

B

72. **Canadian rivers** The table shows four of the longest Canadian rivers.

River	Length (km)
Yukon	3185
St. Lawrence	3058
Nelson	2575
Saskatchewan	1939

Express each of the following percents to the nearest tenth.
a) What is the length of the Nelson as a percent of the length of the St. Lawrence?
b) What is the length of the Nelson as a percent of the length of the Yukon?
c) What is the length of the Saskatchewan as a percent of the length of the Yukon?

73. **Nutrition** One kilogram of chicken that has been cooked without the skin contains about 0.07 kg of fat.
a) What is the percent of fat in the cooked chicken?
b) What percent of the cooked chicken is not fat?

74. **Price increase** A magazine sells for $6.00. Last year it sold for $5.00.
a) What is the increase over last year's price?
b) What is the percent increase over last year's price?
c) What percent of the old price is the new price?

75. Comparing sizes A box of cereal was enlarged to contain 540 g. The original box contained 400 g.
a) What is the percent increase over the original box?
b) What percent of the old size is the new size?

76. Solar system Earth is approximately 150 000 000 km from the sun. Neptune is approximately 4 500 000 000 km from the sun. What percent is Neptune's distance of Earth's distance?

77. The Yukon The Yukon Territory covers about 5% of the area of Canada. Express Canada's area as a percent of the area of the Yukon Territory.

C

78. Conservation research American bison are the first animals to be saved from extinction by breeding them in captivity. In 1830, there were about 60 000 000 bison. By 1894, there were 100.
a) How many bison are there now?
b) What percent of the bison population in 1830 is the bison population today?
c) What percent of the bison population in 1894 is the bison population today?

79. Cost increase research In 1951, it cost $1.00 to go to a movie, and the cost of an LP record was $4.50.
a) What is the average cost of a movie today?
b) What is the percent increase over the cost of a movie in 1951?
c) The CD is the modern equivalent of the LP record. What is the average cost of a CD today?
d) What is the percent increase over the cost of an LP in 1951?
e) Why do you think there has been such a big difference in the percent increases?

80. Rowing The Canadian women's quadruple sculls rowing team finished third at the Olympic Games in Atlanta. There were 8 teams in the final.
a) What percent of the teams finished ahead of Canada?
b) What percent of the teams finished behind Canada?
c) Explain why the sum of your answers to parts a) and b) is not 100%.

81. What is wrong with each statement?
a) The price increased by 200%, which means it doubled.
b) A dollar is worth 400% more than a quarter.

82. Technology Work with a partner to arrange the digits to make a fraction in which the percent is as close as possible to the target given. Use your calculator.

	Digits	Target
a)	1, 3, 6, 7	50%
b)	4, 3, 6, 7	65%
c)	0, 2, 8, 9	2%
d)	1, 2, 4, 0	4%

83. Write a problem that involves a percent greater than 100%. Have a classmate solve your problem.

WORD POWER

Change the word WARM to the word COLD by changing one letter at a time. You must form a real word each time you change a letter. The best solution has the fewest steps.

2.8 Using Percents

A species becomes extinct when the last animal or plant of that species dies. The black rhinoceros is in danger of extinction. In 1979, there were about 15 000 black rhinoceroses. Now there are about 20% of that number.

20% of 15 000 = $0.2 \times 15\ 000$
$= 3000$

So, there are now about 3000 black rhinoceroses.

Explore: Interpret the Data

In 1900, there were about 40 000 tigers in India. By 1972, the number of tigers had decreased to 4% of the number in 1900. Now that hunting tigers has been banned, the number of tigers is 10% of the number in 1900.
a) What is 4% of 40 000?
b) What is 10% of 40 000?

Inquire

1. What is the increase in India's tiger population since 1972?
2. In 1979, there were about 1 300 000 African elephants. Now there are 46% of that number. How many are there now?
3. Write a rule for finding a percent of a number.

Example 1   Recycling
Each Canadian produces approximately 12 kg of garbage per week. Only 15% of this amount is recycled. What mass of each Canadian's garbage is recycled each week?

Solution
Each Canadian produces 12 kg of garbage.
Of this amount, 15% is recycled.
Find 15% of 12 to find the mass recycled each week.
15% of 12 = 0.15×12
$= 1.8$

Estimate
$0.2 \times 10 = 2$

So, 1.8 kg of each Canadian's garbage is recycled each week.

Example 2   Canadian Rivers

The Mackenzie River and the Columbia River are two of the longest rivers in Canada. The length of the Mackenzie River is 212% of the length of the Columbia River. The Columbia River is 2000 km long. How long is the Mackenzie River?

Solution

212% of 2000 = 2.12 × 2000
              = 4240

The Mackenzie River is 4240 km long.

Example 3   Water Conservation

Canadians are being urged to conserve water. A family of 4 uses about 225 L of water per day. If a leaking tap is dripping at a rate of 1 drop/s, water use for a family of 4 goes up to about 250 L per day. What percent of the 250 L of water is wasted because of the leaking tap?

Solution

The leaking tap wastes 250 L − 225 L or 25 L. Find the percent that 25 L is of 250 L.

$$\frac{25}{250} \times 100\% = 0.1 \times 100\%$$
$$= 10\%$$

So, 10% of the 250 L is wasted because of the leaking tap.

Example 4   Butterflies and Orchids

There are 20 000 species of butterflies. This number is 80% of the number of species of orchids. How many species of orchids are there?

Solution 1

Let x represent the number of species of orchids.
Write and solve a proportion.

$$\frac{80}{100} = \frac{20\ 000}{x}$$
$$80x = 20\ 000 \times 100$$
$$80x = 2\ 000\ 000$$
$$\frac{80x}{80} = \frac{2\ 000\ 000}{80}$$
$$x = 25\ 000$$

There are 25 000 species of orchids.

Solution 2

80% of the number of species of orchids is 20 000.

1% of the number of species of orchids is $\dfrac{20\ 000}{80}$.

100% of the number of species of orchids is

$$\dfrac{20\ 000}{80} \times 100 = 25\ 000$$

There are 25 000 species of orchids.

Example 5   Markup

The cost price of a CD for a retailer was $15.50. She marked it up by 30%.
What was the selling price before taxes?

Solution 1

Selling Price = Cost Price + Markup

Markup = 30% of $15.50

$\quad\quad = 0.3 \times \$15.50$

$\quad\quad = \$4.65$

Selling Price = $15.50 + $4.65

$\quad\quad\quad\quad = \$20.15$

The selling price before taxes was $20.15.

Solution 2

For a markup of 30%, the selling price is
130% of the cost price.

Selling Price = 130% of $15.50

$\quad\quad\quad\quad = 1.3 \times \$15.50$

$\quad\quad\quad\quad = \$20.15$

The selling price before taxes was $20.15.

Example 6   Commission

Sandra works at a clothing store. She earns $100 a week, plus a commission
of 15% of all her sales. In one week, she sold $9500 of merchandise. What
did she earn that week?

Solution

Commission = 15% of $9500

$\quad\quad\quad\quad = 0.15 \times 9500$

$\quad\quad\quad\quad = \$1425$

Earnings = Commission + $100

$\quad\quad\quad\quad = \$1425 + \$100$

$\quad\quad\quad\quad = \$1525$

Sandra earned $1525.

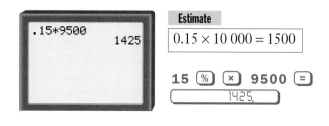

The formula to determine simple interest is $I = Prt$

where I represents the interest paid for 1 year (per annum),

$\quad\quad$ P represents the principal or the money invested or borrowed,

$\quad\quad$ r represents the rate per year (per annum),

$\quad\quad$ t represents the time in years.

Example 7   Investment

Find the simple interest on $2000 invested at 8% per year for 3 years.

Solution

$P = 2000$ $r = 8\%$ $t = 3$
               $= 0.08$

$I = Prt$
   $= 2000 \times 0.08 \times 3$
   $= 480$

The interest is $480.

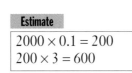

Estimate

$2000 \times 0.1 = 200$
$200 \times 3 = 600$

```
2000*.08*3
              480
```

Example 8   Loan

Find the simple interest on $1500 borrowed for 60 days at 10.75% per year.

Solution

$P = 1500$ $r = 10.75\%$ $t = \dfrac{60}{365}$ 60 days is $\dfrac{60}{365}$ year.
                $= 0.1075$

$I = Prt$
   $= 1500 \times 0.1075 \times \dfrac{60}{365}$
   $= 26.5068$

The interest is $26.51.

Estimate

$1500 \times 0.1 = 150$
$150 \times 60 = 9000$
$9000 \div 300 = 30$

```
1500*.1075*60/36
5
            26.50684932
```

Practice

A

Calculate.

1. 40% of 80
2. 25% of 120
3. 68% of 200
4. 22% of 45
5. 8% of $75.00
6. 200% of 15
7. 120% of 250
8. 175% of 300
9. 5% of $9.50, to the nearest cent
10. 16% of $50.00, to the nearest cent

Calculate.

11. What percent of 150 is 75?
12. What percent of 300 is 81?
13. What percent of 600 is 60?
14. What percent of 30 is 6?

15. What percent of 45 is 18?
16. What percent of 300 is 900?

Determine the number.

17. 50% of a number is 20
18. 25% of a number is 5
19. 20% of a number is 30
20. 10% of a number is 70
21. 2% of a number is 8
22. 150% of a number is 45

Each price is discounted by the percent shown. Find the amount of the discount and the selling price before taxes.

23. 10% of $35
24. 15% of $10
25. 20% of $55.60
26. 25% of $80.76
27. 50% of $5.85
28. 10% of $49.99

Each price is marked up by the percent shown. Find the amount of the markup and the selling price before taxes.

29. 10% of $5.50

30. 15% of $6.00

31. 25% of $8.80

32. 20% of $75.00

33. 30% of $60.00

34. $33\frac{1}{3}$% of $9.75

Express the following percents as decimals.

35. 4%

36. $8\frac{1}{2}$%

37. $6\frac{1}{4}$%

38. $5\frac{3}{4}$%

39. 7.6%

40. $6\frac{9}{10}$%

41. Find the simple interest on $5000 invested for 4 years at 6% per year.

42. Find the simple interest on $7000 invested for 90 days at 6.25% per year, to the nearest cent.

43. Find the simple interest on $2500 borrowed for 2 years at 7% per year.

44. Find the simple interest on $4000 borrowed for 60 days at $8\frac{3}{4}$% per year, to the nearest cent.

Applications and Problem Solving

45. Curling Canadian teams won 7 of the first 15 women's world curling championships. What percent of the championships did they win, to the nearest percent?

46. Election In a student council election, 80% of the students voted. If there are 990 students in the school, how many students voted?

47. Discount Leonor bought a tennis racquet, which regularly cost $94 before tax. During a sale, the discount was 20%. What was the amount of the discount?

48. Discount A portable compact disc player costs $199.99 less a 35% discount.
a) How much is the discount?
b) What is the sale price, excluding taxes?

49. Taxes A video cassette of your favourite musical group costs $39.95 plus PST and GST.
a) Find the PST.
b) Find the GST.

B

50. Marie Curie Marie Curie, who studied radioactivity, was one of the few people to win two Nobel Prizes. She lived for 23 years in Poland and 43 years in France. For what percent of her life was her home in France? Round your answer to the nearest percent.

51. English words There are about 600 000 words in the English language.
a) People use about 5000 of them when talking. What percent of the words do they use, to the nearest tenth of a percent?
b) People use about 10 000 words when writing. What percent of the words do they use, to the nearest tenth of a percent?

52. Canadian islands The area of Vancouver Island is 557% of the area of Price Edward Island. The area of Prince Edward Island is 5620 km². What is the area of Vancouver Island, to the nearest hundred square kilometres?

53. Animal speeds The maximum speed of a hyena is 64 km/h. The maximum speed of a lion is 125% of this speed. What is the maximum speed of a lion?

54. Markup A store owner can purchase a T-shirt for $18.90. The price charged to the customer includes a markup of 40%. What price does the customer pay for the T-shirt?

55. Profit A skate company's total sales were $122 130. The company's profit before taxes was $18 630. What percent of the total sales was the company's profit?

56. Total cost A pair of basketball shoes sells for $129.95, plus PST and GST. What is the total cost of the shoes?

57. Commission Eric works at a shoe store. He earns $150 a week plus a commission of 5% of all his sales. One week he sold $4395 of merchandise. What did he earn that week?

58. Birthday gift Michel received a birthday gift of $500. He plans to deposit the money for 9 months in an account that pays 8% interest per year.
a) How much interest will Michel earn in 9 months?
b) How much money will he have altogether in 9 months?

59. Loan Hania borrowed $1350 for 60 d, at 8.5% interest per year.
a) Calculate the simple interest on the loan.
b) What total amount will Hania have to repay after 60 d?

60. Comparison shopping Two clock radios are on sale. The models have the same features. One sells for $65.50 less 15%. The other sells for $72.50 less 20%. Which is the better buy?

61. Investments The student council invested $6000 of the money collected as student activity fees. The council invested the first $4000 at 6% for 90 d, and the remainder at 5% for 30 d. Calculate the total interest earned.

62. Reinvesting Find the total interest earned when $3000 is invested for 90 d at 5%, and then the total amount is reinvested for 60 d at 4.5%.

63. Working backward Raisa earns $100 a year in interest from her savings, which are invested at 8% simple interest per year. Calculate how much she has in her savings.

C

64. Music research Selling tapes, CDs, and records is a big business. The table shows who buys them.

Age	Percent Bought
10 to 19	24%
20 to 39	57%
40+	19%

Use your research skills to find the total sales, in dollars, of tapes, CDs, and records in Canada last year. Calculate how much was spent by each age group.

65. Measurement Solve these problems, and then communicate your solutions to your classmates. Suggest other ways to solve the problems. Explain each solution, giving a clear reason for each step.
a) The sides of one square are 20% as long as the sides of another square. What percent of the area of the larger square is the area of the smaller square?
b) The edges of one cube are 50% as long as the edges of another cube. What percent of the volume of the larger cube is the volume of the smaller cube?

PATTERN POWER

A triangular pyramid has 3 layers of golf balls. There are 10 golf balls altogether. How many golf balls will there be in a triangular pyramid with 5 layers? 10 layers?

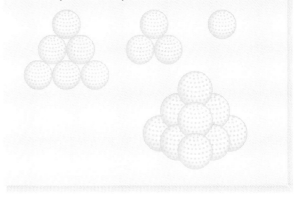

Economics

Economics is the study of how societies use their resources to meet the needs of people.

Canada has a long economic history. Before European settlement, aboriginal peoples were active traders. Hunters might trade with crop growers, for example. In today's market economy, we decide which products and services to buy from businesses. Governments are also part of the economy. They supply many services, such as education and health care, which are financed with tax dollars.

Many organizations, including government departments, banks, industrial companies, and universities, employ economists. Their studies include debt management, trade, employment trends, wages, prices, and spending patterns. Economists have university degrees in economics or business.

1 Consumer Price Index

The Consumer Price Index (CPI) is compiled by Statistics Canada to show price increases. The CPI is a measure of the average prices of household goods and services. The table shows that goods and services costing $100 in 1992 would have cost $37.10 in 1976 and $107.60 in 1997.

Year	CPI	Year	CPI
1976	37.1	1987	81.5
1977	40.0	1988	84.8
1978	43.6	1989	89.0
1979	47.6	1990	93.3
1980	52.4	1991	98.5
1981	58.9	1992	100.0
1982	65.3	1993	101.8
1983	69.1	1994	102.0
1984	72.1	1995	104.2
1985	75.0	1996	105.9
1986	78.1	1997	107.6

1. Suppose a selection of goods and services cost $350.00 in 1985. Explain how to use the CPI to show that the equivalent cost in 1995 was $486.27.

2. For every $500.00 spent on household goods and services in the year you were born, how much was spent in
a) 1978? **b)** 1997?

3. a) The CPI is related to Canada's annual inflation rate. The inflation rate in 1991 was 5.6%. Describe how this rate can be calculated from the CPI for 1990 and 1991.
b) Calculate the inflation rate for 1987, to the nearest tenth of a percent.
c) Which of the years shown in the table had the greatest inflation rate? What was the rate?

2 Locating Information

1. a) What is the meaning of the term *national debt*?
b) What is the size of Canada's national debt?
c) If the national debt were shared equally among all Canadians, how much would each person owe?

2. Find information about a part of Canada's economic history, such as aboriginal trade, farming, the settlement of the West, or the growth of cities.

3. John Kenneth Galbraith is a world-famous Canadian economist. Find information about his life and his contributions to economics.

PROBLEM SOLVING

2.9 Use Logic

Problems that can be solved using logic do not require any special skills in mathematics. These problems sharpen your deductive thinking skills.

A cat, dog, monkey, and elephant are named Trixie, Wags, Snow, and Boots. Use the clues to name each animal.
- Trixie is a friend of the cat and the elephant.
- The dog and Boots enjoy popcorn.
- Snow and Boots play golf with the monkey.
- The elephant does not play outdoor sports.

Understand the Problem

1. What information are you given?
2. What are you asked to find?

Think of a Plan

Make a table and fill in the facts from the clues.

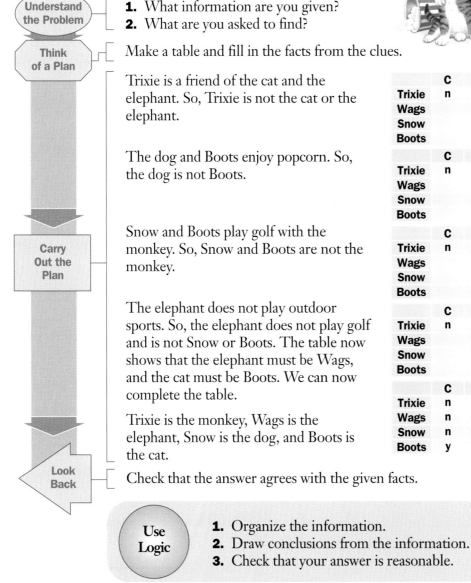

Trixie is a friend of the cat and the elephant. So, Trixie is not the cat or the elephant.

	C	D	M	E
Trixie	n			n
Wags				
Snow				
Boots				

The dog and Boots enjoy popcorn. So, the dog is not Boots.

	C	D	M	E
Trixie	n			n
Wags				
Snow				
Boots		n		

Carry Out the Plan

Snow and Boots play golf with the monkey. So, Snow and Boots are not the monkey.

	C	D	M	E
Trixie	n			n
Wags				
Snow			n	
Boots		n	n	

The elephant does not play outdoor sports. So, the elephant does not play golf and is not Snow or Boots. The table now shows that the elephant must be Wags, and the cat must be Boots. We can now complete the table.

	C	D	M	E
Trixie	n			n
Wags				
Snow			n	n
Boots		n	n	n

Trixie is the monkey, Wags is the elephant, Snow is the dog, and Boots is the cat.

	C	D	M	E
Trixie	n	n	y	n
Wags	n	n	n	y
Snow	n	y	n	n
Boots	y	n	n	n

Look Back

Check that the answer agrees with the given facts.

Use Logic

1. Organize the information.
2. Draw conclusions from the information.
3. Check that your answer is reasonable.

Applications and Problem Solving

1. Students Maria, Paula, and Shelly attend the same school. One is in grade 9, one is in grade 10, and one is in grade 11. Use the clues to find which grade each is in.
• Maria and the grade 9 student eat lunch with Shelly.
• Maria is not in grade 10.

2. Sports Four students named Al, Bjorn, Carl, and Dion each have a favourite sport. The sports are swimming, running, bowling, and golf. Use the clues to match each student with his sport.
• The runner met Bjorn and the golfer for lunch.
• Neither Bjorn's sport nor Carl's sport requires a ball.
• Dion is in the same math class as the golfer's sister.

3. Professions Susan, Irina, Traci, and Delores are a pilot, dentist, doctor, and writer. Use the clues to match each person with her profession.
• Delores is a friend of the doctor.
• Susan and the writer sail with Traci.
• Neither Susan nor Irina has patients.

4. Marathon Four people are running a marathon. Manuel is 30 m behind Margaret. Coreen is 20 m behind Tom. Margaret is 75 m ahead of Coreen. How far ahead of Tom is Manuel? Explain how you used a mathematical model to solve the problem.

5. Coins Sonya had $1.19 in change. None of the coins was a dollar. Gregor asked her for change for a dollar, but Sonya could not make change. What coins did she have?

6. Odometer The odometer on Anitha's car showed 25 952 km. The number 25 952 is called a **palindrome**. It reads the same forward and backward. Anitha drove for 2 h, and the odometer showed the next palindrome. How far did she drive in the 2 h?

7. Building A building has 5 doors. In how many ways can you enter the building by one door and leave by another?

8. Photograph A photographer wants to take a picture of the curling team. In how many ways can the 4 curlers be arranged side by side?

9. Bacteria In a bacterial culture, the number of bacteria doubled every minute. At midnight, the glass jar was full and contained 1 000 000 bacteria. At what time was the jar half full?

10. Committees Twenty-three students have volunteered to prepare for graduation day. The 23 students must be divided into 3 committees. There must be an odd number of people on each committee and at least 3 people on each committee. In how many ways can the committees be formed?

11. Painted cube The cube is yellow. You have some green paint. You must paint at least one of the faces green. In how many distinguishably different ways can you paint the faces?

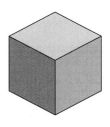

12. Professions Evans, Thompson, Wong, and DiMaggio are a teacher, plumber, artist, and banker. Use the clues to match each person with a profession.
• Thompson met the artist when he hired her to paint a picture of his horse.
• The plumber and DiMaggio are friends who have never had any business dealings.
• Neither Evans nor the plumber has ever met Wong.
• DiMaggio asked the banker for a loan.

13. Make your own logic puzzle like those in questions 2 and 3. First, set up a chart and mark the answers you want. Then, write the clues. Test your puzzle before asking a classmate to solve it.

TECHNOLOGY

Solving Problems Using Spreadsheets

A spreadsheet consists of rows and columns. It allows you to analyze and change data quickly. A spreadsheet can be an important problem solving tool. The following problem solving activities show both the power and the simplicity of a spreadsheet.

1 Coin Collection

A collection of 48 coins has a total value of $7.32. The collection consists of pennies, nickels, dimes, quarters, and half dollars. How many coins of each type are there?

1. Set up the following spreadsheet. Each formula in Column C is typed into that particular cell, as indicated.

	A	B	C
1	Coin	Number	Value
2	Penny		=0.01*B2
3	Nickel		=0.05*B3
4	Dime		=0.1*B4
5	Quarter		=0.25*B5
6	Half Dollar		=0.5*B6
7	Totals	=SUM(B2..B6)	=SUM(C2..C6)

2. Enter numbers for each type of coin into Column B of the spreadsheet until the total number of coins is 48, and the total value of all the coins is $7.32.

3. What strategy did you use to solve the problem?

4. Is there more than one solution?

2 Comparison Shopping

You can use a spreadsheet to help select a store for shopping.
1. Obtain advertising flyers from several stores.

2. Find several items that are common to all the stores. For each item, find the cost of equal sizes at all the stores.

3. Set up a spreadsheet similar to the one shown to determine which store gives you the best value for your money.

	A	B	C	D
1	Item	Store 1	Store 2	Store 3
2		Cost	Cost	Cost
3	Toothpaste			
4	Shampoo			
⋮				
5	Totals			

Electronic Spreadsheets in Sports

Sports statisticians use spreadsheets to keep track of individual and team statistics during a season, so that they can be reported to fans. A spreadsheet allows daily updates of the data.

1 **Hockey Scoring-Leader Statistics**

The spreadsheet gives the partial statistics for several hockey players for a recent season.

GP = Games Played
G = Goals
A = Assists
PTS = Points (1 for each goal and assist)
TGF = Total Goals For
PGF = Goals For on Power Play
TGA = Total Goals Against
PGA = Goals Against on Power Play
+/− = **(TGF − PGF) − (TGA − PGA)**
S = Shots on Goal
Pct = Percent of shots that scored goals

	A	B	C	D	E	F	G	H	I	J	K	L
1	Player	GP	G	A	PTS	TGF	PGF	TGA	PGA	+/−	S	Pct
2	LeClair	82	51	36		124	45	49	0		303	
3	Forsberg	72	25	66		121	52	74	11		202	
4	Francis	81	25	62		126	50	73	9		189	
5	Gretzky	82	23	67		110	41	85	5		201	
6	Jagr	77	35	67		123	46	63	3		262	
7	Palffy	82	45	42		118	52	81	13		277	
8	Bure	82	51	39		118	40	107	34		329	

1. Enter the data and formulas on a spreadsheet that will calculate the missing statistics.

2. Rank the players from best to worst. Give your reasons and compare them with a classmate's.

2 **Sports Research**

1. With a partner, choose a sport of your preference. Find some data for your favourite teams or players.

2. With your partner, set up a spreadsheet that will calculate team statistics or individual player statistics.

MODELLING MATH — THE ENVIRONMENT

2.10 How Can We Model the Population and Distribution of Wildlife Species?

1 Modelling the Population of Black Bears

Black bears come in many colours: blond, cinnamon, light brown, dark brown, and black. There are even white black bears found on islands off the coast of British Columbia.

About 75% of the black bear's diet is vegetarian. Black bears eat for 5 to 7 months and then hibernate for the rest of the year. Adult males have masses between 120 kg and 280 kg. Adult females have masses between 45 kg and 180 kg. Black bears are between 1.5 m and 1.8 m long, and they can run at speeds of up to 40 km/h.

The table shows the estimated population of black bears in Canada by province or territory, and the number killed in each province or territory in a recent year.

Province/Territory	Population Estimate	Number Killed in a Year
Alberta	40 000	3500
British Columbia	120 000–140 000	4000
Manitoba	25 000–30 000	1664
New Brunswick	12 000	1311
Newfoundland	6000–10 000	150–200
Northwest Territories	6000–8000	Unknown
Nova Scotia	7000	339
Nunavut	Unknown	Unknown
Ontario	75 000–100 000	5868
Prince Edward Island	0	0
Quebec	60 000	5045
Saskatchewan	25 000	1550
Yukon	8000	99

1. Estimate the total black bear population in Canada.

2. Estimate the total number of black bears killed in a year.

3. Estimate the percent of black bears killed in Canada in a year.

4. What percent of the black bear population in Canada is in
a) British Columbia?   **b)** Ontario?   **c)** Alberta?

5. The black bear population in North America is 450 000. About what percent of the bears are in Canada?

2 Modelling the Distribution of Black Bears

The map shows where black bears once lived in North America and where they live now.

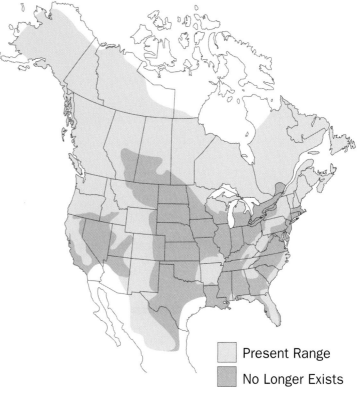

Present Range

No Longer Exists

1. Estimate the percent of its range the black bear has lost in
a) Canada **b)** the United States **c)** North America

2. Which American states that once had black bears no longer have them?

3 Locating Information

1. The black bear population in North America is declining. List some reasons for the decline.

2. List some things that could be done or are being done to protect the black bears in Canada.

3. How do scientists track the movements of animal species?

Review

2.1 *Write each ratio in simplest form.*

1. $4:6$ **2.** $35:28$ **3.** $60:80$

4. 3 to 24   **5.** $\dfrac{9}{33}$ **6.** $\dfrac{48}{20}$

Express as a ratio in simplest form.

7. 3 days to 18 h

8. 4 L to 60 mL

9. Baseball teams Some professional baseball teams have 10 pitchers, 3 catchers, 6 outfielders, and 6 infielders. Express each ratio in lowest terms.

a) pitchers to catchers

b) infielders to catchers

c) outfielders to infielders

Find an equivalent ratio.

10. $3:4$ **11.** 35 to 15   **12.** $\dfrac{8}{5}$

2.3 *Solve for x.*

13. $\dfrac{x}{5} = \dfrac{27}{45}$ **14.** $\dfrac{12}{9} = \dfrac{16}{x}$

15. $10:6 = x:24$ **16.** $4:x = 20:15$

State whether the ratios in each pair are equivalent.

17. $\dfrac{35}{45}, \dfrac{14}{18}$ **18.** $12:8,\ 32:24$

19. Punch recipe A punch recipe calls for orange juice and ginger ale in the ratio $3:5$. How much orange juice should you mix with 6 L of ginger ale?

20. Cutting rope If a 40-m rope is cut into two pieces in the ratio $3:5$, how long is each piece?

2.4 *Express each rate in the stated units.*

21. 720 km in 9 h (kilometres per hour)

22. $61.95 for 3 CDs (dollars per CD)

23. Speed skating Sylvie Daigle of Canada set a world record for speed skating by winning a 500-m race in 46.72 s. What was her average speed, to the nearest tenth of a metre per second?

24. Comparison shopping If 350 mL of shampoo is $4.59 and 150 mL is $2.25, which is the better buy?

25. Homework Christine took 45 min to finish 3 homework questions. At this rate, how long would it take her to finish 5 questions?

26. Swimming Maria can swim 3300 m in 1 h. John can swim 1980 m in 40 min. Who swims faster?

2.6 *Write as a percent.*

27. $\dfrac{51}{100}$ **28.** $\dfrac{4}{100}$ **29.** $\dfrac{96}{100}$

Write as a percent.

30. 0.33   **31.** 0.7   **32.** 0.01

Write as a percent.

33. $\dfrac{3}{5}$ **34.** $\dfrac{19}{20}$ **35.** $\dfrac{11}{25}$

36. Coins For a collection of 5 nickels and 3 quarters, express as a percent of the total value, the value of

a) 5 nickels

b) 1 quarter

c) 3 nickels and 2 quarters

37. Cycling If 24 of 60 people chose cycling as their favourite physical activity, what percent did not choose cycling?

2.7 *Write as percents.*

38. $\dfrac{4}{5}$ **39.** $\dfrac{115}{46}$ **40.** 0.43

41. $2:8$ **42.** 6.4   **43.** 0.008

Write each percent as a decimal.

44. 43 %   **45.** 76.5%   **46.** 0.2%

47. 0.003 %   **48.** 140%   **49.** 600%

50. a) What percent of 65 is 39?

b) What percent of 190 is 95?

c) What percent of 25 is 5?

d) What percent of 25 is 50?

51. Land areas The ratio of the area of land in Ontario to the area of land in Canada is 1:10. What percent of the land in Canada is in Ontario?

52. Planets The diameter of Jupiter is about 140 000 km. The diameter of Uranus is about 50 000 km. What percent of the diameter of Uranus is the diameter of Jupiter?

Calculate.

53. $\frac{1}{2}\%$ of 78

54. $12\frac{1}{2}\%$ of 64

55. 275% of 80

56. 50% of $17.50

57. If 80% of a number is 240, find the number.

2.8 **58. Discount** A sports bag was on sale at 30% off the original price of $45.00. How much was the discount?

59. Markup The cost price of a sweater for a retailer was $80. The retailer marked it up by 60%. Find the selling price before taxes.

60. Commission Sarah sold 2 cars for a total of $60 450. Her rate of commission is 2.5%. How much did she earn?

61. Investment Calculate the simple interest on $500 invested for 3 years at 6% per year.

62. Loan Calculate the simple interest on $2000 borrowed for 120 days at 8.8% per year.

63. Concorde The Concorde has a wingspan of about 25.56 m. The overall length is about 241% of the wingspan. What is the length of the Concorde, to the nearest tenth of a metre?

Exploring Math

Multiples and Divisors

Multiples and Divisors is a game for two players. To play the game, first copy the chart shown.

1	2	3	4	5	6	7	8	9	10
11	12	13	14	15	16	17	18	19	20
21	22	23	24	25	26	27	28	29	30
31	32	33	34	35	36	37	38	39	40
41	42	43	44	45	46	47	48	49	50
51	52	53	54	55	56	57	58	59	60
61	62	63	64	65	66	67	68	69	70
71	72	73	74	75	76	77	78	79	80
81	82	83	84	85	86	87	88	89	90
91	92	93	94	95	96	97	98	99	100

In the following description of the game, we will call the players Amina and Bruno. An important rule of the game is that *the first circled number must be an even number.*

1. Amina plays first by circling an *even* number on the grid.

2. Bruno then circles a number that is an exact multiple or an exact divisor of Amina's number. Bruno also draws a line through Amina's number, so that this number cannot be used again.

3. Amina then circles a number that is an exact multiple or an exact divisor of Bruno's number. Amina also draws a line through Bruno's number.

4. Now it is Bruno's turn again. The two players continue to play until one player is unable to circle a number. This player loses the game.

5. Play the game several times, taking turns to play first. Determine a winning strategy.

6. a) Describe the winning strategy.
b) Explain why the winning strategy works.
c) Explain why you think the game includes the rule that the first circled number must be an even number.

Chapter Check

Express as ratios in simplest form.
1. $6:9$
2. 4 g raisins : 12 g peanuts

Express as a unit rate.
3. $3.32 for 4 cans of soda
4. 12 km in 9 min

Solve for x.
5. $x:5 = 39:13$ **6.** $2:x = 7:21$

Write as a percent.
7. $\dfrac{9}{100}$ **8.** 2.61

9. $\dfrac{1}{10}$ **10.** $1:5$

Write as a decimal and as a fraction in lowest terms.
11. 85%   **12.** 160%   **13.** 0.5%

Find.
14. 50% of 350   **15.** 220% of 25

16. Coinage metal An alloy called coinage metal is used to make "silver" coins. Coinage metal contains copper and nickel in the ratio $3:1$, by mass.
a) What mass of copper is present for every 25 g of nickel?
b) What mass of nickel is present in 200 g of coinage metal?

17. Driving test On a driving test, Rohane answered 80% of the 20 questions correctly. How many questions did she get right?

18. Forested land The ratio of the area of forested land to the area of all land in Ontario is $9:10$. What percent of the land in Ontario is forested?

19. Comparison shopping Twenty-four 355-mL cans of juice cost $4.99, and a 2-L container of the same juice costs $1.49. Which is the better buy?

20. Sale price A bicycle was on sale for 35% off. What was the sale price before tax, if the original price was $375?

21. Markup The cost of producing a manual is $19.50. If the markup is 20%, what is the selling price before taxes?

22. Investment Calculate the simple interest on $300 invested for 3 years at 11% per year.

23. Commission One week, Carlos sold $8000 worth of paintings. He earned $500, plus a commission of 5% of sales. What did he earn?

24. Swimming Marilyn Bell was the first person to swim across Lake Ontario. She completed the 51.5-km trip in 21 h. How fast did she swim? Round your answer to the nearest tenth of a kilometre per hour.

Graham Harrop

Using the Strategies

1. English When you write the whole numbers in words, "one," "two," "three," and so on, what is the first word that has the letters in alphabetical order?

2. Triangle design How many triangles are in the 1st row? the 2nd? the 3rd? the 4th? If the pattern continues, how many triangles are in the 10th row? the 20th row? the 100th row? the *n*th row?

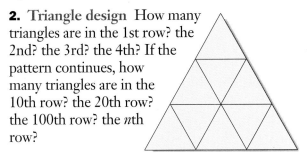

3. Summer job Jennifer works at a hardware store during her summer vacation. She earns $12.50/h for up to 40 h/week. She earns time-and-a-half for hours over 40 h/week. One week she worked 45 h. How much did she earn?

4. Toothpicks The trapezoids are made from toothpicks.

1   2   3

a) How many toothpicks are in the fourth diagram? the fifth diagram?
b) Describe the pattern in words.
c) Write an expression that represents the number of toothpicks needed for the *n*th diagram in terms of *n*.
d) Using the expression from part c), how many toothpicks are there in the 50th diagram? the 80th diagram?

5. Student council In a student council election, there are 2 candidates for president: Ali and Beth. There are 3 candidates for vice-president: Connie, Devo, and Eleanor. There are 3 candidates for treasurer: Franco, Gino, and Helen. One possible set of winners is Beth, Devo, and Helen. How many others are there?

6. Use six 9s and the order of operations to write an expression that equals 100.

7. Team points A team gets 2 points for a win, 1 point for a tie, and no points for a loss. The Bears have played 28 games. They have 27 points and 7 losses. How many wins do they have?

8. Number puzzle Copy the diagram and fill in the squares with the numbers 1 to 8 so that consecutive numbers are not adjacent in any direction — horizontally, vertically, or diagonally.

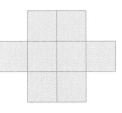

9. Animal speeds The table shows the maximum speeds of some animals.

Animal	Maximum Speed (km/h)
Ostrich	80
Coyote	72
Elephant	40
Porcupine	18

How many minutes less than a porcupine does a coyote take to run 1 km? What assumptions have you made?

10. Placing counters The diagram shows how 20 counters have been placed in 8 squares so that there are 6 counters in each row of 3 squares.

Rearrange the counters so that there are 7 counters in each row of squares.

11. Canadian residents Estimate the percent of Canadian residents whose homes are the south of the 49°N parallel of latitude.

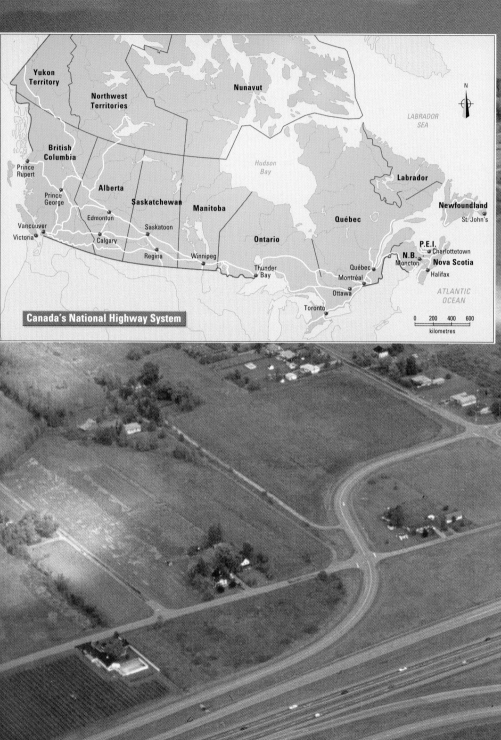

Canada's National Highway System

CHAPTER 3

Real Numbers

How Can We Model Driving Routes?

The map shows Canada's national highway network. There are about 24 500 km of highway.

1. How many hours would it take you to drive along all of Canada's national highway network at a speed of 80 km/h?

2. Could the population of Canada make a hand-to-hand chain 24 500 km long?

3. One highway accounts for almost one third of the length of Canada's highway network.
a) Name this highway.
b) In which cities does it begin and end?

4. Ontario has one fifth of Canada's total length of highways. What is the length of the highways in Ontario?

In Modelling Math — Transportation on pages 154 and 155, a mathcmatical model will be used to compare driving routes.

GETTING STARTED

Fractions

1 Fractions and Words

The first $\frac{1}{2}$ of BASEBALL is BASE.

1. What is the last $\frac{1}{2}$ of BASEBALL?

2. What is the middle $\frac{1}{2}$ of NINE?

3. What is the last $\frac{3}{8}$ of ELEPHANT?

4. What is the first $\frac{2}{3}$ of NUMBER?

5. What is the last $\frac{2}{3}$ of RECTANGLE?

6. What is the first $\frac{3}{8}$ of PENTAGON?

7. What is the middle $\frac{3}{5}$ of STARS?

2 Championship Fractions

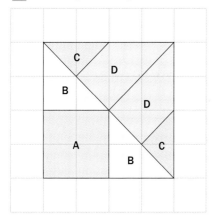

These 7 pieces, similar to a tangram, were used in the first World Puzzle Championships. The pieces are drawn on grid paper.

1. Count squares to find the area of each piece.

2. What fraction of A is B?

3. What fraction of A is C?

4. What fraction of A is D?

5. What fraction of D is C?

6. What fraction of D is B?

7. What fraction of the whole square is A? B? C? D?

3 Operations With Fractions

Add. Write each answer in simplest form.

1. $\frac{3}{8} + \frac{1}{8}$ **2.** $\frac{2}{3} + \frac{1}{3}$

3. $\frac{1}{2} + \frac{1}{6}$ **4.** $\frac{3}{8} + \frac{1}{4}$

5. $\frac{2}{5} + \frac{3}{10}$ **6.** $\frac{2}{3} + \frac{1}{4}$

7. $\frac{1}{4} + \frac{5}{6}$ **8.** $\frac{2}{5} + \frac{1}{2}$

Subtract. Write each answer in simplest form.

9. $\frac{4}{5} - \frac{2}{5}$ **10.** $\frac{5}{8} - \frac{3}{8}$

11. $\frac{1}{2} - \frac{1}{4}$ **12.** $\frac{7}{8} - \frac{1}{4}$

13. $\frac{9}{10} - \frac{3}{5}$ **14.** $\frac{1}{2} - \frac{1}{3}$

15. $\frac{3}{4} - \frac{2}{3}$ **16.** $\frac{1}{2} - \frac{1}{5}$

Multiply. Write each answer in simplest form.

17. $\frac{1}{2} \times \frac{1}{2}$ **18.** $\frac{2}{3} \times \frac{1}{3}$

19. $\frac{1}{2} \times \frac{3}{4}$ **20.** $\frac{5}{6} \times \frac{2}{3}$

21. $\frac{2}{5} \times \frac{3}{4}$ **22.** $\frac{3}{8} \times \frac{1}{2}$

23. $\frac{3}{5} \times \frac{2}{3}$ **24.** $\frac{5}{6} \times \frac{4}{5}$

Divide. Write each answer in simplest form.

25. $\frac{1}{2} \div \frac{1}{2}$ **26.** $\frac{1}{4} \div \frac{3}{4}$

27. $\frac{1}{3} \div \frac{2}{3}$ **28.** $\frac{3}{5} \div \frac{2}{5}$

29. $\frac{3}{4} \div \frac{1}{2}$ **30.** $\frac{3}{8} \div \frac{1}{2}$

31. $\frac{1}{3} \div \frac{1}{2}$ **32.** $\frac{1}{2} \div \frac{1}{3}$

33. $\frac{3}{8} \div \frac{5}{8}$ **34.** $\frac{2}{3} \div \frac{5}{6}$

Perfect Squares

Perfect squares are found by squaring whole numbers. The diagrams model the first four perfect squares.

1	4	9	16

1 Odd Numbers and Perfect Squares

Copy and complete the table.

Odd Numbers	Sum	Diagram
First one	1	■
First two	1 + 3 = 4	
First three	1 + 3 + 5 = ▦	
First four		
First five		

Find the sum of each of the following.

1. the first 8 odd numbers

2. the first 10 odd numbers

3. the first 1000 odd numbers

2 Triangular Numbers and Perfect Squares

The first four triangular numbers are shown.

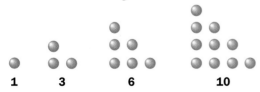

1	3	6	10

1. Why are they called triangular numbers?

Use diagrams to model your solutions to the following.
2. Find the next three triangular numbers.

3. What is the sum of any two consecutive triangular numbers?

Mental Math

Order of Operations

Calculate

1. $14 + 8 + 13$ **2.** $23 + 12 + 6$

3. $32 - 8 - 3$ **4.** $15 - 16 + 20$

5. $3 + 22 - 16$ **6.** $-4 + 15 - 18$

7. $22 + (-15) + 13$ **8.** $-10 + 35 + 12$

9. $42 + 16 + (-10)$ **10.** $-17 + 26 - 3$

11. $10 + (-12) + (-9)$ **12.** $-5 - 31 - 12$

Calculate.

13. $5 \times 2 \times 8$ **14.** $4 \times 6 \div 3$

15. $35 \div 5 \times 4$ **16.** $64 \div 4 \div 8$

17. 2×5^2 **18.** $100 \div (6 + 4)$

19. $50 - 7 \times 5$ **20.** $6 \times 2 + 3$

21. $5 \times (1 + 5)$ **22.** $6^2 \div 9$

23. $(4 + 3) \times (1 - 4)$ **24.** $5^2 + 3^2$

25. $(17 - 11)^2$ **26.** $(11 - 17)^2$

27. $15 \times (65 - 55)$ **28.** $10 \times 5 - 70$

Subtracting in Two Steps

To subtract 92 − 53, first subtract 50, and then subtract 3.

$92 - 50 = 42$
$42 - 3 = 39$
So, $92 - 53 = 39$

Estimate
$90 - 50 = 40$

Subtract.

1. $48 - 23$ **2.** $56 - 31$

3. $75 - 21$ **4.** $43 - 15$

5. $72 - 33$ **6.** $84 - 48$

7. $100 - 36$ **8.** $103 - 42$

9. $121 - 34$ **10.** $144 - 58$

11. $169 - 88$ **12.** $182 - 99$

Adapt the method to subtract the following. Describe how you adapted the method.

13. $3.6 - 1.7$ **14.** $4.2 - 2.3$

15. $6.4 - 3.8$ **16.** $16.2 - 5.4$

17. $22.5 - 4.9$ **18.** $30 - 13.3$

19. $470 - 120$ **20.** $670 - 290$

21. $830 - 540$ **22.** $920 - 450$

23. $1100 - 570$ **24.** $1320 - 440$

INVESTIGATING MATH

Mental Math — Powers of Ten

The place value chart shows the powers of 10 as numbers in standard form and exponential form.

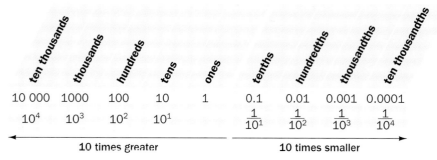

ten thousands	thousands	hundreds	tens	ones	tenths	hundredths	thousandths	ten thousandths
10 000	1000	100	10	1	0.1	0.01	0.001	0.0001
10^4	10^3	10^2	10^1		$\frac{1}{10^1}$	$\frac{1}{10^2}$	$\frac{1}{10^3}$	$\frac{1}{10^4}$

$\longleftarrow$ 10 times greater   10 times smaller $\longrightarrow$

You will complete many calculations using powers of 10. Being able to calculate mentally will simplify the calculations. There will also be times when your skills with powers of 10 will help you to estimate.

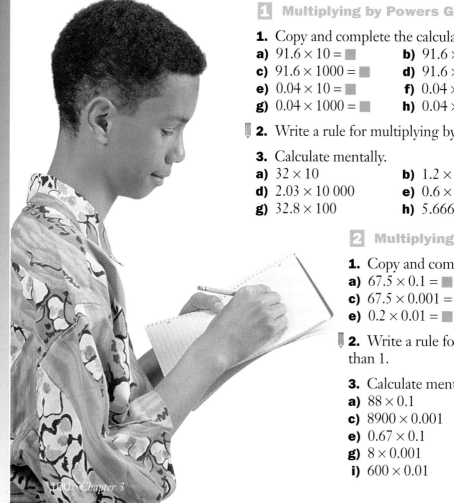

1 Multiplying by Powers Greater Than 1

1. Copy and complete the calculations.
a) $91.6 \times 10 = $ ▨   **b)** $91.6 \times 100 = $ ▨
c) $91.6 \times 1000 = $ ▨   **d)** $91.6 \times 10\ 000 = $ ▨
e) $0.04 \times 10 = $ ▨   **f)** $0.04 \times 100 = $ ▨
g) $0.04 \times 1000 = $ ▨   **h)** $0.04 \times 10\ 000 = $ ▨

2. Write a rule for multiplying by powers of 10 greater than 1.

3. Calculate mentally.
a) 32×10 **b)** 1.2×100 **c)** 346×1000
d) $2.03 \times 10\ 000$ **e)** 0.6×100 **f)** 0.05×1000
g) 32.8×100 **h)** 5.666×1000 **i)** $0.007 \times 10\ 000$

2 Multiplying by Powers Less Than 1

1. Copy and complete the calculations.
a) $67.5 \times 0.1 = $ ▨   **b)** $67.5 \times 0.01 = $ ▨
c) $67.5 \times 0.001 = $ ▨   **d)** $0.2 \times 0.1 = $ ▨
e) $0.2 \times 0.01 = $ ▨   **f)** $0.2 \times 0.001 = $ ▨

2. Write a rule for multiplying by powers of 10 less than 1.

3. Calculate mentally.
a) 88×0.1 **b)** 5.6×0.1
c) 8900×0.001 **d)** 0.4×0.01
e) 0.67×0.1 **f)** 33.3×0.0001
g) 8×0.001 **h)** 1.11×0.1
i) 600×0.01

3 **Dividing by Powers Greater Than 1**

1. Copy and complete the calculations.
a) $700 \div 10 = \blacksquare$ **b)** $700 \div 100 = \blacksquare$
c) $700 \div 1000 = \blacksquare$ **d)** $700 \div 10\ 000 = \blacksquare$
e) $1.4 \div 10 = \blacksquare$ **f)** $1.4 \div 100 = \blacksquare$
g) $1.4 \div 1000 = \blacksquare$ **h)** $1.4 \div 10\ 000 = \blacksquare$

2. Write a rule for dividing by powers of 10 greater than 1.

3. Calculate mentally.
a) $56 \div 10$ **b)** $6.2 \div 100$ **c)** $970 \div 1000$
d) $2000 \div 10\ 000$ **e)** $6 \div 100$ **f)** $55 \div 100$
g) $32.8 \div 100$ **h)** $66 \div 1000$ **i)** $7000 \div 10$

4 **Dividing by Powers Less Than 1**

1. Copy and complete the calculations.
a) $60 \div 0.1 = \blacksquare$ **b)** $60 \div 0.01 = \blacksquare$
c) $60 \div 0.001 = \blacksquare$ **d)** $1.2 \div 0.1 = \blacksquare$
e) $1.2 \div 0.01 = \blacksquare$ **f)** $1.2 \div 0.001 = \blacksquare$

2. Write a rule for dividing by powers of 10 less than 1.

3. Calculate mentally.
a) $34 \div 0.1$ **b)** $9.2 \div 0.01$ **c)** $33 \div 0.0001$
d) $234 \div 0.01$ **e)** $9 \div 0.1$ **f)** $0.04 \div 0.01$
g) $0.8 \div 0.001$ **h)** $4500 \div 0.01$ **i)** $9.9 \div 0.001$

5 **Mixed Questions**

1. Have a classmate time you to see how long you take to write the answers to the following questions.
a) 12×100 **b)** $12 \div 100$ **c)** 70×0.01
d) $12 \div 0.01$ **e)** 88×10 **f)** 8.8×0.1
g) 400×0.001 **h)** $3 \div 0.1$ **i)** $3.4 \div 1000$
j) $0.8 \div 10$ **k)** 0.88×10 **l)** $9.6 \div 0.01$
m) 560×0.1 **n)** 0.004×1000 **o)** $9.9 \div 0.001$

2. Check your answers and use the following formula to calculate your score, S. The time you took is t seconds, and W is your number of wrong answers.
$$S = t + 5W$$
Compare your score with your classmates'. The lower your score is the better.

3.1 Scientific Notation — Large Numbers

A leading Canadian astronomer, Dr. Helen Sawyer Hogg, studied huge balls of stars, known as globular clusters. The stars in these clusters are about 14 000 000 000 years old. The size of a number like 14 000 000 000 depends on the number of zeros. Writing another zero gives 140 000 000 000, which is ten times as large. Removing a zero from 14 000 000 000 gives 1 400 000 000, which is one tenth as large. To avoid mistakes when writing many zeros, large numbers can be written in **scientific notation**.

Explore: Look for a Pattern
Copy and complete the table.

Standard Form	Product Form	Scientific Notation
410	4.1 × 100	4.1×10^2
4 100	4.1 × ▨	▨
41 000	4.1 × ▨	▨
410 000	4.1 × ▨	▨
4 100 000	4.1 × ▨	▨
41 000 000	4.1 × ▨	▨

Inquire

 1. Use the completed table to write the rule for writing large numbers in scientific notation.

2. Write 760 000 000 in scientific notation.

Example 1   Planet Mercury
Mercury is about 58 000 000 km from the sun. Write 58 000 000 in scientific notation.

Solution
In scientific notation, a number has the form $a \times 10^n$, where a is greater than or equal to 1 but less than 10, and 10^n is a power of 10.

The decimal point starts here.

58 000 000

Move the decimal point 7 places to the left.

58000000   5.8ᴇ7

Use the "Sci" (scientific notation) mode on the calculator.

[SCI] **58000000** [=]

5.8 07

$= 5.8 \times 10\ 000\ 000$
$= 5.8 \times 10^7$

Notice that the number of places you moved the decimal point to the left is the exponent in the power of 10.

Example 2   Multiplying
Calculate $(4.5 \times 10^3) \times (8 \times 10^5)$. Write your answer in scientific notation.

Solution

$$(4.5 \times 10^3) \times (8 \times 10^5) = 4.5 \times 8 \times 10^3 \times 10^5$$
$$= 36 \times 10^{3+5}$$
$$= 36 \times 10^8$$
$$= 3.6 \times 10^9$$

Practice

A

Write each number in scientific notation.

1. 81 000
2. 300 000
3. 150 000
4. 200 000 000
5. 4 200 000
6. 71 300 000
7. 760 000 000
8. 5 020 000 000

9. Copy and complete the table. The first line has been completed for you.

Standard Form	Product Form	Scientific Notation
7 200	7.2×1000	7.2×10^3
45 000		
	$8.5 \times 10\ 000$	
	$1.1 \times 100\ 000$	
		9.78×10^8
		2.03×10^7

State each value of n.

10. $600 = 6 \times 10^n$
11. $7\ 100\ 000 = 7.1 \times 10^n$
12. $35\ 000 = 3.5 \times 10^n$
13. $54\ 000\ 000 = 5.4 \times 10^n$
14. $145\ 000 = 1.45 \times 10^n$
15. $460\ 000\ 000 = 4.6 \times 10^n$

Estimate, and then calculate. Write each answer in scientific notation.

16. $(3.4 \times 10^5) \times (5 \times 10^4)$
17. $(4 \times 10^8) \times (1.2 \times 10^7)$
18. $(6.7 \times 10^3) \times (8.9 \times 10^{10})$

Round each number to the highest place value. Then, calculate using scientific notation.

19. $23\ 000\ 000 \times 341\ 000$
20. $870\ 600\ 000 \times 710\ 000$
21. $92\ 000\ 000 \div 56\ 000$
22. $83\ 000\ 000\ 000 \div 777\ 000\ 000$

Applications and Problem Solving

In questions 23–25, express each number in scientific notation.

23. Coastline Canada is the country with the longest coastline, at about 91 000 km.

24. Universe The distance across the universe has been estimated at 800 000 000 000 000 000 000 000 km.

25. Sunken treasure The *HMS Edinburgh* went down with $95 000 000 in gold on board.

B

26. Write the number that is 10 times as large as each of the following.
a) 6.7×10^6 **b)** 7.6×10^5 **c)** 9.8×10^7

27. Write the number that is one tenth as large as each of the following.
a) 2.3×10^6 **c)** 6.7×10^4 **d)** 1.3×10^7

28. Constellation The Andromeda Constellation is the furthest object we can see with the unaided eye. It is about 22 000 000 000 000 000 km from the Earth.
a) Express this distance in scientific notation.
b) Light travels in space at a speed of about 300 000 km/s. Calculate how many years light takes to reach the Earth from the Andromeda Constellation.

C

29. Canada Round each answer to the greatest place value and express it in scientific notation.
a) Write the area of Canada in square metres.
b) Write the population of Canada.
c) Calculate how many square metres there are for each Canadian.

30. Why is 56×10^6 not in scientific notation?

TECHNOLOGY

Calculators and Repeating Decimals

Any repeating decimal can be written as a fraction with a denominator made up of
* one or more 9s

or
* one or more 9s and one or more zeros

```
103/990
        .104040404
```

1 One Digit Repeating

1. Use a calculator to write each fraction as a repeating decimal.

a) $\dfrac{7}{9}$ **b)** $\dfrac{7}{90}$ **c)** $\dfrac{7}{900}$

2. Use the patterns from question 1 to write the following repeating decimals as fractions or mixed numbers in lowest terms.

a) $0.\overline{5}$ **b)** $0.\overline{6}$ **c)** $0.0\overline{8}$ **d)** $0.00\overline{2}$ Recall that $0.\overline{5}$ is $0.55555...$

e) $0.00\overline{1}$ **f)** $1.\overline{3}$ **g)** $2.0\overline{4}$ **h)** $7.00\overline{2}$

3. a) Write the repeating decimal $0.\overline{9}$ as a fraction. Explain your answer.

b) Another way to write the repeating decimal $0.\overline{9}$ is $0.\overline{9} = 3 \times 0.\overline{3}$.

Evaluate $3 \times 0.\overline{3}$ by first writing $0.\overline{3}$ as a fraction. Is the result the same as the result from part a)?

2 Two Digits Repeating

1. Use a calculator to write each fraction as a repeating decimal.

a) $\dfrac{47}{99}$ **b)** $\dfrac{47}{990}$ **c)** $\dfrac{47}{9900}$

2. Use the patterns from question 1 to write the following repeating decimals as fractions or mixed numbers in lowest terms. Check your answers with a calculator.

a) $0.\overline{32}$ **b)** $0.\overline{48}$ **c)** $0.0\overline{45}$ **d)** $0.00\overline{56}$ Recall that $0.\overline{32}$ is $0.3232...$

e) $3.\overline{45}$ **f)** $6.\overline{69}$ **g)** $11.0\overline{35}$ **h)** $22.00\overline{78}$

3 Non-Repeating Parts

For repeating decimals with a non-repeating part, such as $0.1\overline{2}$, write the fraction by breaking the decimal into two parts.

$$0.1\overline{2} = 0.1 + 0.0\overline{2}$$
$$= \frac{1}{10} + \frac{2}{90}$$
$$= \frac{9}{90} + \frac{2}{90}$$
$$= \frac{11}{90}$$

1. Write the following as fractions or mixed numbers in lowest terms.

a) $0.3\overline{4}$ **b)** $0.5\overline{6}$ **c)** $0.1\overline{23}$ **d)** $0.23\overline{4}$ **e)** $4.2\overline{5}$

Writing Decimals as Fractions

Some decimals, like 0.5 and 0.64, terminate or end. Others repeat and never end, like $0.\overline{3}$ or 0.3333…

1 Terminating Decimals to Fractions

To write a terminating decimal as a fraction, use your knowledge of our number system.

0.7 means "seven tenths," so $0.7 = \dfrac{7}{10}$.

0.45 means "forty-five hundredths,"

so $0.45 = \dfrac{45}{100}$ or $\dfrac{9}{20}$.

1. Write each decimal as a fraction or mixed number in lowest terms. Check your answer with a calculator.

a) 0.3   **b)** 0.6   **c)** 1.5

d) 3.75   **e)** 2.06   **f)** 1.875

2 Non-Terminating Repeating Decimals to Fractions

For these types of decimals, eliminate the repeating part of the decimal by subtraction. Study the steps used to change $0.\overline{4}$ and $0.\overline{63}$ to fractions.

Let $F = 0.\overline{4}$ or 0.4444…

Multiply by 10: $10F = 4.\overline{4}$
Write the original: $F = 0.\overline{4}$
Subtract: $9F = 4$

Divide by 9: $\dfrac{9F}{9} = \dfrac{4}{9}$

$F = \dfrac{4}{9}$

Let $G = 0.\overline{63}$ or 0.636363…

Multiply by 100: $100G = 63.\overline{63}$
Write the original: $G = 0.\overline{63}$
Subtract: $99G = 63$

Divide by 99: $\dfrac{99G}{99} = \dfrac{63}{99}$

$G = \dfrac{63}{99}$ or $\dfrac{7}{11}$

1. Write each decimal as a fraction or mixed number in lowest terms. Check your answers with a calculator.

a) $0.\overline{2}$ **b)** $0.\overline{3}$ **c)** $0.\overline{8}$ **d)** $0.\overline{7}$ **e)** $0.\overline{12}$

f) $0.\overline{23}$ **g)** $0.\overline{46}$ **h)** $0.\overline{52}$ **i)** $3.\overline{1}$ **j)** $5.\overline{36}$

2. Write each decimal as a fraction or mixed number in lowest terms. Check your answers with a calculator.

a) $0.2\overline{6}$ **b)** $0.1\overline{5}$ **c)** $0.3\overline{9}$ **d)** $3.8\overline{9}$

3 Writing Decimals

1. Write a non-terminating repeating decimal and convert it to a fraction or mixed number in lowest terms.

2. Have a classmate convert your decimal to a fraction or mixed number in lowest terms.

3. Check your classmate's answer.

TECHNOLOGY

Exploring Zero and Negative Exponents

The equation $y = 2^x$ is called an **exponential equation**.
In this type of equation, one of the variables is an exponent.
For the equation $y = 2^x$,

when $x = 3$, $y = 2^3$
$\qquad\qquad = 8$

1 Exploring $y = 2^x$

The graph of $y = 2^x$ is shown. The table of values for $x = -3, -2, -1, 0, 1, 2, 3$ was found using the TABLE feature of a graphing calculator.

Copy and complete the following table for $y = 2^x$.

x	y (Negative Exponent)	y (Decimal Form)	y (Fraction Form)	y (Positive Exponent)
−3	2^{-3}	0.125	$\frac{1}{8}$	$\frac{1}{2^3}$
−2	2^{-2}			
−1	2^{-1}			

2 Exploring $y = 3^x$

The graph of $y = 3^x$ is shown. The table of values for $x = -2, -1, 0, 1, 2$ was found using the TABLE feature of a graphing calculator.

Copy and complete the following table for $y = 3^x$.

x	y (Negative Exponent)	y (Decimal Form)	y (Fraction Form)	y (Positive Exponent)
−2	3^{-2}			
−1	3^{-1}			

3 Exploring $y = 4^x$

The graph of $y = 4^x$ is shown. The table of values for $x = -2, -1, 0, 1, 2$ was found using the TABLE feature of a graphing calculator.

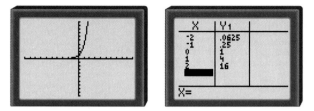

Copy and complete the following table for $y = 4^x$.

x	y (Negative Exponent)	y (Decimal Form)	y (Fraction Form)	y (Positive Exponent)
−2	4^{-2}			
−1	4^{-1}			

4 Exponent Zero

1. From Explorations 1, 2, and 3, what is the value of
a) 2^0?   **b)** 3^0?   **c)** 4^0?

2. Make a conjecture about the value of any number with the exponent 0.

3. Use your conjecture to find the value of each of the following.
a) 5^0 **b)** 7^0 **c)** 10^0 **d)** 19^0

5 Negative Exponents

1. Use the results of Explorations 1, 2, and 3 to copy and complete the following table.

y (Negative Exponent)	y (Positive Exponent)
2^{-3}	
2^{-2}	
2^{-1}	
3^{-2}	
3^{-1}	
4^{-2}	
4^{-1}	

2. Write a rule for writing a number with a negative exponent as a number with a positive exponent.

3. Use your rule to write each of the following with a positive exponent.
a) 5^{-2} **b)** 6^{-2} **c)** 5^{-3} **d)** 8^{-4} **e)** 10^{-5}

3.2 Zero and Negative Exponents

There are eight A notes on a piano.
They can be named as shown in the diagram.

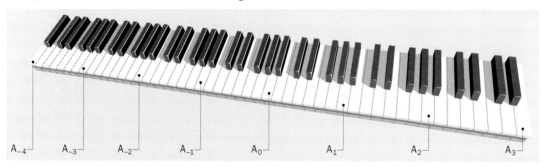

When tuning a piano, a tuner first adjusts the note A_0. This note, called "concert A," is the A above middle C.

The equations to determine the frequencies of the A notes are as follows. The units of frequency are hertz, symbol Hz. One hertz is one vibration per second.

$$A_{-4} = 440 \times 2^{-4} \quad A_{-3} = 440 \times 2^{-3} \quad A_{-2} = 440 \times 2^{-2} \quad A_{-1} = 440 \times 2^{-1}$$
$$A_0 = 440 \times 2^0 \quad A_1 = 440 \times 2^1 \quad A_2 = 440 \times 2^2 \quad A_3 = 440 \times 2^3$$

Calculate the frequencies of notes A_1, A_2, and A_3.

To calculate the other frequencies, we need to know about zero and negative exponents.

Explore: Discover the Relationship

Copy and complete the table by doing each division twice. First expand and divide, and then use the exponent rule for division.

Division	Expand and Divide	Exponent Rule
$2^4 \div 2^4$	$\dfrac{2 \times 2 \times 2 \times 2}{2 \times 2 \times 2 \times 2} = ?$	$\dfrac{2^4}{2^4} = 2^{4-4} = 2^?$
$3^2 \div 3^2$		
$4^3 \div 4^3$		
$10^4 \div 10^4$		
$x^5 \div x^5$		

Inquire

1. How do the two answers in each row compare?

2. What is the value of 5^0? 7^0? y^0?

3. What is the value of any number raised to the exponent 0?

4. Calculate the frequency of A_0 on the piano.

Explore: Discover the Relationship

Copy and complete the table by doing each division twice. First expand and divide, and then use the exponent rule for division.

Division	Expand and Divide	Exponent Rule
$2^3 \div 2^5$	$\dfrac{2 \times 2 \times 2}{2 \times 2 \times 2 \times 2 \times 2} = \dfrac{1}{2^?}$	$\dfrac{2^3}{2^5} = 2^{3-5} = 2^?$
$3^2 \div 3^6$		
$5 \div 5^3$		
$10^4 \div 10^5$		
$x^5 \div x^9$		

Inquire

1. How do the two answers in each row compare?

2. Write a rule for writing a number with a negative exponent as a number with a positive exponent.

3. Write each of the following powers with a positive exponent.
a) 3^{-2} **b)** 4^{-3} **c)** 1^{-4}

4. Evaluate.
a) 2^{-4} **b)** 5^{-2} **c)** 3^{-3} **d)** 4^{-2} **e)** 1^{-7}

5. Calculate the frequencies of the following notes on the piano.
a) A_{-4} **b)** A_{-3} **c)** A_{-2} **d)** A_{-1}

Example 1   Zero Exponents
Evaluate.
a) 4^0 **b)** $(-5)^0$ **c)** -2^0

Solution
$x^0 = 1$, where x can be any number except 0
a) $4^0 = 1$ **b)** $(-5)^0 = 1$ **c)** $-2^0 = -1$

Example 2 Negative Exponents

Evaluate. **a)** 4^{-3} **b)** $(-3)^{-3}$ **c)** $2^0 - 2^{-2}$

Solution

$x^{-m} = \dfrac{1}{x^m}$, where x can be any number except 0

a) $4^{-3} = \dfrac{1}{4^3}$

$\quad\;\; = \dfrac{1}{64}$

b) $(-3)^{-3} = \dfrac{1}{(-3)^3}$

$\qquad\qquad = -\dfrac{1}{27}$

c) $2^0 - 2^{-2} = 1 - \dfrac{1}{2^2}$

$\qquad\qquad = 1 - \dfrac{1}{4}$

$\qquad\qquad = \dfrac{3}{4}$

Note that, in Example 2, evaluating with a scientific calculator would give a decimal answer. For example, in part a), **4** $\boxed{y^x}$ **3** $\boxed{+/-}$ $\boxed{=}$ $\boxed{\;\;\;0.015625\;\;\;}$

Example 3 Evaluating Expressions

Evaluate.

a) $3^{-3} \times 3^5 \times 3^{-4}$ **b)** $(-2)^{-5} \div (-2)^{-2}$ **c)** $(4^{-1})^2$ **d)** $\dfrac{1}{5^{-2}}$

Solution 1 Using Paper and Pencil

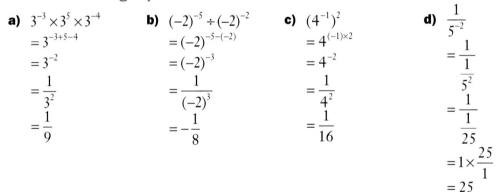

a) $3^{-3} \times 3^5 \times 3^{-4}$
$= 3^{-3+5-4}$
$= 3^{-2}$
$= \dfrac{1}{3^2}$
$= \dfrac{1}{9}$

b) $(-2)^{-5} \div (-2)^{-2}$
$= (-2)^{-5-(-2)}$
$= (-2)^{-3}$
$= \dfrac{1}{(-2)^3}$
$= -\dfrac{1}{8}$

c) $(4^{-1})^2$
$= 4^{(-1)\times 2}$
$= 4^{-2}$
$= \dfrac{1}{4^2}$
$= \dfrac{1}{16}$

d) $\dfrac{1}{5^{-2}}$
$= \dfrac{1}{\dfrac{1}{5^2}}$
$= \dfrac{1}{\dfrac{1}{25}}$
$= 1 \times \dfrac{25}{1}$
$= 25$

Solution 2 Using a Graphing Calculator

The first answer given by a graphing calculator may be a decimal. If necessary, this answer can be converted to a fraction.

a) $3^{-3} \times 3^5 \times 3^{-4} = \dfrac{1}{9}$ **b)** $(-2)^{-5} \div (-2)^{-2} = -\dfrac{1}{8}$ **c)** $(4^{-1})^2 = \dfrac{1}{16}$ **d)** $\dfrac{1}{5^{-2}} = 25$

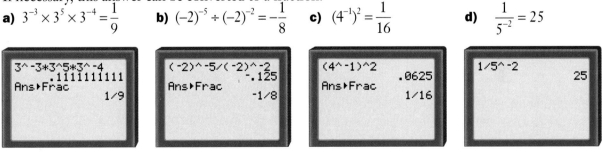

Practice

Evaluate.

1. 5^0 **2.** 2^6 **3.** 3^{-1}

4. 4^{-2} **5.** $(-1)^7$ **6.** 10^{-3}

7. $(-6)^0$ **8.** 8^{-1} **9.** $(-3)^{-4}$

10. $(-10)^{-3}$ **11.** 0.1^{-3} **12.** $(-1)^{-6}$

13. $\dfrac{1}{3^{-1}}$ **14.** $\dfrac{1}{4^{-2}}$ **15.** $\dfrac{1}{6^{-1}}$

Write each power with a positive exponent.

16. 2^{-3} **17.** 4^{-1} **18.** 10^{-7}

19. 9^{-8} **20.** 1^{-4} **21.** 0.5^{-6}

22. $(-7)^{-6}$ **23.** $(-2)^{-3}$ **24.** $\dfrac{1}{2^{-3}}$

25. $\dfrac{1}{4^{-2}}$ **26.** $\dfrac{1}{5^{-4}}$ **27.** $\dfrac{1}{3^{-5}}$

Write each expression as a power.

28. $7^4 \times 7^5$ **29.** $9^6 \times 9^{-4}$

30. $8^{-3} \times 8^{-5}$ **31.** $6^7 \div 6^3$

32. $5^{-7} \div 5^{-2}$ **33.** $4^{-2} \div 4^6$

34. $(3^3)^4$ **35.** $(9^{-2})^4$

36. $(8^{-1})^{-5}$ **37.** $-(2^{-3})^{-2}$

Write each expression as a power.

38. $2^4 \times 2^{-3} \times 2^2$

39. $3^{-5} \times 3^{-3} \times 3^2$

40. $5^6 \times 5^{-9} \times 5$

41. $8^4 \times 8^{-5} \div 8^{-2}$

42. $(-2)^{-4} \times (-2)^{-3} \div (-2)^{-1}$

43. $(-3)^{-6} \div (-3)^{-2} \times (-3)^4$

Evaluate.

44. $3^2 \times 3^2$ **45.** $4^7 \div 4^5$ **46.** $2^4 \times 2^{-3}$

47. $3^2 \div 3^{-1}$ **48.** $5^2 \times 5^{-4}$ **49.** $6^{-2} \div 6^0$

50. $7^{-4} \div 7^{-5}$ **51.** $6^{-3} \div 6^{-3}$ **52.** $\dfrac{(2^2)^2}{(5^3)^{-1}}$

53. $\dfrac{(3^{-1})^3}{(2^{-3})^{-2}}$ **54.** $\dfrac{(6^0)^{-4}}{(10^2)^{-2}}$ **55.** $\dfrac{(7^{-3})^0}{(0.1^{-1})^{-2}}$

Evaluate.

56. $2^3 \times 2^{-2} \times 2^{-2}$ **57.** $3^4 \div 3^5 \times 3$

58. $3^0 + 3^3$ **59.** $4^2 - 2^{-1}$

60. $5^3 + 3^2$ **61.** $2^{-2} + 5^0$

62. $2^3 \times 2^{-1} + 5$ **63.** $(6 - 3)^{-2}$

64. $(9^0 + 2^0)^{-1}$ **65.** $\dfrac{1}{2^{-2}} + \dfrac{1}{3^{-1}}$

66. $\dfrac{2^{-1}}{3^{-1}}$ **67.** $\dfrac{-3^{-3}}{3^{-1}}$

Evaluate.

68. $\left(\dfrac{1}{3}\right)^{-1}$ **69.** $\left(-\dfrac{1}{5}\right)^2$ **70.** $\left(-\dfrac{7}{8}\right)^0$

71. $\left(\dfrac{1}{10}\right)^{-2}$ **72.** $\left(-\dfrac{2}{3}\right)^{-3}$ **73.** $\left(-\dfrac{3}{4}\right)^{-2}$

Simplify. Express each solution with a positive exponent.

74. $x^4 \times x^3$ **75.** $x^{-2} \times x^3$ **76.** $y^{-1} \times y^{-3}$

77. $t^8 \div t^4$ **78.** $m^6 \div m^{-2}$ **79.** $b^{-2} \div b^{-4}$

80. $(m^4)^2$ **81.** $(t^{-2})^4$ **82.** $(y^{-5})^{-2}$

83. $m^3 \times m^{-2} \times m^4$ **84.** $\dfrac{a^{-4} \times a^{-2}}{a^2}$

85. $\dfrac{t^4 \times t^3}{t^9}$ **86.** $y^{-3} \times y^7 \times y^{-5}$

87. $t^{-4} \div t^{-6} \times t^6$ **88.** $n^5 \times n^{-6} \div n$

Applications and Problem Solving

89. State whether all the numbers in each row are equal. If they are not, state which number does not equal the other three. Explain.

a) $\dfrac{1}{5 \times 5}$ 0.25 $\dfrac{1}{25}$ 5^{-2}

b) $\dfrac{1}{3 \times 3 \times 3}$ 0.027 $\dfrac{1}{27}$ 3^{-3}

c) $\dfrac{1}{2 \times 2 \times 2 \times 2}$ 0.0625 $\dfrac{1}{16}$ 2^{-3}

d) $\dfrac{1}{10 \times 10 \times 10}$ 0.001 $\dfrac{1}{1000}$ 10^{-2}

90. Algebra Evaluate for $a = 2$ and $b = 3$.

a) a^3 **b)** b^4

c) a^0 **d)** a^{-3}

e) b^{-2} **f)** a^{-4}

g) $(a \times b)^{-2}$ **h)** $(a + b)^{-1}$

i) $(a - b)^{-1}$ **j)** $(b^2 - a^2)^{-2}$

91. Algebra Find the value of x.

a) $2^x = 8$ **b)** $3^x = 81$

c) $4^x = 1$ **d)** $3^x = \dfrac{1}{9}$

e) $5^x = \dfrac{1}{125}$ **f)** $x^3 = 27$

g) $x^{-2} = \dfrac{1}{4}$ **h)** $x^{-3} = \dfrac{1}{1000}$

92. Evaluate.

a) $\left(\dfrac{1}{2}\right)^0$ **b)** $\left(\dfrac{2}{3}\right)^{-3}$

c) $\left(\dfrac{1}{3}\right)^2\left(-\dfrac{1}{2}\right)^{-3}$ **d)** $\left(\dfrac{4}{5}\right)^0 - \left(\dfrac{3}{4}\right)^2$

e) $\left(\dfrac{4}{5}\right)^6\left(\dfrac{4}{5}\right)^{-8}$ **f)** $\left(\dfrac{5}{3}\right)^3 \div \left(\dfrac{5}{3}\right)^5$

93. Radioactivity The radioactivity of a sample of carbon-14 drops to $\dfrac{1}{2}$ or 2^{-1} of its original value in about 5700 years. After 11 400 years, the radioactivity is $\dfrac{1}{4}$ or 2^{-2} of its original value.

a) What fraction of the radioactivity remains after 28 500 years?

b) Write the fraction as a power with a negative exponent.

c) Write the fraction as a power with a positive exponent.

d) After how long is the radioactivity $\dfrac{1}{128}$ or 2^{-7} of its original value?

C

94. Is each statement always true, sometimes true, or never true? Explain.

a) The value of a power with a negative exponent is less than 0.

b) The value of a power with a fractional base is less than 1.

c) Two powers in which the exponents are both 0 have equal values.

95. On a test, three students evaluated $2^{-2} \times 2^0$ as follows.

$$Terry \quad 2^{-2} \times 2^0 = 4^{-2}$$
$$= \dfrac{1}{4^2}$$
$$= \dfrac{1}{16}$$
$$Sean \quad 2^{-2} \times 2^0 = 2^0$$
$$= 1$$
$$Michel \quad 2^{-2} \times 2^0 = 4^0$$
$$= 1$$

a) What errors did each student make?

b) What is the correct answer? Justify your reasoning in each step of your solution.

96. Describe how to evaluate such powers as $(-3)^{-2}$ and -3^{-2}. Compare your description with your classmates'.

PATTERN POWER

Some pairs of 2-digit numbers have the same product when the digits are reversed.

$$12 \times 42 = 21 \times 24$$
$$24 \times 63 = 42 \times 36$$
$$24 \times 84 = 42 \times 48$$

There are 11 other pairs of these numbers. Look for the pattern, and then find the pairs of numbers.

3.3 Scientific Notation — Small Numbers

Light from the sun and from other sources is transmitted as electromagnetic waves. The wavelength of an electromagnetic wave is the distance from one peak to the next.

|←——— wavelength ———→|

Sunlight can be separated into a spectrum of colours. The average wavelengths of the colours are given in the table. To work with such small numbers, we need to extend our knowledge of scientific notation.

Colour	Average Wavelength (cm)
Red	0.000 067
Orange	0.000 062
Yellow	0.000 058
Green	0.000 053
Blue	0.000 046
Violet	0.000 041

Explore: Look for a Pattern

Copy and complete the table.

Standard Form	Product Form	Scientific Notation
0.52	$\dfrac{5.2}{10}$ or $5.2 \times \dfrac{1}{10^1}$	5.2×10^{-1}
0.052	$\dfrac{5.2}{?}$ or $5.2 \times \dfrac{1}{10^?}$	$5.2 \times 10^?$
0.0052	$\dfrac{5.2}{?}$ or $5.2 \times \dfrac{1}{10^?}$	$5.2 \times 10^?$
0.000 52	$\dfrac{5.2}{?}$ or $5.2 \times \dfrac{1}{10^?}$	$5.2 \times 10^?$

Inquire

1. Write a rule for writing numbers less than 1 in scientific notation.

2. Write in scientific notation the average wavelength, in centimetres, of
a) red light   **b)** yellow light   **c)** violet light

Example 1   Writing in Scientific Notation
Write in scientific notation.
a) 5100   **b)** 0.0051

Solution
Write the number in the form $a \times 10^n$, where a is greater than or equal to 1 but less than 10.

a) $5100 = 5.1 \times 1000$
$\quad\quad = 5.1 \times 10^3$

b) $0.0051 = 5.1 \times \dfrac{1}{1000}$
$\quad\quad\quad\quad = 5.1 \times \dfrac{1}{10^3}$
$\quad\quad\quad\quad = 5.1 \times 10^{-3}$

For 5100, the decimal point is moved 3 places to the left, and the exponent is 3.
$5100 = 5.1 \times 10^3$

5100

For 0.0051, the decimal point is moved 3 places to the right, and the exponent is −3.
$0.0051 = 5.1 \times 10^{-3}$

0.0051

Example 2   Multiplying
Evaluate $(3.2 \times 10^{-2}) \times (5 \times 10^{-4})$.

Solution
$(3.2 \times 10^{-2}) \times (5 \times 10^{-4}) = 3.2 \times 5 \times 10^{-2} \times 10^{-4}$
$\quad\quad\quad\quad\quad\quad\quad\quad = 16 \times 10^{(-2)+(-4)}$
$\quad\quad\quad\quad\quad\quad\quad\quad = 16 \times 10^{-6}$
$\quad\quad\quad\quad\quad\quad\quad\quad = 1.6 \times 10^{-5}$

Example 3 Dividing
Evaluate $(4.8 \times 10^4) \div (5 \times 10^{-3})$.

Solution
$(4.8 \times 10^4) \div (5 \times 10^{-3}) = (4.8 \div 5) \times (10^4 \div 10^{-3})$
$\quad\quad\quad\quad\quad\quad\quad\quad = 0.96 \times 10^{4-(-3)}$
$\quad\quad\quad\quad\quad\quad\quad\quad = 0.96 \times 10^7$
$\quad\quad\quad\quad\quad\quad\quad\quad = 9.6 \times 10^6$

Practice

A

Write in scientific notation.
1. 4 500 000
2. 0.089
3. 0.2
4. 0.000 055
5. 0.0013
6. 0.000 000 101

Write in standard form.
7. 2.3×10^4
8. 4.7×10^{-3}
9. 7×10^{-5}
10. 10^{-6}

Write in scientific notation.
11. 45×10^7
12. 0.34×10^6
13. 33×10^{-8}
14. 10^{-8}
15. 0.06×10^{-7}
16. 100×10^{-14}

Estimate, then calculate. Write each answer in scientific notation.
17. $(2.5 \times 10^{-3}) \times (5 \times 10^{-4})$
18. $(8 \times 10^{-5}) \times (1.2 \times 10^{-1})$
19. $(3.2 \times 10^{-3}) \times (4.1 \times 10^{-2})$
20. $(5.2 \times 10^3) \div (2 \times 10^{-2})$
21. $(3.5 \times 10^{-4}) \div (7 \times 10^{-3})$

Applications and Problem Solving

22. **Energy** Energy is measured in joules, symbol J. If you tap your finger 10 times on your desk, you use about 1 J of energy. Express the following quantities of energy in scientific notation.
a) If you run for 1 h, you use about 2 000 000 J of energy.
b) When a cricket chirps, it uses about 0.0008 J of energy.
c) The food energy in a slice of apple pie is about 1 500 000 J.
d) The energy released by splitting one uranium atom is about 0.000 000 000 08 J.

B

23. Write the number that is 10 times as large as each of the following.
a) 2.3×10^6
b) 4.5×10^{-9}
c) 5×10^{-7}
d) 10^{-11}

24. Write the number that is one tenth as large as each of the following.
a) 7.8×10^9
b) 6.8×10^{-6}
c) 8×10^{-10}
d) 10^{-7}

25. Order from greatest to least.
a) $4.3 \times 10^{-3}, 4.35 \times 10^{-3}, 8.4 \times 10^{-4}, 10^{-3}$
b) $5.6 \times 10^{-9}, 10^{-9}, \dfrac{1}{10^8}, 5.6 \times 10^{-8}$
c) $\dfrac{1}{1000}, 2.1 \times 10^{-3}, 10^{-2}, 2.12 \times 10^{-3}$

26. **Lake Superior** One water molecule has a mass of about 3×10^{-26} kg. Calculate the number of water molecules in Lake Superior, which holds about 1.2×10^{16} kg of water.

C

27. Why is 0.23×10^{-9} not in scientific notation?

28. **Electromagnetic waves a)** The waves that bombard us every day have wavelengths that range from 0.000 000 000 000 01 cm to 1 000 000 000 cm. Write these numbers in scientific notation.
b) Draw a number line showing the wavelengths in powers of 10.

Mark the range of wavelengths visible to humans.
c) Use your research skills to find out if there are creatures that can see outside the human range.

29. If the product of two numbers, $(a \times 10^m) \times (b \times 10^n)$ is written in scientific notation as $c \times 10^{m+n}$, what do you know about the value of the product ab? Explain.

WORD POWER

A certain vowel appears in the names of 8 of the 10 Canadian provinces. Which vowel?

PROBLEM SOLVING

3.4 Guess and Check

One way to solve a problem is to guess at the answer and then check to see if it is correct. If it is not, you can keep guessing and checking until you get the right answer.

Jacques Villeneuve was the first Canadian to win the Indy 500 car race. The year he won, there were two other Canadians in the race, Paul Tracy and Scott Goodyear. The three of them drove a total of 538 laps of the track. Goodyear drove 64 laps more than Tracy, and Villeneuve drove 2 laps more than Goodyear. How many laps did each of them drive?

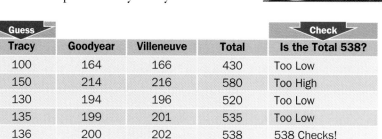

Understand the Problem

1. What information are you given?
2. What are you asked to find?
3. Do you need an exact or an approximate answer?

Think of a Plan

Set up a table. Guess at the number of laps Tracy drove. Use this guess to write the number of laps driven by Goodyear and Villeneuve. If the total number of laps is not 538, make another guess at the number of laps driven by Tracy.

Carry Out the Plan

Guess				Check
Tracy	**Goodyear**	**Villeneuve**	**Total**	**Is the Total 538?**
100	164	166	430	Too Low
150	214	216	580	Too High
130	194	196	520	Too Low
135	199	201	535	Too Low
136	200	202	538	538 Checks!

Tracy drove 136 laps, Goodyear drove 200 laps, and Villeneuve drove 202 laps.

Look Back

Check the answer against the given information.
Since $200 - 136 = 64$, Goodyear drove 64 laps more than Tracy.
Since $202 - 200 = 2$, Villeneuve drove 2 laps more than Goodyear.
How could you set up a spreadsheet to solve the problem by guess and check?

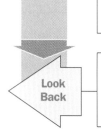

Guess and Check

1. Guess an answer that fits one of the facts.
2. Check the answer against the other facts.
3. If necessary, adjust your guess and check again.

Applications and Problem Solving

1. Multiplying a number by 7 and adding 13 gives 55. What is the number?

2. Multiplying a number by 14 and subtracting 12 gives 114. What is the number?

3. What 3 consecutive numbers have a sum of 237?

4. What 4 consecutive even numbers have a sum of 196?

5. Band The square of the number of students in the band is close to 3000. About how many students are in the band?

6. Ticket costs The 7 Trudeaus went to the fair. Adult tickets cost $11. Children's tickets cost $7. The total cost was $65. How many adults were there?

7. Darts In how many ways could 4 darts hit the board to give a total score of 19?

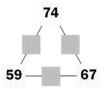

8. Measurement The perimeter of a rectangle is 60 m. The length is 4 m more than the width. What are the dimensions of the rectangle?

9. Missing numbers The number in each yellow square is found by adding the numbers in the two small green squares adjacent to it. Find the numbers in the green squares.

10. Swim team The cube of the number of people on the swim team is close to 4000. About how many are on the swim team?

11. Coins Justine has some rare quarters and nickels. She has 8 more nickels than quarters. The face value of the coins is $2.50. How many are quarters?

12. Measurement The dimensions of a rectangular solid are whole numbers. The areas of the faces are 42 cm^2, 48 cm^2, and 56 cm^2. What are the dimensions of the solid?

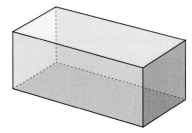

13. Number puzzle Copy the diagrams. Use the numbers 1, 2, 3, 4, 5, and 6 once in each triangle. Place the numbers in the circles so that each side of triangle A adds to 10, each side of triangle B adds to 11, and each side of triangle C adds to 12.

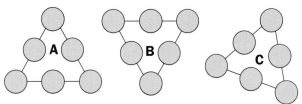

14. Order of Canada Canada's top honour is the Order of Canada. There are 3 categories — Companion, Officer, and Member. A total of up to 165 awards can be given in any year. If all the awards are given, the number of new Members is twice the number of new Officers. There are 35 more new Officers than new Companions. How many awards are made in each category?

15. Write a problem that can be solved using the guess and check strategy. Ask a classmate to solve the problem.

3.5 Rational Numbers

You have already found the quotient of two integers.

$$\frac{6}{2} = 3 \qquad -\frac{6}{2} = -3 \qquad \frac{12}{-3} = -4 \qquad \frac{-20}{-4} = 5$$

The quotient of two integers is not always another integer.

$$3 \div 5 = \frac{3}{5} \text{ (a fraction) or } 0.6 \text{ (a decimal)}$$

Explore: Use a Number Line

The table shows the average early morning temperatures in April for five Canadian cities.

City	Temperature (°C)
Edmonton	–2.7
Québec	–1.5
Regina	–2.4
Sault Ste. Marie	–2
Whitehorse	–5.1

Plot the temperatures on a number line like the one below.

Inquire

1. Which two integers are closest to the Edmonton temperature?

2. Which two integers are closest to the Whitehorse temperature?

3. Here are two ways to write the Sault Ste. Marie temperature as the ratio of two integers.

$$\frac{-4}{2} \qquad \frac{6}{-3}$$

Write two other ways.

4. Write the Québec temperature as the ratio of two integers in two ways.

5. Write the Regina temperature as the ratio of two integers in two ways.

Rational numbers are numbers that can be written as the ratio of two integers, that is, in the form $\frac{a}{b}$, where a is any integer, and b is any integer except 0.

All fractions and mixed numbers are rational numbers. $3\frac{1}{2} = \frac{7}{2}$

All integers are rational numbers. $7 = \frac{7}{1}$ $-5 = -\frac{5}{1}$

All terminating and repeating decimals are rational numbers.

$0.5 = \frac{1}{2}$ $0.27272727\ldots = \frac{3}{11}$

terminating
decimal

non-terminating
but **repeating** decimal

The repeating decimal $0.27272727\ldots$ is also written as $0.\overline{27}$.
The digits that repeat are called the **period**.
The number of digits that repeat is called the **length of the period**.
In $0.\overline{27}$, the period is 27, and the length of the period is 2.

Numbers that cannot be written as the ratio of two integers are called **irrational numbers**. These numbers are non-repeating, non-terminating decimals. Examples of irrational numbers are $\sqrt{2}, \sqrt{3}$, and π.

Real numbers include all the rational and irrational numbers.
This diagram shows the relationships among the sets of numbers.

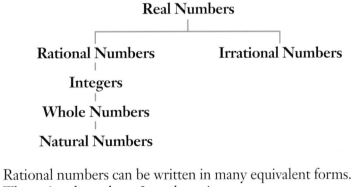

Real Numbers

Rational Numbers   **Irrational Numbers**

Integers

Whole Numbers

Natural Numbers

Rational numbers can be written in many equivalent forms.
The rational number -2 can be written as
$\frac{2}{-1}, \frac{-4}{2}, \frac{-2}{1}, -\frac{-2}{-1}$, and so on.

The rational number 3 can be written as
$\frac{3}{1}, \frac{-3}{-1}, \frac{-6}{-2}$, and so on.

Example 1   Equivalent Forms

Express each rational number in an equivalent form.

a) $\dfrac{-4}{7}$ b) -6 c) $-\dfrac{-6}{-8}$ d) $\dfrac{5}{-7}$

Solution

a) $\dfrac{-4}{7} = \dfrac{-4}{7} \times 1$

$= \dfrac{-4 \times (-1)}{7 \times (-1)}$

$= \dfrac{4}{-7}$

b) $-6 = \dfrac{-6}{1} \times 1$

$= \dfrac{-6 \times 2}{1 \times 2}$

$= \dfrac{-12}{2}$

c) $-\dfrac{-6}{-8} = -\dfrac{-6}{-8} \div 1$

$= -\dfrac{-6 \div 2}{-8 \div 2}$

$= -\dfrac{-3}{-4}$

$= -\dfrac{3}{4}$

d) $\dfrac{5}{-7} = \dfrac{5}{-7} \times 1$

$= \dfrac{5 \times (-3)}{-7 \times (-3)}$

$= \dfrac{-15}{21}$

The results of Example 1 suggest the following general statement.

$\dfrac{-a}{b} = \dfrac{a}{-b} = -\dfrac{a}{b} = -\dfrac{-a}{-b}$, where $b \neq 0$.

Rational numbers can be located on a number line. Recall that numbers increase in value as you go from left to right on the number line.

For example, $-1\dfrac{3}{4}$ is less than $\dfrac{1}{2}$.

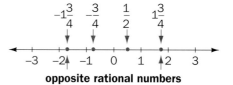

opposite rational numbers

Example 2   Comparing Rational Numbers

Which is greater, $\dfrac{-2}{3}$ or $\dfrac{-4}{5}$?

Solution 1

The LCD of $\dfrac{-2}{3}$ and $\dfrac{-4}{5}$ is 15.

$\dfrac{-2 \times 5}{3 \times 5} = \dfrac{-10}{15}$ $\dfrac{-4 \times 3}{5 \times 3} = \dfrac{-12}{15}$

Compare numerators. $-10 > -12$

> means greater than.
< means less than.

Therefore, $\dfrac{-2}{3} > \dfrac{-4}{5}$

Solution 2

Use your calculator to compare numbers.

$\dfrac{-2}{3} = -0.\overline{6}$ $\dfrac{-4}{5} = -0.8$

$-0.\overline{6} > -0.8$

So, $\dfrac{-2}{3} > \dfrac{-4}{5}$.

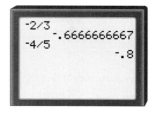

Example 3 Quotients of Two Integers

Write each of the following as the ratio of two integers.

a) $1\frac{1}{2}$ **b)** -0.7 **c)** 3 **d)** -2.51

Solution

a) $1\frac{1}{2} = \frac{3}{2}$

b) 0.7 means 7 tenths

so $-0.7 = -\frac{7}{10}$

c) $3 = \frac{3}{1}$

d) 2.51 is $2\frac{51}{100}$ or $\frac{251}{100}$

so $-2.51 = -\frac{251}{100}$

Example 4 Decimals to Fractions

Express each decimal as a fraction in simplest form.

a) 0.4 **b)** 0.85 **c)** -0.26 **d)** -1.825

Solution

a) $0.4 = \frac{4}{10}$
$= \frac{4 \div 2}{10 \div 2}$
$= \frac{2}{5}$

b) $0.85 = \frac{85}{100}$
$= \frac{85 \div 5}{100 \div 5}$
$= \frac{17}{20}$

c) $-0.26 = -\frac{26}{100}$
$= -\frac{26 \div 2}{100 \div 2}$
$= -\frac{13}{50}$

d) $-1.825 = -\frac{1825}{1000}$
$= -\frac{1825 \div 25}{1000 \div 25}$
$= -\frac{73}{40}$

Practice

A

1. State which of the following are rational numbers.

a) $\frac{1}{2}$ **b)** $\frac{2}{5}$ **c)** $\frac{-1}{3}$ **d)** $\frac{-3}{0}$

e) $\frac{-0}{4}$ **f)** 0 **g)** -7 **h)** $\sqrt{5}$

i) π **j)** $\frac{-8}{-1}$ **k)** $\frac{18}{-19}$ **l)** $\frac{7}{0}$

Express each rational number in an equivalent form.

2. $\frac{-2}{5}$ **3.** 7 **4.** $\frac{-6}{12}$ **5.** $\frac{8}{-3}$

6. $-\frac{3}{4}$ **7.** -5 **8.** $\frac{2}{-3}$ **9.** $\frac{-2}{-5}$

Write each rational number in lowest terms.

10. $\frac{4}{8}$ **11.** $\frac{-3}{6}$ **12.** $\frac{-2}{8}$ **13.** $-\frac{14}{2}$

14 $\frac{-18}{21}$ **15.** $-\frac{8}{10}$ **16.** $-\frac{3}{9}$ **17.** $\frac{12}{15}$

Write each of the following as the ratio of two integers in lowest terms.

18. $2\frac{3}{4}$ **19.** $5\frac{1}{3}$ **20.** $-3\frac{1}{2}$ **21.** $\frac{-12}{18}$

Which is greater?

22. $\frac{-1}{2}$ or $\frac{3}{4}$ **23.** $\frac{3}{5}$ or $\frac{8}{3}$

24. $\frac{-3}{4}$ or $\frac{5}{-4}$ **25.** 0 or $\frac{-4}{-5}$

Express in the form $\frac{a}{b}$ *and reduce to lowest terms.*

26. 0.5   **27.** -0.4 **28.** 1.4
29. 0.8   **30.** -2.75 **31.** 1.25
32. -0.36 **33.** 3.25   **34.** 1.62
35. -7.4 **36.** -2.32 **37.** 3.1

Write each repeating decimal using bar notation.

38. $0.31313\ldots$ **39.** $0.666\ldots$
40. $0.9555\ldots$ **41.** $5.6161\ldots$
42. $32.42874287\ldots$ **43.** $-18.5252\ldots$

Write as a decimal.

44. $\frac{2}{3}$ **45.** $-\frac{7}{8}$ **46.** $\frac{9}{2}$

47. $-\frac{5}{12}$ **48.** $-\frac{11}{5}$ **49.** $\frac{4}{11}$

50. $\frac{3}{7}$ **51.** $-\frac{7}{9}$ **52.** $\frac{-7}{20}$

Identify the period and the length of the period of each rational number.

53. $\frac{2}{9}$ **54.** $\frac{7}{11}$ **55.** $-\frac{1}{6}$

56. $-\frac{1}{3}$ **57.** $\frac{5}{6}$ **58.** $-\frac{7}{12}$

Replace each ● with <, >, or = to make each statement true.

59. $\frac{1}{2}$ ● $\frac{3}{4}$ **60.** $\frac{-3}{5}$ ● $\frac{-2}{5}$

61. $\frac{8}{3}$ ● $2\frac{2}{3}$ **62.** $\frac{-2}{3}$ ● $\frac{-3}{4}$

63. $\frac{11}{12}$ ● $\frac{5}{6}$ **64.** $\frac{3}{-4}$ ● $\frac{-1}{8}$

Replace each ● with <, >, or = to make each statement true.

65. 0.3 ● $0.\overline{3}$ **66.** 0.007 ● 0.07

67. 1.21 ● $1\frac{21}{100}$ **68.** $0.\overline{61}$ ● $\frac{3}{5}$

69. $-\frac{7}{8}$ ● -0.875 **70.** $5\frac{1}{3}$ ● $5.\overline{3}$

71. $-\frac{7}{11}$ ● $-0.\overline{71}$ **72.** $6.\overline{001}$ ● $6.00\overline{1}$

73. $-1\frac{1}{6}$ ● -1.6 **74.** $6\frac{3}{4}$ ● 6.75

Write in order from least to greatest.

75. $\frac{1}{2}, \frac{1}{3}, \frac{3}{5}, 0.59$

76. $0.71, 0.7\overline{1}, \frac{711}{1000}, 0.\overline{7}$

77. $-9.01, -8.93, -9.\overline{1}, -8.\overline{9}$

78. $0.113, 0.1\overline{13}, 0.11\overline{3}, 0.\overline{1}$

79. $\frac{3}{8}, \frac{4}{7}, 0.3\overline{7}, 0.3\overline{75}$

Applications and Problem Solving

80. Write an example of a rational number
a) with a numerator of 1 and a denominator greater than 5
b) with a numerator less than -3 and a denominator greater than 0
c) with a denominator of -16 and a numerator that makes a rational number in lowest terms

81. Provinces How many times more provinces are there to the east of Manitoba than there are to the west of Manitoba? Write your answer as a ratio of two integers in lowest terms.

B

82. English Divide the number of consonants by the number of vowels in each name. Express each answer as a ratio of two integers in lowest terms.
a) Montréal
b) Red Deer
c) Nanaimo
d) Saskatoon
e) Barrie
f) Truro
g) Fredericton
h) Gander

83. a) List your answers from question 82 in order from greatest to least.
b) Which name has the greatest ratio?

84. Olympic medals At the Summer Olympics in Barcelona, Spain, Canadians won 6 gold medals, 5 silver medals, and 7 bronze medals.
a) State in lowest terms the fraction of the Canadian medals of each kind.
b) Write each fraction as a decimal.

85. Game farm The following game report was published by the operators of a game farm.

Game Report		
Animal	Population 5 Years Ago	Population Now
Elephants	18	14
Monkeys	6	12
Giraffes	14	19
Rhinoceroses	3	1
Hyenas	8	8

The growth factor for each type of animal can be calculated using the following formula.

$$GF = \frac{\text{Pop. now} - \text{Pop. 5 years ago}}{\text{Pop. 5 years ago}}$$

Calculate the growth factor for each type of animal. Express each answer as the ratio of two integers in lowest terms.

86. Highrise buildings How many times taller is a 60-storey building than a 50-storey building? Write your answer as a decimal. What assumptions have you made?

87. Pattern a) Express each of the following as a repeating decimal.

$$\frac{1}{11} \qquad \frac{2}{11} \qquad \frac{3}{11}$$

b) Describe the pattern.
c) Use the pattern to predict the following.

$$\frac{7}{11} \qquad \frac{10}{11}$$

C

88. Temperature scales The Celsius temperature scale uses positive and negative rational numbers to represent temperatures. The Kelvin temperature scale does not use negative rational numbers. Use your research skills to investigate the Kelvin temperature scale. Explain why it does not use negative rational numbers.

89. Is $\frac{-3}{4}$ the opposite of $\frac{-4}{3}$? Explain.

90. Since $4 \times 2 = 8$, $\frac{8}{2} = 4$. Use this idea to show why $\frac{8}{0}$ is not possible. Explain and justify your reasoning.

91. State whether each statement is always true, sometimes true, or never true. Explain.
a) The ratio of two integers has a value greater than 1 if the numerator is greater than the denominator.
b) The value of the ratio of two integers decreases as the denominator increases.
c) An integer is a rational number.
d) A rational number is a real number.
e) A real number is a rational number.

LOGIC POWER

Copy the grid, with the letters A, E, I, and O placed as shown.

Place the letters B, C, D, F, G, H, J, K, L, M, N, and P in the empty squares of the grid, according to the following directions.

• H and B are in the top row.
• F is in the left column.
• G, M, and N are in corners.
• P is in the third column but not in the third row.
• L is in the same row as E.
• C is in the same column as I.
• No row or column contains two consecutive letters of the alphabet.

INVESTIGATING MATH

Canada's Musical Place Names

Each letter in the table represents a different number.

Letter	A	B	C	D	E	F	G
Number							
Letter	H	I	K	L	M	N	O
Number							
Letter	P	R	S	T	U	V	Z
Number							

1 Completing the Table

Evaluate the left side of each of the following equations. Express each answer as a fraction or mixed number in simplest form. Use the results to copy and complete the above table.

1. $\dfrac{1}{4} + \dfrac{2}{3} = A$

2. $\dfrac{2}{3} - \dfrac{1}{4} = B$

3. $\dfrac{3}{4} \times \dfrac{1}{2} = C$

4. $\dfrac{3}{8} \div \dfrac{1}{2} = D$

5. $\dfrac{3}{5} - \dfrac{1}{2} = E$

6. $\dfrac{7}{8} \times \dfrac{2}{3} = F$

7. $\dfrac{5}{6} + \dfrac{1}{4} = G$

8. $4 \div \dfrac{3}{5} = H$

9. $3 \times 1\dfrac{3}{4} = I$

10. $3\dfrac{3}{5} + 2\dfrac{4}{5} = K$

11. $3\dfrac{1}{6} - 1\dfrac{5}{6} = L$

12. $2\dfrac{3}{4} \div 1\dfrac{1}{4} = M$

13. $1\dfrac{1}{2} + 2\dfrac{2}{3} = N$

14. $2\dfrac{3}{4} \times 3\dfrac{1}{3} = O$

15. $5 \div 1\dfrac{1}{3} = P$

16. $1\dfrac{3}{8} - \dfrac{3}{4} = R$

17. $3\dfrac{4}{5} \div 2 = S$

18. $3\dfrac{1}{2} - 2\dfrac{1}{5} = T$

19. $6 - 2\dfrac{5}{8} = U$

20. $2\dfrac{1}{2} \times 1\dfrac{1}{9} = V$

21. $2\dfrac{1}{4} \div 3\dfrac{1}{3} = Z$

2 Finding Place Names

Use the results of Exploration 1 to replace each of the following numbers with its corresponding letter. Each resulting word is all or part of a musical place name in Canada. If a word is part of a place name, the rest of the name is given beside the question. The one-word place names are the names of towns.

1. $\dfrac{3}{4}$ $\dfrac{5}{8}$ $3\dfrac{3}{8}$ $2\dfrac{1}{5}$ ▬▬▬ Creek

2. $\dfrac{1}{10}$ $1\dfrac{1}{3}$ $2\dfrac{7}{9}$ $5\dfrac{1}{4}$ $1\dfrac{9}{10}$ Lac ▬▬▬

3. $4\dfrac{1}{6}$ $\dfrac{11}{12}$ $1\dfrac{9}{10}$ $6\dfrac{2}{3}$ $2\dfrac{7}{9}$ $5\dfrac{1}{4}$ $1\dfrac{1}{3}$ $1\dfrac{1}{3}$ $\dfrac{1}{10}$ ▬▬▬

4. $\dfrac{3}{4}$ $\dfrac{11}{12}$ $4\dfrac{1}{6}$ $\dfrac{3}{8}$ $\dfrac{1}{10}$ ▬▬▬

5. $\dfrac{5}{12}$ $1\dfrac{1}{3}$ $3\dfrac{3}{8}$ $\dfrac{1}{10}$ $1\dfrac{1}{12}$ $\dfrac{5}{8}$ $\dfrac{11}{12}$ $1\dfrac{9}{10}$ $1\dfrac{9}{10}$ ▬▬▬ Brook

6. $\dfrac{3}{4}$ $5\dfrac{1}{4}$ $1\dfrac{9}{10}$ $\dfrac{3}{8}$ $9\dfrac{1}{6}$ Lac du ▬▬▬

7. $2\dfrac{1}{5}$ $9\dfrac{1}{6}$ $\dfrac{27}{40}$ $\dfrac{11}{12}$ $\dfrac{5}{8}$ $1\dfrac{3}{10}$ ▬▬▬

8. $1\dfrac{1}{12}$ $3\dfrac{3}{8}$ $5\dfrac{1}{4}$ $1\dfrac{3}{10}$ $\dfrac{11}{12}$ $\dfrac{5}{8}$ ▬▬▬ Creek

9. $3\dfrac{3}{4}$ $9\dfrac{1}{6}$ $1\dfrac{1}{3}$ $6\dfrac{2}{5}$ $\dfrac{11}{12}$ ▬▬▬ Lake

3 Locating Information

1. Use your research skills to find the location of each place in Exploration 2. Describe each location.

3.6 Multiplying Rational Numbers

Explore: Study the Table

The value of one share of a company's stock changes, depending on what people are willing to pay. The following table shows the change in value of one share of some stocks at the Toronto Stock Exchange in one day.

Stock	Change in Value ($)
Corel	−0.04
Imax	+0.10
Loblaw	−0.30
Petro-Canada	+1.10
TD Bank	−1.00

Inquire

1. By how much did the value of 500 Imax shares increase?
2. By how much did the value of 1000 TD Bank shares decrease?
3. By how much did the value of 400 Loblaw shares decrease?
4. Did the value of 500 Corel shares increase or decrease during the day? by how much?

When multiplying rational numbers in decimal form, multiply as you did with decimals and use the sign rules you used with integers. Use a calculator, when convenient.

Example 1   Multiplying Decimals

Multiply. **a)** 3.2×0.9 **b)** $8.5 \times (-0.125)$ **c)** $-1.1 \times (-0.69)$

Solution

a) 3.2×0.9
   $= 2.88$

Estimate

$3 \times 1 = 3$

b) $8.5 \times (-0.125)$
   $= -1.0625$

Estimate

$10 \times (-0.1) = -1$

c) $-1.1 \times (-0.69)$
   $= 0.759$

Estimate

$-1 \times (-0.7) = 0.7$

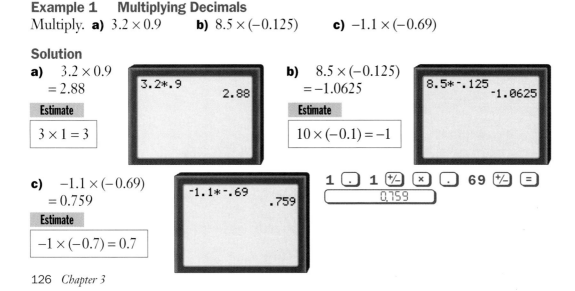

When multiplying rational numbers in fraction form, use the rule you used to multiply fractions and the sign rules you used with integers.

Example 2   Multiplying in Fraction Form

Multiply.

a) $\dfrac{1}{3} \times \dfrac{3}{5}$ **b)** $\dfrac{-4}{7} \times (-3)$ **c)** $\dfrac{-3}{-4} \times \dfrac{2}{-5}$ **d)** $-2\dfrac{1}{4} \times 1\dfrac{2}{3}$

Solution

a) $\dfrac{1}{3} \times \dfrac{3}{5} = \dfrac{3}{15}$
$\qquad = \dfrac{1}{5}$

b) $\dfrac{-4}{7} \times (-3) = \dfrac{12}{7}$

c) $\dfrac{-3}{-4} \times \dfrac{2}{-5} = \dfrac{-6}{20}$
$\qquad = \dfrac{-3}{10}$

d) $-2\dfrac{1}{4} \times 1\dfrac{2}{3} = \dfrac{-9}{4} \times \dfrac{5}{3}$
$\qquad = \dfrac{-45}{12}$
$\qquad = \dfrac{-15}{4}$

Example 3   Multiplying Rational Numbers

Multiply $2\dfrac{1}{4} \times \left(-1\dfrac{1}{2}\right)$.

Solution 1

Multiply the numbers in fraction form.

$2\dfrac{1}{4} \times \left(-1\dfrac{1}{2}\right) = \dfrac{9}{4} \times \dfrac{-3}{2}$

$\qquad = \dfrac{-27}{8}$

$\qquad = -3\dfrac{3}{8}$

A graphing calculator will find the answer in decimal or fraction form.

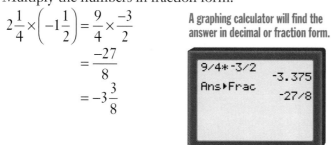

```
9/4* -3/2
              -3.375
Ans▶Frac
              -27/8
```

Solution 2

Multiply the numbers in decimal form.

$2\dfrac{1}{4} \times \left(-1\dfrac{1}{2}\right) = 2.25 \times (-1.5)$

$\qquad = -3.375$

Estimate

$2 \times (-1.5) = -3$

2 [.] 25 [×] 1 [.] 5 [+/−] [=]
‾‾‾‾‾‾‾‾‾‾‾‾‾‾
     -3.375

Example 4   Powers With Rational Bases

Evaluate.

a) $\left(\dfrac{3}{8}\right)^2$ **b)** $\left(-\dfrac{5}{4}\right)^3$ **c)** -3.5^2 **d)** $(-1.5)^4$

Solution

a) $\left(\dfrac{3}{8}\right)^2 = \dfrac{3}{8} \times \dfrac{3}{8}$

$\qquad = \dfrac{9}{64}$

b) $\left(-\dfrac{5}{4}\right)^3 = \left(-\dfrac{5}{4}\right) \times \left(-\dfrac{5}{4}\right) \times \left(-\dfrac{5}{4}\right)$

$\qquad = -\dfrac{125}{64}$

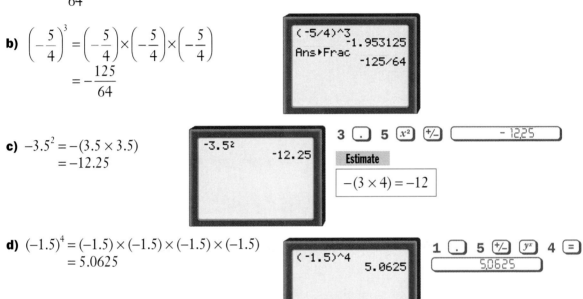

c) $-3.5^2 = -(3.5 \times 3.5)$

$\qquad = -12.25$

Estimate

$-(3 \times 4) = -12$

d) $(-1.5)^4 = (-1.5) \times (-1.5) \times (-1.5) \times (-1.5)$

$\qquad = 5.0625$

Practice

A

Estimate each product.

1. $-8\dfrac{1}{2} \times \left(-1\dfrac{1}{4}\right)$ **2.** $-6\dfrac{2}{3} \times 3\dfrac{1}{2}$

3. $3\dfrac{1}{5} \times \left(-2\dfrac{5}{6}\right)$ **4.** -4.9×2.2

5. $-5.6 \times (-7.8)$ **6.** $3.4 \times (-9.7)$

Multiply.

7. $\dfrac{-1}{4} \times \dfrac{3}{5}$ **8.** $-\dfrac{2}{7} \times \left(-\dfrac{7}{2}\right)$

9. $\dfrac{3}{4} \times \left(-\dfrac{2}{5}\right)$ **10.** $\dfrac{5}{8} \times \dfrac{2}{3}$

11. $0.3 \times (-0.25)$ **12.** -0.5×0.75
13. $-0.46 \times (-0.5)$ **14.** 0.9×0.55

Multiply.

15. $1\dfrac{1}{2} \times 3\dfrac{1}{4}$ **16.** $0 \times \left(-\dfrac{3}{4}\right)$

17. $-\dfrac{3}{4} \times 2\dfrac{1}{2}$ **18.** $-1\dfrac{1}{2} \times \left(-1\dfrac{2}{3}\right)$

19. 3.5×1.25 **20.** -1.5×3.6
21. $4.2 \times (-2.5)$ **22.** $-2.25 \times (-1.4)$

Evaluate.

23. $\left(\dfrac{3}{4}\right)^3$ **24.** $\left(-\dfrac{2}{5}\right)^2$ **25.** $-\left(\dfrac{1}{2}\right)^4$

26. -1.5^3 **27.** $(-0.8)^4$ **28.** -3.8^2

Applications and Problem Solving

29. Algebra Evaluate when $p=\dfrac{1}{2}$, $q=\dfrac{3}{5}$, and $r=-\dfrac{3}{4}$.

a) $p\times q$ **b)** $q\times r$ **c)** $p\times q\times r$ **d)** r^3

30. Stock market The price of Canadian Pacific stock fell by $0.90 one day. What was the change in the value of 400 shares of Canadian Pacific?

31. Cycling Martina can ride 11.5 km/h on her mountain bike. What distance can she ride in 2.5 h?

32. Temperature change The temperature in Hamilton changed by an average of −1.3°C/h overnight. What was the temperature change from 01:00 to 06:00?

B

33. Time How many hours are there in $3\dfrac{1}{4}$ weeks?

34. Space junk One year, about 6600 satellites were orbiting the Earth. There were also about $2\dfrac{3}{11}$ times that number of pieces of junk in orbit. The junk included used rockets and debris from explosions in space. About how many pieces of junk were orbiting the Earth?

35. Environment It is estimated that the loon population today is about $\dfrac{1}{2}$ what it was 10 years ago.
a) If the population 10 years ago was approximately one million, what is the loon population today?
b) What factors might be responsible for this decline in the loon population?

36. Measurement A cube has an edge length of 2.4 cm. What is the volume of the cube?

C

37. Decide whether each statement is always true, sometimes true, or never true. Explain.
a) The square of a non-zero rational number is negative.
b) The product of 2 negative rational numbers is greater than either of them.
c) The product of 2 rational numbers is not zero.

38. For each statement what are the possible values of n, if n is a natural number? Explain and justify your reasoning.
a) The value of $(-1.5)^n$ is greater than 0.
b) The value of $(-2.3)^n$ is less than 0.
c) The value of -0.6^n is less than 0.

39. Advertising Work with a classmate. Use your research skills to find the cost of advertising space in your local newspaper or your favourite magazine. Determine the cost of a $\dfrac{1}{4}$-page, $\dfrac{1}{2}$-page, and $\dfrac{1}{8}$-page advertisement. List any factors other than size that might affect the cost of an advertisement.

LOGIC POWER

1. How many triangles are in this figure?

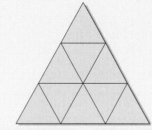

2. Make up a similar type of problem using a different geometric shape. Ask a classmate to solve it.

3.7 Dividing Rational Numbers

From 1759 to 1858, the official money in what was to become Canada consisted of British pounds, shillings, and pence. In 1858, a decision was made to switch to the decimal system being used in the United States, and so the dollar replaced the pound. In 1858, one Canadian dollar bought one US dollar. In 1865, the Canadian dollar was valued at US$1.45, that is, one Canadian dollar bought $1.45 in US money.

Explore: Complete the Table

The table shows the approximate value of one Canadian dollar in US funds at different times during its first 100 years. To determine how much Canadian money bought one US dollar in 1865, divide one Canadian dollar by the number of US dollars it bought.

$$US\$1.45 = CDN\$1.00$$

Divide by 1.45: $\quad US\$1.00 = CDN\$\dfrac{1.00}{1.45}$

Copy the table and use a calculator to complete it. Round answers to the nearest cent.

Year	Value of 1 Canadian Dollar in US Dollars	Division	Cost of 1 US Dollar in Canadian Dollars
1865	1.45	1 ÷ 1.45	
1920	0.84		
1930	0.80		
1935	1.04		
1940	0.91		
1958	1.03		

Inquire

1. How much did it cost, in Canadian dollars, to buy
a) US$200 in 1865? **b)** US$500 in 1930?
c) US$2000 in 1940? **d)** US$250 in 1958?

2. Use your research skills to determine how much it costs, in Canadian dollars, to buy US$800 today.

> When dividing rational numbers, use the same sign rules used to divide integers. Use a calculator, when convenient.

Example 1   Dividing Decimals
Divide.
a) $-3.5 \div 0.07$ **b)** $-1.68 \div (-1.4)$ **c)** $2.76 \div (-0.16)$

Solution

a) $-3.5 \div 0.07 = -50$

> **Estimate**
>
> $$-4 \div 0.1 = -40$$

b) $-1.68 \div (-1.4) = 1.2$

> **Estimate**
>
> $$-1.5 \div (-1.5) = 1$$

c) $2.76 \div (-0.16) = -17.25$

> **Estimate**
>
> $$3 \div (-0.2) = -15$$

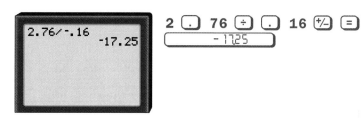

Example 2   Dividing in Fraction Form

Divide.

a) $\dfrac{1}{4} \div \dfrac{1}{2}$ **b)** $3 \div \dfrac{1}{3}$ **c)** $-\dfrac{2}{5} \div \dfrac{3}{10}$ **d)** $1\dfrac{1}{4} \div (-3)$

Solution

Replace the divisor by its reciprocal, and then multiply.

a)
$$\dfrac{1}{4} \div \dfrac{1}{2}$$
$$= \dfrac{1}{4} \times \dfrac{2}{1}$$
$$= \dfrac{2}{4}$$
$$= \dfrac{1}{2}$$

b)
$$3 \div \dfrac{1}{3}$$
$$= 3 \times \dfrac{3}{1}$$
$$= 9$$

c)
$$-\dfrac{2}{5} \div \dfrac{3}{10}$$
$$= -\dfrac{2}{5} \times \dfrac{10}{3}$$
$$= -\dfrac{20}{15}$$
$$= -\dfrac{4}{3}$$

d)
$$1\dfrac{1}{4} \div (-3)$$
$$= \dfrac{5}{4} \div \dfrac{-3}{1}$$
$$= \dfrac{5}{4} \times \dfrac{1}{-3}$$
$$= \dfrac{5}{-12}$$

Example 3   Dividing Rational Numbers

Divide $-1\dfrac{1}{2} \div \dfrac{4}{7}$.

Solution

$$-1\dfrac{1}{2} \div \dfrac{4}{7}$$
$$= -\dfrac{3}{2} \div \dfrac{4}{7}$$
$$= -\dfrac{3}{2} \times \dfrac{7}{4}$$
$$= -\dfrac{21}{8} \text{ or } -2.625$$

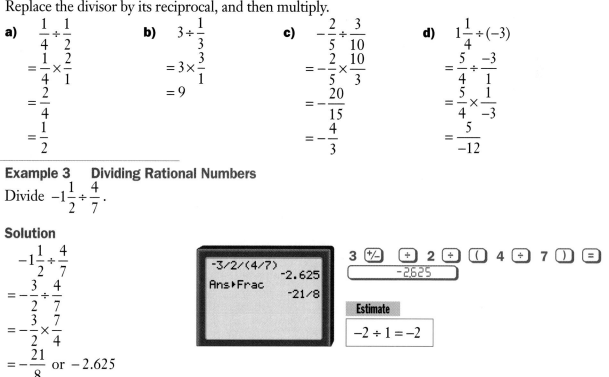

> **Estimate**
>
> $$-2 \div 1 = -2$$

Practice

State whether each answer will be positive or negative.

1. $-\dfrac{1}{3} \div \dfrac{1}{2}$ **2.** $6 \div \dfrac{1}{3}$

3. $\dfrac{7}{9} \div \left(-\dfrac{1}{3}\right)$ **4.** $-4\dfrac{1}{2} \div \left(-1\dfrac{1}{2}\right)$

5. $-0.25 \div 0.5$ **6.** $0.8 \div (-0.3)$

7. $-5.2 \div (-1.3)$ **8.** $0.4 \div 0.15$

State the reciprocal.

9. $\dfrac{1}{4}$ **10.** $-\dfrac{1}{2}$ **11.** $\dfrac{-5}{3}$ **12.** $\dfrac{7}{2}$

13. 3 **14.** $1\dfrac{3}{4}$ **15.** 0 **16.** $-2\dfrac{1}{5}$

Estimate each quotient.

17. $3\dfrac{1}{2} \div 2\dfrac{1}{4}$ **18.** $-4\dfrac{1}{4} \div 1\dfrac{7}{8}$

19. $1\dfrac{2}{5} \div \left(-5\dfrac{1}{2}\right)$ **20.** $-2\dfrac{2}{3} \div \left(-1\dfrac{1}{2}\right)$

21. $4.6 \div 8.2$ **22.** $-0.4 \div 1.7$

23. $8.5 \div (-1.4)$ **24.** $-9.7 \div (-2.5)$

Divide.

25. $2 \div \dfrac{2}{7}$ **26.** $-\dfrac{7}{8} \div \left(-\dfrac{1}{4}\right)$

27. $-10.5 \div 0.25$ **28.** $-50 \div 0.4$

29. $\dfrac{1}{2} \div 0$ **30.** $\dfrac{-4}{5} \div \left(-\dfrac{8}{10}\right)$

31. $2\dfrac{1}{3} \div \left(-\dfrac{1}{2}\right)$ **32.** $\dfrac{-7}{4} \div 4$

33. $-6.75 \div (-3)$ **34.** $-8.75 \div (-2.5)$

35. $4.48 \div (-1.6)$ **36.** $2.52 \div 4.2$

Applications and Problem Solving

37. **Chemistry** A chemist is measuring the acid needed for an experiment. If she has 2.2 cylinders of acid and needs 0.2 of a cylinder for each experiment, how many experiments can she do?

38. **Driving speed** Latika drove the 299 km from Calgary to Edmonton in $3\dfrac{1}{4}$ h. What was her average speed?

39. **British pound** There are 100 pennies in a British pound. If a Canadian dollar is worth 38.96 British pennies, how many Canadian dollars does it cost to buy
a) a British pound?   **b)** 250 British pounds?

40. **Slicing bread** If $\dfrac{1}{2}$ a loaf of bread is cut into 8 equal slices, what fraction is each slice of the original loaf?

41. **Fuel consumption** If a car travels 12.5 km on 1 L of gasoline, how many litres of gasoline does it use when it travels 100 km?

42. **Stock market** The value of an Inco share changed by -0.45 one day. If Lisa's Inco shares decreased in value by \$189 that day, how many Inco shares did she have?

43. **Lake Ontario** If the water in Lake Ontario was shared equally between all the residents of Ontario, what volume of water would each person receive, to the nearest thousand cubic metres?

44. What is the value of the quotient of two opposite rational numbers? Explain.

45. Write the following numbers. Compare your answers with a classmate's.
a) two rational numbers with a quotient of $\dfrac{5}{4}$
b) two rational numbers with a quotient of $-\dfrac{1}{2}$
c) two rational numbers whose quotient is an integer

46. Write a problem that requires division of rational numbers to solve it. Have a classmate solve your problem.

Astronomy

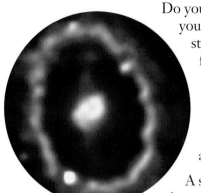

Do you think about conditions that exist far beyond the Earth? Do you wonder how far it is to the edge of the universe, how many stars are in the sky, or how long it has taken light to reach us from the stars? If you do, a career in astronomy may interest you.

Most astronomers work for government agencies, universities, or observatories. Astronomers study many aspects of the universe. Most astronomers then specialize in an area that interests them, such as the study of supernovas.

A supernova is the explosive destruction of a massive star, which is a star with a mass four or more times the mass of the sun. The explosions are so powerful that a supernova can give out as much energy in a few seconds as the sun does in millions of years.

Canadian astronomer Ian Shelton discovered a supernova from an observatory in Chile in 1987. This supernova, now called Supernova Shelton, was bright enough to be visible to the naked eye.

The first discovery of a supernova from a Canadian observatory was made from the Burke-Gaffney Observatory at St. Mary's University in Halifax, Nova Scotia, in 1995. The supernova, named 1995-F, was discovered by David Lane, a community college student and amateur astronomer, and Paul Gray, observatory technician and president of the Halifax branch of the Royal Astronomical Society of Canada.

1 Calculating Distances

1. Light travels through space at a speed of about 3×10^5 km/s. How far does light travel in
a) 5 s?
b) 30 s?
c) 5 min?

2. a) A light-year is the distance that light travels through space in a year. Calculate this distance in kilometres. Express your answer in scientific notation, and round the decimal part of the number to the first decimal place.
b) Supernova 1995-F is about 7×10^7 light-years from Earth. Express this distance in kilometres.
c) How many years did it take light from the explosion of 1995-F to reach the Earth? Explain.

2 Comparing Sizes

The diameter of the sun is about 1.4×10^6 km. The diameter of the moon is about 3476 km.

1. About how many moons could fit along the diameter of the sun?

2. After a massive star explodes, a neutron star as little as 20 km across may remain. About how many neutron stars could fit along
a) the diameter of the moon?
b) the diameter of the sun?

3 Locating Information

Where would you look to find information on the following?

1. the education needed for a career in astronomy

2. how to become an amateur astronomer

PROBLEM SOLVING

3.8 Use a Diagram

You can simplify many problems by drawing a diagram. Architects and interior designers use diagrams to solve design problems. The director of a play uses a diagram to block out where the actors should be.

Tom and Margarita are park rangers. They patrol the park by driving around the outside of the park. They start on opposite sides and drive at different speeds. Margarita takes 15 min to drive halfway around the park. Tom takes 20 min. They start their patrols at 20:00 and travel in opposite directions. If they stay on schedule, what are the approximate times at which they pass each other between 20:00 and 22:00?

Understand the Problem

1. What information are you given?
2. What are you asked to find?
3. Do you need an exact or an approximate answer?

Think of a Plan

Draw a diagram to show the time taken to drive around the park. Show Tom in red. Show Margarita in blue. Use the diagram to find when they pass each other.

Carry Out the Plan

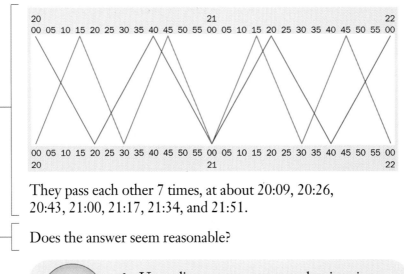

They pass each other 7 times, at about 20:09, 20:26, 20:43, 21:00, 21:17, 21:34, and 21:51.

Look Back

Does the answer seem reasonable?

Use a Diagram

1. Use a diagram to represent the situation.
2. Use the diagram to solve the problem.
3. Check that the answer is reasonable.

Applications and Problem Solving

1. Measurement How many different-sized rectangles have a perimeter of 16 m and side lengths that are whole numbers of metres?

2. Measurement In a scalene triangle, no two sides are equal. How many scalene triangles have a perimeter of 12 cm or less, if the side lengths are whole numbers of centimetres?

3. Stamps Roberto bought 4 stamps attached as shown.

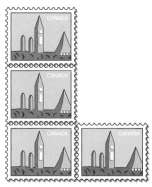

In how many different ways can 4 stamps be attached to each other?

4. Fence posts Lenore wants to fence a rectangular yard that measures 15 m by 9 m. She wants posts at the corners and every 3 m. How many posts does she need?

5. Swimming widths Yoshiko and Carla are water polo players. Part of their training program is to swim widths of the pool. Carla swims a width in 15 s. Yoshiko swims a width in 12 s. They start swimming widths at the same time from opposite sides of the pool. How many times do they pass each other in 2 min? What assumptions have you made?

6. Dinner seating When Terry, Rocky, Indu, and Lennox arrived at a restaurant for dinner, they were led to a square table. In how many different ways could they sit at the table, with one person on each side?

7. Signal flags Ships at sea use flags to send signals. Different orders of the same flags mean different messages. How many different messages could you send by using 3 flags?

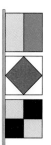

8. Round pies You can cut a round pie into 4 pieces with 2 straight cuts. If you do not care about the sizes of the pieces, you can cut a round pie into 7 pieces using 3 straight cuts. What is the greatest number of pieces you can get using 5 straight cuts?

9. River crossing A farmer must get a wolf, a goat, and some cabbages across a river. The boat will hold the farmer and one of the wolf, the goat, or the cabbages. Only the farmer can row the boat. The farmer cannot leave the goat alone with the cabbages, because the goat will eat them. The farmer cannot leave the wolf alone with the goat, because the wolf will chase the goat away. How does the farmer get the goat, wolf, and cabbages safely across the river?

10. Expedition A photography expedition planned an 8-day crossing of a desert. Each person could carry, at most, a 5-day supply of water. What is the smallest number of people needed to start the trip so that one person can cross the desert and the others can return to the starting point? Explain how you used a mathematical model to solve the problem.

11. Write a problem that can be solved with a diagram. Have a classmate solve your problem.

3.9 Adding and Subtracting Rational Numbers

The opening price of a stock tells you how much one share of a stock cost when the stock market opened for the day. The closing price of a stock tells you what one share was worth when the stock market closed for the day.

Explore: Complete the Table

The table shows the opening price for Nortel stock on a Monday at the Toronto Stock Exchange, and the daily change in price for 5 days. Copy and complete the table. The closing price on Monday becomes the opening price on Tuesday, and so on.

Stock	Opening Price ($)	Change ($)	Closing Price ($)
Monday	67.75	+0.25	
Tuesday		−0.60	
Wednesday		+0.60	
Thursday		+0.15	
Friday		+0.55	

Inquire

1. What was the closing price on Friday?
2. What was the sum of the Change column for the week?
3. What number do you get when you subtract the opening price on Monday from the closing price on Friday?
4. How does this number compare with the sum of the Change column? Explain.
5. What number do you get when you subtract the closing price on Friday from the opening price on Monday?
6. How does this number compare with the sum of the Change column?

When adding or subtracting rational numbers in decimal form, add or subtract as you did with decimals and use the sign rules you used for integers. Use a calculator, when convenient.

Example 1   Adding and Subtracting in Decimal Form
a) Add −3.42 + 1.35.   **b)** Subtract 6.75 − (−2.48).

Solution

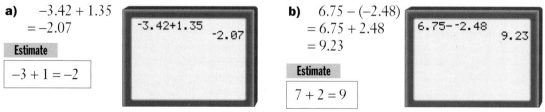

a)   −3.42 + 1.35
   = −2.07

Estimate
−3 + 1 = −2

-3.42+1.35
-2.07

b)   6.75 − (−2.48)
   = 6.75 + 2.48
   = 9.23

Estimate
7 + 2 = 9

6.75--2.48
9.23

When adding or subtracting rational numbers in fraction form, use the same rules you used for adding or subtracting fractions and use the sign rules you used for integers.

Example 2   Adding and Subtracting in Fraction Form

Simplify.

a) $-\dfrac{7}{8}+\dfrac{3}{4}$ **b)** $-3-1\dfrac{2}{3}$

Solution

a) $-\dfrac{7}{8}+\dfrac{3}{4}$ | Estimate | $-1+1=0$

$=-\dfrac{7}{8}+\dfrac{6}{8}$

$=-\dfrac{1}{8}$

b) $-3-1\dfrac{2}{3}$ | Estimate | $-3-2=-5$

$=-\dfrac{9}{3}-\dfrac{5}{3}$

$=-\dfrac{14}{3}$

Example 3   Subtracting Rational Numbers

Simplify $1\dfrac{1}{4}-2\dfrac{3}{8}$.

Solution

$1\dfrac{1}{4}-2\dfrac{3}{8}$ | Estimate | $1-2=-1$

$=\dfrac{5}{4}-\dfrac{19}{8}$

$=\dfrac{10}{8}-\dfrac{19}{8}$

$=-\dfrac{9}{8}$ or -1.125

Practice

A

State the lowest common denominator for each pair of fractions.

1. $\dfrac{1}{2},\dfrac{1}{5}$ **2.** $\dfrac{-3}{8},\dfrac{-1}{4}$ **3.** $1\dfrac{2}{3},-2\dfrac{3}{4}$

Estimate.

4. $1\dfrac{1}{3}+2\dfrac{3}{4}$

5. $-1\dfrac{1}{2}+3\dfrac{1}{8}$

6. $4\dfrac{2}{3}-6\dfrac{1}{4}$

7. $-\dfrac{5}{6}-2\dfrac{1}{4}$

8. $2\dfrac{1}{8}+\left(-2\dfrac{3}{4}\right)$

9. $4\dfrac{1}{3}-\left(-2\dfrac{1}{2}\right)$

10. $3.56+6.21$ **11.** $4.85+(-7.52)$

12. $9.69-2.86$ **13.** $-8.77-(-2.01)$

Write true or false for each number sentence.

14. $\dfrac{1}{4}-\dfrac{7}{8}=-\dfrac{5}{8}$ **15.** $-2\dfrac{1}{3}+\dfrac{5}{6}=-\dfrac{2}{6}$

16. $\dfrac{7}{10}+\dfrac{11}{20}=\dfrac{18}{20}$ **17.** $-\dfrac{11}{30}-\dfrac{7}{6}=-\dfrac{23}{15}$

18. $8.3-(-1.5)=6.8$ **19.** $-4.4-(-2.6)=-1.8$

Estimate, and then simplify.

20. $\dfrac{1}{4}-2\dfrac{1}{3}$ **21.** $-2.55+6.3$

22. $\dfrac{7}{9}+\dfrac{1}{3}$ **23.** $\dfrac{9}{10}-\dfrac{3}{10}$

24. $8.83-9.75$ **25.** $\dfrac{3}{5}-\dfrac{1}{4}$

26. $-1\dfrac{4}{5} - \dfrac{1}{10}$ **27.** $-\dfrac{5}{8} + 2\dfrac{3}{16}$

28. $-4\dfrac{8}{9} - 2\dfrac{2}{3}$ **29.** $-\dfrac{1}{4} + \dfrac{21}{100}$

30. $6.23 - (-3.65)$ **31.** $-\dfrac{3}{10} + \dfrac{53}{100}$

32. $1 - \dfrac{1}{100}$ **33.** $-8.93 + (-5.63)$

34. $-4.61 - 1.84$ **35.** $-3.65 - (-2.99)$

36. $2\dfrac{1}{4} - \left(-1\dfrac{1}{2}\right)$ **37.** $3\dfrac{1}{2} - 5\dfrac{1}{3}$

Applications and Problem Solving

38. Share prices Shares of ABC Foods opened at 9.10 and closed at 7.65. What was the change that day?

B

39. Weather The nightly low temperatures one week in Kingston were $-1.5°C$, $+2.1°C$, $-3.8°C$, $-2.2°C$, $+4.3°C$, $-5.3°C$, and $-6.9°C$. What was the average low temperature that week?

40. Eating pizza Six friends bought 3 pizzas. Each person ate $\dfrac{3}{8}$ of a pizza. How much pizza was left over?

41. Vacation spending On their vacation, the Reikos spent $\dfrac{1}{4}$ of their money on gas, $\dfrac{3}{5}$ on food and lodging, and $\dfrac{1}{8}$ on tourist attractions.
a) What fraction of their money did they spend?
b) If they started with $1840.00, how much money did they have left?

42. Skiing When Canada's Kate Pace won the gold medal at the World Alpine Ski Championships, her winning time was 1 min 27.38 s. She finished $\dfrac{28}{100}$ of a second ahead of Astrid Loedemal of Norway. What was Astrid's time?

43. Gold mining About $\dfrac{2}{5}$ of Canada's gold production comes from Ontario. About $\dfrac{3}{10}$ comes from Quebec and $\dfrac{1}{10}$ from British Columbia. What fraction of Canada's gold production comes from the rest of the country? Write your answer in lowest terms.

C

44. a) If the sum of two different rational numbers is zero, what can you say about the numbers?
b) If the sum of two equal rational numbers is zero, what can you say about the numbers?

45. Decide whether each statement is always true, sometimes true, or never true. Explain.
a) If a negative rational number is subtracted from another negative rational number, the result is less than 0.
b) The sum of two non-zero rational numbers is greater than either of the numbers.
c) Subtracting one rational number from another gives an integer.

46. Write the following numbers. Compare your answers with a classmate's.
a) two rational numbers with a sum of -0.6
b) three rational numbers with a sum of $-2\dfrac{1}{4}$
c) two rational numbers with a difference of $\dfrac{5}{8}$

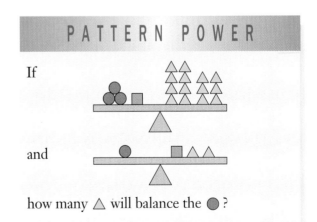

PATTERN POWER

If

and

how many △ will balance the ● ?

Budgets From a Spreadsheet

A spreadsheet is a useful tool for keeping track of expenses and the amount of money that remains in a budget.

1 Finding the Total Cost

1. Work with a partner. Use magazines, catalogues, and newspapers to choose 5 prizes of different values. They will be 1st, 2nd, 3rd, 4th, and 5th prizes for the students who raise the most in a fund-raising project. Keep the total cost below $500.00.

2. Copy the following spreadsheet into your notebook. Calculate and record the entries. You will need to enter the rate of provincial tax and the rate of the GST.

	A	B	C	D	E	F
1		**Prize**	**Price**	**Provincial Tax**	**GST**	**Item Cost**
2	1st			=C2*■	=C2*■	=C2+D2+E2
3	2nd					
4	3rd					
5	4th					
6	5th					
7					Total Cost	=SUM(F2..F6)

3. Is the calculation method shown in the spreadsheet correct for all provinces? Explain.

2 Adjusting the Total Cost

1. Set up the above spreadsheet on a computer, and have the computer calculate the total cost.

2. Adjust your 5 prizes until you have spent no more than $350.00 and no less than $300.00.

3. Redo the spreadsheet to allow for 8 prizes, with a total cost of no more than $700.00 and no less than $650.00.

3.10 Order of Operations With Rational Numbers

A new band made a demo tape and sent copies to music publishers, hoping to get a recording contract. The band received no response from the publishers. One reason might be that the band did not follow the usual steps. The suggested steps, in order, are as follows.
- Hire an agent.
- Develop a marketing package.
- Contact publishers.
- Select a publisher.
- Negotiate and sign a contract.

The order in which calculation steps are performed in mathematics is also important.

Explore: Solve the Problem
Suni worked 10 h at Champions Fitness Centre on the holiday weekend.
She worked at the reception desk for $4\frac{1}{2}$ h and earned $10.00/h.
She worked for $5\frac{1}{2}$ h as manager for the centre and earned $12.50/h.
She received a bonus of $20.00 for working on the holiday weekend.
a) How much did she earn at the reception desk?
b) How much did she earn as manager?
c) What were her total earnings?

Inquire
1. The company computer calculated her earnings by evaluating the expression $4.5 \times 10.00 + 5.5 \times 12.50 + 20.00$. Which operation does the computer do first?

2. Does adding the hourly rates, multiplying by 10 h, and then adding $20.00 give the correct result? Explain.

3. Does averaging the hourly rates, multiplying by 10 h, and then adding $20.00 give the correct result? Explain.

Example 1   Using BEDMAS
Evaluate.
a) $0.7 + 0.5 \times 0.4$ **b)** $\frac{1}{2} - 3\left(\frac{1}{3} + 2\right)$

Solution

a)
$$0.7 + 0.5 \times 0.4 \quad \text{multiply}$$
$$= 0.7 + 0.2 \quad \text{add}$$
$$= 0.9$$

b)
$$\frac{1}{2} - 3\left(\frac{1}{3} + 2\right) \quad \text{brackets}$$
$$= \frac{1}{2} - 3\left(\frac{7}{3}\right) \quad \text{multiply}$$
$$= \frac{1}{2} - 7 \quad \text{subtract}$$
$$= -6\frac{1}{2}$$

Example 2   Using BEDMAS With Powers

Evaluate.

a) $-6.2 \div 0.5^2 + 1.6$ **b)** $\left(\dfrac{5}{6} - \dfrac{1}{2}\right)^3 \div \dfrac{2}{3}$

Solution

a) $-6.2 \div 0.5^2 + 1.6$ exponent

$= -6.2 \div 0.25 + 1.6$ divide

$= -24.8 + 1.6$ add

$= -23.2$

6 [.] 2 [+/−] [÷] [.] 5 [x²] [+]

1 [.] 6 [=] [−23.2]

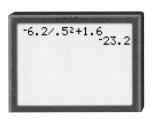

b) $\left(\dfrac{5}{6} - \dfrac{1}{2}\right)^3 \div \dfrac{2}{3}$ brackets

$= \left(\dfrac{5}{6} - \dfrac{3}{6}\right)^3 \div \dfrac{2}{3}$

$= \left(\dfrac{2}{6}\right)^3 \div \dfrac{2}{3}$

$= \left(\dfrac{1}{3}\right)^3 \div \dfrac{2}{3}$ exponent

$= \dfrac{1}{27} \div \dfrac{2}{3}$ divide

$= \dfrac{1}{27} \times \dfrac{3}{2}$

$= \dfrac{3}{54}$

$= \dfrac{1}{18}$ or $0.0\overline{5}$

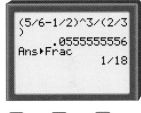

(5 [÷] 6 [−] 1

[÷] 2) [yˣ] 3 [÷]

(2 [÷] 3) [=]

[0.055555555]

Practice

A

Evaluate.

1. $8 + 6 \times 2$

2. $18 + 6 \div 2$

3. $-6.5 \times 4 - 8$

4. $\dfrac{18 + 6}{5 + 1} - 4$

5. $9.8 - 1.4 \div 0.7$

6. $7(3 - 2 + 6)$

7. $-4[8 + 7(6 - 3)]$

8. $\dfrac{7}{10} - \dfrac{1}{10} \div \dfrac{1}{10}$

Evaluate. Justify the steps in your solutions.

9. $-3 + \left(\dfrac{3}{4} - \dfrac{1}{4}\right)^2$

10. $-3 - (1 - 2)^2$

11. $(0.75 + 0.25)^3 \div 0.2$

12. $2\left(\dfrac{1}{4} - \dfrac{1}{2}\right) - \left(\dfrac{1}{2}\right)^3$

13. $\dfrac{3}{4} + \left(\dfrac{2}{3}\right)^2 \times \dfrac{1}{2}$

14. $(4.5 \div 1.5 - 5)^4$

15. $(3.6 - 4.1)^3 \times 1.2$

16. $\left(\dfrac{7}{9} - \dfrac{4}{9}\right)^3 - \left(\dfrac{5}{3} - \dfrac{4}{3}\right)^2$

Use brackets to make each statement true.

17. $\dfrac{2}{3} + 4 \times \dfrac{1}{2} + \dfrac{1}{4} \div 3 = \dfrac{5}{3}$

18. $0.5^2 - 0.1 \times 8 \div 2 = 0.6$

19. $-2 \times 18.5 - 6.3 \div 4 = -6.1$

Applications and Problem Solving

B

20. Algebra Evaluate each expression for $a = 3$, $b = 6$, and $c = -\dfrac{1}{2}$.

a) $a(b + c)$ **b)** $ab + ac$

c) $b^2 + a$ **d)** $a \times b \times c$

e) $b \div c \times a$ **f)** $b \times c + 3$

g) $a \div b \div c$ **h)** $a \div (b \div c)$

i) $a \times b \div c^3$ **j)** $(b \times c)^3 + a^2$

21. Algebra Evaluate each expression for $x = 0.5$, $y = 7.2$, and $z = -1.8$.

a) $x(y + z)$ **b)** $xy + xz$

c) $y \div z \times x$ **d)** $x \times y \times z$

e) $x^2 - z$ **f)** $x^2 + y^2$

g) $x^2 - y^2$ **h)** $y \div x + z$

i) $(y - z)^2$ **j)** $z \div x^3$

22. Puzzle Copy the cross-number puzzle into your notebook. Evaluate the following expressions to complete the puzzle.

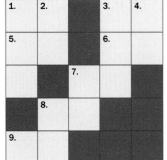

Across

1. $17 + 5 - 3$

3. $[(6 - 3)^2 - 4]^2$

5. $5^2 - 16 + 3$

6. $(75 - 10) - (23 - 8)$

7. $96 - 3(4.2 - 0.2)$

8. $9 + 4 \div \dfrac{1}{6} \times 3$

9. $(19.5 - 6.5)^2 - (8.4 - 4.4) - 7 \times 10$

Down

1. $323 - 2(121 - 16)$

2. $(12 - 7)^3 + 6 - 39$

3. $2^8 - 2$

4. $10 \div \dfrac{1}{2} \times 2.5$

7. $(6 \div 6 \times 3)^4$

8. $5(18 - 3) + 10$

23. Three of the following skill-testing questions were answered incorrectly. Identify the incorrect answers and correct them. Explain and justify your reasoning.

a) $8 \div 2 \times 3 + (6 - 1) \div 5 = 13$

b) $7 - 8 \times 0.5 - 0.5 = 7$

c) $2^2 \times 3 - 1 = 8$

d) $(1 - 3)^3 \div (5 - 7)^2 = 2$

C

24. Make up your own skill-testing question. Have a classmate solve your question.

25. For each part, compare your expressions with a classmate's.

a) Here is a way of using four $\dfrac{1}{2}$s and the order of operations to make the number 1.

$$\dfrac{\dfrac{1}{2} + \dfrac{1}{2}}{\dfrac{1}{2} + \dfrac{1}{2}} = 1$$

Write three other ways of using four $\dfrac{1}{2}$s to make the number 1.

b) Write three ways of using four $-\dfrac{1}{2}$s to make the number 1.

c) Use four $\dfrac{1}{2}$s to make the number 3.

d) Use four $-\dfrac{1}{2}$s to make the number 3.

NUMBER POWER

Use each of the numbers from 1 to 9 only once to make each statement true.

$$(\blacksquare - \blacksquare) \div \blacksquare = 1$$

$$\blacksquare + \blacksquare - \blacksquare = 1$$

$$\blacksquare - \blacksquare \times \blacksquare = 1$$

Box Office Hits

From the Computer Data Bank, use the *Movies* database, which is about top money-making movies each year, to complete the following.

1 Favourite Type of Movie

The movies in this database are classified by type. There are 8 different types of movies — Action, Comedy, Drama, Family, Horror, Musical, Science Fiction, and Western.

1. Find all the records for your favourite type of movie. How many records are displayed?

2. Find all of those records that have a 4-star rating. How many records are displayed? What percent is this of the records displayed in question 1?

3. Repeat questions 1 and 2 for the other types of movies, sharing the work with classmates.

4. Which type of movie has the greatest percent with 4 stars? the least percent? Would you have predicted these answers? Explain.

2 Academy Awards

1. Sort the records from greatest to least star rating, and, within each star rating, from greatest to least number of Academy Awards. Which movie with 4 stars has the greatest number of Academy Awards? How many does it have?

2. Do movies with higher star ratings have more Academy Awards than movies with lower star ratings? Explain.

3 Comparing Profits

1. Find all the records for which the cost and income are available. How many records are displayed?

2. a) How could you calculate profit in millions of dollars?
b) Add a calculated field for profit in millions of dollars.

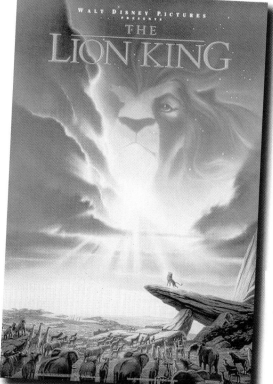

©Disney Enterprises, Inc.

3. Sort the records from greatest to least profit in millions of dollars. Which are the top five movies?

4. Did any movies lose money? Explain.

5. The profits can be multiplied by the inflation factor to get profits in millions of 1996 dollars. Add a calculated field for profits in millions of 1996 dollars, rounding the profits to 1 decimal place.

6. Sort the records from greatest to least profit in millions of 1996 dollars. Which are the top five movies? Compare with your answers to question 3.

4 Making Movies

1. If you were a movie producer interested in making a lot of money, receiving a 4-star rating, and winning several Academy Awards, which type of movie would you produce? Explain.

PROBLEM SOLVING

3.11 Solve Fermi Problems

"About how many buckets of water would it take to empty Loch Ness and find the monster?" Problems like this one that involve large numbers and give approximate answers are known as *Fermi problems*. They are named after the great Italian physicist Enrico Fermi (1901–1954), who liked to pose them. Solving Fermi problems will help you to improve your estimation skills.

About how many Canadian $1 coins are needed to cover a basketball court?

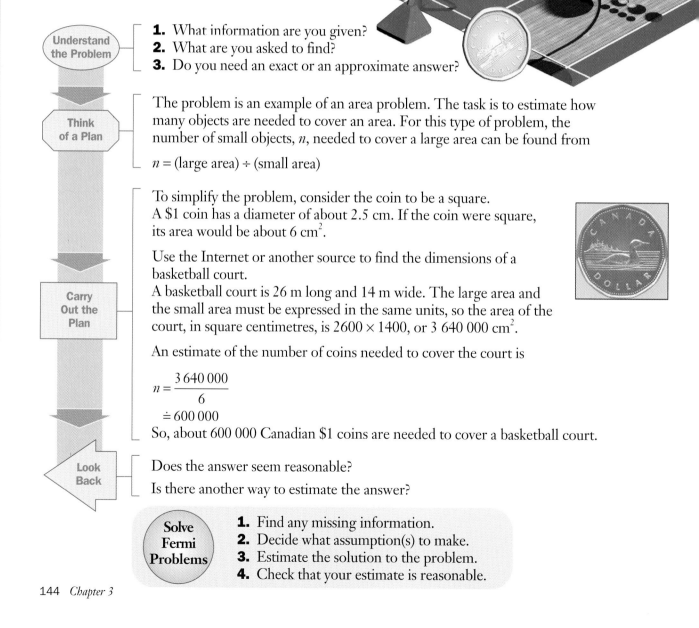

Understand the Problem

1. What information are you given?
2. What are you asked to find?
3. Do you need an exact or an approximate answer?

Think of a Plan

The problem is an example of an area problem. The task is to estimate how many objects are needed to cover an area. For this type of problem, the number of small objects, n, needed to cover a large area can be found from

$n = (\text{large area}) \div (\text{small area})$

Carry Out the Plan

To simplify the problem, consider the coin to be a square. A $1 coin has a diameter of about 2.5 cm. If the coin were square, its area would be about 6 cm^2.

Use the Internet or another source to find the dimensions of a basketball court.
A basketball court is 26 m long and 14 m wide. The large area and the small area must be expressed in the same units, so the area of the court, in square centimetres, is 2600 × 1400, or 3 640 000 cm^2.

An estimate of the number of coins needed to cover the court is

$$n = \frac{3\,640\,000}{6}$$
$$\doteq 600\,000$$

So, about 600 000 Canadian $1 coins are needed to cover a basketball court.

Look Back

Does the answer seem reasonable?

Is there another way to estimate the answer?

Solve Fermi Problems

1. Find any missing information.
2. Decide what assumption(s) to make.
3. Estimate the solution to the problem.
4. Check that your estimate is reasonable.

To solve a Fermi problem that involves volume, you may find it convenient to assume that an object approximates a cube or other simple shape.

Suppose you want to estimate how many golf balls are needed to fill a 10 m by 8 m by 5 m room. A golf ball has a diameter of about 4 cm. If a golf ball were a cube, it would have a volume of about 64 cm^3.

The volume of the room, in cubic centimetres, is $1000 \times 800 \times 500$, or 400 000 000 cm^3.

For this type of problem, the number of small objects, n, needed to fill a large object can be found from

$n = $ (large volume) $\div$ (small volume)

$= \dfrac{400\,000\,000}{64}$

$\doteq 6\,000\,000$

So, the number of golf balls needed to fill the room is about 6 000 000.

Applications and Problem Solving

For each of the following problems, state any assumptions you make. Use the Internet or another source to find the data you need. Explain and justify the reasoning you use to solve each problem.

1. Toonies About how many Canadian $2 coins would cover the floor of your classroom?

2. Gymnasium Estimate the number of CDs, in their cases, that would cover the floor of the gymnasium in your school.

3. Football field About how many students could stand on a football field?

4. Volleyballs About how many volleyballs would fill your principal's office?

5. Popcorn About how many pieces of popped popcorn would fill your classroom?

6. Table tennis balls About how many table tennis balls would fill a school bus?

7. Soccer field About how many blades of grass are there on a soccer field?

8. Textbooks About how many math textbooks, lying end to end, would reach from St. John's to Vancouver along the Trans-Canada Highway?

9. Tennis balls About how many tennis balls would fill a minivan?

10. Loch Ness Loch Ness contains about 9×10^{12} L of water. About how many buckets of water would it take to empty Loch Ness?

11. Grand Canyon The Grand Canyon in Arizona is about 440 km long, and averages 1.5 km deep and 15 km wide. If you built a cubic apartment in the Grand Canyon for each person on Earth, what would be the dimensions of each apartment? Would each apartment be larger than your classroom?

12. Cars About how many cars are there in your city or town?

13. Pencil line You have a new pencil and a pencil sharpener. What is the length of the longest line you can draw?

14. Telephones About how many telephones are there within 1 km of your school?

15. Pets About how many cats are kept as pets in Ontario?

16. Sneakers About how many kilometres can you walk in one pair of sneakers?

3.12 Square Roots

About 1 in every 5 Canadian adults plays chess. The world's top chess players are called grandmasters. At only 13 years of age, Alexandre Lesiège of Quebec beat a Russian grandmaster at the World Open. Alexandre went on to become Canada's youngest-ever grandmaster, at age 21.

The playing surface of a chessboard is a square. It is covered by 64 smaller squares that are equal in area. There are 8 squares along each side of the board. We can say that 64 is the square of 8, but how can we describe 8 in relation to 64?

Explore: Use the Diagrams

Draw figures A, B, C, and D on 1-cm grid paper.

a) Determine the areas of squares A, B, and C.
b) Count squares to determine the area of square D.

Inquire

1. The length of each side of a square is the **square root** of its area. What is the square root of area A? area B? area C?

2. Measure the side of square D. What is the approximate square root of area D?

3. Write your definition of the square root of a number.

4. a) What is the square root of 64?
b) Is any other integer also the square root of 64? Explain.

5. A Snakes and Ladders game board is a square with 100 smaller squares marked on it.
a) How many of the smaller squares lie along each side of the board?
b) What are the square roots of 100?

Since $5 \times 5 = 25$ and $(-5) \times (-5) = 25$, then 5 and -5 are the square roots of 25. Since $1.2 \times 1.2 = 1.44$ and $(-1.2) \times (-1.2) = 1.44$, then 1.2 and -1.2 are the square roots of 1.44.

The **radical sign**, $\sqrt{}$, is used to represent the positive square root of a number.
$$\sqrt{25} = 5, \text{ and } \sqrt{1.44} = 1.2$$
The positive square root is also called the **principal square root**. To avoid confusion, mathematicians use the radical sign only for non-negative square roots.

Example 1   Evaluating Square Roots
Evaluate.
a) $\sqrt{81}$ **b)** $\sqrt{0.36}$ **c)** $-\sqrt{6400}$

Solution

a) $9 \times 9 = 81$ **b)** $0.6 \times 0.6 = 0.36$ **c)** $80 \times 80 = 6400$
so $\sqrt{81} = 9$ so $\sqrt{0.36} = 0.6$ so $-\sqrt{6400} = -80$

Many numbers, such as $\sqrt{2}$ and $\sqrt{3}$, cannot be written as a fraction or a terminating decimal. These square roots are non-terminating, non-repeating decimals, or **irrational numbers**. To determine the approximate values of such square roots, we estimate or use a calculator.

Example 2   Estimating Square Roots
Estimate $\sqrt{356}$.

Solution
Start with numbers whose squares you know.
$30 \times 30 = 900$ (too high)
$20 \times 20 = 400$ (too high)
$10 \times 10 = 100$ (too low)
Since 356 is between 100 and 400, and is closer to 400, a good estimate for $\sqrt{356}$ is $\sqrt{400}$ or 20.

Another way to estimate the square root of a number is to divide the number into groups of two digits, starting at the decimal point. Then, for numbers greater than 1, estimate the square root of the group furthest from the decimal point and add one zero for each other group. Thus, for $\sqrt{1535}$, we consider the two groups 15 and 35.
$\sqrt{15} \doteq 4 \leftarrow$ square root of the group furthest from the decimal point
There is one other group of digits, so we add one zero. So, $\sqrt{1535} \doteq 40$.

$\sqrt{1535}$
$\sqrt{15\ 35}$
$\quad 4\quad 0$

For numbers less than 1, estimate the square root of the non-zero group closest to the decimal point. Thus, for $\sqrt{0.096}$, we consider the two groups 09 and 60.
$\sqrt{09} = 3$, so $\sqrt{0.096} \doteq 0.3$.

$\sqrt{0.096}$
$0.\sqrt{09\ 60}$
$0.\quad 3$

Example 3 Estimating Square Roots

Estimate the square roots.

a) $\sqrt{567}$ **b)** $\sqrt{12\,300}$ **c)** $\sqrt{0.45}$ **d)** $\sqrt{0.006}$

Solution

a) $\sqrt{567}$
$\sqrt{5\ 67}$
$\downarrow\ \ \downarrow$
$2\ \ \ 0$
$\sqrt{567} \doteq 20$

b) $\sqrt{12\,300}$
$\sqrt{1\ 23\ \ 00}$
$\downarrow\ \ \downarrow\ \ \ \downarrow$
$1\ \ 0\ \ \ 0$
$\sqrt{12\,300} \doteq 100$

c) $\sqrt{0.45}$
$0.\sqrt{45}$
$\downarrow\ \ \downarrow$
$0.\ \ 7$
$\sqrt{0.45} \doteq 0.7$

d) $\sqrt{0.006}$
$0.00\ \sqrt{60}$
$\downarrow\ \ \downarrow\ \ \ \downarrow$
$0.\ 0\ \ \ 8$
$\sqrt{0.006} \doteq 0.08$

Example 4 Approximate Square Roots

Evaluate, to the nearest tenth.

a) $\sqrt{42}$ **b)** $-\sqrt{164}$

Solution

Use a calculator.

a)

Estimate

$6 \times 6 = 36$, so $\sqrt{42} \doteq 6$

$\sqrt{42} = 6.5$, to the nearest tenth.

b)

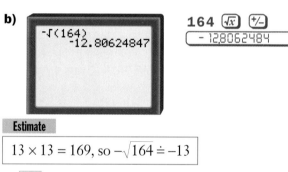

Estimate

$13 \times 13 = 169$, so $-\sqrt{164} \doteq -13$

$-\sqrt{164} = -12.8$, to the nearest tenth.

Example 5 Evaluating Expressions

Evaluate, to the nearest tenth.

a) $5\sqrt{3} + 7\sqrt{2}$ **b)** $\dfrac{6\sqrt{11}}{7}$

Solution

a) $5\sqrt{3}$ means $5 \times \sqrt{3}$ and $7\sqrt{2}$ means $7 \times \sqrt{2}$

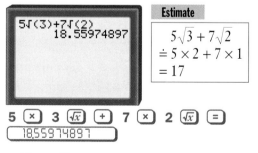

Estimate

$5\sqrt{3} + 7\sqrt{2}$
$\doteq 5 \times 2 + 7 \times 1$
$= 17$

$5\sqrt{3} + 7\sqrt{2} = 18.6$, to the nearest tenth.

b)

Estimate

$\dfrac{6\sqrt{11}}{7} \doteq \dfrac{6 \times 3}{6}$
$= 3$

$\dfrac{6\sqrt{11}}{7} = 2.8$, to the nearest tenth.

Example 6   Distance to the Horizon

The distance to the horizon for a person standing on a beach and looking out to sea is given by the formula
$$d = 0.35\sqrt{h}$$
In this formula, d is the distance to the horizon, in kilometres, and h is the height of the person's eyes above the water, in centimetres.

Sandra is a lifeguard. When she sits on a lifeguard tower, her eyes are 375 cm above the water. What distance can she see to the horizon, to the nearest tenth of a kilometre?

Solution
$$d = 0.35\sqrt{h}$$
$$= 0.35\sqrt{375}$$
$$\doteq 6.8$$
Sandra can see 6.8 km to the horizon, to the nearest tenth of a kilometre.

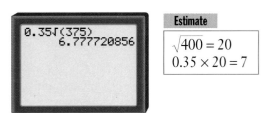

```
0.35√(375)
          6.777720856
```

Estimate

$\sqrt{400} = 20$

$0.35 \times 20 = 7$

Practice

A

Find the square roots of each number.

1. 49   **2.** 81   **3.** 121   **4.** 625

5. 0.64   **6.** 0.01   **7.** 1.96   **8.** 0.25

Evaluate.

9. $\sqrt{25}$ **10.** $\sqrt{100}$ **11.** $\sqrt{225}$

12. $\sqrt{256}$ **13.** $-\sqrt{169}$ **14.** $\sqrt{0.36}$

15. $\sqrt{0.04}$ **16.** $\sqrt{1.21}$ **17.** $-\sqrt{0.81}$

Estimate.

18. $\sqrt{30}$ **19.** $\sqrt{66}$ **20.** $-\sqrt{92}$

21. $\sqrt{765}$ **22.** $\sqrt{989}$ **23.** $\sqrt{3245}$

24. $\sqrt{7800}$ **25.** $\sqrt{56\ 000}$ **26.** $-\sqrt{880\ 000}$

Estimate.

27. $\sqrt{0.8}$ **28.** $\sqrt{0.77}$

29. $-\sqrt{0.05}$ **30.** $\sqrt{0.067}$

31. $\sqrt{0.0382}$ **32.** $\sqrt{0.0023}$

33. $-\sqrt{0.009}$ **34.** $\sqrt{0.0006}$

35. $\sqrt{0.000\ 22}$ **36.** $\sqrt{0.000\ 34}$

Estimate. Then, calculate to the nearest tenth.

37. $\sqrt{31}$ **38.** $\sqrt{44}$

39. $\sqrt{62}$ **40.** $-\sqrt{79}$

41. $\sqrt{101}$ **42.** $\sqrt{206}$

43. $\sqrt{1123}$ **44.** $\sqrt{20\ 183}$

45. $\sqrt{86\ 003}$ **46.** $\sqrt{202\ 183}$

Estimate. Then evaluate, to the nearest tenth.

47. $\sqrt{3} + \sqrt{7}$ **48.** $\sqrt{10} - \sqrt{5}$

49. $3\sqrt{11}$ **50.** $-6\sqrt{23}$

51. $(\sqrt{3})(\sqrt{2})$ **52.** $2\sqrt{12} - 8$

53. $\sqrt{14} \div \sqrt{5}$ **54.** $\dfrac{\sqrt{20} - \sqrt{10}}{\sqrt{31}}$

55. $3\sqrt{7} + 6\sqrt{91}$ **56.** $\dfrac{2\sqrt{45}}{3}$

57. $\dfrac{5\sqrt{10} + 6\sqrt{21}}{4}$ **58.** $\dfrac{\sqrt{123}}{\sqrt{60}}$

Applications and Problem Solving

59. Measurement Given the area of each square, determine the length of its side and its perimeter. Round to the nearest tenth of a unit, if necessary.
a) 25 cm^2 **b)** 225 m^2 **c)** 55 m^2
d) 90 cm^2 **e)** 200 m^2 **f)** 800 cm^2

B

60. Algebra Evaluate for $a = 5$ and $b = -2$.
a) $\sqrt{4a + 2b}$ **b)** $\sqrt{\dfrac{125}{a}}$

c) $\sqrt{-18b}$ **d)** $\sqrt{a^2 - 12b}$

e) $-\sqrt{(ab)^2}$ **f)** $\sqrt{10a - 5b + 4}$

g) $\sqrt{-10ab^3}$ **h)** $-3\sqrt{a^2 + 2ab + b^2}$

i) $7.3\sqrt{a^2 - 2ab + b^2}$ **j)** $\sqrt{-2a^2b^3}$

61. Measurement Calculate the perimeter of each figure, to the nearest tenth of a unit.

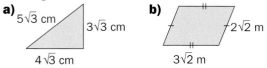

62. Measurement The Greek mathematician Heron found the following formula for the area of a triangle.
$$A = \sqrt{s(s-a)(s-b)(s-c)}$$
where a, b, and c are the side lengths, and s is half the perimeter.
$$s = \frac{a + b + c}{2}$$
Calculate the area of each triangle.

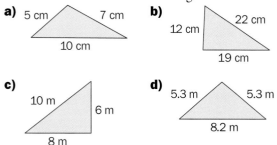

63. Land areas Land areas are measured in hectares (ha). 1 ha = 10 000 m^2
a) If a square field has an area of 1 ha, what are its dimensions?
b) A house lot in a big city may be about 0.04 ha in area. If this amount of land were square, what would its dimensions be?

64. Measurement The area, A, of an equilateral triangle can be modelled algebraically by the formula
$$A \doteq 0.433s^2$$
where s is the side length. For each area, find the side length, to the nearest tenth of a unit.
a) 15.6 cm^2 **b)** 44 m^2
c) 346.9 mm^2 **d)** 876.4 cm^2

65. Water speeds The water at the surface of a river moves faster than the water near the bottom. The formula that relates these two speeds is
$$\sqrt{b} = \sqrt{s} - 1.3$$
where b is the speed near the bottom and s is the speed at the surface. Both speeds are in kilometres per hour.
a) What is the speed of the water near the bottom of a river, to the nearest tenth of a kilometre per hour, if the surface speed is 16 km/h? 20 km/h?
b) What is the surface speed of the water, to the nearest tenth of a kilometre per hour, if the speed near the bottom is 9 km/h? 7 km/h?

66. Gravity The formula for calculating the time it takes an object to fall to the ground is
$$t = 0.45 \times \sqrt{h}$$
where h is the height, in metres, and t is the time, in seconds. The Leaning Tower of Pisa is 54.5 m tall. How long does it take an object dropped from the top to reach the ground, to the nearest tenth of a second?

67. a) Evaluate $2\sqrt{2}$.
b) Evaluate $\sqrt{8}$.
c) Compare your answers and explain your findings.

68. Velocity of sound The velocity of sound changes with temperature and with the material the sound passes through. The formula to calculate the velocity in air is
$$V = 20\sqrt{273+T}$$
where V is the velocity, in metres per second, and T is the temperature, in degrees Celsius. Calculate the velocity of sound in air, to the nearest metre per second, at
a) 16°C　　**b)** 0°C　　**c)** −10°C

C

69. Measurement A square has an area of 169 cm². What is the radius of the largest circle you can fit inside it? Explain.

70. How are the square roots of a perfect square related?

71. Technology Try to evaluate $\sqrt{-9}$ on your calculator. What is the result? Why?

72. Measurement For a square of area 2 cm², Nyla said that the perimeter was $4\sqrt{2}$ cm. Jill said that the perimeter was 5.66 cm. Who gave the exact value of the perimeter? Explain.

73. Measurement a) What is the exact value of the perimeter of a square with an area of 5 cm²?
b) Starting with the diagram shown, describe the steps you would follow to construct a square with an area of 5 cm². Explain how you used a mathematical model to solve the problem.

1 cm
2 cm

74. To find the square root of a perfect square by subtraction, subtract the odd numbers in increasing order until the result is 0.
$$25 - 1 = 24$$
$$24 - 3 = 21$$
$$21 - 5 = 16$$
$$16 - 7 = 9$$
$$9 - 9 = 0$$
We need five subtractions to reach 0 from 25, so $\sqrt{25} = 5$.
a) Use this method to find the following.
$$\sqrt{289} \quad \sqrt{576} \quad \sqrt{784} \quad \sqrt{1089}$$

b) Explain why this method works. Compare your explanation with your classmates'.

75. Satellites For a satellite to stay in orbit, its speed must satisfy the formula
$$s = \sqrt{\frac{5.15 \times 10^{12}}{d}}$$
where s is the speed, in kilometres per hour, and d is the distance from the satellite to the centre of the Earth, in kilometres. If a satellite is in orbit 35 880 km above the Earth, it hovers over one spot on the Earth. Use your research skills to find the radius of the Earth, and then determine the speed of a satellite that hovers over one spot on the Earth. Compare your answer with a classmate's.

LOGIC POWER

The Riddler has invited you to a party at his apartment. The elevator buttons are shown below. They are lettered from A to I, but the letters are hidden. You must press the buttons in order from A to I to get to the party. Use the clues to find the button letters.

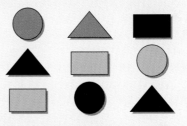

1. The D button is green.
2. The G button is red.
3. The F button is directly below a triangle.
4. The I button is in the left column.
5. The B button is not round.
6. The E button is in the middle row.
7. The H button is in the top row.
8. The F button is lower than the C button.
9. The C button is directly to the left of a round button.

3.13 Applying Formulas

Hailstones are balls of ice that grow as they are held up in the clouds by thunderstorm updrafts. While they are held up, supercooled water drops hit them and freeze, causing the hailstones to grow. Large hailstones can fall at speeds of up to 150 km/h and can have masses of up to 2 kg. Because of the damage that can occur during a hailstorm, weather forecasters try to warn people when hail is probable.

Explore: Use a Formula

Weather forecasters can use a formula to estimate the size of hailstones, if the speed of the thunderstorm updraft is known. The formula is
$$d = 0.05s$$
where s is the speed of the updraft, in kilometres per hour, and d is the diameter of a hailstone, in centimetres. What is the predicted diameter of a hailstone when the updraft speed is

a) 30 km/h?   **b)** 80 km/h?   **c)** 100 km/h?

Inquire

1. The smallest hailstone possible is about 0.5 cm in diameter. What is the approximate updraft speed that produces this hailstone?

2. The formula $r = 0.025s$ relates the radius of a hailstone, in centimetres, to the speed of the updraft, in kilometres per hour. In what way is this formula related to the one above?

3. How do weather forecasters determine the speed of an updraft?

Example   Tidal Waves

Tidal waves are caused by underwater earthquakes or large storms at sea. Tidal waves can be very destructive if they crash into populated areas. The speed of a tidal wave, s metres per second, can be found using the formula
$$s = 3.1 \times \sqrt{d}$$
where d is the depth of the ocean, in metres. To the nearest tenth of a metre per second, what is the speed of a tidal wave in 300 m of water? in 50 m of water?

Solution

$s = 3.1 \times \sqrt{d}$

In 300 m of water,
$s = 3.1 \times \sqrt{300}$
$\doteq 53.7$
In 300 m of water, the speed is about 53.7 m/s.

In 50 m of water,
$s = 3.1 \times \sqrt{50}$
$\doteq 21.9$
In 50 m of water, the speed is about 21.9 m/s.

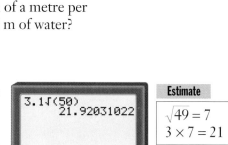

Estimate

$\sqrt{49} = 7$

$3 \times 7 = 21$

Applications and Problem Solving

A

1. Rental charges A rental company charges for chair rentals and delivery according to the formula
$$C = 5.50n + 50.00$$
where n is the number of chairs rented and C is the cost, in dollars. Calculate the cost of renting 60 chairs for a garden party.

2. Coin collection The face value, f dollars, of a collection of dimes and nickels is given by the equation
$$f = 0.1d + 0.05n$$
where d is the number of dimes and n is the number of nickels. What is the face value of 35 dimes and 48 nickels?

3. Stopping distances The stopping distance a car requires in good road conditions can be modelled by the formula
$$d = 0.4s + 0.002s^2$$
where d represents the approximate stopping distance, in metres, and s represents the speed, in kilometres per hour. Calculate the distance required to stop at the following speeds.
a) 50 km/h   **b)** 80 km/h
c) 100 km/h   **d)** 120 km/h

B

4. Fund-raising The school band decided to raise money by performing in a music marathon. Pledges averaged $15.50 per musician for every hour of playing. Write a formula to calculate the amount each member could earn for the band. Let h represent the number of hours each member plays and v represent the amount of money earned.

5. Car rental For a mid-size car, a car rental company charges $45.00 per day, plus $0.15 per kilometre driven.
a) Write a formula to model the cost of a one-day rental, C dollars, if the car is driven d kilometres.
b) Determine the rental cost when the car is driven 175 km in a day.

6. Falling object The following formula calculates the time, t seconds, it takes for an object to fall from a height, h metres.
$$t = \sqrt{h \div 4.9}$$
The High Level Bridge in Lethbridge, Alberta, is the highest railway bridge of its type in the world. It stands 96 m above the river valley below. To the nearest tenth of a second, how long does it take for an object to fall from the top of the High Level Bridge to the ground below it?

7. Solar system The period of revolution of a planet around the sun is the time it takes for the planet to complete one orbit of the sun. The period, P years, is given by Kepler's third law
$$P^2 = D^3$$
where D is the average distance of the planet from the sun, in astronomical units (AU). One astronomical unit is the average distance of the Earth from the sun. Use the average distance from the sun to find the period of revolution for each of the following planets, to the nearest tenth of a year.
a) Jupiter; 5.20 AU
b) Mercury; 0.387 AU
c) Uranus; 19.2 AU

C

8. Write a problem that requires a formula. Have a classmate solve your problem.

MODELLING MATH — TRANSPORTATION

3.14 How Can We Model Driving Routes?

The road map shows part of Eastern Ontario. There are four type of roads, primary roads, secondary roads, regional roads, and local roads. Driving distances are shown in kilometres. Assume that you can average 80 km/h on primary roads, 60 km/h on secondary and regional roads, and 40 km/h on local roads.

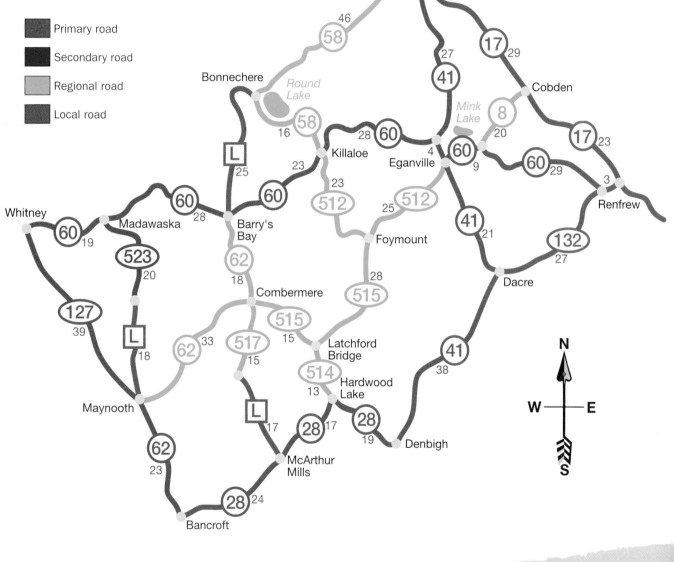

Primary road

Secondary road

Regional road

Local road

1 Modelling Directions

1. The compass directions north, south, east, and west are marked on the map. Using these compass directions, and the roads and towns on the map, write a set of directions for someone who wants to drive from Barry's Bay to Latchford Bridge, passing through Pembroke and not travelling on the same road twice.

2. Write a set of directions for someone who wants to drive from Whitney to Combermere to McArthur Mills and then to Dacre, without travelling on any local roads.

2 Modelling Distances and Times

1. a) Find the shortest driving distance from Cobden to Maynooth using any of the four types of roads.
b) Suppose regional road 8 is closed for construction. Find the shortest driving distance from Cobden to Maynooth using at least one primary road, and at least one secondary or regional road.
c) Find the shortest driving distance from Cobden to Maynooth using only primary roads.

2. a) Which of the routes you found in question 1 takes the least time? How long does it take, to the nearest minute?
b) Can you find a route that takes less time than the route in part a)? If so, describe the route, and find how long it takes, to the nearest minute.
c) Which route from question 1 takes the longest time? How long does it take, to the nearest minute?

3. a) Find the shortest driving distance from Whitney to Denbigh, if you can use any of the four types of roads and you must pick up a parcel in Bonnechere on your way.
b) Find the shortest driving distance from Whitney to Denbigh through Bonnechere using at least one primary road, at least one secondary or regional road, and no local roads.

4. a) Which of the routes you found in question 3 takes the least time? How long does it take, to the nearest minute?
b) Which route takes the longest time? How long does it take, to the nearest minute?

3 Applying the Model

One year, the Great North American Race for antique cars started in Ottawa and travelled through or near Toronto, Buffalo, Syracuse, Philadelphia, Washington, D.C., Charleston, Lexington, Nashville, Little Rock, Dallas, Austin, San Antonio, Laredo, and Monterrey, ending in Mexico City. Each car had a driver and a navigator. The race took 15 days. There were 108 teams in the race, 12 of them from Canada.

1. Use your research skills to determine the approximate length of the race, in kilometres.

2. About what distance, in kilometres, did the cars average each day?

Review

3.1 *Write in scientific notation.*

1. 27 300 000   **2.** 701 000 000

Write in standard form.

3. 2.53×10^8 **4.** 5.2×10^6

Calculate. Write your answer in scientific notation.

5. $(2.5 \times 10^3)(3.1 \times 10^5)$

6. $(8.6 \times 10^{12}) \div (2.5 \times 10^7)$

3.2 *Evaluate.*

7. $3^{-1} - 3^0$ **8.** $2^{-3} + 2^{-2}$

Simplify.

9. $2^3 \times 2^{-5}$ **10.** $n^{-4} \div n^{-6}$

11. $((-3)^{-2})^4$ **12.** $((-x)^5)^{-1}$

13. $(-0.4)^{-5}(-0.4)^{-3}$ **14.** $4^2 \times 4^{-3} \times 4^{-1}$

Evaluate.

15. $5^3 \times 5^2 \times 5$ **16.** $2^0 \times 2^3$

17. $3^2 \div 3^{-1}$ **18.** $(2^3)^4$

19. $2^{-3} \times 2^2$ **20.** $(4^2)^3 \div 4^4$

21. $(2^3)^{-2}$ **22.** $((-3)^2)^{-1}$

23. Evaluate for $x = 3$ and $y = -2$.

a) x^2y^2 **b)** y^5

c) $-6xy$ **d)** $(x - y)^3$

e) $6x^3 - 5y$ **f)** $(-x)^2(-y)^2$

3.3 *Write in scientific notation.*

24. 0.000 007   **25.** 0.000 000 019

Write in standard notation.

26. 3.4×10^{-4} **27.** 5.2×10^{-5}

Calculate. Write your answer in scientific notation.

28. $(6.2 \times 10^{-4})(3.7 \times 10^2)$

29. $(7.8 \times 10^{-15}) \div (1.3 \times 10^{-9})$

30. Population The area of Welland is about 80 km^2. One year, the population of Welland was about 50 000. How many square kilometres were there per person in Welland? Write your answer in scientific notation.

3.5 *Write each rational number in lowest terms.*

31. $\dfrac{4}{8}$ **32.** $\dfrac{-3}{6}$

33. $\dfrac{-2}{8}$ **34.** $-\dfrac{14}{2}$

35. $-\dfrac{18}{21}$ **36.** $\dfrac{-8}{10}$

37. $-\dfrac{3}{9}$ **38.** $\dfrac{12}{15}$

Arrange the rational numbers in order from greatest to least.

39. $\dfrac{1}{2}, \dfrac{4}{5}, \dfrac{7}{5}, 0, \dfrac{-1}{2}, \dfrac{-7}{-10}, 2$

40. $\dfrac{-5}{3}, \dfrac{11}{8}, \dfrac{-11}{-9}, \dfrac{4}{-3}$

Write as a decimal.

41. $\dfrac{-3}{5}$ **42.** $-\dfrac{11}{3}$ **43.** $\dfrac{1}{7}$

Write in the form $\dfrac{a}{b}$ and reduce to lowest terms.

44. -0.24 **45.** -0.06 **46.** 0.625

3.6 *Calculate.*

47. $\dfrac{1}{2} \times (-9)$ **48.** -7×0.5

49. $-2\dfrac{1}{2} \times \left(-3\dfrac{1}{4}\right)$ **50.** $\dfrac{-2}{7} \times \dfrac{14}{3}$

51. $\left(-\dfrac{3}{4}\right)^2$ **52.** $1.2 \times (-2.5)$

53. $-1.6 \times (-4.5)$ **54.** -2.1^3

3.7 *Calculate.*

55. $-\dfrac{3}{4} \div (-4)$ **56.** $21 \div \dfrac{7}{3}$

57. $\dfrac{3}{100} \div 1$ **58.** $9.6 \div (-0.4)$

59. $-3.8 \div 1.9$ **60.** $-2.08 \div (-1.6)$

61. Measurement A rectangle with an area of 6.75 cm^2 has a width of 1.25 cm. What is the length?

3.9 *Calculate.*

62. $18 - 12\dfrac{1}{2}$ **63.** $-6 - \dfrac{1}{2}$

64. $-3.6 + 5.4$ **65.** $9.1 - 3.7$

66. Share price Find today's closing price for one share of ABC Magazine Publishing stock, if it closed yesterday at 64.25 and the change today was −1.4.

3.10 *Simplify.*

67. $\left(\dfrac{7}{2}+\dfrac{1}{4}\right)\times\dfrac{1}{2}$

68. $\dfrac{8}{3}-3\times\dfrac{1}{6}$

69. $7.16-1.16\div 2$

70. $9^2-6+2.5$

71. $11.1\times 100\div 10$

72. $(12-10)^4\div\left(-\dfrac{1}{8}\right)$

73. $\dfrac{1}{3}\times\dfrac{2}{5}\div 2$

74. $-7.2-7\dfrac{1}{5}$

75. $(1.14-2.14)^3+2$

76. $3\div\dfrac{1}{3}\times\dfrac{1}{27}$

3.12 *Estimate. Then, calculate to the nearest tenth.*

77. $\sqrt{372}$ **78.** $-\sqrt{41\,093}$ **79.** $\sqrt{0.0187}$

Calculate to the nearest tenth.

80. $\sqrt{5}-\sqrt{7}$ **81.** $\sqrt{18}\div\sqrt{5}$

82. Velocity of sound The velocity of sound in air may be found from the formula
$$V = 20\sqrt{273+T}$$
where V is the velocity, in metres per second, and T is the temperature, in degrees Celsius. Calculate the velocity of sound in air, to the nearest metre per second, when the temperature is

a) 18°C **b)** 30°C **c)** −5°C

3.13 83. Coins The face value, v dollars, of a collections of dimes and quarters is given by the formula
$$v = 0.1d + 0.25q$$
where d is the number of dimes and q is the number of quarters. What is the face value of 22 dimes and 31 quarters?

84. Car rental The formula that a car rental company uses to determine the daily cost of renting a compact car is
$$C = 39.95 + 0.125d$$
where C is the daily cost, in dollars, and d is the distance driven, in kilometres. Find the rental cost for a day, if the car is driven 120 km.

Exploring Math

Impossible Scores

1. Suppose that, in a flag football league, a team gets 3 points for a field goal and 5 points for a touchdown. No other ways of scoring are possible.
a) It is impossible for a team to score 1 or 2 points. What are the other impossible team scores?
b) What is the highest impossible score?
c) Explain why all the scores higher than your answer to part b) are possible.

2. Suppose that a team gets 3 points for a field goal and 7 points for a touchdown.
a) What team scores are impossible?
b) What is the highest impossible score?
c) Explain why all the scores higher than your answer to part b) are possible.

3. Repeat question 2, but with 4 points for a field goal and 7 points for a touchdown.

4. Suppose that a team gets 4 points for a field goal and 6 points for a touchdown.
a) List the first 10 impossible team scores.
b) Is there a highest impossible score? Explain.

5. Repeat question 4, but with 3 points for a field goal and 6 points for a touchdown.

6. a) Can you use the numbers of points for a field goal and a touchdown to predict whether there is a highest impossible team score? Explain.
b) Devise 3 new scoring systems that will give a highest impossible team score.
c) Without giving 1 point for either a touchdown or a field goal, devise 3 new scoring systems that will not give a highest impossible team score.
d) Test your scoring systems from parts b) and c).

Chapter Check

Write in scientific notation.

1. 610 000　　　　**2.** 50 100 000

Write in scientific notation.

3. 0.0004　　　　**4.** 0.000 000 000 002 31

Estimate, and then calculate. Express your answer in scientific notation.

5. $(4.4 \times 10^{7}) \times (3.6 \times 10^{6})$

6. $(9.5 \times 10^{-2}) \times (5.1 \times 10^{-6})$

7. $(6.3 \times 10^{-4}) \div (1.8 \times 10^{-7})$

Simplify.

8. $(-3)^{4} \div (-3)^{5}$　　　　**9.** $s^{2} \times s^{-5}$

10. $((2)^{-3})^{-1}$　　　　**11.** $3^{-1} \div 3^{-2} \times 3^{-3}$

12. Evaluate for $m = -2$.

a) $3m^{4}$　　　　**b)** $4m^{3} + 5$

Write in order from greatest to least.

13. $\dfrac{1}{2}, \dfrac{4}{5}, \dfrac{7}{10}$　　　　**14.** $-1\dfrac{1}{2}, -1\dfrac{1}{4}, -2$

15. $1.1, 1.12, \dfrac{8}{7}$　　　　**16.** $\dfrac{4}{3}, \dfrac{3}{2}, 1.7$

Write as a fraction in lowest terms.

17. -0.35　　**18.** 1.4　　**19.** -1.3　　**20.** 0.6

Write as a decimal.

21. $\dfrac{2}{7}$　　**22.** $-\dfrac{13}{5}$　　**23.** $3\dfrac{1}{3}$　　**24.** $-2\dfrac{6}{11}$

Simplify.

25. $\dfrac{1}{2} + \dfrac{5}{6}$　　　　**26.** -1.8×0.2

27. $-\dfrac{8}{3} \div \left(-\dfrac{1}{3}\right)$　　　　**28.** $1\dfrac{1}{4} \div 2\dfrac{1}{3}$

29. $\left(-\dfrac{1}{2}\right)^{3}$　　　　**30.** $(-0.1)^{4}$

Simplify.

31. $9 - \left(7 \times 2 \times \dfrac{1}{2}\right)$　　　　**32.** $(8-2)^{2} \div 6$

33. $7.6 + 2 \times \left(\dfrac{1}{2} + \dfrac{1}{4}\right)$　　**34.** $2.375 - (1.2 + 0.3)^{3}$

35. Evaluate $x + y + z$ when $x = \dfrac{1}{2}, y = \dfrac{1}{4}$, and $z = -\dfrac{1}{3}$.

36. Evaluate $s \times r \div t$ when $s = 0.75$, $r = -1.3$, and $t = 2.6$.

Calculate.

37. $\sqrt{36}$　　**38.** $5\sqrt{16}$　　**39.** $-\sqrt{121}$　　**40.** $\sqrt{1.69}$

Estimate. Then, calculate to the nearest tenth.

41. $\sqrt{93}$　　　　**42.** $(\sqrt{8})(\sqrt{39})$

43. $2\sqrt{5} - 3\sqrt{6}$　　　　**44.** $\dfrac{\sqrt{61}}{\sqrt{15}}$

45. Car rental The cost of renting a car from a car rental agency is given by the formula
$$C = 50n + 0.25d$$
where C is the cost, in dollars, n is the number of days the car is rented, and d is the total distance driven, in kilometres.

a) Calculate the cost of renting a car for 3 days and driving 350 km/day.

b) How much money do you have left for food and accommodations if you have $750 budgeted for the trip?

46. Philippine peso If a Philippine peso is worth 4¢ Canadian, how many Philippine pesos can you buy for $50 Canadian?

Using the Strategies

1. Measurement The figure is made up of 11 identical squares. The area of the figure is 539 cm².

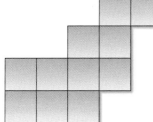

What is the perimeter of the figure?

2. Number pattern Determine the pattern and write the next 3 rows.

```
1   1   1
1   2   3   2   1
1   3   6   7   6   3   1
1   4   10  16  19  16  10  4   1
```

3. Measurement The perimeter of an isosceles triangle is 8 cm. The length of each side is a whole number. How long is the shortest side?

4. Leap year If New Year's Day in a leap year is on a Tuesday, on what day of the week does July 1 fall?

5. Trees Estimate the number of trees within a 2 km radius of your school.

6. Numbers Find three consecutive whole numbers whose sum is 144.

7. Letters Assume that the following pattern continues.

A, BBB, CCCCC, DDDDDDD, ...

a) How many letter Ms will there be?
b) How many letter Zs will there be?

8. Calendar In one year, December had exactly four Tuesdays and four Saturdays. On what day did December 1 fall that year?

9. Apartments An apartment building has six floors. The top floor has one apartment. Each of the other floors has twice the number of apartments as the floor above it. How many apartments are there?

10. River crossing Two grade 6 students and two grade 9 students want to cross a river in a canoe. The canoe is big enough to hold the two grade 6 students or one grade 6 student and one grade 9 student. How many times must the canoe cross the river to get all the students to the other side?

11. Perfect cubes The number 8 is a perfect cube.
$2^3 = 2 \times 2 \times 2 = 8$ or $2^3 = 8$
The number 27 is also a perfect cube.
$3^3 = 3 \times 3 \times 3 = 27$ or $3^3 = 27$
We can write 8 as the sum of two consecutive odd numbers.
$$3 + 5 = 8$$
We can write 27 as the sum of three consecutive odd numbers.
$$7 + 9 + 11 = 27$$
a) The next perfect cube is 64 because $4^3 = 64$. Write 64 as the sum of 4 consecutive odd numbers.
b) The next perfect cube is 125. Write 125 as the sum of five consecutive odd numbers.
c) The next perfect cube is 216. Write 216 as the sum of six consecutive odd numbers.
d) How does the square of the number that is cubed fit into the sum of the consecutive odd numbers?
e) Use this pattern to write 7^3 as the sum of seven consecutive odd numbers.

12. Great Lakes a) Which of the Great Lakes lie partially in Canada and partially in the United States?
b) For which of the Great Lakes is the percent of the area within Canada closest to 50%?

CHAPTER 4

Statistics

How Can We Model Word Use?

The table gives the average number of words in the spoken vocabulary of a child at various ages.

Age	Number of Words
15 months	10
18 months	50
2 years	200
3 years	1000
4 years	1600
5 years	2200
6 years	2800

1. Plot the points on a grid and draw a broken-line graph.

2. For which four ages do the data in the table lie on the same straight line?

3. What is the percent increase in the number of words in the spoken vocabulary
a) from age 15 months to age 18 months?
b) from age 4 years to age 5 years?

4. Estimate the number of words in the spoken vocabulary at age 4.5 years.

5. For each age in the table, the number of words a child understands but does not use is 5 times the number of words the child uses. How many more words are understood but not used by a 2 year-old than by an 18 month-old?

In Modelling Math — English on pages 226 and 227, a mathematical model will be used to investigate the "fingerprint" that writers leave by the words they use.

Displaying Data

1 Bar Graphs

Bar graphs are used to make comparisons. The bars can be horizontal or vertical.

1. Sleeping habits The double bar graph shows the percents of people in different age groups who snore or talk in their sleep.

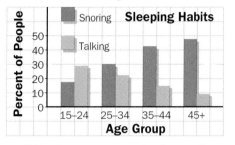

a) List the age groups in decreasing order of the percent of people who snore.
b) In which age group is the percent of people who snore closest to 3 times the percent of people who talk in their sleep?
c) Why is a bar graph more effective than a list of numbers for displaying these data?

2. Continents The table shows the percent of the world's land and the percent of the world's population on each continent.

Continent	Percent of Land	Percent of Population
Africa	20	13
Antarctica	9	0
Asia	30	62
Europe	7	10
North America	16	8
Oceania	5	0.5
South America	12	6

a) Display the data on a double bar graph.
b) Which is the most crowded continent? Explain.
c) Which two continents are equally crowded? Explain.

2 Circle Graphs

A circle graph is used to show how something is divided.

1. Blood types The circle graph shows the percents of people with different blood types.

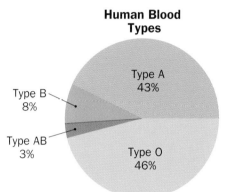

a) In a sample of 5000 Canadians, how many would you expect to have Type A blood? Type AB blood?
b) Express the ratio of the number of people with Type O blood to the number of people with Type B blood as a fraction in lowest terms and as a decimal.

2. Bird species The table shows the numbers of species of different types of birds that breed in Canada. Draw, label, and title a circle graph to display these data.

Type of Bird	Breeding Species in Canada
Ducks	36
Raptors	19
Shorebirds	71
Owls	14
Perching Birds	180
Other	80

3 Pictographs

Pictographs display data visually with pictures or symbols.

1. Telephones The pictograph shows the number of telephones per 100 people in different countries.

Bahamas	☎☎🕿
Canada	☎☎☎☎☎☎
France	☎☎☎☎☎
Japan	☎☎☎☎🕿
Kuwait	☎🕿
Lithuania	☎☎
Switzerland	☎☎☎☎☎☎☎☎
U.S.A.	☎☎☎☎☎☎🕿

Each ☎ represents 10 telephones.

a) About how many telephones are there per 100 people in each country?
b) Would it be appropriate to represent these data on a circle graph? Explain.

2. Fish speeds The table gives the top speeds of 5 fish. Display the data on a pictograph.

Fish	Top Speed (km/h)
Barracuda	43
Mackerel	33
Sailfish	110
Shark	69
Swordfish	90

3. Magazines The table shows the approximate circulations of 6 magazines in Canada.

Magazine	Circulation
Canadian Geographic	230 000
Canadian Living	560 000
Chatelaine	800 000
L'Actualité	190 000
Maclean's	510 000
TV Guide	710 000

a) Display the data on a pictograph.
b) What are the advantages and disadvantages of using a bar graph instead of a pictograph to display these data?
c) Would it be appropriate to display these data on a circle graph? Explain.

Mental Math

Percents

Write as a percent.

1. 0.3   **2.** 0.07   **3.** 0.98   **4.** 0.425
5. $\dfrac{1}{4}$ **6.** $\dfrac{3}{10}$ **7.** $\dfrac{1}{20}$ **8.** $\dfrac{3}{25}$

Calculate.

9. 10% of 30   **10.** 20% of 40
11. 50% of 38   **12.** 80% of 60
13. 25% of 80   **14.** 15% of 20

Adding a Column of Numbers

To add the numbers shown, first add the numbers in the tens column. To the result, add the numbers in the ones column one at a time.

$$
\begin{array}{r} 35 \\ 21 \\ 49 \\ 60 \\ +87 \end{array}
\rightarrow
\begin{array}{r} 30 \\ 20 \\ 40 \\ 60 \\ +80 \\ \hline 230 \end{array}
$$

$230 + 7 = 237; 237 + 0 = 237; 237 + 9 = 246;$
$246 + 1 = 247; 247 + 5 = 252.$
So, the sum is 252.

Add.

1. 11, 19, 23, 51, +46
2. 38, 41, 92, 17, +33
3. 77, 65, 84, 17, 24, +32
4. 93, 14, 28, 55, 40, 59, 62, +71
5. 56, 58, 80, 11, 29, 91, 44, 35, +36

Describe how you could modify the method to complete each of the following. Then, add.

6. 2.3, 7.5, 6.6, 4.1, +3.2
7. 9.9, 0.4, 1.8, 5.7, 9.2, +4.3
8. 110, 430, 230, 580, 750, +290
9. 330, 520, 980, 590, 400, +190
10. 102, 201, 333, 407, 522, +690

4.1 Hypotheses, Surveys, and Inferences

Does one battery last longer than another? Which hockey team will win the Stanley Cup this year? Does one cola taste better than another? What percent of Canadian homes have computers? When someone poses questions such as these, the answers may be found in **statistics**, which is the science of collecting, organizing, and interpreting data.

Explore: Make Predictions

Work in groups of four or five and come to a group decision for the answers to the following questions.
a) What percent of the students in grade 9 in your school know the capitals of all the Canadian provinces?
b) What percent of the students in your school put on their right shoe before their left shoe in the morning?
c) What is the favourite weeknight TV show of high school students in Ontario, and what percent of students choose this show as their favourite?

Inquire

1. Compare your group's answers to those of the other groups in the class. Is there a consensus in your class about the answers?

2. For each of questions a), b), and c), what group of students could you survey next to improve the accuracy of your answer? Explain.

When answering questions a), b), and c), above, you were suggesting possible answers to statistical questions. This is one of the following eight stages involved in using statistics to investigate relationships.

• Pose a problem, that is, state the question that you want to answer, and identify the variable or variables.
• Make a **hypothesis**, which is a possible answer to the question.
• Decide how to collect the data.
• Collect and record the data.
• Organize and analyze the data using tables, graphs, and calculations.
• Use trends and relationships to make an **inference**, which is a generalization based on the data. Decide whether the inference supports or contradicts the hypothesis.
• Communicate the results of the investigation and justify your conclusions.
• Pose and/or solve problems related to the investigation.

Large amounts of data can be collected and organized by computers. Smaller amounts of data can be recorded by hand. One way of doing this is to use a **frequency distribution table**, which lists each item once. Each piece of data is recorded in the tally column. Then, the tallies are counted, and the results are recorded in the frequency column.

Example 1   Student Council Election

Sara was undecided about running for president of the Student Council. Her friend, Miguel, thought that she would be elected. To persuade her to run, he conducted a survey in which he asked 30 students at the school to name the person they would vote for. He recorded these results.

Henri	Sara	Sara	Henri	Henri
Sara	Monique	Claudio	Sara	Claudio
Claudio	Claudio	Henri	Sara	Claudio
Henri	Sara	Monique	Sara	Sara
Claudio	Sara	Henri	Monique	Monique
Claudio	Monique	Monique	Sara	Claudio

a) Record the results in a frequency distribution table.
b) State Miguel's hypothesis.
c) Make an inference about whether Sara was likely to be elected.
d) Compare the inference with the hypothesis.

Solution

a)

Chosen Candidates		
Candidate	**Tally**	**Frequency**
Henri	⊬⊦⊦		6
Sara	⊬⊦⊦ ⊬⊦⊦	10
Claudio	⊬⊦⊦ |||	8
Monique	⊬⊦⊦		6
Total		30

b) Miguel's hypothesis was that Sara would be elected if she ran for president of the Student Council.
c) The survey results suggest the inference that Sara was the most likely person to be elected.
d) The inference agrees with the hypothesis.

All the people eligible for a survey make up the **population**. In Example 1, the population that could be surveyed included all the students in the school. In a **census**, data are collected from every member of the population. When a population is very large, a **sample** of the population may be surveyed. Example 1 included a sample of 30 students chosen from the population.

A sample is often used to make a prediction about a population. For the result to be reliable, the sample must be **representative** of the population. To predict who would win the student election in Example 1, a representative sample was chosen from among the students at the school. Teachers were not included, because teachers could not vote in the election.

Example 2   Listening to Music

Sampa thought that the majority of students in her school would choose CDs as their favourite way of listening to music. To test this hypothesis, she completed a survey of 20 of the 520 students in the school. The results were as shown.

Favourite Music Sources

Music Source	Number of Students
AM Radio	3
CDs	9
FM Radio	5
Records	1
Tapes	2
Total	20

a) Did the survey results support the hypothesis?
b) Predict the number of students in the school who preferred to listen to CDs.

Solution

a) Sampa's hypothesis was that the majority of students would choose CDs. Of the 20 students surveyed, 9 chose CDs but 11 did not.
So, the survey results did not support Sampa's hypothesis.

b) Of the 20 students surveyed, 9 preferred CDs.

$$\frac{9}{20} = 0.45$$
$$= 45\%$$

Assuming that this percent is true for the whole school, find 45% of 520.
$520 \times 0.45 = 234$

Estimate
$500 \times 0.5 = 250$

So, the prediction is that 234 students in the school preferred to listen to CDs.

If you use a survey or an experiment to gather your own information, you are using a **primary data-gathering method**. The people who carried out surveys in Examples 1 and 2 were using primary methods. If you did an experiment in which you measured the daily high temperatures in July and August, and compared the averages for the two months, your temperature measurements would be primary data.

If you use someone else's data, you are using a **secondary data-gathering method**. Secondary methods include the use of books and databases. If you compared the average high temperatures in July and August by looking up the values of the daily highs in a database, you would be using secondary data to calculate the averages.

Practice

A

Would each of the following likely come from a sample or a census? Explain.

1. The student enrolment at Silver Springs High School is 574.

2. Two-fifths of teenage students prefer sugarless gum.

3. A Canadian family spends $55/year on books.

4. Of last year's 490 subscribers, 452 will buy season tickets to the theatre this year.

5. There are 25 000 fish in the lake.

State whether each of the following is a primary or secondary source of data.

6. an article in a newspaper or magazine

7. a table of data on a CD-ROM

8. finding opinions by conducting interviews

9. measuring the thickness of the ozone layer

10. downloading data from the Internet

11. an almanac

12. performing a door-to-door survey

13. testing the effectiveness of a drug in a laboratory

14. an encyclopedia

Applications and Problem Solving

15. Would you use a primary or a secondary data-gathering method to find each of the following? Explain.

a) the world's 10 biggest countries

b) the populations of the provincial capitals

c) your classmates' favourite movies

d) the most popular radio station in your home town

B

State a hypothesis for each of the questions 16–20. Use a secondary data-gathering method to test each hypothesis.

16. Farming Which Canadian province grows the most wheat?

17. Populations What are the three countries with the greatest populations?

18. Areas of countries How many times the area of the United States is the area of Canada?

19. Great Lakes What percent of the total area of the Great Lakes lies inside Canada?

20. Border length How long is Canada's border with the United States, including the border with Alaska?

21. Apartment living In a city school with 1040 students, a survey of 40 students showed that 18 of them lived in apartments. If the survey used a representative sample, how many students at the school lived in apartments?

C

22. Rain forests a) State a hypothesis about the percent of the world's rain forests that have been destroyed.

b) The table shows the results of a survey in which people estimated the percent of the world's rain forests that have been destroyed.

10	20	40	80	20	40
20	30	50	20	40	40
20	40	30	60	30	10
20	40	40	10	20	30
40	60	30	50	30	50

Complete a frequency distribution table for these data.

c) Is the most frequent estimate necessarily the correct value? Explain.

d) The percent with the greatest frequency is actually the correct value. What percent of the rain forests have been destroyed?

e) Does the answer to part d) agree with your hypothesis?

Write a hypothesis for each of the questions 23-25. Use a primary data-gathering method to write an inference. Compare the inference with the hypothesis.

23. Sports What is the favourite sport of students in your class?

24. Radio What is the favourite radio station of students in your class?

25. Pets What percent of the students in your class have a dog?

TECHNOLOGY

Graphing Calculators and Random Sampling

1 Generating Random Numbers

The following list of random numbers was generated by a scientific calculator.

0.538	0.383	0.826	0.755
0.017	0.404	0.304	0.385

The following list of random numbers was generated by a graphing calculator.

.6485679703	.6976612527	.0151786158
.1018231622	.7916268018	.3688383045

1. How are the random numbers generated by each calculator the same? How are they different?

2. Describe how you can generate random numbers with your calculator.

2 Random Sampling

One way of choosing a sample of a population is to choose randomly. In a random sample, every member of the population has an equal chance of being selected for the sample

A way to select a random sample of students in a school is to list the students alphabetically, number each student, and generate random numbers to define the sample. Suppose the 750 students in a school are numbered from 1 to 750.

1. What command would you enter into your graphing calculator to generate random integers from 1 to 750?

2. If you wanted a sample of 60 students and generated 60 random integers, what would you do if the same integer were generated twice?

4.2 Sampling Techniques

Explore: Use the Survey

In a Gallup poll conducted by telephone, 1026 Canadians 18 years of age or older were asked this question.

Would you say that your standard of living is higher, lower, or the same as the standard of living of your parents?

a) State a hypothesis describing how you would expect people to respond to the question.

b) The results of the poll were as follows. State an inference based on the results.

Response	Percent
Higher	50
Lower	23
Same	25
Don't Know	2

c) Compare your hypothesis and your inference.

Inquire

1. How many people gave each response to the question?

2. The results of the survey were rounded to the nearest percent. Explain why.

3. Why did the survey include only people who were 18 years of age or older?

4. Why were about 1000 people surveyed and not
a) 2 people?
b) 5000 people?
c) all the adults in Canada?

5. Did the people who conducted the poll use a primary or a secondary data-gathering method? Explain.

6. When you interpreted the results of the poll, were you using a primary or a secondary data-gathering method? Explain.

Before collecting data, you must make two decisions.
• Decide what type of data to collect. This decision involves identifying variables. A **variable** is a characteristic that can be classified, counted, ordered, or measured. Examples of variables include temperature, length, colour, and opinion.
• Decide from whom or from where to collect data. This decision involves identifying populations and choosing samples. You must ensure that the sample is large enough to give reliable results. For example, you cannot determine the number of hours people spend watching TV per week by asking only one person. Instead, you could perform **multiple trials** by asking a number of people and repeating the survey in different weeks of the year.

Example 1   Variables, Populations, and Samples

Identify the variable and the population, and suggest a sample that could be used to answer each of the following questions.
a) How many hours of homework does a grade 9 student in your school have each week?
b) What percent of the teenagers in your city or town wear a chain around their necks?

Solution

a) The variable is the number of hours of homework per week.
The population is all the grade 9 students in your school.
A sample might include all the students in your class.
b) The variable is whether or not a chain is worn around the neck.
The population includes all the teenagers in your city or town.
A sample might include all the students in your school.

The procedure used for collecting information from the sample is called the sampling technique. To collect reliable data, statisticians use techniques designed to eliminate **sampling error**. Sampling error is the difference between the results obtained by sampling and the truth about the whole population.

Sampling techniques can be divided into two categories, **probability sampling** and **non-probability sampling**. Probability sampling involves the random selection of units from a population. One probability sampling technique is called **simple random sampling**. Units are drawn at random from the population and every unit has the same probability of being selected.

Example 2   Simple Random Sampling

Design a simple random sampling procedure to select students in
your school to study the following question.
*Should the school year be changed so that there are 4 blocks of 13 weeks, with
10 weeks of classes and 3 weeks vacation in each block?*

Solution

The population is all the students in your school. Suppose there are
800 students. Let the sample size be 8% of the population.
8% of 800 = 64
The simple random sampling procedure might include the following
steps:
• Obtain an alphabetical list of all the students.
• Assign each student a different number from 1 to 800.
• Generate 64 random numbers from 1 to 800 using a calculator or a
computer.
• The sample is the 64 students whose numbers were generated. Ask
each of the 64 students the question and record the answers.

A second probability sampling technique is called **systematic
sampling**. Units are selected from a list using a selection interval, for
example, 8. Then, every 8th element on the list is sampled.

Example 3   Systematic Sampling

Design a systematic sampling procedure to study the following
question among students in your school.
If you had the chance, would you travel in space?

Solution

The population is all the students in your school.
Suppose there are 500 students. Sample 10% of them.
10% of 500 = 50
Suppose you wanted to cover all age groups fairly.
The systematic sampling procedure might include the following
steps:
• Sort a list of all the students in the school in order of age.

Find the selection interval, k. $k = \dfrac{500}{50}$
$$= 10$$

• Choose a random number, x, from 1 to 10 to be the starting point
of the systematic sample. If $x = 4$, start with the 4th student in the
sorted list.
• Sample every 10th student in the sorted list. If you start with the 4th
student, also sample the 14th, 24th, and 34th students, and so on.
• Ask each sampled student the question and record the answers.

A third probability sampling technique is called **stratified sampling**. The population is divided into groups, or strata, from which random samples are taken.

Example 4 Stratified Sampling

Design a stratified sampling procedure to study the following question among students in your school.

Should school start one hour earlier and end one hour earlier each school day?

Solution

The population is all the students in your school.
Suppose there are 660 students. Sample 15% of them.
15% of 660 = 99
The stratified sampling procedure might include the following steps:
• Divide the population into two groups — female and male.
• Survey 15% of the females and 15% of the males.
If the school population includes 340 females and 320 males,

$$f = 0.15 \times 340 \qquad\qquad m = 0.15 \times 320$$
$$= 51 \qquad\qquad\qquad\qquad = 48$$

• From the list of all students, prepare an alphabetical list of female students and an alphabetical list of male students.
• Use simple random sampling to identify 51 females and 48 males.
• Ask each of the 99 students the question and record the answers.

Non-probability sampling techniques generally give less reliable results than probability sampling techniques. The main advantages of non-probability sampling techniques are that they are cheap and convenient. Two non-probability sampling techniques are called **convenience sampling** and **sampling of volunteers**.

An example of convenience sampling occurs when television reporters sample people on the street to determine public opinion. Little planning goes into the selection of the sample.

An example of sampling of volunteers occurs when a researcher studying the effects of sleep deprivation asks for volunteers to participate in the study.

Example 5 Non-Probability Sampling

Describe a non-probability sampling technique that might be used to study the following two questions.
a) Does being good in mathematics affect a person's musical ability?
b) What percent of people are vegetarians?

Solution

a) A researcher could try sampling volunteers by inviting members of the general public to participate in the study. The researcher might advertise in a local newspaper and offer payment to those who volunteer.

b) A student could use the convenience sampling technique by surveying some students in the cafeteria at lunch.

Practice

A

Identify the population implied in each statement.

1. *Hockey Night in Canada* is watched by 23% of people.

2. Two out of three people prefer to use *Toothtaste* to brush their teeth.

3. Today's youth prefer comfort over style in fashion.

4. Water-skiing is the most popular summer water activity.

Identify the variable and the population, and suggest a sample that could be used to answer each of the following questions.

5. Who is the most popular movie star for students in your school?

6. How many hours a month do grade 9 students in your city or town spend using a computer?

7. How many secondary school students in Ontario have part-time jobs?

8. What percentage of Canadians like spinach?

Describe how simple random sampling could be used to answer each of the following questions.

9. What is the average time spent by shoppers on each visit to a mall?

10. What are the favourite vacation destinations of Canadians?

11. What is the average mass of the salmon in a certain river?

Describe how the list of units could be organized if the systematic sampling technique were used to answer each of the following questions.

12. How many days per year does the average skier spend on the slopes?

13. Do grade 9 students think that humanity should spend money on exploring the planets?

14. Do parents think that Canadian high school students should take a Canadian history course every year?

15. What is the average speed of the cars on a section of highway?

Suggest appropriate stratifications of the population for each of the following questions.

16. Which school-related extra-curricular activity is the most popular?

17. What restrictions should be placed on young drivers?

18. Should the area of Canada's national and provincial parks be increased?

19. Should the federal government control fishing quotas?

Applications and Problem Solving

20. Mineral water A mineral water company wants to find out why people choose a particular brand of mineral water. Name each of the following sampling techniques that could be used. Identify the population in each case.

a) Attach a mail-in response card to the neck of each bottle of mineral water the company sells.

b) Phone every 200th person who mails in a coupon as part of a money-back offer on the purchase of mineral water.

c) Phone 400 numbers chosen randomly from all the residential phone numbers in a province.

d) Mail questionnaires to 200 men and 200 women chosen randomly from a list of men and a list of women compiled from a market research company's mailing list.

e) Ask the first 20 people seen carrying mineral water in a park on a summer day.

21. Car ownership A survey of car ownership among shoppers was conducted in a shopping mall. Passers-by were asked how many cars were owned by all the people in their household.
a) Name the sampling technique used.
b) Identify the population.
c) Design a probability sampling technique that would be appropriate in this study.

22. Stranded airline travellers A television reporter interviewed travellers stranded at an airport during a snow storm about the efficiency of Canadian air travel.
a) Name the sampling technique used.
b) Design a probability sampling technique that could be used to study the efficiency of Canadian air travel.

23. Mosquito repellent A researcher was studying a new mosquito repellent. The study required people to apply the repellent to part of an arm and then expose it in a closed environment infested with mosquitos.
a) Name the sampling technique required in this case.
b) Suggest a possible source of sample units.

B

24. Soup choice The school cafeteria wants to introduce a new soup, to be chosen from three possibilities. How would you conduct a survey to decide which soup should be the new one?

25. Movie viewing A newspaper has asked you to find out how many times people 15 years old and older go a movie theatre in a year in your town or city. The data must be organized in the table shown.

Number of Times	Percent of People
0	
1 to 4	
5 to 8	
9 to 12	
13+	

a) What sampling technique would you use?
b) How would you collect the data?

26. Shopping habits To get a sense of people's shopping habits in a mall, a survey was conducted on a Friday morning. The first 50 customers were asked where they would spend most of their money that day — in a department store, music store, clothing store, or restaurant. The results are shown in the table.

Place	Percent of People
Department store	54
Music store	12
Clothing store	26
Restaurant	8

a) What generalization, if any, can be made from this survey?
b) Does the sample adequately represent the shopping habits of mall shoppers? Explain.
c) Design a more reliable method of obtaining information about the shopping habits of mall shoppers. Include the details you would put on the questionnaire. Describe the method you would use to select the sample.

27. Clustered sampling For the probability sampling technique known as clustered sampling, a random sample is chosen from one group within a population. For example, to determine the most popular place to ski, the group to sample includes all skiers. Design a clustered sampling procedure to determine each of the following.
a) the best place in your neighbourhood to buy pet supplies
b) the musical instrument that the most students in your city or town learn to play

28. Technology In a school, there are 460 male students, numbered from 1 to 460, and 420 female students, numbered from 1 to 420. A stratified sample of students is to contain 23 male students and 21 female students. Describe how you would use your graphing calculator to choose the students for the sample. Specify any commands you would use.

29. Technology A school has 260 grade 9 students, 250 grade 10 students, 220 grade 11 students, and 200 grade 12 students. A sample stratified by grade is to include a total of 93 students. Describe how you would use your graphing calculator to choose the students for the sample. Specify any commands you would use.

C

30. Social activities There were 250 girls and 275 boys in a school. A random sample of 30 students was surveyed to decide on social activities for the following year.
a) Is it possible that the sample contained only boys?
b) Would a sample containing only boys represent all the students? Explain.

31. Decide whether each of the following methods will produce a random sample of the students in your class. Explain.
a) One student lists the names of six students from memory.
b) Five letters of the alphabet are chosen randomly. Students whose surnames begin with these letters form the sample.
c) Choose the five oldest students in the class.
d) The name of each student is written on a piece of paper, and all the pieces of paper are placed in a hat. The names of eight students are drawn.
e) The sample consists of the first six students to arrive in class in the morning.

32. Library books To find the average number of pages in a book, you could use all the books in a public library as a population. How would you select 30 books to obtain each of the following types of samples?
a) simple random **b)** stratified
c) convenience **d)** systematic

33. Jury duty research How are people chosen to appear for possible jury duty in the area where you live? Is a sampling technique used? Are some people excluded from jury duty?

34. School vacation experiment a) Design a sampling technique that could be used to survey opinions on the following statement.

The two-month vacation students have in July and August should be changed to January and February. That way, the cost of heating schools would be reduced.

b) What difficulties do you anticipate with this survey? How will you get around these difficulties?
c) Conduct the survey on your school population.
d) Might there be a better choice of population for the survey? Explain.

35. Daily life experiment Statistics Canada has found that all Canadian adults averaged, over a seven-day period, 3.6 h a day on paid work, 3.6 h a day on unpaid work (domestic chores, volunteering), 5.7 h a day of free time, 8.1 h a day sleeping, and 2.4 h a day on personal care, including eating. The remaining 0.5 h in the day was spent on education.
a) What sampling technique was probably used?
b) Design a survey in which you analyze the day of the students at your school.
c) Conduct the survey and conclude with a statement similar to the one above.

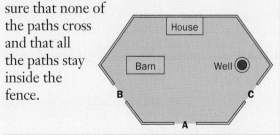

LOGIC POWER

In the 1880s, some companies put their advertising on puzzle cards to get people's attention. The following farmer's puzzle was very popular. Copy the diagram into your notebook. Draw 3 paths, one from the house to gate A, another from the barn to gate C, and the third from the well to gate B. Make sure that none of the paths cross and that all the paths stay inside the fence.

4.3 Bias

Surveying samples of a population is an attempt to make inferences about the population. For inferences to be reliable, a survey should use a suitable probability sampling technique and be as unbiased as possible. However, an absolute lack of bias is rarely possible.

Explore: Analyze the Questions

Work in groups. Analyze the four questions to decide what response is being encouraged by the wording of each question.

a) Without commercials, there would be no private radio stations. Are commercials a small price to pay for being able to listen to the radio for free?

b) In-line skaters on sidewalks endanger pedestrians. Should in-line skaters be allowed to skate on sidewalks?

c) Shakespeare's plays are written in a style that is hard to understand and, besides, they are old. Should high school students be required to study one of Shakespeare's plays?

d) Do you really think fast food is nutritious?

Inquire

1. How might the information in the first sentence of questions a), b), and c) influence the responses?

2. How could questions a), b), and c) be reworded so that a certain response is not encouraged?

3. How does the wording of question d) direct the response?

4. How could you reword question d) so that it is unbiased?

5. Give two examples of these types of forced response questions you have seen or heard in advertising.

Bias that arises from the phrasing or construction of a survey question, as in questions a) to d) above, is called **response bias**.

Bias can also occur within the sampling technique itself. One example is to exclude one or more groups of people from the sample. This type of bias is called **selection bias.**

Example 1   Selection Bias

A newspaper conducted a survey to identify the sports its readers wanted to have highlighted in the sports section. The newspaper obtained lists of members of golf and tennis clubs. A simple random sample was taken from these lists.

a) Identify the population that was of interest in this survey.

b) What form of bias appeared in the sample design? Explain.

c) Design a different sampling method that would more accurately have represented the population.

Solution

a) The population of interest was all readers of the newspaper's sports section.

b) This sampling technique had selection bias, because some members of the population were excluded from the sample. Not all of the newspaper's readers were members of the golf or tennis clubs.

c) The newspaper could have chosen a simple random sample from its list of subscribers and conducted a phone survey. This method would have excluded fewer people from the sample.

A second form of bias within the sampling technique may arise if a large number of the people selected for the sample do not complete the survey. This type of bias is called **non-response bias.** For example, after a polling firm has selected the people in a sample, the firm still has to get their opinions. This process can be difficult. If a large number of the people selected do not respond to a questionnaire, interview, or telephone call, the results of the poll may be distorted.

Example 2   Non-Response Bias

A magazine publisher used a systematic sampling method to get the opinions of readers on a new feature for a magazine. The company took its list of subscribers and mailed a questionnaire to every five hundredth subscriber. Of the readers who received the mailing, 20% responded, and 60% of the respondents were in favour of the new feature.

a) What inference about the population can be drawn from this information? Is the inference reliable?

b) How could the sampling method be improved to reduce the possibility of a non-response bias?

Solution

a) Because 60% of the respondents were in favour of the new feature, it could be inferred that the readers approve of it. However, the inference may not be reliable, because only 20% of the people in the sample responded. The fact that 80% did not respond may mean that there is a non-response bias in the result.

b) To reduce the possibility of a non-response bias, the company could offer an incentive, such as a gift, to anyone who returns a completed survey. Another approach would be to contact each subscriber in the sample by telephone and conduct a personal interview. A typical response rate for personal interviews is 75%, compared with 25% for mailed questionnaires.

To give reliable results, polling companies must know how different types of bias can affect the results of a survey. The companies should make every effort to reduce the influence of bias on the results.

Practice

A

Identify the type(s) of bias that are most likely to influence the results of each of the following surveys.

1. City traffic A traffic survey was taken at a major intersection between the hours 13:00 and 16:00 to study the traffic volume in the centre of a city.

2. Voluntary work A survey to determine the types of voluntary work people were willing to do was conducted by leaving a stack of questionnaires on a counter at a recreation centre. The questionnaires were to be filled out and dropped into a collection box.

3. Examinations A survey question is worded as follows.

Should there be national examinations for all grade 9 students? In what subjects?

4. Welfare A stratified sample, using the two strata male and female, was chosen in the workplace, to determine the attitude of the public to government welfare.

5. Driving age A survey question is worded as follows.

Is it really fair that young people are not allowed to drive until they are 16?

6. Transportation A travel agency obtained a list of department store credit card holders. The agency surveyed a random sample of them as to their preference for either air or ground transportation when they went on vacation. The survey was conducted by telephone interview.

Reword the following questions to remove the response bias.

7. Colas Why does Cola A taste better than Cola B?

8. Dogs Do you think that small, yappy dogs make good pets?

9. Logging Deforestation of the tropical rain forest in Brazil occurs at a rate of about 14 000 km^2/year. Should logging be restricted in Canada?

10. Art If you cannot understand a painting, is it still art?

11. School projects Do long, challenging projects make school work more interesting?

12. Power Is hydro-electric power less damaging to the environment than nuclear power, with its radioactive waste?

13. Skiing Does the thrill of skiing make it Canada's favourite winter sport?

Applications and Problem Solving

B

14. School diplomas A newspaper reported that thousands of Canadian high school dropouts are returning to school to get high school diplomas. The newspaper determined the students' reasons for dropping out and returning by surveying 892 students who returned to school.
a) What organizations would be interested in the results of this type of survey?
b) What type of sampling technique could be used for this survey?
c) Design a questionnaire that could be used in this survey.
d) Suppose the results of the survey suggested that most dropouts returned to school because there was a high unemployment rate for high school dropouts. What follow-up survey could be conducted to test this suggestion?

15. Federal election To predict the winner of a federal election, a national magazine compiled a list of 10 000 names from its subscription list, telephone books, and lists of homeowners. The questionnaire was mailed to all 10 000 people, and 1203 people returned it. The magazine used the 1203 responses to make its prediction. Describe the potential sources of bias in this survey.

16. Highway bypass The Ministry of Transportation is studying the possibility of building a highway bypass around a town of 5000 people. The ministry plans to survey 320 town residents about the bypass, using a telephone survey.
a) How is the ministry attempting to control non-response bias?
b) Describe fully how you would choose the sample of 320 people. Should they be drawn from the whole population of the town or from the people most affected by the bypass?
c) Design a sequence of questions that could be used in the telephone survey.

17. Phone-in poll To get the public reaction to a government decision announced on the news, a television station asked viewers to dial one phone number if they agreed with the decision and another if they disagreed. Identify the potential sources of bias in such a poll.

18. The Internet A radio station posts a questionnaire on the Internet to get responses to a possible switch in format from country music to all-talk radio. What are the potential sources of bias in this survey?

19. Suggestion box If you set up a suggestion box in the school cafeteria and asked for suggested improvements to the menu,
a) in what way might the results be biased? Explain.
b) how could you gain a more accurate impression of students' opinions?

C

20. Census In a census of a population, can the following types of bias exist? Explain.
a) response bias
b) selection bias
c) non-response bias

21. Advertising A company that makes headache tablets advertises that three out of four doctors prefer their product.
a) Analyze this statement for its accuracy in terms of population, possible sampling method, and bias.
b) What inference does the company hope you will draw from its claim?

22. Destructive sampling In some situations, sampling methods may be **destructive**, which means that the sample cannot be returned to the population. For a firecracker manufacturer, testing the quality of firecrackers by setting off a sample of them is an example of destructive sampling.
a) Give two other examples of situations in which you think destructive sampling might be used.
b) When carrying out destructive sampling, what are the advantages and disadvantages of using a small number of units in the sample? a large number of units in the sample?

23. Media research Use various media, such as newspapers, magazines, radio, and television, to find three examples of data from samples being used to make generalizations about populations. Explain why you agree or disagree with the generalizations. Share your findings with your classmates.

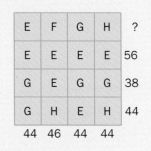

NUMBER POWER

Find the missing sum.

E	F	G	H	?
E	E	E	E	56
G	E	G	G	38
G	H	E	H	44
44	46	44	44	

PROBLEM SOLVING

4.4 Work Backward

Working backward can be a very useful problem solving technique. To solve some crimes, a detective will start at the scene of the crime and retrace the criminal's steps, or work backward, until the crime is solved.

The departure time for the Orient Express train from Calais to Paris is 21:20. Sam Orwell, a government agent, plans to board the train 35 min before departure. Orwell's hotel in Calais, The Rampant Lion, is a 25-min cab ride from the train station.

Before leaving the hotel, Orwell needs 30 min to eat dinner. After dinner, he needs 10 min to pack and 15 min to send and read his e-mail. On the way to the train station, Orwell needs to stop for 15 min at police headquarters to get some documents. To reach the train on time, when should Orwell

a) leave his hotel for the train?   **b)** go to dinner?

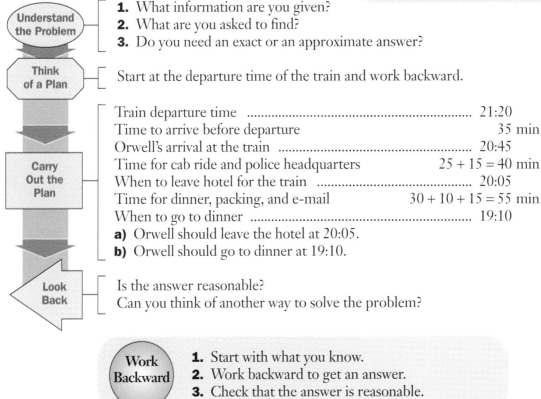

Understand the Problem
1. What information are you given?
2. What are you asked to find?
3. Do you need an exact or an approximate answer?

Think of a Plan
Start at the departure time of the train and work backward.

Carry Out the Plan

Train departure time	21:20
Time to arrive before departure	35 min
Orwell's arrival at the train	20:45
Time for cab ride and police headquarters	25 + 15 = 40 min
When to leave hotel for the train	20:05
Time for dinner, packing, and e-mail	30 + 10 + 15 = 55 min
When to go to dinner	19:10

a) Orwell should leave the hotel at 20:05.
b) Orwell should go to dinner at 19:10.

Look Back
Is the answer reasonable?
Can you think of another way to solve the problem?

Work Backward
1. Start with what you know.
2. Work backward to get an answer.
3. Check that the answer is reasonable.

Applications and Problem Solving

1. Departure time Helga's plane leaves at 08:15. She has to be at the airport 40 min early. The cab ride to the airport is about 55 min. Helga wants to spend 30 min at her office on her way to the airport. When should she leave home?

2. County fair Michiko went to the county fair. She spent half her money on rides. She spent half of what was left on food. Of the remainder, she spent half at the arcade. She had $6 left. How much money did she start with?

3. Gold chain Elaine bought a gold chain for $150. The jeweller added one half of his cost price to get the price of $150. What did the jeweller pay for the chain?

4. School exam The exam starts at school at 09:00. You want to get there 15 min early. It takes 20 min to 30 min to get to school, depending on the buses. You plan to study for 1 h at home. It will take you 1 h to shower, dress, and eat breakfast. For what time should you set your alarm?

5. Jacket Karina wants a jacket that costs $230, including tax. She has saved $70. If she saves the rest in equal amounts over the next 4 months, how much will she save each month?

6. Departure time Ahmed's plane leaves at 12:30. Ahmed can drive 120 km to the airport at an average speed of 80 km/h. He needs to be at the airport 45 min before departure. When should he leave home?

7. Band trip Tanya saved for a band trip costing $885. She worked part-time at a convenience store and earned $9.50/h. Then, her aunt gave her $125 toward the trip. For how many hours did Tanya have to work to pay for the trip?

8. Age Dino multiplied his age by 3. Then he subtracted 3, divided by 7, and added 12. The result was 18. How old was Dino?

9. Train passengers The train left Sutton for Bent Creek. At Brownsville, 35 people got on and 27 got off. Next came Liberty, where 24 people got on and 11 got off. At Long Lake, 55 people got on and 42 people got off. At Bent Creek, 105 people got off and 10 got on. There were 203 people on the train when it left Bent Creek. How many people were on the train when it left Sutton?

10. Painting Mike works for an art gallery. An art dealer offers him a painting for $72 000. The dealer says the painting has increased in value by one half of the previous year's value in each of the past 2 years.
a) What was its value 2 years ago?
b) If the painting's value continues to increase at this rate, what will it be worth 3 years from now?

11. Population The Canadian population was about 30 300 000 in 1998. It had increased by about 5 500 000 since 1981. The 1981 figure was about 7 times the figure at Confederation in 1867. What was the Canadian population at Confederation, to the nearest 100 000?

12. Write a problem that can be solved by working backward. Have a classmate solve your problem.

PATTERN POWER

The diagrams show coloured 3 by 3, 4 by 4, and 5 by 5 grids.

If the pattern continues, how many grid squares of each colour are there on grids with the following dimensions?
a) 6 by 6   **b)** 7 by 7
c) *n* by *n*   **d)** 100 by 100

4.5 Mean, Median, Mode, and Range

Statisticians often use graphs to describe and display data. Statisticians are also interested in finding a number to describe the middle or centre of a set of data.

Explore: Use the Table

It is dangerous for aircraft to fly through thunderstorms, so air traffic controllers keep a careful watch on thunderstorm activity. The table shows the days of thunderstorms per year at airports in some Canadian cities.

Airport	Days of Thunderstorms
Edmonton	27
Halifax	9
Montréal	25
Ottawa	24
Regina	23
St. John's	3
Toronto	27
Vancouver	6
Winnipeg	27

Rank the data in ascending order, that is, from lowest to highest.

Inquire

1. a) What is the middle number in the new order?

b) What is the number that occurs most often?

c) Take the average of the numbers in the list.

2. The numbers from question 1 are three different ways to describe the centre of a set of data. Compare how effective they are at showing the centre of the data in the table.

3. What is the difference between the highest and lowest values in the data?

The three numbers you determined in question 1, above, are known **as measures of central tendency**.

The **mean**, or arithmetic average, is calculated by finding the sum of the data and dividing by the number of pieces of data. It is the most sensitive to changes in the data, because each piece of data helps determine it.

The **median** is the middle value when the data are arranged in numerical order. If the number of pieces of data is even, there are 2 middle values. The median is the arithmetic average of these 2 values. The median is especially useful when there are unusual data that distort the mean.

The **mode** represents popularity. It is the number that occurs most frequently. A set of data may have more than one mode or no mode.

In Inquire question 3, you determined the **range**, which is the difference between the highest and lowest values in a set of data. The range is not a measure of central tendency, because the range does not give any information about values other than the highest and lowest. The range does tell us how spread out the data are.

The mean, median, mode, and range help you analyze data and determine how they are grouped.

Explore: Use the Data

The golf coach asked Carla and Alicia to play 9 holes of golf to decide who would make the golf team. The score card shows the results. Alicia hit her ball into the lake on the fifth hole.

Hole	1	2	3	4	5	6	7	8	9	Total
Carla	6	4	3	7	7	6	3	4	6	46
Alicia	4	4	3	4	15	5	4	3	6	48

a) Who won the match?
b) Who won more holes?

Inquire

1. a) Calculate the mean score for each player. Round each answer to the nearest tenth.
b) Who had the better mean score?

2. a) Calculate the median score for each player.
b) Who had the better median score?

3. a) Determine the mode of each player's scores.
b) Who had the better mode?

4. Who should make the golf team? Explain.

Example 1   British Monarchs

The table shows the lengths of the reigns of some British monarchs who directly preceded Queen Elizabeth II.

a) Calculate the mean, median, and mode of the data.

b) Which measure of central tendency best represents the data? Explain.

Monarch	Reign (years)
George I	13
George II	33
George III	59
George IV	10
William IV	7
Victoria	63
Edward VII	9
George V	25
Edward VIII	1
George VI	15

Solution

a) *Method 1: Using Pencil and Paper*

$$\text{Mean} = \frac{13+33+59+10+7+63+9+25+1+15}{10}$$

$$= 23.5$$

Estimate

$$10 + 30 + 60 + 10 + 10 + 60 + 10 + 30 + 0 + 20$$
$$= 240$$
$$240 \div 10 = 24$$

To find the median, arrange the numbers in order.
1, 7, 9, 10, 13, 15, 25, 33, 59, 63
There are two middle numbers, 13 and 15.

The median is $\frac{13+15}{2}$ or 14.

Since each piece of data appears the same number of times, exactly once, there is no mode.

So, the mean is 23.5 years, the median is 14 years, and there is no mode.

Method 2: Using a Graphing Calculator
Use the mean function and the median function to find the mean and median of the data.

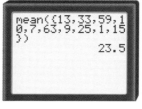

Alternatively, enter the data as a list and find the mean and median of the list.

To help identify any mode(s), use the SortA instruction to sort the list of data in ascending order.

There is no mode.

So, the mean is 23.5 years, the median is 14 years, and there is no mode.

b) The median value, 14, probably best represents the data.
The mean is distorted by the two high values, 59 and 63.

Practice

State the measure of central tendency that best describes each of the following.
1. the most requested song on a radio station
2. the marks 12, 80, 82, 84, and 87 on a test
3. the most popular baseball cap size
4. the mass of an adult elephant
5. the typical salary paid by a company
6. your bowling ability

Find the mean, median, mode, and range for each set of data.
7. 21, 25, 27, 26, 25
8. 13, 21, 16, 25, 18, 28, 32, 31
9. 8, 16, 28, 41, 16, 11, 8
10. 80, 40, 35, 62, 11, 80
11. 3800, 2700, 1650, 1120, 1360, 4500

Applications and Problem Solving

12. Describe the effect of each change on the mean of this set of numbers.

    10   11   12   13   14   15

a) Increase each number by 2.
b) Decrease each number by 2.
c) Double each number.

B

13. **Hockey** The list gives the shots on goal for the Hornets in their last 10 games.

    18   18   25   19   27
    18   25   19   22   27

a) Find the mean, mode, and median.
b) Explain how the following calculates the mean.

$$\frac{3\times18+2\times19+22+2\times25+2\times27}{10}$$

14. **Bowling** These are Tamara's bowling scores.
    145   145   168   170   174   182

a) Does the mode give an accurate indication of how well she bowls? Why?
b) Does the median give a more accurate indication of how well she bowls? Why?

15. **Resale houses** The table gives the average values, in thousands of dollars, for resale homes in the 10 cities in Canada with the highest prices one year.

City	Resale Value ($000)
Calgary	143
Edmonton	111
Halifax	110
Hamilton	151
Mississauga	194
Montréal	112
Ottawa	143
Toronto	211
Vancouver	287
Victoria	218

a) Calculate the mean, median, and mode of the data.
b) Which measure of central tendency best represents the data? Explain.

16. **University degrees** The table gives the percent of the population of each province with a university degree one year.

Province	Percent
Alberta	13.3
British Columbia	13.6
Manitoba	11.6
New Brunswick	10.2
Newfoundland	8.1
Nova Scotia	12.2
Ontario	14.9
Prince Edward Island	10.6
Québec	12.2
Saskatchewan	9.8

a) Calculate the mean, median, and mode of the data.
b) Which measure of central tendency best represents the data? Explain.

17. Salaries The table shows the salaries of all the employees in a small company.

Position	Number	Annual Salary ($)
President	1	100 000
Vice-President	1	60 000
Senior Staff	4	40 000
Junior Staff	2	30 000

a) List all eight salaries in ascending or descending order.

b) Find the mean, median, and mode.

c) Which measure of central tendency best represents the data? Explain.

d) Drop the highest salary. Find the mean, median, and mode of the remaining seven salaries.

e) Drop the lowest salary. Find the mean, median, and mode of the remaining seven salaries.

f) Which measure of central tendency is most affected by the extreme (highest and lowest) salary values?

C

18. Music research The Rock and Roll Hall of Fame was established to preserve the status of rock and roll as an art form.

a) Use your research skills to find the number of artists who were inducted into the Hall of Fame each year for the past 10 years.

b) Calculate the mean, median, and mode of the data.

c) Which measure of central tendency best represents the data? Explain.

19. Is each statement always true, sometimes true, or never true? Explain.

a) If a list of numbers has a mode, it is one of the numbers in the list.

b) The median of a list of whole numbers is a whole number.

c) The mean of a list of numbers is one of the numbers in the list.

d) The mean, median, and mode of a list of numbers are not equal.

20. List eight numbers for which the mean is
a) less than all but one of the numbers
b) greater than all but one of the numbers

21. The mean of a set of eight numbers is 6. When the greatest number in the set is removed, the mean of the new set of numbers is 5. What number was removed?

22. When a set of data is represented using a bar graph, what can you say about the appearance of the graph if there is
a) one mode?
b) two modes?
c) no mode?

23. Write the following sets of numbers in ascending order. Compare your answers with a classmate's. Decide whether different answers are possible in each case.

a) 5 numbers with a mean of 15, a median of 12, and a mode of 11

b) 4 numbers with a mean of 12.5, a median of 11.5, and a mode of 10

c) 6 numbers with a mean of 20, a median of 22.5, and no mode

d) 5 numbers whose mean, median, mode, and range all equal 16

LOGIC POWER

Nine playing cards are in a 3 by 3 arrangement. There are at least two aces, two kings, two queens, and two jacks. The cards border on each other horizontally and vertically, but not diagonally. Every jack borders on a king and a queen. Every queen borders on a king and an ace. Every king borders on an ace. Find an arrangement for the cards.

Geology

Geology is the scientific study of the composition and structure of the Earth. For example, geologists might study how mountains form or how continents may slowly drift across the Earth's surface. A specialized branch of geology is volcanology, which is the study of volcanoes.

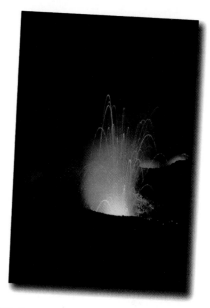

Over 80% of the Earth's surface is of volcanic origin. There are about 500 active volcanoes around the world, excluding those under the ocean. Hundreds of other volcanoes are inactive, or dormant, but they could become active again. Most of the active volcanoes are arranged in the so-called "Ring of Fire" around the Pacific Ocean.

There are at least 21 known volcanic regions in Canada. The volcanic mountains in these regions include Mount Edziza and Mount Garibaldi in British Columbia. The most recent volcanic eruption in Canada took place about 200 years ago, near Terrace in northwestern British Columbia.

Millions of people around the world live close to volcanoes. The people who study volcanoes, called volcanologists, try to predict when a volcano will erupt. Efforts can then be made to move people out of harm's way.

1 Volcanic Eruptions

1. About a third of volcanic eruptions take place on the island of Iceland. One eruption of the Icelandic volcano known as Askja threw a fountain of lava 500 m into the air. How does this height compare with the height of the tallest building in Canada?

2. One of the largest known volcanic eruptions occurred on the island of Krakatoa, in southwestern Indonesia, in 1883. The explosions that accompanied the eruption reduced the area of the island from 47 km^2 to 16 km^2. One explosion was heard almost 5000 km away and may have been the loudest noise ever produced on Earth. The eruption produced about 18 km^3 of lava. If the lava formed a uniform layer of rock across Ontario, how thick would the layer be, to the nearest tenth of a centimetre?

2 Numbers of Volcanoes

The volcanoes in the United States are distributed as shown in the table.

1. Determine the mean, median, mode, and range of the numbers in the table. Round to the nearest tenth, if necessary.

2. The other U.S. states have no volcanoes. If these states were included in the table, what would the mean of the numbers be, to the nearest tenth?

State	Number of Volcanoes
Alaska	108
Arizona	9
California	24
Colorado	1
Idaho	6
Hawaii	19
Nevada	7
New Mexico	16
Oregon	34
Utah	6
Washington	9
Wyoming	2

3 Locating Information

1. Explore the education and training needed to become a volcanologist. Also, find out who employs volcanologists and where they work.

2. Use your research skills to locate Canada's volcanic regions. How far is the closest one from where you live?

INVESTIGATING MATH

Histograms

1 Space Shuttle Launches

The table shows the numbers of space shuttle launches in the first 18 years of shuttle missions.

Years	1981–82	1983–84	1985–86	1987–88	1989–90	1991–92	1993–94	1995–96	1997–98
Number of Launches	5	9	11	2	11	14	14	14	10

We can display the data on a type of graph called a **histogram.**

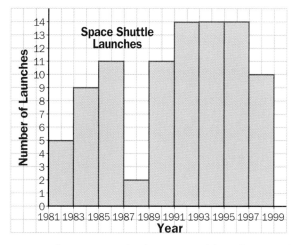

1. In what ways is the histogram like a bar graph?

2. In what ways is the histogram different from a bar graph?

3. Why are there no spaces between the bars of the histogram?

4. Can you tell from the histogram how many launches there were in 1998? Explain.

5. How many shuttle flights were there from the beginning of 1981 to the end of 1998?

2 Precipitation

The histogram shows the average number of days it rains in Toronto each month.

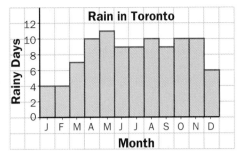

1. a) Which month has the most rainy days?
b) How many rainy days does this month have?

2. a) Which months have the least rainy days?
b) How many rainy days does each of these months have?

3. Toronto receives a greater depth of rainfall in July than in June. What can you conclude about the amounts of rainfall on rainy days in these two months?

4. a) List the number of rainy days for each month. Find the mean, median, and mode of the data.
b) Which measure of central tendency best describes the data? Explain.

5. a) As a hypothesis, draw a histogram that shows the average number of days it snows in Toronto each month.
b) Use your research skills to find out the actual monthly values. Display the data on a histogram.
c) Compare the histograms from parts a) and b).

3 Personal Stereos

A survey of the owners of 100 personal stereos gave the following data.

Age	0–9	10–19	20–29	30–39	40–49	50–59	60–69	70–79	80–89
Frequency	19	26	17	13	7	6	5	4	3

1. Use grid paper to display the data on a histogram.

2. The window displays show some of the steps in displaying the histogram on a graphing calculator.

Display the histogram on your graphing calculator and describe all the steps you followed.

TECHNOLOGY

Graphics Software Packages

Research has shown that some people learn better when information is presented to them visually. One way to present information visually is to use graphics software packages. There are two types of packages.

An *analytical* graphics package takes numerical data that are in rows and columns and displays them in bar graphs, broken-line graphs, and circle graphs. The graphical display is much easier to analyze than rows and columns of numbers. You can display analytical graphics on a monitor or print them out.

Presentation graphics packages are used to deliver a message by people who work in sales and marketing. Presentation graphics look more sophisticated than analytical graphics and use techniques a graphic artist might use. The graphics displays can be converted into overhead transparencies or slides. Some packages allow you to make animated graphics on a computer and run them on a VCR.

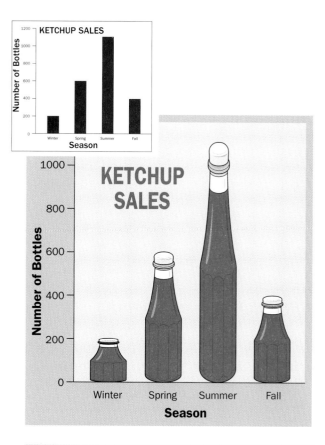

1 Displaying Data

1. If a computer with a graphics software package is available, try different graphs to display these survey data.

Type of Shoe	Frequency (%)
Running	10
Golf	6
Tennis	11
Basketball	26
Aerobics	6
Walking	11
Cross-training	18
Other	12

2. Display the data on a bar graph in a creative way.

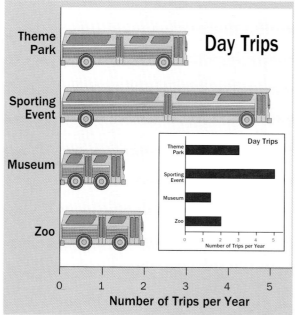

2 Comparing Graphs

The following three graphs display the data from Exploration 1.
Which graph do you think best represents the data?
Give reasons for your choice.

Graph A

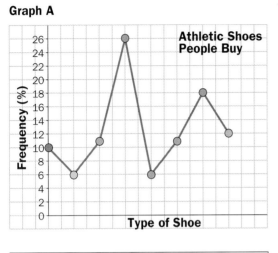

Graph B

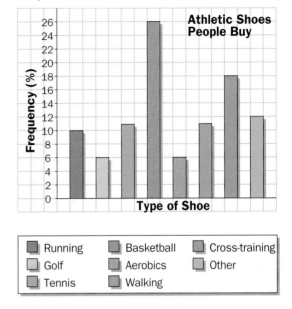

Graph C

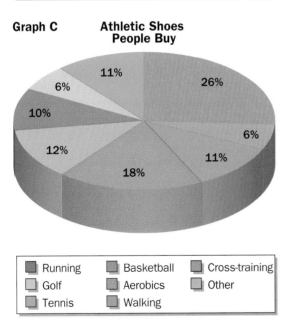

3 Choosing Graphs

1. What type of graph would you use to display each of the following? Explain.

a) the CDs sold at a music store on each day of the week for one week

b) the CDs sold at a music store by type of music in one week

2. a) For an imaginary music store, make up some data showing CD sales by type of music for each day of one week.

b) Display the data on the types of graphs you suggested in question 1.

4 Animated Graphs

Suppose you had a presentation graphics package you could use to design animated graphics and run them on a VCR. How would you display the data from Exploration 1?

4.6 Stem-and-Leaf Plots

Explore: Interpret the Data

Babe Ruth was one of the greatest home run hitters. He hit these numbers of home runs in 15 seasons with the New York Yankees.

Babe Ruth's Home Runs in 15 Seasons				
54	59	35	41	46
25	47	60	54	46
49	46	41	34	22

Organize the data by listing the tens digits, called **stems**. Beside them, list the units digits, called **leaves**.

```
2 | 5  2
3 | 5  4
4 | 1  6  7  6  9  6  1
5 | 4  9  4
6 | 0
```

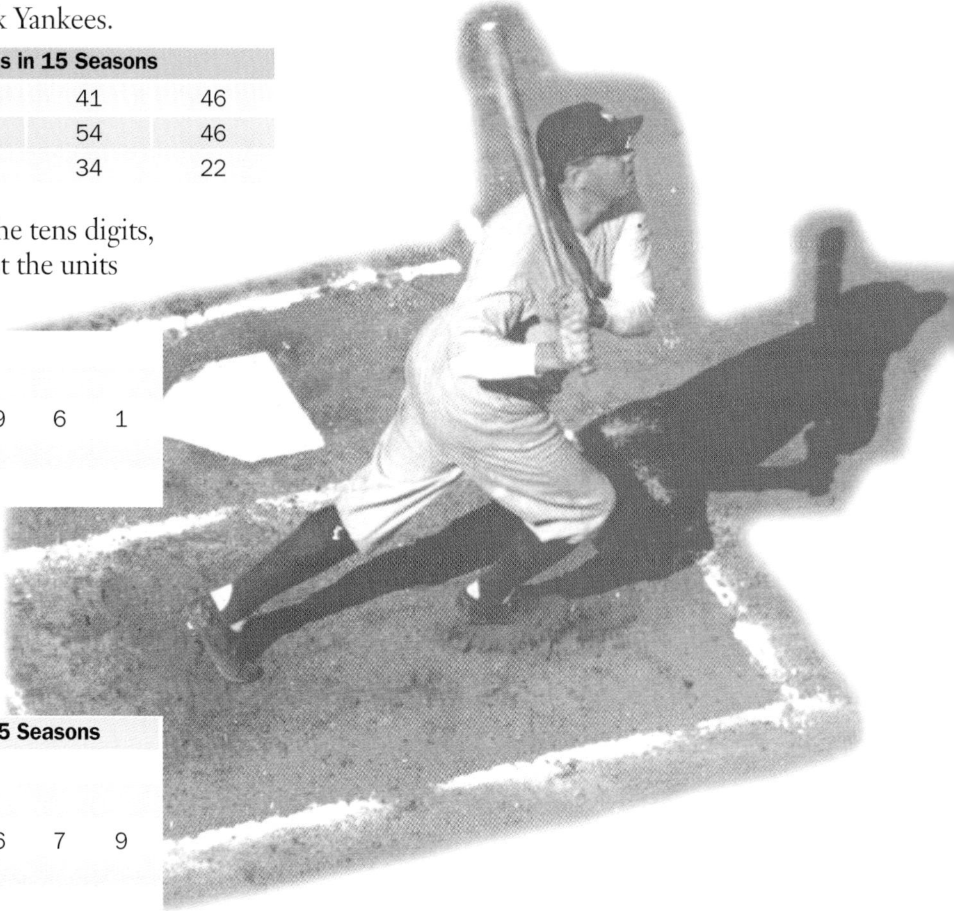

The same data are shown below in a type of table called a **stem-and-leaf plot**. Describe how the data are organized in this plot.

Babe Ruth's Home Runs in 15 Seasons	
2	2 5
3	4 5
4	1 1 6 6 6 7 9
5	4 4 9
6	0

Inquire

1. From which table can you read the median most easily? Explain.

2. What was Babe Ruth's median number of home runs?

3. What other type of representation does the stem-and-leaf plot resemble? Why?

4. What was the mode of Babe Ruth's numbers of home runs?

5. What was Babe Ruth's mean number of home runs?

6. Which measure of central tendency best represents these data? Explain.

Back-to-back stem-and-leaf plots can be used to compare data from 2 groups.

Example   Television Viewing Habits
a) Construct a back-to-back stem-and-leaf plot for these data.

Hours Spent Watching Television Per Week	
Female	**Male**
13, 16, 17, 18, 19	11, 18
21, 27	21, 26, 26
35, 38	31, 34, 34, 36
40, 42	41

b) How many people were surveyed?
c) Was the mean value higher for males or for females?

Solution
a) The stem is the 10s digit in each number.
The leaf is the 1s digit in each number.

Hours Spent Watching Television Per Week		
Female		**Male**
9 8 7 6 3	1	1 8
7 1	2	1 6 6
8 5	3	1 4 4 6
2 0	4	1

b) There were 21 people surveyed, 11 females and 10 males.
c) The 10 males watched 278 h of television for a mean of 27.8 h.
The 11 females watched 286 h of television for a mean of 26 h.
So, the mean value was higher for males.

Applications and Problem Solving

A

1. Wind speeds The list shows the peak wind speeds, in kilometres per hour, recorded at 16 Canadian airports.

109	129	127	148	153	129	124	135
161	177	146	132	177	193	106	106

a) Construct a stem-and-leaf plot.
b) What is the range of the data?
c) What is the median peak wind speed?

2. Basketball The following data show the points scored by the Celtics girls basketball team in home and away games.

Home Games   62, 68, 73, 43, 51, 55, 53, 78, 64, 66, 67
Away Games   42, 50, 62, 51, 53, 58, 63, 64, 71, 57, 43

a) Construct a back-to-back stem-and-leaf plot to show the comparison.
b) What was the median number of points in each category?

B

3. Hot weather Weather stations in each of Canada's provinces have recorded the greatest number of consecutive days with the highest temperature above 32°C. The data are shown in the stem-and-leaf plot.

Stem	Leaf
0	3 4 7 8
1	1 6 6
2	2 2
3	1

a) How many weather stations were considered?

b) The greatest number of consecutive days with the highest temperature above 32°C occurred in British Columbia in 1971. What was the number of days?

c) Do you agree that most of Canada's provinces have had at least 15 consecutive days with the highest temperature above 32°C? Explain.

d) What are the two modes in the data?

4. Television viewing habits **a)** How many more 14-year-olds than 18-year-olds are represented in this back-to-back plot?

Weekly Television Viewing (h/week)		
14-Year-Olds		**18-Year-Olds**
9 7	0	7 7 9 9
9 8 8 4 4 2 1	1	2 3 4 4 4 8 8 9 9
8 8 6 6 4 3 1	2	1 2 3 4 8
8 8 5 5 5	3	6
2 2	4	1
6	5	0

b) What is the range of hours of television watched by 14-year-olds?

c) Describe the difference in viewing habits of the two age groups.

d) What might contribute to the difference in part c)?

5. Technology The SortA and SortD or equivalent instructions on a graphing calculator can be used to sort a list of data into ascending or descending order. Explain why using a calculator to sort data can be helpful for constructing stem-and-leaf plots.

C

6. Hockey In the 12 seasons Mario Lemieux played for the Pittsburgh Penguins, he scored the following numbers of goals.
43, 48, 54, 70, 85, 45, 19, 44, 69, 17, 69, 69

a) Display the data on a stem-and-leaf plot.

b) Find the mean, median, and mode of the data.

c) Which measure of central tendency best represents the data? Explain.

7. Football research The Grey Cup is awarded to the Canadian Football League champion.

a) Use your research skills to find the total number of points scored in each of the last 20 Grey Cup games.

b) Display the data on a stem-and-leaf plot.

c) Find the mean, median, and mode of the data.

d) Which measure of central tendency best represents the data? Explain.

8. Birthday experiment If you consider the days of the month on which the members of your class were born, there are 31 possible dates.

a) As a hypothesis, show how you think a stem-and-leaf plot of the actual birth dates for your class would look. Explain your reasoning.

b) Collect the birth date data for your class. Display the data on a stem-and-leaf plot.

c) Does the plot from part b) agree with your hypothesis? If not, describe the ways in which they are different.

9. Multiple trials experiment For this experiment, you need a piece of string with a length between 30 cm and 70 cm.

a) As a hypothesis, show how you think a stem-and-leaf plot of 30 people's estimates of the length, to the nearest centimetre, would look.

b) Ask 30 people to estimate the length of the string, to the nearest centimetre. Display the data on a stem-and-leaf plot.

c) Does the plot from part b) agree with your hypothesis? If not, describe the ways in which they are different.

4.7 Box-and-Whisker Plots and Percentiles

Kim Campbell was 46 years old when she became Canada's nineteenth Prime Minister. The mean age of Canada's first 19 Prime Ministers when they began their terms in office was about 55 years.

Sir John A. Macdonald

Sir Wilfrid Laurier

Explore: Interpret the Data

Beginning with Sir John A. Macdonald, the first 19 Canadian Prime Ministers had the following ages when they began their terms.

52, 51, 70, 48, 70, 74, 54, 57, 46, 47, 60, 66, 61, 65, 48, 39, 55, 45, 46

List the ages in order from youngest to oldest.

Inquire

1. What is the lowest value in the data?

2. What is the highest value in the data?

3. What is the median value?

4. Consider the nine values above the median. What is the median of these nine values?

5. Consider the nine values below the median. What is the median of these nine values?

Sir Robert L. Borden

Lester B. Pearson

The number you found in question 4 is known as the **upper quartile**. The number you found in question 5 is known as the **lower quartile**. The five numbers you found in questions 1–5 are known as a **five-number summary**.

Brian Mulroney

Kim Campbell

Example 1 Canadian Prime Ministers

a) Use the data from the previous page to construct a box-and-whisker plot.
b) About what percent of the values lie in the box? in each whisker?

Solution

a) *Method 1: Using Pencil and Paper*
The 5-number summary is 39, 47, 54, 65, 74. Plot these 5 numbers on a number line. Then, draw vertical line segments through the median and the upper and lower quartiles. Draw a box between the upper and lower quartiles. Draw horizontal segments to the highest and lowest values from the ends of the box. These segments are the whiskers.

Method 2: Using a Graphing Calculator
There is no need to sort the data into ascending or descending order. Enter the data as a list. Use the STAT PLOTS menu to select a boxplot. Then, display the graph.

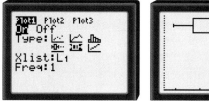 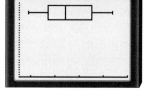

If you need the five-number summary to interpret the graph, you can use the TRACE instruction and the right and left arrow keys to display the five values.

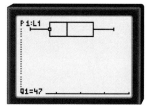

b) About 50% of the numbers lie in the box. Each whisker contains about 25% of the numbers.

Example 2 Percentile Scores

Mariko scored 75 on a math test. The results, in ascending order, for the whole class, were as shown.

| 40 | 45 | 52 | 52 | 58 | 64 | 64 | 64 | 65 | 66 | 67 | 67 | 70 |
| 71 | 72 | 73 | 75 | 75 | 75 | 80 | 82 | 82 | 86 | 88 | 90 | |

a) In what percentile was Mariko's score?
b) What did this percentile show?

Solution

a) The percentile of Mariko's score, or her percentile rank, is given by

$$\frac{b + \frac{1}{2}e}{n} \times 100$$

where b represents the number of scores below hers, e represents the number of scores that equalled hers, and n represents the total number of scores.

In this case, $b = 16$, $e = 2$, and $n = 25$.
Mariko's percentile rank is

$$\frac{16 + \frac{1}{2}(2)}{25} \times 100 = \frac{17}{25} \times 100$$
$$= 0.68 \times 100$$
$$= 68$$

So, Mariko's score was in the 68th percentile.

b) Her percentile rank of 68 showed that Mariko scored better than about 68% of the students, and that about 32% of the students scored better than Mariko.

Applications and Problem Solving

A

1. Practising songs The number of hours some bands spend practising a new song before they record is shown below.

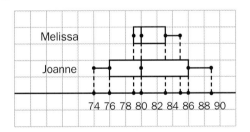

a) What fraction of the bands spend more than 30 h practising?
b) What fraction of the bands spend from 20 h to 45 h practising?
c) What fraction of the bands spend less than 45 h practising?

2. Test scores Diego scored 81 on a test. The results for the whole class are shown.

| 65 | 74 | 81 | 92 | 63 | 55 | 83 | 77 | 77 | 80 |
| 96 | 95 | 90 | 56 | 68 | 70 | 81 | 91 | 81 | 96 |

In what percentile was Diego's score?

3. Test scores a) Draw a box-and-whisker plot to represent the following test scores.

40	47	50	50	50	54	56	56
60	60	62	62	63	65	70	70
72	76	77	80	85	85	95

b) Find the percentile rank of a score of 60.

B

4. Test scores Melissa and Joanne had the following scores on seven tests.

| Melissa | 79 | 79 | 80 | 80 | 83 | 83 | 85 |
| Joanne | 74 | 76 | 76 | 80 | 85 | 86 | 89 |

The following two box-and-whisker plots represent their scores.

a) Why is the plot of Joanne's scores longer than the plot of Melissa's scores?
b) Why is the median score not in the middle of either box?
c) Why is there no left whisker on the plot of Melissa's scores?
d) Why is the right whisker on the plot of Joanne's scores longer than the left whisker?
e) For each student, predict whether the mean score is above, below, or equal to the median score. Explain your reasoning. Then, check whether your prediction is correct.

5. Math marks The plots model the math marks for three students.

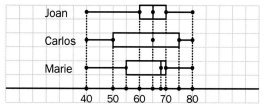

a) What fraction of Joan's marks are from 60 to 70?

b) Which student's marks are the most inconsistent? Explain.

c) What percent of Marie's marks are above 70%?

C

6. Tax research The day of the year on which Canadians begin to keep the money they earn is known as tax freedom day. Until that day, all the money earned in the year is paid in taxes that year.

a) Use your research skills to determine the number of "tax-free days" there were in each province last year.

b) Write the five-number summary for the data.

c) Construct a box-and-whisker plot.

d) Write a paragraph to describe the data. Include the answers to such questions as the following. In which province do people pay the most in taxes? In which province do people pay the least in taxes?

7. Airport research One way to rank how busy airports are is to determine the total number of passengers who arrive at and depart from the airports in a year.

a) Use your research skills to find the total number of passenger arrivals and departures for each of the 15 busiest airports in the world last year. Round each number to the nearest million.

b) Construct a box-and-whisker plot for the rounded data.

c) Write a paragraph to describe the rounded data.

8. Climate Environment Canada's Climate Severity Index (CSI) rates the climate of a place on a scale from 1 to 100. A higher score indicates a more severe climate. The table gives the CSI values for Canada's provincial capitals.

City	CSI
Charlottetown	48
Edmonton	37
Fredericton	41
Halifax	43
Québec City	52
Regina	47
St. John's	56
Toronto	35
Winnipeg	51
Victoria	13

a) Write the five-number summary for the data.

b) Draw a box-and-whisker plot to model the data.

c) Which cities have CSI values that lie entirely within the box?

d) Predict whether the mean CSI value is above, below, or equal to the median value. Explain your reasoning. Then, check whether your prediction is correct.

e) Which measure of central tendency best describes the data? Explain.

f) Write a paragraph to describe the data.

9. a) The median of a set of data is also the 50th percentile. Explain why.

b) What percentiles represent the upper and lower quartiles? Explain.

10. If you score 80% on a test, are you at the 80th percentile? Explain.

> ### LOGIC POWER
>
> Lin drove from her home to her office at 90 km/h. At the end of the day, there was more traffic, and Lin drove home from her office along the same highway at 60 km/h. What was her average speed for the two journeys?

4.8 Broken-Line Graphs

A broken-line graph shows how something changes.

Explore: Interpret the Graph

The broken-line graph shows how the world's annual fresh water consumption changed over 60 years.

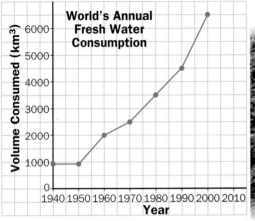

About how much fresh water was used in
a) 1940?   **b)** 1960?
c) 1980?   **d)** 1990?

Inquire

1. About how many times more fresh water was used in 1990 than in 1940?

2. a) What will the world's fresh water consumption be in the year 2010?
b) State the assumptions you made.

3. It is estimated that there are 39 000 km³ of fresh water available for use in the world each year. Why is there concern about the use of fresh water?

4. Could you use each of the following types of graphs to represent the water consumption data? Explain.
a) bar graph   **b)** pictograph   **c)** circle graph

Example   Land Speed Record

The table shows changes in the approximate land speed record with time. Plot the data on a broken-line graph.

Year	Land Speed Record (km/h)
1900	60
1920	240
1940	600
1960	750
1980	1000
2000	1200

Solution 1   Graphing Manually

Draw and label the axes. Choose a scale that allows you to plot all the data.

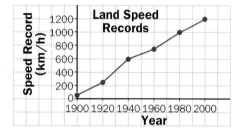

Plot the data and join the points with straight lines. Give the graph a title.

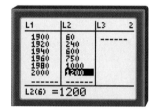

Solution 2   Using a Graphing Calculator

Enter the year and speed data into your calculator as two lists.

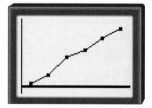

Using the STAT PLOTS or equivalent menu, select a broken-line graph, which may be called an xyLine plot. Specify the list to be plotted on each axis.

Set the window variables to suitable values and display the graph, or use the ZoomStat or equivalent instruction to adjust the window automatically.

Applications and Problem Solving

A

1. Javelin and discus The diagram shows two broken-line graphs on the same set of axes. The graphs show the winning throws in the women's discus and the women's javelin at the Olympics.

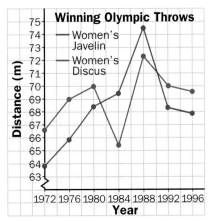

a) In which years was the javelin thrown further than the discus?
b) What was the difference in the winning distances in 1976?
c) What does the jagged line on the vertical axis mean?

2. Atlantic crossings The winners of the Blue Riband Award for the fastest Atlantic crossing by a liner are listed in the table.

Year	Winner	Speed (km/h)
1840	Britannia	19.6
1863	Scotia	25.9
1882	Alaska	31.9
1897	Kaiser Wilhelm der Grosse	41.5
1909	Mauretania	48.0
1929	Bremen	51.7
1938	Queen Mary	58.7
1952	United States	66.0

a) Display the data on a broken-line graph.
b) Which liner crossed at about half the speed of the *Bremen*?

B

3. Education The table shows changes in the percent of Canadian adults with two levels of education.

Year	Education Level	
	Less Than Grade 9	University Degree
1976	25.4	6.4
1981	20.7	8.0
1986	17.7	9.6
1991	14.3	11.4
1996	12.4	13.3

a) Represent the data by drawing two broken-line graphs on the same set of axes.
b) Describe the trends in the data.

4. Canadian population The table shows the changes in the percent of the Canadian population in different age groups.

Year	Age		
	Under 19	20–44	Over 44
1966	42	32	26
1971	39	34	27
1976	36	36	28
1981	32	39	29
1986	29	41	30
1991	27	41	32
1996	27	40	33

a) Represent the data by plotting three broken-line graphs on the same set of axes.
b) Describe the trend in the average age. Explain and justify your reasoning.

C

5. Ontario population **a)** Use your research skills to find the population of Ontario in every tenth year from 1911 to the most recent year possible. Plot the data on a broken-line graph.
b) In which 10-year period was there the biggest change in population?

PROBLEM SOLVING

4.9 Interpret Graphs

Much of the information you receive from newspapers and magazines is displayed on graphs. Therefore, the ability to interpret graphs correctly is an important life skill. The graph shows the distance from Port Colborne to Brampton versus the time taken for a car to travel this distance. What is happening between P and Q; Q and R; R and S; S and T?

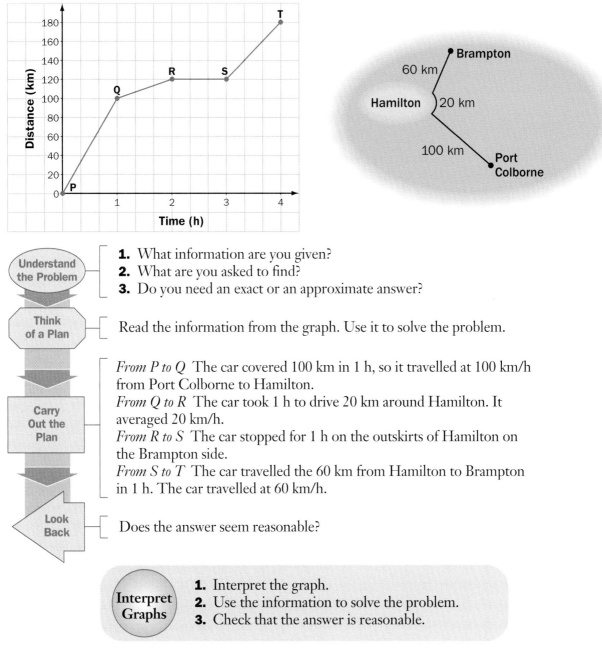

Understand the Problem

1. What information are you given?
2. What are you asked to find?
3. Do you need an exact or an approximate answer?

Think of a Plan

Read the information from the graph. Use it to solve the problem.

Carry Out the Plan

From P to Q The car covered 100 km in 1 h, so it travelled at 100 km/h from Port Colborne to Hamilton.
From Q to R The car took 1 h to drive 20 km around Hamilton. It averaged 20 km/h.
From R to S The car stopped for 1 h on the outskirts of Hamilton on the Brampton side.
From S to T The car travelled the 60 km from Hamilton to Brampton in 1 h. The car travelled at 60 km/h.

Look Back

Does the answer seem reasonable?

Interpret Graphs
1. Interpret the graph.
2. Use the information to solve the problem.
3. Check that the answer is reasonable.

Applications and Problem Solving

1. Travelling salesperson The graph shows the amount of gasoline in the tank of a salesperson's car at different times on a work day. Describe how the salesperson might have spent the day.

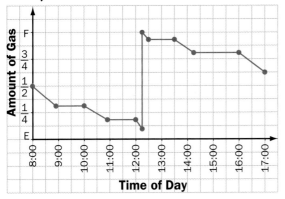

2. Pleasure boats The two graphs describe two pleasure boats. Compare the boats by age, cost, speed, and length.

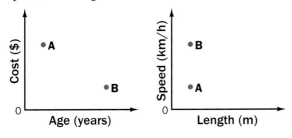

3. Car trip a) The graph models the distance versus time for a car travelling from Fredericton to Moncton. Describe what is happening between A and B; B and C; C and D; D and E.

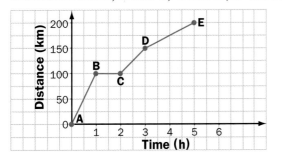

b) Sketch a graph of the car's speed versus time.

4. Ferris wheel You are the first person to get on and off a Ferris wheel with eight cars. Once the cars are loaded, the Ferris wheel makes three revolutions before letting people off. Sketch a graph of your height versus time.

5. Hot-water tap Suppose someone turned on the hot-water tap on a kitchen sink and left it running. Sketch a graph of the water temperature versus time as the tap is running.

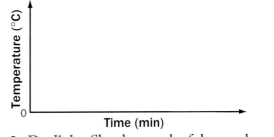

6. Daylight Sketch a graph of the number of minutes of daylight versus the month of the year.

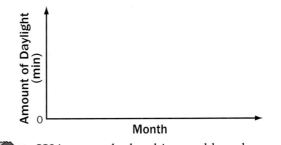

7. Write a graph-sketching problem that involves each of the following. Have a classmate solve each problem.
a) the temperature of water in a kettle versus time
b) the depth of water in a bathtub versus time

4.10 Scatter Plots

A scatter plot can be used to show whether a relationship exists between two variables.

Explore: Interpret the Graph

The scatter plot shows the relationship between the lengths and wingspreads of 22 birds.

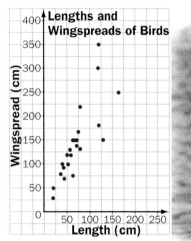

a) Describe the pattern made by the points.

b) Describe any relationship you see between the lengths of birds and their wingspreads.

c) How does the scatter plot show this relationship?

Inquire

1. a) Estimate the least wingspread shown.
b) Estimate the length of the bird with this wingspread.

2. Estimate the length of the bird with a wingspread close to
a) 220 cm   **b)** 180 cm

3. Estimate the wingspread of most birds that are about
a) 50 cm long   **b)** 75 cm long

When you have collected data for two variables, you may choose to display the data on a scatter plot.

Example   Book Prices

The table gives the prices of some books, to the nearest dollar, in Canada and the United States.

Book	Price In Canada (CDN$)	In the U.S. (US$)
The Far Side Gallery	18	13
Joy of Cooking	23	17
Chicken Soup for the Teenage Soul	20	13
The Everything Bicycle Book	16	12
Hoyles Rules of Games	9	7
First Field Guide: Rocks and Minerals	15	11
Romeo and Juliet	5	4

a) Draw a scatter plot for the data.
b) Describe any relationship you see on the scatter plot.
c) Do individual points suggest a relationship between the prices of the books in U.S. dollars and in Canadian dollars? Explain.
d) If the price of a book is CDN$12.00, use the scatter plot to estimate its price in U.S. dollars.
e) If the price of a book is US$15.00, use the scatter plot to estimate its price in Canadian dollars.

Solution

a) *Method 1: Graphing Manually*
• Draw and label the axes. Choose a scale that allows you to plot all the data.
• Plot a point to represent the data for each book.
• Give the graph a title.

Method 2: Using a Graphing Calculator
• Input the data as two lists.
• Using the STAT PLOTS or equivalent menu, select a scatter plot. Specify the list to be plotted on each axis.
• Set the window variables to suitable values, or use the ZoomStat or equivalent instruction to adjust the window automatically.

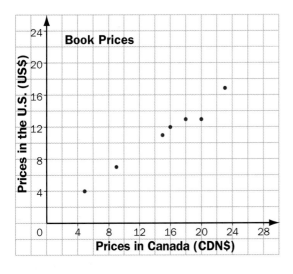

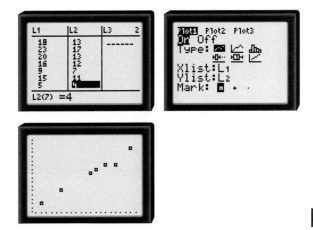

b) The points on the scatter plot seem to lie close to a straight line. The points suggest the relationship that, as the book prices in Canadian dollars increase, the book prices in U.S. dollars also increase.

c) Find the ratio of the price in U.S. dollars to the price in Canadian dollars for each book. Round to the nearest hundredth, where necessary.

$$\frac{13}{18} \doteq 0.72 \qquad \frac{17}{23} \doteq 0.74 \qquad \frac{13}{20} = 0.65 \qquad \frac{12}{16} = 0.75$$

$$\frac{7}{9} \doteq 0.78 \qquad \frac{11}{15} \doteq 0.73 \qquad \frac{4}{5} = 0.8$$

The average ratio is close to 0.75.
So, the prices of books in U.S. dollars are approximately 0.75 or $\frac{3}{4}$ of the prices in Canadian dollars.

d) From the scatter plot, a book with a price of CDN$12.00 has a price of about US$9.00.

e) From the scatter plot, a book with a price of US$15.00 has a price of about CDN$20.00.

Applications and Problem Solving

A

1. Women's track records The scatter plot shows the world records that stood in five women's track events one year.

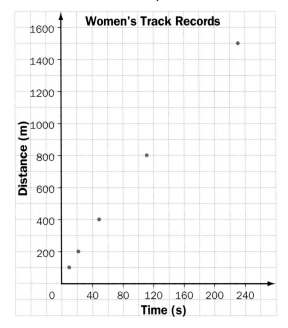

a) What was the approximate world record for the 400-m event?
b) About how many times greater was the world record for the 800-m event than for the 100-m event?
c) If there had been a 1000-m event, what world record would you estimate for it?
d) Estimate how far a top female athlete can run in 3 min.

2. Bears This scatter plot compares the masses and lengths of different kinds of bears.

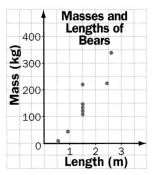

a) Estimate the length of the kind of bear that has the greatest mass.

b) What is the approximate length of the kind of bear with a mass of about 45 kg?

c) If a kind of bear had a mass of about 300 kg, about what length would you expect it to have?

d) What relationship between mass and length does the scatter plot suggest?

3. Commonwealth Games The table shows the number of gold medals and the total number of medals for the top 10 countries when the Commonwealth Games were held in Victoria, British Columbia.

Country	Gold Medals	Total Medals
Australia	87	182
Canada	40	128
England	31	125
New Zealand	5	41
Nigeria	11	37
India	6	24
Scotland	6	20
Kenya	7	19
Wales	5	19
South Africa	2	11

a) Draw a scatter plot of total medals versus gold medals.

b) Describe any relationship you see.

4. Cats The table shows the lengths, from the nose to the end of the tail, and the masses of different types of cats.

Type of Cat	Length (cm)	Mass (kg)
Lion	300	180
Lioness	270	140
Cheetah	180	45
Mountain Lion	240	90
Jaguar	260	140
Leopard	265	70
Tiger	270	190
Tigress	240	135
Lynx	90	30

a) Display the data on a scatter plot of mass versus length.

b) Describe any relationship you see.

B

5. Ocean temperatures The scatter plot models how the average temperature of the ocean changes with latitude in the southern hemisphere.

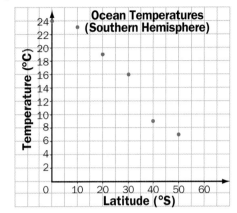

a) Describe the relationship between average ocean temperature and latitude in the southern hemisphere.

b) Estimate the average ocean temperature at a latitude of 35°S; 22°S.

c) Would you expect to see a similar relationship for the northern hemisphere? Explain.

d) At what latitude is the border between the United States and Canada's Western Provinces?

e) What do you think is the average ocean temperature at this latitude? Explain.

6. Summer Olympics The table shows the number of countries represented at the Summer Olympics in different years.

Year	1920	1924	1928	1932	1936
Number of Countries	29	44	46	37	49

Year	1948	1952	1956	1960	1964
Number of Countries	59	69	67	83	93

Year	1968	1972
Number of Countries	112	122

a) Draw a scatter plot of the number of countries versus the year.

b) Describe any relationship you see.

c) Use your scatter plot to estimate the numbers of countries represented in 1976, 1984, and 1996.

d) Use your research skills to find the actual numbers of countries represented in 1976, 1984, and 1996.

e) Compare your estimates from part c) with your findings from part d). Give reasons for any differences.

C

7. Lizards The scatter plot shows the lengths of lizards, not including their tails, and the lengths of their tails.

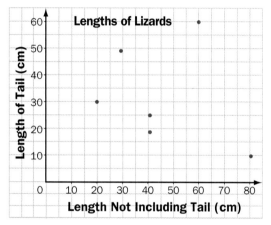

a) Does the scatter plot suggest a relationship between the lengths of lizards and the lengths of their tails? Explain.

b) Do all scatter plots show a relationship? Explain.

8. a) How does a scatter plot show whether there is a relationship between two variables?

b) Refer to the scatter plot in question 2. Consider only the five points that represent kinds of bears with lengths of about 1.5 m. What relationship do these five points suggest between the lengths and masses of bears?

c) Is it possible for a scatter plot to mislead you about whether a relationship exists? Explain.

9. Travel experiment Different students travel to school in different ways — by car, on foot, and so on.

a) For students who travel to school in the same way, write a hypothesis to describe how the distance travelled is related to the time taken.

b) Ask 10 students who travel to school in the same way as you to estimate the distance, in kilometres, from their home to the school. Also, ask them the average time, in minutes, the trip takes.

c) Use your data to draw a scatter plot of distance versus time.

d) Describe any relationship you see and compare it with your hypothesis.

e) Aside from the way in which a student travels and the distance from home to school, what factors can affect the time taken for the trip?

LOGIC POWER

The diagram shows the locations of five pieces of furniture in rooms in a recreation centre.

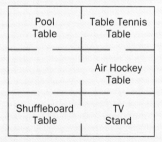

You need to switch the locations of the TV stand and the shuffleboard table. Because of lack of space, you can only move each piece of furniture into an adjacent empty room. What is the smallest number of moves you need to switch the TV stand and the shuffleboard table?

4.11 Lines of Best Fit

Explore: Use the Graph

The scatter plot shows the relationship between the areas and the greatest depths of seas.

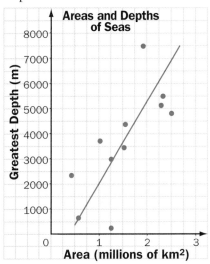

The line shown on the graph is called the **line of best fit**. This line is as close as possible to the points. There are about as many points above the line as there are below the line.

a) Describe the relationship between the areas and the greatest depths of seas.

b) How does the line of best fit help to show this relationship?

Inquire

1. a) How well does the line of best fit match the points on the scatter plot?

b) In what ways does the line of best fit not match the points?

2. Is it possible to draw a different line of best fit for this scatter plot? Explain.

3. When you **interpolate**, you estimate values within the range of given values. Use the line of best fit to interpolate the greatest depth of a sea with an area of about 1 400 000 km^2.

4. When you **extrapolate**, you extend a line to estimate values outside the range of given values. Use the line of best fit to extrapolate the area of a sea with a greatest depth of about 9000 m.

Example   Rural Population

Statistics Canada divides the Canadian population into two categories — urban and rural. The urban population includes people who live in communities with a population of at least 1000, and with at least 400 people per square kilometre. The rural population includes people who live outside these communities. The table shows Canada's rural population as a percent of the total population in different years.

Display the data on a scatter plot of percent rural population versus year. Draw a line of best fit.

Year	Percent Rural Population (%)
1951	37.1
1956	33.4
1961	30.4
1966	26.4
1971	23.9
1976	24.5
1981	24.3
1986	23.5
1991	23.4
1996	22.1

Solution 1   Using Paper and Pencil

Draw the scatter plot. Then draw a straight line that is as close as possible to the points plotted on the grid.

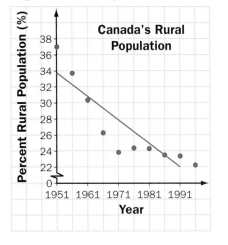

Solution 2   Using a Graphing Calculator

Enter the data as two lists. Then, use the linear regression instruction from the STAT CALC or equivalent menu to draw the scatter plot and the line of best fit.

Applications and Problem Solving

A

1. High jump The table shows some winning heights in the men's high jump at the Olympic Games.

Year	Winning Height (m)
1912	1.93
1924	1.98
1936	2.03
1948	1.98
1960	2.16
1972	2.23
1984	2.35
1996	2.39

a) Draw a scatter plot of winning height versus year. Draw a line of best fit.

b) Canada's Duncan McNaughton won the event in 1932. Interpolate to estimate his winning height.

c) Duncan McNaughton's actual winning height was 1.97 m. Compare this height with your estimate from part b).

d) Extrapolate to estimate the winning heights in 2020; in 2060.

e) Are your estimates in part d) reasonable? Explain.

f) Display the data in the table on a broken-line graph. Does a line of best fit or a broken-line graph more clearly model the relationship between the winning height and the year? Explain.

2. Video rentals The table shows, for a major video chain, the number of rentals of a particular video in each week the video has been available.

Week	Number of Rentals
1	642
2	635
3	762
4	695
5	564
6	508
7	455
8	293
9	215
10	160

a) Draw a scatter plot of number of rentals versus the week. Draw a line of best fit for the data.

b) Describe the relationship.

c) Estimate the number of rentals of the video in the 15th week.

B

3. Tree growth The table shows the height and the circumference of a tree at different ages.

Age (years)	Height (m)	Circumference (cm)
1	1.1	15.2
2	1.1	18.2
3	2.4	20.7
4	2.5	23.2
5	3.1	27.0
6	4.3	29.5
7	4.5	32.0
8	5.3	33.9

a) Draw a scatter plot of height versus circumference. Draw a line of best fit.

b) Describe the relationship.

c) Estimate the circumference for a height of 2 m; 6 m.

d) Estimate the height for a circumference of 25 cm; 10 cm.

e) What other scatter plots could you construct from the data in the table?

f) Draw another scatter plot and use it to write two problems. Have a classmate solve them.

4. Technology Investigate how the TRACE instruction and the Value operation can be used to interpolate and extrapolate from a line of best fit. Describe your findings.

C

5. a) How can you decide whether interpolations based on a line of best fit are reasonable?

b) How can you decide whether extrapolations based on a line of best fit are reasonable?

6. Physiology experiment a) Your arm stretch is the distance between your fingertips when your arms are fully extended. Measure and record the height and the arm stretch for 12 classmates.

b) Draw a scatter plot of arm stretch versus height. Draw a line of best fit.

c) Describe the relationship between the arm stretch and the height. Explain how you can judge whether your answer is reasonable.

TECHNOLOGY

Scatter Plots and Computer Spreadsheets

1 Drawing a Scatter Plot

A computer spreadsheet program can be used
to draw a scatter plot.

1. a) The table shows temperature forecasts
for a September day.

City	Temperature Forecasts	
	Low (°C)	High (°C)
Amsterdam, Holland	10	19
Beijing, China	15	26
Cairo, Egypt	21	33
Geneva, Switzerland	9	18
Kingston, Jamaica	25	34
London, England	11	21
Mexico City, Mexico	14	24
New Delhi, India	23	34
Oslo, Norway	5	16
Rome, Italy	15	22
Sydney, Australia	13	22
Toronto, Canada	10	21
Vancouver, Canada	12	21
Yellowknife, Canada	5	17

Open a spreadsheet and enter the data.

	A	B	C
1	City	Low (°C)	High (°C)
2	Amsterdam, Holland	10	19
3	Beijing, China	15	26
4	Cairo, Egypt	21	33

b) Select the cells containing the data you want to
display on a scatter plot of high temperature versus
low temperature. Choose the chart option. Select the
scatter plot icon. Follow the instructions to create a
scatter plot.
c) Format to make the changes you want to the type,
labels, gridlines, and scales.

2. Draw a line of best fit for your scatter plot. You might use a draw feature on a toolbar or copy your chart into a word processing program and use its drawing feature. If you cannot draw the line of best fit with your computer, print the scatter plot and draw the line of best fit with a pencil.

2 Using the Line of Best Fit

1. The table shows the average high or low in September for eight cities in Canada. Use your line of best fit from Exploration 1 to complete the table.

City	Low (°C)	High (°C)
Churchill, Manitoba		9
Edmonton, Alberta		17
Montréal, Québec	10	
Prince Rupert, British Columbia		15
Regina, Saskatchewan		19
St. John's, Newfoundland	8	
Whitehorse, Yukon	3	
Winnipeg, Manitoba	6	

 2. Use your research skills to check the accuracy of the values you added to the table in question 1. Describe your findings.

3. a) The highest temperature ever recorded in Toronto in September was 37°C. Use your line of best fit to estimate the low temperature that day.
b) The lowest temperature ever recorded in Vancouver in September was 0°C. Use your line of best fit to estimate the high temperature that day.

3 Weather Experiment

1. Think of weather statistics that might be related. Examples might include data on temperatures or precipitation. Write a hypothesis to describe how you think the data might be related.

2. Use your research skills to find data you can use to test your hypothesis.

3. Use your data to draw a scatter plot. If a relationship exists, draw a line of best fit.

4. Use your scatter plot to write an inference based on the data.

5. Compare your hypothesis with your inference and explain any differences.

INVESTIGATING MATH

🤝 Scientific Data and the Line of Best Fit

1 Measuring Mass and Volume

You will need a material, such as Plasticine, that can be made into pieces of different sizes. An alternative is a set of rubber stoppers of different sizes. Make sure that the material you use sinks in water. Also, make sure that the material does not soak up water, like a sponge or paper towel.

1. Write a hypothesis to describe the relationship you expect between mass and volume for different-sized pieces of a material.

2. a) Measure the mass of a piece of the material.
b) Measure the volume of the same piece of material by using it to displace water in a graduated cylinder.

3. Repeat step 2 for seven more different-sized pieces of the same material. Record your data in a table.

4. a) If you used a material that floats in water, the volume measurements would be misleading. Explain why.
b) If you used a material that floats in water, how could you change the way the volume is measured to get accurate values?

2 Displaying the Data

1. a) Use your data to draw a scatter plot of mass versus volume. Draw a line of best fit.
b) What relationship does the scatter plot suggest?
c) Compare the relationship from part b) with your hypothesis in Exploration 1, above.

2. Choose a mass within the range of masses you measured. Interpolate to estimate the volume of a piece of the material with this mass.

3. Choose a volume greater than any of the volumes you measured. Extrapolate to estimate the mass of a piece of the material with this volume.

🤝 Internet Experiment

✒ 1 Designing a Survey

1. With your classmates, write a list of questions for a survey of students in other schools. The questions may be affected by the scope of the survey. For example, are you restricting the survey to grade 9 students, or can all students respond? Is the survey local, provincial, national, or worldwide?

2. Write a hypothesis for each question on the survey.

3. Write instructions about how the survey should be completed. For example, do you want each school to use a specific sampling technique? Do you want each school to organize the results in a certain way, or do you just want a list of the data? What is the deadline for completing the survey?

2 Carrying Out the Survey

🌏 **1.** Use your research skills to investigate how you can use the Internet to make teachers and students in other schools aware of your survey. Decide the way(s) you wish to use.

✒ **2.** Draft an announcement of your survey and use the Internet to find out which schools wish to participate. Give a deadline for responses.

3. Send the survey to the schools that wish to participate. Include the deadline date and the instructions for completing the survey and returning the results.

4. Collect the responses as they arrive. Store the data until after the deadline date.

✒ 3 Writing a Report

1. Analyze the responses of the participants. Display the data in the most suitable ways, including tables and graphs. Calculate measures of central tendency, if appropriate.

2. Write an inference based on the responses to each question in the survey.

3. Compare your hypothesis and your inference for each question. Explain any differences.

4. Write a report on your survey. To justify your conclusions, include your tables, graphs, calculations, and explanations. Indicate any questions for which you need more data to give a reliable conclusion. If there are any questions you wish you had worded differently, explain why. List any related questions that could be included in a follow-up survey.

5. Send a copy of your report to each school that participated in the survey.

4.12 Determining Relationships

Page 164 in Section 4.1 included the following list of eight stages involved in using statistics to investigate relationships.

• Pose a problem, that is, state a question that you want to answer, and identify the variable or variables.
• Make a hypothesis, which is a possible answer to the question.
• Decide how to collect the data.
• Collect and record the data.
• Organize and analyze the data using tables, graphs, and calculations.
• Use trends and relationships to make an inference, which is a generalization based on the data. Decided whether the inference supports or contradicts the hypothesis.
• Communicate the results of the investigation and justify your conclusions.
• Pose and/or solve problems related to the investigation.

You will use these stages in the following Exploration and problems.

Explore: Conduct an Experiment

If you stand 2 m from a wall and look through a paper tube at the wall, you can see an area of a certain height on the wall. If you move farther away from the wall, or closer to it, the height of the area you can see changes.

The following problem has been posed for you.

Is there a relationship between the height of the area you can see and your distance from the wall?

a) What are the variables in this problem?
b) Make a hypothesis about the relationship between the variables.
c) Conduct an investigation to answer the problem. Use multiple trials, if necessary.

Inquire

1. How did you collect and record the data?
2. How did you organize and analyze the data?
3. Make an inference about the relationship. Does the inference support or contradict the hypothesis?
4. a) What factors might affect the outcome of this investigation?
b) How could you redesign the investigation to account for these factors?
5. Communicate your results and justify your conclusions.
6. How might you vary this investigation to examine other relationships?
7. Pose and solve a problem related to this investigation.

When you conduct an investigation and plot the data, a graph like the one shown might result. All the data points, except point A, suggest there is a relationship between the variables. Point A is an outlying point or **outlier**. An outlier may exist because the data used to plot it are not correct, or because some unusual event has occurred. An outlier on a graph should be investigated and explained.

Applications and Problem Solving

B

In problems 1–6, the first stage, posing a problem, has been done for you. Each problem involves one variable. To solve each problem, use a primary or secondary data-gathering method. Use multiple trials when appropriate. Present your results to the class.

1. Rolling coins How far can you roll a toonie before it falls over?

2. Balancing act What is the average number of seconds a student can balance a ball on top of his or her head?

3. Eating habits What percent of the students in your school eat breakfast?

4. Class sizes How does the average class size in Ontario high schools compare with the average class size in high schools in other provinces?

5. School year What percent of parents of school-aged children think that the school year should be increased in length?

6. Library visits How often did people 13 years old and older visit a public library last year?

In problems 7-15, the first stage, posing a problem, has been done for you. Each problem involves two variables. To solve each problem, use a primary or secondary data-gathering method. Use multiple trials when appropriate. Present your results to the class.

7. Physiology Is there a relationship between the length of a person's ear and the circumference of the person's wrist?

8. Provinces Is there a relationship between the areas and the populations of Canada's provinces?

9. Cars Is there a relationship between the lengths and the widths of mid-size cars?

10. Olympic Games Is there a relationship between the number of nations represented at Summer Olympic Games and the number of competitors?

11. Great Lakes Is there a relationship between the lengths and the widths of the Great Lakes?

12. Cars Is there a relationship between the cost of a new car and the number of litres of gas used to drive 100 km?

13. Cities Is there a relationship between the areas and the populations of Canada's cities?

14. Sport-utility vehicles Is there a relationship between the heights and the widths of sport-utility vehicles?

15. Senators Is there a relationship between the number of senators that represent a province or territory and the population of the province or territory?

C

16. Related problem — one variable
a) Pose a problem that is related to one of the one-variable problems, 1 to 6.
b) With a classmate, complete the usual stages in solving the problem and communicating the solution.

17. Related problem — two variables
a) Pose a problem that is related to one of the two-variable problems, 7 to 15.
b) With a classmate, complete the usual stages in solving the problem and communicating the solution.

18. Independent study
a) Decide on a problem that interests you.
b) Solve the problem and communicate the solution. Explain how you used mathematical modelling to solve the problem.

TECHNOLOGY

Collecting Voltage Data Using CBL™

In this experiment, the remaining voltage of batteries will be measured.

For this experiment, you will need:

1 CBL unit
1 graphing calculator
1 TI voltage probe

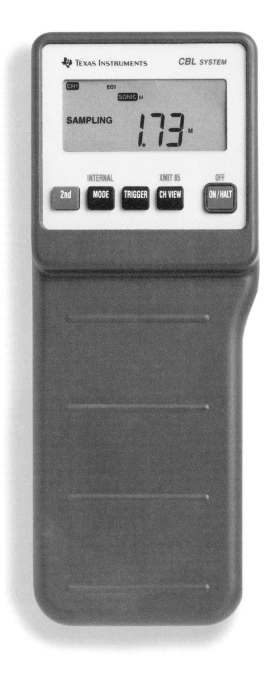

1. Press the MODE button on the CBL unit until the word MULTIMETER appears. Connect the voltage probe to the port labelled CH1.

2. Have members of the class remove one battery from their calculators. Use the probe to determine the remaining voltage of each battery. The value will be shown on the CBL display.

3. Record the data in one of the lists in the calculator.

4. Using the STAT PLOTS menu, select a boxplot and display the data as a box-and-whisker plot. Copy it into your notebook.

5. Use the TRACE feature and the left and right arrow keys to display the numbers in the five-number summary. Record the numbers on the graph in your notebook.

6. Write a paragraph to describe the data.

7. Why was it suggested that only one battery from each calculator be removed, instead of all four?

8. Suppose the experiment were repeated after the batteries were used for another month. How would the values in the five-number summary compare with today's values?

9. Would there be any difference in the results if the data were collected the day after all the batteries were recharged or new batteries were installed? Explain.

10. If any students in the class have portable cassette or CD players, remove one battery from each and measure the voltage. Add these values to the data and redraw the graph. Describe the data.

Collecting Jump-Height Data Using CBL™

1 Measuring Jump Heights

In this experiment, the jump heights for the students in the class will be measured.
For this experiment, you will need:
1 CBL unit
1 TI-82, TI-83, or other suitable graphing calculator with unit-to-unit link cable
1 TI light probe
1 flashlight

1. Load the program JUMP into the calculator, and follow the directions to connect the CBL to the light probe.

2. Place the flashlight and the light probe about 1 m apart, so that the flashlight is pointing at the light probe.

3. Take turns standing between the flashlight and the light probe and jumping into the air. The program will automatically store the height of each student's jump into list L2 of the calculator.

4. Using the STAT PLOTS menu, select a boxplot and display the data as a box-and-whisker plot. Copy it into your notebook.

5. Use the TRACE feature and the left and right arrow keys to display the numbers in the five-number summary. Record the numbers on the graph in your notebook.

6. Write a paragraph to describe the data.

7. a) If a student came late and wanted to participate, would this additional jump change the values of all of the statistics?
b) Would it be necessary to redraw the graph to include the jump for this student?

8. If the class practised jumping, and then repeated the experiment, greater jump heights should be obtained. How would this change be reflected in the values of the five-number summary?

TECHNOLOGY

Collecting Rebound-Height Data Using CBR™ or CBL™

1 Measuring Rebound Heights

In this experiment, the rebound heights of balls will be measured. For this experiment, you will need:
1 CBR unit, or 1 CBL unit with a motion detector
1 TI-82, TI-83, or other suitable graphing calculator with a unit-to-unit link cable
a variety of balls to bounce (Do not use a soft or felt-covered ball.)

1. If you use a CBR, set the UNITS? menu to METERS and run the BALL BOUNCE program. If you use a CBL and motion detector, load and run the BOUNCE program.

2. Hold the CBR or the motion detector under the top of a door frame. A classmate should hold a ball below the CBR or the motion detector, and should drop the ball when you are ready to take measurements. Make sure the plot shows at least 3 complete bounces.

3. Copy the following table. Move the cursor along the ball bounce plot, and record the starting height and the rebound heights in a table. Round heights to the nearest hundredth of a metre.

Starting Height (m)	
First Rebound Height (m)	
Second Rebound Height (m)	
Third Rebound Height (m)	

4. Copy and complete the following table. Complete the calculations listed in the first column to find each height ratio, to the nearest hundredth. Express each height ratio as a percent to find the rebound percent.

Calculation	Height Ratio	Rebound Percent
First Rebound Height / Starting Height		
Second Rebound Height / First Rebound Height		
Third Rebound Height / Second Rebound Height		

5. How do the rebound percents compare?

6. Calculate the average rebound percent. Then, copy and complete the following statement.

When the ball rebounded, its new height was ■% of the previous height.

7. Repeat the experiment using different types of balls. Is the rebound percent the same for all types? Explain.

Collecting Distance and Time Data Using CBR™ or CBL™

In these experiments, you will create distance-time motion plots.
For these experiments, you will need:
1 CBR unit, or 1 CBL unit with a motion detector
1 TI-82, TI-83, or other suitable graphing calculator with a unit-to-unit link cable
1 TI motion detector

1 Matching Distance-Time Graphs

1. Connect your calculator to a CBR, or to a CBL and motion detector. If you use a CBR, choose the DIST MATCH option from the APPLICATIONS menu, so that the calculator plots a graph of distance versus time. If you use a CBL and motion detector, load and run the program DTMATCH, so that the calculator plots a graph of distance versus time.

2. Place the CBR, or the CBL and motion detector, on a flat table or desk. Starting in front of the CBR, or the CBL and motion detector, walk toward or away from it to try to match the graph that the calculator drew.

3. Should you move away from or toward the CBR, or the CBL and motion detector, to match a part of the graph that slopes upward from left to right?

4. Should you move away from or toward the CBR, or the CBL and motion detector, to match a part of the graph that slopes downward from left to right?

5. What should you do to match a horizontal part of the graph?

6. With paper and pencil, sketch your own graph like the ones produced by the calculator program. Try to match your graph using the CBR or CBL.

 ## 2 Measuring and Graphing Distance and Time

1. For the CBR, use the option SETUP/ SAMPLE. Set the time to 5 s. For the CBL, load and run the program HIKER.

2. Work in pairs. If you use a CBR, take turns standing about 0.5 m from a wall, while holding both the calculator and the CBR. Point the CBR at the wall. If you use a CBL and motion detector, both students should stand side by side about 0.5 m from the wall. One student should point the motion detector at the wall, while the other student holds the CBL and the calculator.

3. If you use a CBR, walk at a steady rate away from the wall. If you use a CBL and motion detector, both students should walk away from the wall together at a steady rate. A graph of distance versus time is plotted. It should be close to a straight line. If the graph is not close to a straight line, repeat the experiment.

4. The time data are saved in L1 and the distance data in L2. Draw a scatter plot for the data.

5. Using the Y= editor, try to find an equation of a line that matches the scatter plot as closely as possible.

6. Use the linear regression instruction to draw the line of best fit. How does this line compare with the one you found in step 5?

7. Write a hypothesis in which you predict how the graph would change if, in step 3, the students
a) walked faster?   **b)** walked more slowly?

8. Write a hypothesis in which you predict how the graph would change if, in step 3, the students
a) sped up as they walked?
b) slowed down as they walked?
c) stopped for a few seconds?

9. Perform experiments to test your hypotheses and use your findings to write inferences.

PROBLEM SOLVING

4.13 Use A Table or Spreadsheet

Much of the information you see in newspapers and magazines is displayed in tables. A table or an organized list is an efficient way to arrange information and solve problems.

You are a member of an archaeological team working at a site in North Africa. The site, S, is 80 km north of a road that runs east-west. The closest point on the road is 100 km from a town, T, where you buy supplies. Your all-terrain vehicle can average 20 km/h across the sand between the site and the road. Your vehicle can travel 40 km/h on the road. Where should you meet the road so that the travel time to the town is as short as possible?

Understand the Problem

1. What information are you given?
2. What are you asked to find?

Think of a Plan

If you drive straight to the road at point A, you will take 4 h to reach the road. It will then take you 2.5 h on the road to get to the town. The total time is 6.5 h.
Suppose you aim for a point closer to the town and get on the road there. Will the total time to the town be shorter?

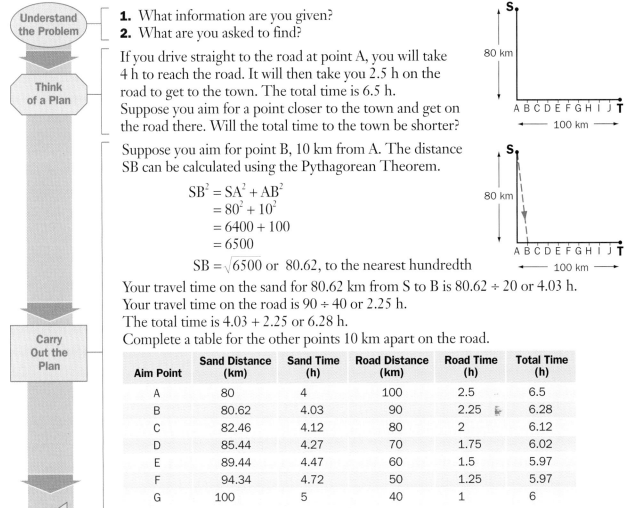

Suppose you aim for point B, 10 km from A. The distance SB can be calculated using the Pythagorean Theorem.

$$SB^2 = SA^2 + AB^2$$
$$= 80^2 + 10^2$$
$$= 6400 + 100$$
$$= 6500$$

$SB = \sqrt{6500}$ or 80.62, to the nearest hundredth

Your travel time on the sand for 80.62 km from S to B is 80.62 ÷ 20 or 4.03 h.
Your travel time on the road is 90 ÷ 40 or 2.25 h.
The total time is 4.03 + 2.25 or 6.28 h.

Carry Out the Plan

Complete a table for the other points 10 km apart on the road.

Aim Point	Sand Distance (km)	Sand Time (h)	Road Distance (km)	Road Time (h)	Total Time (h)
A	80	4	100	2.5	6.5
B	80.62	4.03	90	2.25	6.28
C	82.46	4.12	80	2	6.12
D	85.44	4.27	70	1.75	6.02
E	89.44	4.47	60	1.5	5.97
F	94.34	4.72	50	1.25	5.97
G	100	5	40	1	6

Look Back

Beyond point F, the total time is getting longer.
The shortest time is 5.97 h, if you meet the road at point E or point F.

Does the answer seem reasonable?

Another way to solve a problem of this type is to use a spreadsheet.

Set up a spreadsheet to calculate the shortest time.

	A	B	C	D	E	F	G
1	Aim	Distance From	Sand	Sand	Road	Road	Total
2	Point	Point A	Distance	Time	Distance	Time	Time
3		(km)	(km)	(h)	(km)	(h)	(h)
4	A	0	=sqrt(80^2+B4^2)	=C4/20	=100-B4	=E4/40	=D4+F4
5	B	=B4+10					
6	C						
7	D						
8	E						
9	F						
10	G						

Use a Table or Spreadsheet

1. Organize the given information in a table or set up a spreadsheet.
2. Complete the table with the results of your calculations or use the spreadsheet to complete the calculations.
3. Find the answer from the table or spreadsheet.
4. Check that your answer is reasonable.

Applications and Problem Solving

1. Survival course As part of a survival course, Laura has to run from point P to point Q. Point P is in the bush, 4 km from a road. The nearest point on the road is 10 km from point Q.

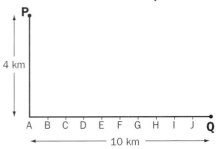

Laura estimates that she can average 6 km/h through the bush and 10 km/h on the road. At what point should she meet the road in order to reach point Q in the shortest possible time? Round distances to the nearest hundredth of a kilometre, and times to the nearest hundredth of an hour.

2. What is the total number of digits in all the whole numbers from 1 to 1999?

3. How many whole numbers from 1 to 500 begin or end in a 2?

4. Football In Canadian football, a team can score points in the following ways.

Single: 1 point
Safety: 2 points
Field Goal: 3 points
Touchdown: 6 points
Touchdown plus Convert: 7 points
Touchdown plus Conversion: 8 points

Make an organized list to determine the number of different ways a team could score 21 points without kicking a single.

5. Two whole numbers have a product of 240. The sum of the two numbers is an odd number. What are the possible pairs of whole numbers?

6. Measurement A rectangle has an area of 72 m². The width and length are whole numbers of metres.
a) What are the possible dimensions of the rectangle?
b) Which dimensions give the greatest perimeter?
c) Which dimensions give the smallest perimeter?

7. Vending machine A vending machine sells cold drinks. Each drink costs $1.00. The machine accepts only exact change. How many combinations of coins must the machine be programmed to accept if it accepts only
a) dollars and quarters?
b) dollars, quarters, and dimes?
c) dollars, quarters, dimes, and nickels?

8. Hockey The table shows part of the statistics for a hockey league after each team has played each of the other teams once. A win is worth 2 points, a tie 1 point, and a loss 0 points. Copy and complete the table.

Team	Games Played	Wins	Losses	Ties	Points
Aces		1			3
Bears			1	1	
Lions					
Pintos				2	2

9. Stock-car racing The manager of a stock-car-racing facility can sell 2000 tickets each evening when the price per ticket is $32. A researcher has informed the manager that, for every $1 decrease in the ticket price, 100 more tickets will be sold. Find the ticket price that will give the greatest revenue from ticket sales.

10. Palindromes Palindromes are words or numbers that read the same forward and backward. The word *noon* and the number 3223 are examples of palindromes. How many palindromes between 100 and 1000 are perfect squares?

11. Measurement How many isosceles triangles, with side lengths that are whole numbers of centimetres, have a perimeter of 20 cm?

12. Darts The regions of the dart target have point values of 2, 4, and 6, as shown. How many different point totals are possible, if three darts are thrown and each dart lands on the target?

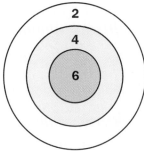

13. The sum of the digits in the number 629 is 6 + 2 + 9 or 17. How many whole numbers between 100 and 1000 have digits with a sum of 20?

14. Polyominoes Polyominoes are made from squares joined along entire sides. If polyominoes are made from squares with side lengths of 1 cm, how many different polyominoes can have a perimeter of 12 cm?

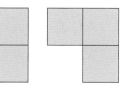

15. Running Céline and Ann-Marie ran around the same track in the same direction from the same starting point. Céline began running 6 min before Ann-Marie. Céline ran at 10 km/h, and Ann-Marie ran at 12 km/h. They ran until they had covered the same distance.
a) How far did they run?
b) For how many minutes did Céline run?

16. Service calls Suzanne and Marcus are both plumbers. Suzanne charges $55 for a service call, plus $35/h. Marcus charges $43 for a service call, plus $38/h. One day, they each made two service calls. If they earned the same amount of money that day, for how many hours did each plumber work?

17. Write a problem that can be solved using a table or organized list, or a spreadsheet. Have a classmate solve your problem.

Nations of the World

Use the *Nations* database from the Computer Data Bank to complete the following.

1 Labour Force in Asia

1. Find all the nations in Asia for which the population and labour force are available.

2. a) How could you calculate labour force as a percent of the population?
b) Add a calculated field for labour force as a percent of the population, rounding the percents to the nearest whole number.

3. Sort the records from least to greatest labour force as a percent of the population.

4. What is the median labour force as a percent of the population? Explain how you know.

5. What is the mode labour force as a percent of the population? How frequently does it occur?

6. Determine the mean labour force as a percent of the population, to the nearest whole number.

7. Compare the three measures of central tendency. Which do you consider to be the best measure? Explain.

8. Which is greater — the median labour force as a percent of the population for Asia or the labour force as a percent of the population for Canada? How much greater is it?

2 Educational Expenditure in Europe

The educational expenditures given are percents of the expenditures given.

1. Find all the nations in Europe for which the expenditures in billions of dollars and educational expenditures percents are available.

2. a) How could you calculate educational expenditures in billions of dollars?
b) Add a calculated field for educational expenditures in billions of dollars, rounding the number of billions to 3 decimal places.

3. Determine the three measures of central tendency for educational expenditures in billions of dollars. Compare the measures. Explain why they are quite different.

3 Exports and Imports

1. Find all the nations in Africa for which the values of exports and imports are available.

2. For a nation with a positive balance of trade, the value of exports is greater than the value of imports. How many nations in Africa have a positive balance of trade?

3. Copy, and paste, the exports and imports values for the records found in question 1 onto a spreadsheet. Then, create a scatter plot.

4. Describe any trends you observe.

5. Repeat questions 1 to 4 for another continent. Then, compare the scatter plots.

4 Standard of Living

Gross domestic product (GDP) measures the value of all goods and services produced in a nation. GDP per capita (per person) is a strong indicator of standard of living.

Based on GDP per capita, which country has the highest standard of living? the lowest? Where does Canada rank?

4.14 How Can We Model Word Use?

Did Sir Francis Bacon write some of the plays attributed to Shakespeare? This is one of the questions a stylometer tries to answer. Stylometry is the science of measuring written words. It is used to show that one particular person has written something.

Authors leave "fingerprints." The "fingerprints" of an author are verbal. From year to year, a certain author uses roughly the same percent of 5-letter words in written pieces. The same is true for words of any other length. But the percent of 5-letter words will likely differ from one author to another. When analyzing writing, the first task of a stylometer is to graph how someone writes.

The following excerpt is from a piece by Canadian humorist Stephen Leacock (1869–1944).

"I've been reading some very interesting statistics," he was saying to the other thinker.

"Ah, statistics!" said the other; "wonderful things, sir, statistics; very fond of them myself."

"I find, for instance," the first man went on, "that a drop of water is filled with little…with little…I forgot just what you call them…little — er — things, every cubic inch containing — er — containing…let me see…"

"Say a million," said the other thinker, encouragingly.

"Yes, a million, or possibly a billion…but at any rate, ever so many of them."

"Is it possible?" said the other. "But really, you know, there are wonderful things in the world. Now, coal…take coal…."

"Very good," said his friend, "let us take coal," settling back in his seat with the air of an intellect about to feed itself.

"Do you know that every ton of coal burnt in an engine will drag a train of cars as long as…I forget the exact length, but say a train of cars of such and such a length, and weighing, say so much…from…from…hum! for the moment the exact distance escapes me…drag it from…"

"From here to the moon," suggested the other.

"Ah, very likely; yes, from here to the moon. Wonderful, isn't it?"

"But the most stupendous calculation of all, sir, is in regard to the distance from the earth to the sun. Positively, sir, a cannon-ball — er — fired at the sun…"

"Fired at the sun," nodded the other, approvingly, as if he had often seen it done.

"And travelling at the rate of …of…"

"Of three cents a mile," hinted the listener.

"No, no, you misunderstand me — but travelling at a fearful rate, simply fearful, sir, would take a hundred million — no, a hundred billion — in short would take a scandalously long time in getting there —"

1 Modelling Word Use

1. To draw a word-use graph to show how Stephen Leacock wrote, copy and complete the table for the excerpt.

Word Length in Letters	Frequency	
	Number of Words	Percent of Total
1		
2		
3		
4		
5		
6		
7		
8		
9		
10		
11		
12		
13+		

2. Using a grid like the one shown, draw a broken-line graph of the frequency (percent of total) versus the word length.

2 Applying the Model

1. Choose a newspaper or magazine article, and use an excerpt to construct a word-use graph. Do not count any proper names.

2. Compare the graph with the graph you drew for Stephen Leacock. Describe the similarities and differences.

3. Construct a word-use graph for something you have written. Do not count any proper names.

4. Compare the graph for your writing with the graph for
   a) Stephen Leacock's writing
   b) a classmate's writing

3 Extending the Model

1. a) Write a hypothesis about whether the graph of your writing depends on the subject you write about.
b) Carry out an experiment to test your hypothesis.
c) Use your results to write an inference.
d) Compare your hypothesis with your inference.

2. What could you do to improve the accuracy of the graphs for Stephen Leacock's writing and your writing?

Review

State whether each of the following is a primary or a secondary data-gathering method.

1. reading baseball statistics in a newspaper

2. measuring the blood pressure of hospital patients

3. Fresh water a) State a hypothesis for the question: "Which Canadian province contains the greatest area of fresh water?"
b) Use a secondary data-gathering method to test your hypothesis.

4. Rain On the average, it rains on 40% of spring and summer days in Charlottetown, Prince Edward Island. Predict the number of days it rains in June in Charlottetown.

4.2 *In questions 5 and 6, identify the population and suggest a sampling procedure that could be used to answer the questions.*

5. Eating habits How many high school students in Ontario are vegetarians?

6. Vacations What is the country outside North America that Canadians most like to visit?

7. School teams Design a simple random sampling procedure to select students in your school to study the question: Should all students be required to pay $10 a year to support school teams?

8. Part-time jobs Design a systematic sampling procedure to select high school students in your city or town to study the question: What is the best part-time job for high school students?

9. Running shoes Design a stratified sampling procedure to study the question: What percent of the people in Ontario own running shoes but do not run?

10. Extra-terrestrials Describe a non-probability sampling technique to study the question: Has the Earth had visitors from outer space?

4.3 *In questions 11–13, identify the type(s) of bias in each situation.*

11. Swimming pool A neighbourhood group trying to get support for a new swimming pool puts petition forms in all variety stores in the neighbourhood.

12. Teen drivers A survey question is worded as follows: Teenagers drive too fast. Should the cars they drive have speed regulators?

13. Mail delivery A survey mailed to every hundredth person in the telephone book asked the following question: Should there be mail delivery twice a day?

14. Radio listening times A radio station conducted a survey to determine the time of day most people listened to the radio. A simple random sample was taken from the telephone book. People were surveyed by telephone between 09:00 and 16:00 on weekdays in May.
a) Identify the population that is of interest.
b) Describe the bias in the sample design.
c) Design another sampling method that would more accurately represent the population.

4.5 **15. Sailing** These are Stephan's marks on nine sailing tests.

 35   86   88   37   90   41   12   89   37

a) Determine the mean, median, and mode of the data.
b) Which of the three measures best represents Stephan's sailing ability?

4.6 **16. Driving speeds** The following speeds, in kilometres per hour, were measured for cars passing through a 50 km/h zone.

44   50   52   63   46   50   54   56
59   63   56   39   44   45   51

a) Display the data on a stem-and-leaf plot.
b) What was the median speed?

4.7 **17. Driving test** Draw a box-and-whisker plot to represent the following driving test scores.

85   86   60   55   73   75   81   83   84
98   56   64   68   66   88   90   92

18. Swimming test Tara scored 78 on a swimming test. The scores of the other students in the class were as follows.

56 57 66 68 70 72
74 78 80 82 84 88

In what percentile was Tara's score?

4.8 19. Comparing weather The table gives the average daily high temperatures, in degrees Celsius, in Montréal and Alice Springs for each month of one year.

	Temperature (°C)	
Month	Montréal	Alice Springs
Jan	–3	38
Feb	0	33
Mar	9	30
Apr	11	26
May	19	19
Jun	22	20
Jul	25	21
Aug	22	24
Sep	18	31
Oct	12	33
Nov	0	35
Dec	–2	36

a) Display the data as 2 broken-line graphs on the same set of axes.

b) Is the summer warmer in Montréal or Alice Springs? Explain.

4.10 20. Vintage airplanes The table shows the
4.11 wingspans and lengths of some vintage airplanes.

Plane (Year built)	Length (m)	Wingspan (m)
Flyer (1903)	6.43	12.29
June Bug (1908)	9.1	13.89
Demoiselle (1909)	6.1	5.5
Blériot XI (1909)	8	7.8
Deperdussin Racer (1912)	6.1	6.65
Grand (1913)	20.02	28.02
Junkers J-1 (1915)	9.04	16.8
Fokker DVII (1918)	7.01	8.94
Ford Trimotor (1926)	15.19	22.6
Lockheed Vega (1927)	8.38	12.5

a) Display the data on a scatter plot of wingspan versus length.
b) Draw a line of best fit.
c) Interpolate the wingspan of an airplane with a length of 10 m.
d) Extrapolate the length of an airplane with a wingspan of 30 m.

Exploring Math

Scheduling Games

A round robin is a way of scheduling games so that each team plays every other team once.

1. Four basketball teams are entered in a round robin. A table can be used to decide which teams play each other in each round. The 1s in the table show that, in round 1, the Lions play the Bears, and the Eagles play the Tigers.

	Lions	Bears	Eagles	Tigers
Lions		1		
Bears	1			
Eagles				1
Tigers			1	

a) Copy the table and complete it using the numbers 2 and 3 to show the teams that play each other in round 2 and in round 3.
b) Keeping in mind that two teams play in each game, decide how many games will be played.

2. Three soccer teams are entered in a round robin.

	Giants	Sting	Colts
Giants		1	
Sting	1		
Colts			

Because 3 is an odd number, one team will get a bye in each round and not play. As the table shows, the Colts get a bye in round 1.
a) Copy and complete the table.
b) How many rounds are needed?
c) How many games will be played?

3. a) Copy and complete the table for round robins with different numbers of teams.

Number of Teams	Number of Rounds Needed	Number of Games Played
2		
3		
4		
5		
6		

b) How many rounds would be needed for 12 teams? 19 teams? 50 teams?
c) How many games would be played for 12 teams? 19 teams? 50 teams?

Chapter Check

1. Commonwealth countries **a)** Write a hypothesis for the question: "How many countries are members of the Commonwealth?"
b) Use a method of your choice to test your hypothesis.
c) State whether your data-gathering method is primary or secondary.

2. Car colours In a survey of 25 students in a school, 3 chose red as their favourite car colour. If there were 1200 students at the school, and the sample was representative, predict how many students at the school would have chosen red as their favourite car colour.

3. Favourite videos Describe how you could use each of the following sampling methods to find the favourite type of video among students in your school.
a) simple random sampling
b) systematic sampling
c) stratified sampling

4. Politics **a)** Describe a non-probability sampling technique that might be used to study the following question.
What percent of Canadians would like to be a Member of Parliament?
b) If you drew inferences from the results in part a), how reliable would the inferences be? Explain.

In questions 5 and 6, identify the type(s) of bias in each situation.
5. Advertising A survey question reads as follows.

Research shows that most people would rather watch television than listen to the radio or read a newspaper. Is television the best place to advertise?

6. Education A newspaper reporter asked people entering a bank on a Wednesday afternoon the following question.

Should elementary school students be allowed to use calculators in math class?

7. Test scores Find the mean, median, and mode of these test scores.
64 85 86 70 72 80 83 72 65 80

8. Music test Lucia got 62 on a music test. The marks of the other students were as follows.
50 56 58 60 62 62
64 68 70 78 80
In what percentile was Lucia's mark?

9. Passenger cars The table shows the numbers of sales of new passenger cars in Canada in different years.

Year	New Passenger Cars (thousands)
1989	985
1990	885
1991	873
1992	798
1993	739
1994	749
1995	670
1996	661
1997	739

a) Display the data on a scatter plot of new passenger cars versus year.
b) Draw a line of best fit.
c) Describe the relationship between the variables.
d) Use the graph to estimate the number of new passenger cars sold in Canada in 1985.
e) Use the graph to predict the year in which there will be no sales of new passenger cars in Canada. Do you think the prediction is valid? Explain.

Using the Strategies

1. Asterisks The rectangular shapes are made from asterisks.

Diagram 1   2   3

a) How many asterisks will there be in the 4th rectangle? the 5th rectangle?
b) How many asterisks will there be in the nth rectangle?
c) How many asterisks will there be in the 26th rectangle?
d) Which rectangle is made from 92 asterisks?

2. Picture border A picture 20 cm by 20 cm is to be bordered by 1-cm squares. How many squares are needed for the border?

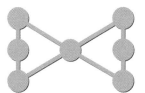

3. Number puzzle Place the digits 1, 2, 3, 4, 5, 6, and 7 in the circles so that the sum of each line of connected circles is the same.

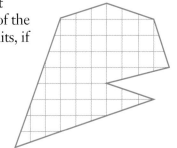

4. Cruise departure The ship will leave the harbour at 08:30. You have to be on board 20 min before departure. It takes 25 min to drive to the ship from your hotel. You must allow 15 min to check out of the hotel. It will take you 20 min to pack. You need half an hour to eat breakfast and at least 45 min to shower and dress. For what time should you place your wake-up call?

5. Islands About how many islands are there in Ontario?

6. Time How many hours are in 1 000 000 s?

7. Buying chicken Chicken pieces come in boxes of 6, 9, and 20. You can buy 21 pieces by buying two boxes of 6 pieces and one box of 9 pieces.

$$6 + 6 + 9 = 21$$

Can you buy
a) 41 pieces?   **b)** 42 pieces?
c) 43 pieces?   **d)** 44 pieces?

8. Railway crossing A train travelling at 90 km/h passed a car sitting at a railway crossing. It took 45 s for the train to pass. How long was the train, in metres?

9. Walking Sketch a graph that shows the distance you walk in a school day. Label the vertical axis "Distance Walked" and the horizontal axis "Time of Day." Represent a complete 24-h period, starting at midnight. Compare your graph with a classmate's and explain any differences.

10. Sentence Copy the sentence. Then, fill in the blank with a number, written in words, to make the sentence true.

This sentence has ▓▓▓▓ letters.

11. Measurement Calculate the area of the figure, in square units, if each grid square represents 1 square unit.

12. Time zones What time is it at the North Pole? Explain using time zones.

13. Canadian provinces If the Canadian province with the greatest area had the shape of a square, what would be the length of each side, to the nearest kilometre?

Chapter 1

Estimate, and then calculate.

1. $347 + 786 + 88$ **2.** $47.2 + 0.98 - 17.6$

3. 53×82 **4.** 5.3×220

5. $1820 \div 35$ **6.** $46.8 \div 7.2$

7. Evaluate for $x = 3$ and $y = 5$.

a) $4x + 6y$ **b)** $2x + 4xy$

c) $22 - y - x$ **d)** $8y - 6x - 7$

8. Evaluate $5g - 3$ when g equals

a) 7.1 **b)** 8.3 **c)** 10.2

Evaluate.

9. $4^3 - 5^2$ **10.** $3^4 - 2^4$

11. $8^2 \div 2^4$ **12.** 7×3^3

13. Evaluate for $x = 3$ and $y = 2$.

a) $x^2 + y^4$ **b)** $(x - y)^3$

c) $5x^2 - 3xy$ **d)** $6y^2 + 4xy$

Simplify. Express each answer in exponential form.

14. $3^4 \times 3^5$ **15.** $6^8 \div 6^5$

16. $(4^3)^3$ **17.** $x^2 \times x^6$

18. $x^7 \div x^4$ **19.** $(x^4)^5$

Evaluate.

20. $-2 + 4 + 5 - 1$ **21.** $1 - 6 - 7 - 8$

22. $7 - (-6) - 3 + 9$ **23.** $-5 + 2 - (-3) + 4$

24. -9×8 **25.** $-6 \times (-3)$

26. $-24 \div 6$ **27.** $-40 \div (-10)$

28. $(-3)^2$ **29.** -2^4

Evaluate.

30. $(-2^3)^2$ **31.** $(-5)^5 \div (-5)^3$

32. $12^2 \div (-3)^2$ **33.** $(1.5)^2(-4)^2$

Evaluate.

34. $8 \times (-5) - 3^2 - 1$ **35.** $(7 - 4)^2 \times (-3 + 5)^3$

36. $-7 \times 3 - 8$ **37.** $(-16 + 13) \div (-3)$

38. $5 \times (-2) - 32 \div 8$ **39.** $4 \times (-2)^2 + 5 \times (-3)$

40. Evaluate for $x = -3$ and $y = -2$.

a) $4x + 6y$ **b)** $5xy$

c) $-2(y - x)$ **d)** $3x^2 - 6xy$

e) $x^3 - y^3$ **f)** $x^2 - 3xy - y^2$

Chapter 2

Write each ratio in simplest form.

1. $12:4$ **2.** 15 to 60 **3.** 3 to 24

4. $\dfrac{42}{14}$ **5.** $\dfrac{16}{40}$ **6.** $18:8$

Write each ratio in simplest form in 3 ways.

7. 8 days to 2 weeks   **8.** 3 years to 30 months

Find an equivalent ratio.

9. $5:2$ **10.** 20 to 15 **11.** $16:30$

State whether the ratios in each pair are equivalent.

12. $15:3,\ 5:1$ **13.** $16:20,\ 5:6$

Solve for x.

14. $\dfrac{x}{3} = \dfrac{18}{27}$ **15.** $\dfrac{5}{1.2} = \dfrac{10}{x}$

16. $6:8 = x:0.4$ **17.** $0.8:1.5 = 4:x$

18. Telescope A telescope costs $350. Thao and her brother share the cost in a ratio of 4:3. What is Thao's share?

19. Centipede A centipede travels at a speed of 0.5 m/s. How long will it take to travel 100 m?

20. Comparison shopping Decide which is the better value.

a) 150 envelopes for $9.00 or 50 envelopes for $3.50

b) 19 L of gas for $11.97 or 31 L of gas for $18.91

Write as percents.

21. 0.34 **22.** 0.07 **23.** 1.65

24. $\dfrac{11}{25}$ **25.** $\dfrac{13}{20}$ **26.** $\dfrac{5}{4}$

27. $3:5$ **28.** $7:10$ **29.** $7:16$

Write each percent as a decimal.

30. 13% **31.** 24.6% **32.** 4.6%

33. 0.9% **34.** 200% **35.** 124%

36. What percent is 30 of 120?

37. Markup The cost price of a jacket for a retailer was $150. The retailer marked it up by 40%. What was the selling price before taxes?

38. Investment Find the simple interest on $8000 invested for 3 years at 5% per year.

Chapter 3

Write in scientific notation.

1. 340 000 **2.** 13 000 000

3. 0.000 006 **4.** 0.000 56

Write in standard form.

5. 4.7×10^6 **6.** 7.8×10^{-7}

Calculate. Write each answer in scientific notation.

7. $(5.2 \times 10^3)(4.5 \times 10^{-6})$

8. $(3.6 \times 10^{-5}) \div (1.8 \times 10^{-7})$

Simplify.

9. $3^5 \times 3^{-2}$ **10.** $5^{-3} \div 5^{-7}$

11. $(2^5)^{-3}$ **12.** $((-4)^{-1})^{-4}$

Evaluate.

13. $2^0 \times 2^4$ **14.** $5^3 \div 5^4$

15. $(2^{-2})^{-2}$ **16.** $3^{-3} \div 3^{-4}$

Calculate.

17. $-1.2 \times (-5.5)$ **18.** -3.2^2

19. $-\dfrac{3}{8} \times \dfrac{16}{5}$ **20.** $-1\dfrac{1}{2} \times (-2\dfrac{1}{4})$

21. $8.6 \div (-0.2)$ **22.** $-4.8 \div (-3.5)$

23. $-\dfrac{4}{5} \div (-2)$ **24.** $-\dfrac{5}{3} \div \dfrac{5}{6}$

25. $-19 + 15\dfrac{3}{4}$ **26.** $3\dfrac{2}{5} - (-5)$

27. $-4.8 - 3.7$ **28.** $6.6 - 8.9$

29. Stock market The value of a Silverado share increased by $0.15 one day. If Tom's Silverado shares increased in value by $30 that day, how many Silverado shares did he have?

Evaluate.

30. $2(3.7 - 1.2) \div 0.5$ **31.** $2.1 \times 10 \div 100$

32. $\dfrac{2}{3} \times \dfrac{3}{5} - 6$ **33.** $(13 - 10)^3 \div \dfrac{1}{3}$

Estimate. Then, calculate to the nearest tenth.

34. $\sqrt{515}$ **35.** $-\sqrt{2366}$ **36.** $\sqrt{0.013}$

37. Measurement A square has an area of 40 m². Calculate its side length and its perimeter, to the nearest tenth of a metre.

Chapter 4

1. a) Write a hypothesis for the question: "What percent of the students in your school like camping?"
b) Describe how you would test your hypothesis.

2. Identify the population and suggest a sampling procedure to answer the question: "What percent of Canadian adults can swim?"

3. Identify the type of bias in the following situation: In order to determine if there was support for a new public art gallery, a radio station conducted a survey on its web site.

4. Winter Olympics The table gives the total numbers of medals won by the top ten countries at the Winter Olympics in Nagano, Japan. Calculate the mean, median, mode, and range of the data.

Country	Medals
Germany	29
Norway	25
Russia	18
Austria	17
Canada	15
United States	13
Finland	12
Netherlands	11
Italy	10
Japan	10

5. Test scores Draw a box-and-whisker plot to represent the following history test scores.
56 77 84 92 66 90 59 60 74 80
63 71 83 90 54 70 88 50 81

6. Science test Paul scored 88 on a science test. The scores of the other students were as follows. In what percentile was Paul's score?
77 66 91 88 77 55 68 68 88 70
65 68 91 93 60 57 68 72 66

7. Education The table shows the changes in the percent of Canadian adults with some post-secondary education but no university degree.

Year	1976	1981	1986	1991	1996
Percent of Adults	24	28	30	32	34

a) Display the data on a scatter plot.
b) Draw the line of best fit.
c) Use the graph to estimate the percent of Canadian adults in this category in the year 2010.

CHAPTER 5

Linear and Non-Linear Relations

How Can We Model the Flight of an Object?

A batted or thrown baseball, the water arcs from a fountain, the trails of rocks spewed from a volcano, and the trails of rockets in a fireworks display all follow a curved path that is sometimes called gravity's rainbow curve. A red flare fired from a boat in an emergency situation also traces gravity's rainbow curve.

Suppose a red flare is fired at an angle of 70° to the horizontal. The table gives the height of the flare, in metres, and the time, in seconds, since it was fired.

Time (s)	Height (m)
0	0
1	35
2	60
3	75
4	80
5	75
6	60
7	35
8	0

1. Plot the height versus the time, and join the points with a smooth curve.

2. What is the maximum height reached by the flare?

3. If the flare burns until it hits the water, for how many seconds does it burn?

 4. Why is the trail of a rocket in a fireworks display called gravity's rainbow curve?

5. List three events or situations, not mentioned above, that might be modelled by gravity's rainbow curve.

In Modelling Math — Sports on pages 288 and 289, you will learn about modelling the flight of a punted football.

GETTING STARTED

Using Graphs

1 A Grid Game

1. Draw 2 grids like the one shown. Mark each of them from 0 to 8 along the horizontal and vertical axes.

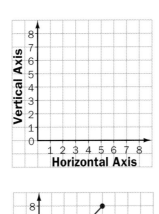

2. Use 1 of the 2 grids and draw 4 vehicles on it, as horizontal, vertical, or diagonal straight lines. Vehicles should be drawn through the following numbers of points on the grid.
Truck: 5 points
Bus: 4 points
Van: 3 points
Car: 2 points

3. Flip a coin to decide who will begin the game.

4. Call out a pair of numbers such as (4, 5), where 4 is the value along the horizontal axis and 5 is the value along the vertical axis. Your opponent should tell you if that pair successfully locates a vehicle. For example, the location of the van shown in the diagram includes (4, 3), (4, 4), and (4, 5), in any order.

If you successfully locate a point on a vehicle, you take another turn. Once all of the points of a vehicle have been called, it is removed from the game. If you call out a point that is not part of a vehicle, your opponent takes a turn. Keep track of your "hits" and "misses" on the second grid. The winner is the first player to remove all of the opponent's vehicles.

2 Writing Statements

Write as many statements as you need to describe fully the information shown on each graph.

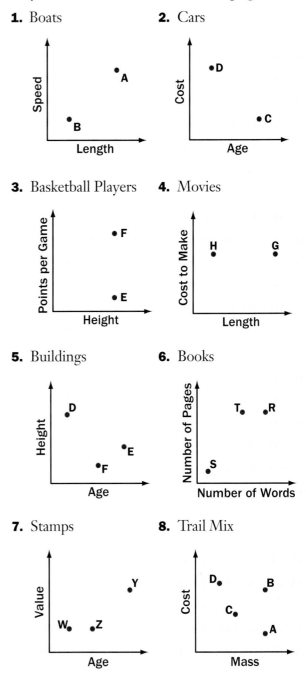

1. Boats

2. Cars

3. Basketball Players

4. Movies

5. Buildings

6. Books

7. Stamps

8. Trail Mix

Warm Up

Copy and complete each table of values.

1.

x	x + 7
13	
5	
–2	
–5	

2.

x	x – 4
5	
2	
–3	
–5	

3.

b	5b
7	
4	
0	
–6	

4.

n	n + 3
12	
6	
–18	
–30	

Study the patterns. Write an equation to show how y is related to x for each table.

5.

x	2	1	0	–1
y	2	1	0	–1

6.

x	1	2	3	4
y	2	4	6	8

7.

x	2	3	4	5
y	–6	–9	–12	–15

8.

x	2	1	0	–1
y	3	2	1	0

9.

x	2	1	0	–1
y	7	6	5	4

10.

x	2	1	0	–1
y	–1	–2	–3	–4

11.

x	4	3	2	1
y	2	1.5	1	0.5

12.

x	2	3	4	5
y	–2	–3	–4	–5

13.

x	2	3	4	5
y	4	9	16	25

14.

x	1	2	3	4
y	–1	–8	–27	–64

Mental Math

Equations and Expressions

Solve for x.

1. $x + 1 = 4$ **2.** $x - 15 = 9$

3. $x + 3 = -9$ **4.** $x - 2 = -15$

5. $x + 7 = -2$ **6.** $x - 9 = 15$

7. $x + 2 = -8$ **8.** $x - 3 = 12$

9. $2x = 12$ **10.** $3x = -18$

11. $\dfrac{x}{2} = 6$ **12.** $\dfrac{x}{4} = -1$

13. $6 + x = -2$ **14.** $9 - x = 3$

15. $14 = 2 + x$ **16.** $12 = 15 - x$

17. Evaluate each expression for $x = 2$.
a) $12 - x$ **b)** $x + 17$ **c)** $3x$

18. Evaluate each expression for $x = -2$.
a) $9 + x$ **b)** $7 - x$ **c)** $5x$

Multiplying in Two Steps

It is sometimes easier to multiply two numbers mentally by factoring one of them and multiplying in two steps.

$$55 \times 16 = 55 \times 2 \times 8$$
$$= 110 \times 8$$
$$= 880$$

Estimate
$$50 \times 20 = 1000$$

or

$$55 \times 16 = 11 \times 5 \times 16$$
$$= 11 \times 80$$
$$= 880$$

Estimate
$$50 \times 20 = 1000$$

Multiply.

1. 9×18 **2.** 8×17 **3.** 12×11

4. 15×13 **5.** 14×14 **6.** 16×15

7. 13×16 **8.** 25×28 **9.** 12×45

10. 17×24 **11.** 35×26 **12.** 27×27

13. Explain why the method of multiplying in two steps works.

14. The product of 23×37 cannot be found more easily in two steps. Explain why.

Relationships in Polygons

In this section, you will make polygons from squares. The squares must be joined along whole edges.

These polygons are allowed.

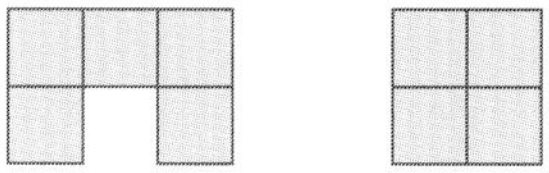

These polygons are not allowed.

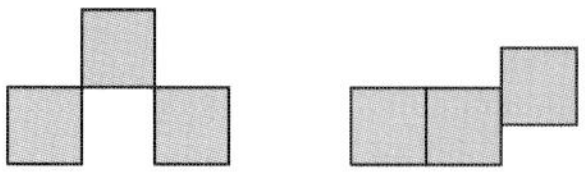

1 Polygons From 8 Squares

1. Polygon A is made up of 8 squares. The area, A, of the polygon is 8 square units. A common vertex within a polygon is called an **interior point**. Polygon A has 2 interior points, marked 1 and 2. The perimeter, P, of the polygon is 14 units. Half the perimeter, H, is 7 units.

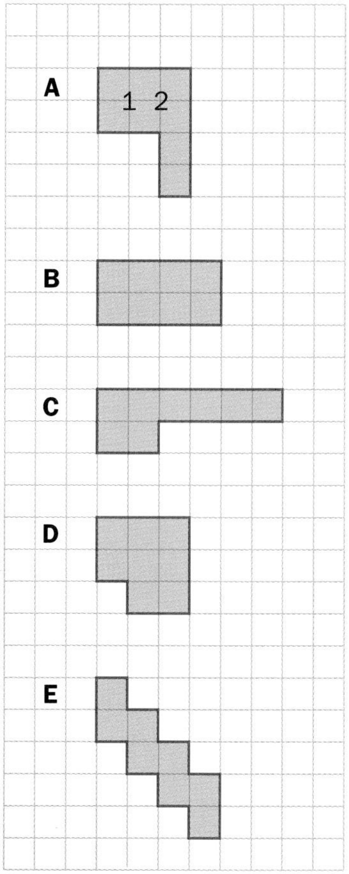

Copy and complete the table for the other polygons shown.

Polygon	Area (A)	Interior Points (I)	Perimeter (P)	Half the Perimeter (H)
A	8	2	14	7
B				
C				
D				
E				

2. Describe the relationship between half the perimeter, H, the area, A, and the number of interior points, I.

3. Write an expression for H in terms of A and I.

$H = $ ▒▒

4. Write an expression for the perimeter, P, in terms of A and I.

$P = $ ▒▒

5. Draw 4 more polygons made up of 8 squares. Use the polygons to test your expressions.

2 Other Polygons

1. On grid paper, draw 7 different polygons made up of 6, 7, 9, 10, 11, 12, and 13 squares. Draw at least one polygon with 4 interior points, one with 3, one with 2, one with 1, and one with no interior points.

2. Name the polygons from A to G. Then, copy and complete the table.

Polygon	Area (A)	Interior Points (I)	Perimeter (P)
A			
B			
C			
D			
E			
F			
G			

3. Use your earlier expression for P in terms of A and I to calculate the perimeter of each polygon. Does the expression work for all the polygons?

3 Using an Expression

1. Use your expression for P in terms of A and I to calculate the perimeter of a polygon with an area of 16 square units and with 5 interior points. Check your answer by drawing the polygon and finding the perimeter.

2. Calculate the perimeter of a polygon made up of 50 squares and with 10 interior points.

3. Calculate the perimeter of a polygon made up of 200 squares and with 1 interior point.

5.1 Relations as Ordered Pairs

Halley's comet enters our solar system about every 75 years. It will return next in the year 2061. A comet's tail always points away from the sun. There is a relationship between the length of the tail and the comet's distance from the sun. The closer the comet is to the sun, the longer the tail.

There are many examples of how things relate or depend on each other. For example:
• The cost of a concert ticket depends on the popularity of the group.
• The distance travelled over time in a car depends on the speed of the car.
• The number of people in a mall depends on the time of day.

Mathematics has been described as the study of patterns or how numbers relate to each other.

Explore: Look for a Pattern

One cube has a surface area of 6 square units. Two cubes, attached as shown, have a surface area of 10 square units. Three cubes can be attached in the same way. Copy and complete the table.

Number of Cubes	Surface Area
1	6 square units
2	10 square units
⋮	
7	

Inquire

1. What is the surface area of 3 attached cubes? 4 attached cubes? 7 attached cubes?

2. What is the pattern in the surface area column?

3. Write the results from the table as a set of ordered pairs. For 1 cube, the ordered pair is (1, 6), where the first number is the number of cubes and the second number is the surface area.

4. What is the surface area of 8 attached cubes? 9 attached cubes?

5. Describe in words the relationship between the number of cubes and the surface area.

6. Let n represent the number of cubes. Write an equation in the form $S =$ ▮▮▮▮ to find the surface area from the number of cubes.

7. Use your equation to calculate the surface area for 20 cubes; 50 cubes.

8. For the cubes and surface area,
a) what does the ordered pair (15, 62) mean?
b) why does the ordered pair (10, 10) have no meaning for this relationship?

A **relation** is a set of ordered pairs. They are called ordered pairs because the order of the two values or **elements** is important. The set of the first elements in the ordered pairs is called the **domain** of the relation. The set of the second elements is called the **range** of the relation.

For example, for the relation (1, 2), (2, 4), (3, 6), the domain is {1, 2, 3}, and the range is {2, 4, 6}.

A relation can be described in other ways than as a set of ordered pairs. Some of these ways are:
• by a table of values
• in words
• by an equation

Many relations in mathematics are expressed as formulas with two or more variables. Here are some of the familiar ones.

$$A = l \times w \qquad P = 2(l + w) \qquad A = \frac{1}{2}b \times h$$

Example 1 Describing Relations
Use the equation $x + y = 5$.
a) Describe the relation in words.
b) Complete a table of values for the domain {2, 1, 0, −1, −2}.
c) Write the relation as a set of ordered pairs.
d) What is the range?

Solution
a) The sum of the x- and y-values equals five.
b) Calculate the y-values.   Complete the table of values.

$x + y = 5$
$2 + 3 = 5$
$1 + 4 = 5$
$0 + 5 = 5$
$-1 + 6 = 5$
$-2 + 7 = 5$

x	y
2	3
1	4
0	5
−1	6
−2	7

c) The set of ordered pairs is (2, 3), (1, 4), (0, 5), (−1, 6), (−2, 7).
d) The range is {3, 4, 5, 6, 7}.

Example 2   Describing Relations

Use the equation $y = 2x + 1$.
a) Describe the relation in words.
b) Complete a table of values for the domain $\{2, 1, 0, -1, -2\}$.
c) Write the relation as a set of ordered pairs.
d) What is the range?

Solution
a) The value of y is two times the value of x, plus one.
b) Calculate the y-values.   Complete the table of values.

$2x + 1$
$2(2) + 1$
$2(1) + 1$
$2(0) + 1$
$2(-1) + 1$
$2(-2) + 1$

x	y
2	5
1	3
0	1
-1	-1
-2	-3

c) The set of ordered pairs is $(2, 5)$, $(1, 3)$, $(0, 1)$, $(-1, -1)$, $(-2, -3)$.
d) The range is $\{5, 3, 1, -1, -3\}$.

Example 3   The Gemini Project

The Gemini project involves Canada, Argentina, Brazil, the United Kingdom, Chile, the United States, and Australia. These countries cooperated to build two 8-m telescopes. One telescope is on Mauna Kea in Hawaii, and the other is on Cerro Pachon in Chile. There is a relationship between the amount of money a country invested and the number of nights in a year that the country's astronomers get to use the two telescopes.

Country	Money Invested (millions of dollars)	Total Nights on the Two Telescopes
Argentina	7.5	15
Brazil	7.5	15
Australia	15	30
Chile	15	30
Canada	45	90
United Kingdom	75	150
United States	150	300

a) Write the relation as a set of ordered pairs.
b) What is the domain? the range?
c) How many nights on the telescopes does each 1 million dollars provide?
d) Write an equation in the form $N = \blacksquare m$ to describe the relation, where N is the number of nights on the telescopes, and m is the number of millions of dollars invested.
e) Describe the relation in words.

Solution
a) (7.5, 15), (15, 30), (45, 90), (75, 150), (150, 300)
b) The domain is {7.5, 15, 45, 75, 150}.
The range is {15, 30, 90, 150, 300}.
c) As 7.5 million dollars provides 15 nights, 1 million dollars
provides $\dfrac{15}{7.5}$ or 2 nights.
d) $N = 2m$
e) For every million dollars invested, a country's astronomers get
two nights per year on the telescopes.

Practice

A

1. Describe the relationship between the
following.
a) the length of a tree's shadow on a sunny day
and the time of day
b) the number of greeting cards sold by a store
and the month of the year
c) the number of stars you can see on a clear
night and where you live

For each relation,
a) *write the domain and range*
b) *describe the relation in words*
2. (2, 6), (3, 9), (5, 15), (8, 24)
3. (9, 7), (12, 10), (18, 16), (32, 30)
4. (4, 9), (5, 9), (7, 9), (21, 9)
5. (3, 4), (3, 7), (3, 11), (3, 30)

Use each of the following equations.
a) *Describe the relation in words.*
b) *Copy and complete the table of values for the
domain shown.*
c) *Write the relation as a set of ordered pairs.*
d) *State the range.*
6. $x + y = 4$

x	y
2	
1	
0	
−1	
−2	

7. $x - y = 1$

x	y
3	
4	
5	
6	
7	

8. $m + n = -2$

m	n
2	
1	
0	
−1	
−2	

9. $s - t = 3$

s	t
4	
3	
2	
1	
0	

Use each of the following equations.
a) *Describe the relation in words.*
b) *Copy and complete the table of values for the
domain shown.*
c) *Write the relation as a set of ordered pairs.*
d) *State the range.*
10. $y = 4x + 2$

x	y
2	
1	
0	
−1	
−2	

11. $y = 3x - 4$

x	y
2	
1	
0	
−1	
−2	

12. $y = -2x + 7$

x	y
2	
1	
0	
−1	
−2	

13. $y = -x - 2$

x	y
−4	
−3	
−2	
−1	
0	

14. For the equation $x + y = 8$, find the missing value in each ordered pair.
a) $(1, \blacksquare)$ **b)** $(6, \blacksquare)$ **c)** $(-5, \blacksquare)$
d) $(\blacksquare, 2)$ **e)** $(\blacksquare, -2)$ **f)** $(\blacksquare, -5)$

15. For the equation $x - y = 2$, find the missing value in each ordered pair.
a) $(5, \blacksquare)$ **b)** $(8, \blacksquare)$ **c)** $(-3, \blacksquare)$
d) $(\blacksquare, 7)$ **e)** $(\blacksquare, 0)$ **f)** $(\blacksquare, -3)$

Find 5 ordered pairs for each relation.
16. $x + y = 11$ **17.** $x - y = 3$
18. $y = 4x + 5$ **19.** $y = 2x - 7$

Write an equation that describes each relation.

20.

x	y
1	8
2	7
3	6
4	5

21.

x	y
1	3
2	6
3	9
4	12

22.

x	y
4	2
3	1
2	0
1	-1
0	-2

23.

x	y
2	-4
1	-2
0	0
-1	2
-2	4

Applications and Problem Solving

B

24. Baseball A baseball commentator uses ordered pairs to describe the ball and strike count for a batter. What are the possible ordered pairs? Is there any relationship between the 2 numbers?

25. Train travel a) Copy and complete the table for a train travelling at 80 km/h.

Time (h)	Distance (km)
1	
2	
3	
4	

b) How far would the train travel in 5 h? 6 h?
c) Describe the pattern in the distance column.

d) Write the results from the table as a set of ordered pairs.
e) Describe in words the relationship between the time and the distance travelled.
f) Let t represent the number of hours travelled. Write an equation in the form $D = \blacksquare$ to find the distance travelled.
g) Use your equation to determine how far the train will travel in 13 h; 21 h.

26. Geometry A diagonal is a straight line that joins 2 non-adjacent vertices of a polygon. A quadrilateral has 2 diagonals.

a) Copy and complete the table.

Name of Polygon	Number of Sides	Number of Diagonals
Quadrilateral	4	2
Pentagon	5	
Hexagon	6	
Heptagon	7	
Octagon	8	
Nonagon	9	
Decagon	10	
Hendecagon	11	

b) What is the pattern in the number of diagonals?
c) How many diagonals are there for a polygon with 12 sides? 13 sides?
d) Write the results from the table as a set of ordered pairs.
e) Describe in words the relationship between the number of sides and the number of diagonals.
f) Let s represent the number of sides. Write an equation in the form $D = \blacksquare$ to find the number of diagonals from the number of sides.
g) Use your equation to find the number of diagonals for a polygon with 20 sides; 50 sides; 100 sides.

27. Paper folding If you fold a
piece of paper once, you divide it
into 2 regions. If you fold it again,
perpendicular to the last fold, you
get 4 regions.
a) Copy and complete the table.

Number of Folds	Number of Regions
1	2
2	4
3	
4	
5	
6	

b) What is the pattern in the number of regions
column?
c) How many regions would there be after
7 folds? 8 folds?
d) Write the results from the table as a set of
ordered pairs.
e) Describe in words the relationship between
the number of folds and the number of regions.
f) Let n represent the number of folds. Write an
equation in the form $R = \blacksquare$ to find the
number of regions from the number of folds.
g) Use your equation to calculate the number of
regions after 10 folds; 12 folds.

28. Mirrors To see a complete reflection of
yourself in a mirror fixed to a flat wall, you must
use a mirror that is long enough. The table
shows the minimum mirror lengths, l, for people
of different heights, h.

Height of Person, h (cm)	Length of Mirror, l (cm)
140	70
150	75
160	80
170	85
180	90

a) Write the relation as a set of ordered pairs of
the form (h, l).
b) Write the domain and range of the relation.
c) Describe the relation in words.
d) Write an equation of the form $l = \blacksquare$ to
express the minimum mirror length, l, in terms
of the height of a person, h.

C

29. Months a) Write a set of ordered pairs of
the form (l, d) for the relation, where l is the
number of letters in the name of the month and d
is the number of days in the month in a leap year.
b) Write the domain and range for the relation.
c) Can this relation be described by an equation?
Explain.

30. Social Insurance Numbers a) A Social
Insurance Number is the first element of a set of
ordered pairs that defines a relation. What is the
second element of the set of ordered pairs?
b) What is the range of this relation?

LOGIC POWER

Opposite faces of the large cube are shaded
in the same way. The interior of the large
cube is filled with small cubes of the same
size as those on the exterior. All interior
faces are white.

How many of the small cubes have
a) 3 blue faces?
b) 2 blue faces?
c) 1 blue face?
d) 0 blue faces?

5.2 Graphing Ordered Pairs

Air traffic controllers at a busy airport, such as Lester B. Pearson International Airport in Toronto, must quickly and easily identify an approaching aircraft's position.

To do this, air traffic controllers observe the lighted, electronic dots on their radar screens. Each aircraft is represented by a dot that is labelled with the aircraft's flight number, altitude, and ground speed.

Explore: Analyze the Number Lines

a) Is an approaching aircraft's distance along the ground from the airport a horizontal or a vertical dimension?

b) Is an approaching aircraft's height above the ground a horizontal or a vertical dimension?

c) On which of the following number lines would you plot the aircraft's distance along the ground from the airport, in kilometres?

d) On which of the number lines would you plot the aircraft's height above the ground, in metres?

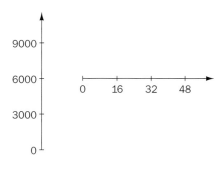

Inquire

1. Can either number line show both the distance along the ground and the height above the ground at the same time?

2. Describe how the two number lines can be put together so that both sets of values can be plotted at once.

3. What is the advantage of the system you described in question 2?

René Descartes, a 17th century mathematician, developed a system for graphing ordered pairs on a grid. This system is called the **Cartesian Coordinate System**.

In this system, ordered pairs are graphed on a grid made up of two perpendicular number lines. The lines meet at a point called the **origin**. The horizontal number line is called the **x-axis**. The vertical number line is called the **y-axis**. The x- and y-axes divide the plane into four quadrants.

For any point on the grid, such as A(4, 2), the first number in the ordered pair is the **x-coordinate**. The second number in the ordered pair is the **y-coordinate**. To plot the point A(4, 2) on the grid, start at the origin and move 4 units to the right and 2 units up.

Example 1   Naming Points

What ordered pairs describe the points shown on this grid?

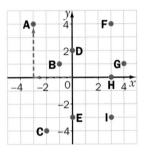

Solution

First, read along the x-axis to identify the x-coordinate.
Then, read along the y-axis to identify the matching y-coordinate.
For point A, the x-coordinate is −3 and the y-coordinate is 4.
The ordered pair is (−3, 4).
The ordered pairs that describe the points are:
A(−3, 4), B(−1, 1), C(−2, −4), D(0, 2), E(0, −3), F(3, 4), G(4, 1), H(3, 0), and I(3, −3)

Example 2   Plotting Points

a) Plot the points A(−2, 3), B(2, 3), C(2, −3), and D(−2, −3) on a grid.
b) Join AB, BC, CD, and DA.
c) Identify the polygon and its dimensions.

Solution

a)

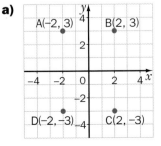

b)

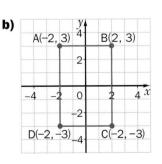

c) The polygon is a rectangle, where $l = 6$ units and $w = 4$ units.

Because a relation is a set of ordered pairs, graphing the ordered pairs is one way to represent the relation.

Example 3 Reading a Graph

For the graph shown,
a) express the relation as a set of ordered pairs
b) write the domain and range

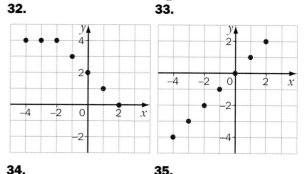

Solution

a) The set of ordered pairs is $(-2, -2)$, $(1, 2)$, $(3, -2)$, $(4, 0)$.
b) The domain is $\{-2, 1, 3, 4\}$. The range is $\{-2, 0, 2\}$.

Practice

A

Name the point with the given coordinates on the following grid.

1. $(3, 1)$
2. $(-5, 1)$
3. $(2, 3)$
4. $(4, -1)$
5. $(0, -2)$
6. $(5, 2)$
7. $(-3, 0)$
8. $(1, -5)$
9. $(-6, -4)$
10. $(-2, 2)$
11. $(3, 5)$
12. $(6, -3)$
13. $(-1, -4)$
14. $(0, 0)$
15. $(-4, -1)$

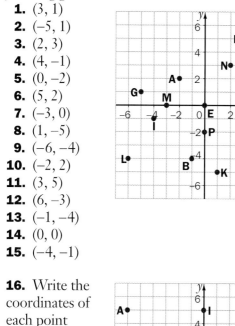

16. Write the coordinates of each point shown on the grid.

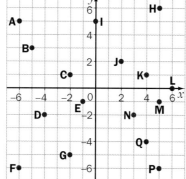

Plot each point on a grid.

17. A(3, 5)
18. B(5, 3)
19. C(-3, 5)
20. D(-5, 3)
21. E(3, -5)
22. F(5, -3)
23. G(0, 4)
24. H(4, 0)
25. I(-4, 0)
26. J(0, -4)
27. K(1, 1)
28. L(-1, 1)
29. M(1, -1)
30. N(-1, -1)
31. O(0, 0)

For each graph,
a) *express the relation as a set of ordered pairs*
b) *write the domain and range*

32.   **33.**

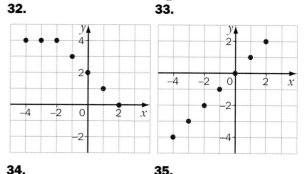

34.   **35.**

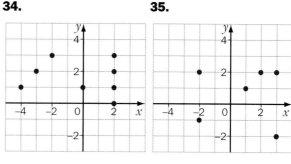

Graph each relation.
36. (0, 2), (0, 3), (1, 4), (3, 2)
37. (–2, 2), (–1, 1), (2, 3), (4, 5)
38. (–4, –5), (–4, –3), (–1, 0), (0, –2), (2, 2)
39. (–2, –2), (–1, –1), (0, 0), (1, 1), (2, 2)

Applications and Problem Solving

40. Measurement Plot and join these sets of points in order. Join the last point to the first point to form a closed figure. Identify each figure. Calculate the area of each figure in square units.
a) A(3, 1), B(3, 5), C(8, 4)
b) D(1, 1), E(1, –2), F(–5, –2), G(–5, 1)
c) J(6, 0), K(9, 1), L(9, –4), M(6, –5)
d) Q(–3, 1), R(–3, –1), S(3, –1), T(3, 1)
e) G(–3, 0), H(0, –4), I(5, –4), J(8, 0), N(5, 4), T(0, 4)

B

41. Geometry Plot the points A(–2, 3) and B(5, –1). Find the coordinates of a third point that will form a right triangle with these two points. There is more than one solution.

42. Geometry Plot the points D(5, 1) and E(3, –3) on a grid. Find the coordinates of a third point, F, so that △DEF is isosceles and DE = DF. How many solutions are there? Explain how you solved the problem. Justify your reasoning.

43. Geometry a) Plot the points X(–4, 1), Y(–3, –4), and Z(5, 0) on a grid.
b) Find all the possible points that form a parallelogram with these three points.
c) How many solutions are there?

44. Geometry Let x equal the number of sides of each figure and y equal the number of diagonals from one vertex.

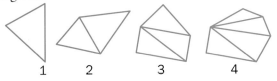

1   2   3   4

a) Complete a table of x and y values for the first six figures.
b) Graph the relation.

45. Pattern Let x equal the number of hexagons in each diagram and y equal the number of toothpicks in each diagram.

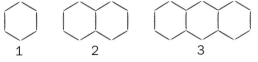

1   2   3

a) Make a table of x and y values for the first five diagrams.
b) Graph the relation.

C

46. Decide if each statement is always true, sometimes true, or never true. Explain.
a) A point with one positive coordinate and one negative coordinate lies in the 4th quadrant.
b) A point whose x- and y-coordinates are equal lies in the 1st or 3rd quadrant.
c) The points on a vertical line have the same x-coordinate.

47. Make up a problem where the solution requires that points be plotted on a grid. Have a classmate solve your problem.

NUMBER POWER

Copy the diagram.

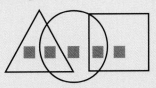

Identify 5 consecutive whole numbers and arrange them in the 5 small squares so that
• the sum of the numbers in the triangle is 28
• the sum of the numbers in the circle is 39
• the sum of the numbers in the rectangle is 30
• the sum of all 5 numbers is 70

List the 5 numbers in order from left to right in the diagram.

5.3 Graphing Linear Relations

The advertisement shown was used to help raise money to save rain forests.

"IN THE TIME IT TAKES YOU TO READ THIS, ABOUT SIX HECTARES OF RAIN FOREST WILL BE LOST FOREVER!"

Please help to save our trees.

Explore: Draw the Graph

Assume it takes 10 s to read the above advertisement. Copy and complete this table of values.

Time (s)	Area of Rain Forest Lost (ha)
0	
10	
20	
30	
40	
50	

Inquire

1. Copy the grid and plot the ordered pairs for this relation. Join the points.

2. Is the graph a straight line?

3. Extend the line to $t = 60$ s. How much rain forest is lost in this amount of time?

4. Use the graph to estimate how much time it takes for 10 ha of rain forest to be lost.

5. Use the graph to estimate the number of hectares of rain forest lost in 25 s.

6. Work with a partner.
a) Use the variables A, r, and t to write an equation in the form $A = \rule{2cm}{0.4cm}$ that relates the number of hectares of rain forest lost to the elapsed time. A is the number of hectares of rain forest lost, r is the rate of rain forest loss, and t is the time in seconds.
b) What is the value of r in your equation?

7. Describe how you can check that your equation is correct.

A relation whose graph is a straight line is called a **linear relation**.

Example 1 Thunderstorms

You can calculate your distance from a flash of lightning by counting the number of seconds that elapse before you hear the thunderclap. With every kilometre, the time that elapses increases by 3 s.
a) Make a table of values for distances from 0 km to 4 km.
b) Graph distance versus time for this relation. State what type of relation it is.
c) How much time elapses before you hear the thunderclap if you are at a distance of 3.5 km from the lightning?
d) How far away are you if you hear the thunderclap in 1.5 s?

Solution

a) The table of values that satisfies this relation is:

Time (s)	Distance (km)
0	0
3	1
6	2
9	3
12	4

b)

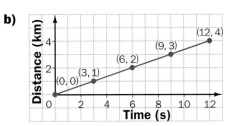

The relation is a linear relation.

Recall that a graphing calculator can be used to plot the ordered pairs and draw the line of best fit.

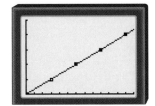

c) From the graph, the time that elapses before you hear the thunderclap at 3.5 km is about 10.5 s.

The TRACE instruction can be used to interpolate from the graph.

If necessary, zoom in and trace again to find a more accurate answer

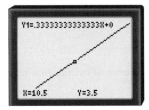

d) From the graph, if you hear the thunderclap in 1.5 s, you are about 0.5 km away from the lightning.

Example 2 Air Temperature

The temperature of the air varies with the altitude.

Altitude (m)	Temperature (°C)
0	16
2000	12
4000	8
6000	4
8000	0

a) Use the values in the table to graph the relation between air temperature and altitude.
b) Mount Logan is 5959 m high. Estimate the temperature at the peak of Mount Logan when the temperature at the base is 16°C.

Solution

a) Plot the data and join the points with a straight line.

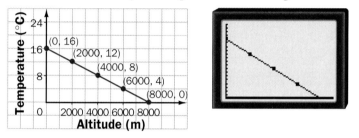

b) Mount Logan is 5959 m high. The temperature at its peak is approximately 4°C when the temperature at the base is 16°C.

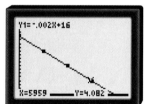

On a graphing calculator, when the first coordinate of a point on the line is known, the Value operation can be used to find the second coordinate.

Practice

A

Name the coordinates of the indicated points for each linear relation.

1.

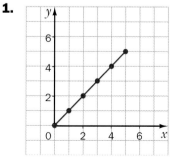

2.

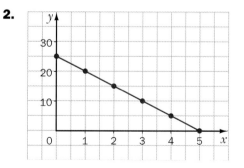

Copy and complete these tables of values. Graph each relation.

3.

Time (h)	Distance (km)
0	0
1	5
2	10
3	
4	
5	

4.

Time (h)	Cost ($)
0	0
1	6.00
2	12.00
3	
4	
5	

5.

Time (h)	Distance (km)
0	0
1	30
2	60
3	
4	
5	

6.

Time (h)	Cost ($)
0	30
1	80
2	130
3	
4	
5	

Applications and Problem Solving

7. Canadian Navy The *HMCS Vancouver* cruises at 20 km/h.
a) Copy and complete the table for this ship at cruise speed.

Time (h)	Distance Travelled (km)
1	20
2	
3	
4	
5	

b) Graph the relation.
c) Use the graph to estimate the time the ship takes to travel 48 km.

B

8. Numbers The sum of two positive numbers, *x* and *y*, is 10. Graph this relation.

9. Gas volume This table of values shows the effect of temperature on the volume of a gas.

Temperature (°C)	Volume (mL)
10	849
15	864
20	879
25	894
30	909

a) Graph the relation.
b) By how many millilitres does the volume of the gas change per degree?
c) What is the volume of the gas at 21°C? at 29°C?
d) Determine the volume of the gas when the temperature is 0°C.

C

10. Computer repairs Tina repairs computers. She charges $45.00 for a service call and $55.00 for each hour of labour needed.
a) Complete a table of values that shows her fees for up to and including 3 h of labour.
b) Graph the relation.
c) Does this graph pass through the origin? Explain.

11. Integers The sum of two positive integers, *x* and *y*, is 8.
a) Graph this relation.
b) Should the points be joined with a straight line? Explain.

12. Write a problem that involves graphing a relation. Have a classmate solve your problem.

WORD POWER

How many real words of four letters or more can you form using the letters in the word CARTESIAN? Compare your list of words with a classmate's.

5.4 Graphing Linear Equations

The *Pathfinder-Plus* is an experimental plane that is guided from the ground. Its uses include taking atmospheric samples and relaying telecommunications signals. The plane holds the world altitude record for a propeller-driver aircraft, at 24 445 m.

Solar energy powers the propellers during daylight. With the motors off, the plane can glide 21 km for every 1 km of altitude. The glide distance, d kilometres, can be calculated from the altitude, a kilometres, using the equation $d = 21a$.

Explore: Graph an Equation

Use the equation $d = 21a$ to copy and complete the table.

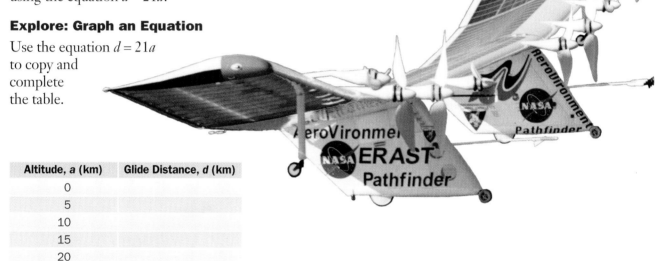

Altitude, a (km)	Glide Distance, d (km)
0	
5	
10	
15	
20	

Plot the ordered pairs for this relation on a grid like the one shown. Join the points.

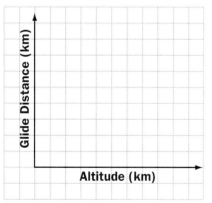

Inquire

1. Why is the equation $d = 21a$ called a linear equation?

2. Use the graph to find how far the plane glides from an altitude of

a) 18 km   **b)** 24 km

Example 1 Graphing a Linear Equation
Graph the equation $y = 1 - x$ for the domain $\{-2, -1, 0, 1, 2\}$.

Solution
Make a table. Substitute the values of x to determine the corresponding values of y.

x	1 − x	y	Ordered Pair (x, y)
−2	1 − (−2)	3	(−2, 3)
−1	1 − (−1)	2	(−1, 2)
0	1 − (0)	1	(0, 1)
1	1 − (1)	0	(1, 0)
2	1 − (2)	−1	(2, −1)

Plot the ordered pairs on a grid. Do not join the points, because the domain does not include values of x between the given values.

Example 2 Graphing a Linear Equation
Graph $y = 2x - 3$ for each of the following domains.
a) $\{3, 2, 1, 0, -1\}$ **b)** the real numbers, R

Solution 1 Using Paper and Pencil
a) Complete a table of values.

x	2x − 3	y	(x, y)
3	2(3) − 3	3	(3, 3)
2	2(2) − 3	1	(2, 1)
1	2(1) − 3	−1	(1, −1)
0	2(0) − 3	−3	(0, −3)
−1	2(−1) − 3	−5	(−1, −5)

Plot the points on a grid. Do not join them, because the domain does not include values of x between the given values.

b) Plot the same 5 points determined in part a). Draw a line through the points, because the domain includes all real values of x.

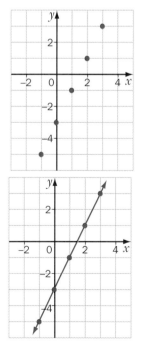

Solution 2   Using a Graphing Calculator
a) Enter the data to be plotted. Graph the data as a set of unconnected points.

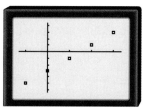

b) To graph the linear equation with domain R, there is no need to complete a table of values or to plot individual points. Press the ⟨Y=⟩ key and enter 2X–3 for Y1. Then, display the graph in a suitable viewing window.

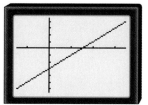

In part a) of Example 2, the graph is a series of separate points. This type of graph is said to be **discrete**. In part b) of Example 2, the graph is an unbroken line. This type of graph is said to be **continuous**.

Example 3   Writing Linear Equations
Given the points on the grid, write an equation to describe each relation.

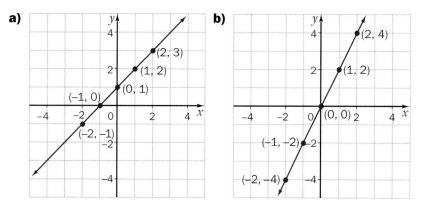

a)

b)

Solution
a) Each y-value is 1 more than each x-value.
The equation is $y = x + 1$.

b) Each y-value is double each x-value.
The equation is $y = 2x$.

Practice

A

Copy and complete each table of values.

1. $y = x - 1$

x	y
-2	
-1	
0	
1	
2	

2. $y = x + 2$

x	y
-2	
-1	
0	
1	
2	

3. $y = 3 - x$

x	y
-2	
-1	
0	
1	
2	

4. $y = 2x + 2$

x	y
-2	
-1	
0	
1	
2	

The domain of each of the following equations is $\{-2, -1, 0, 1, 2\}$. Complete a table of values. Then, graph each equation.

5. $y = x + 1$ **6.** $y = x - 2$

7. $y = 2x + 1$ **8.** $y = 2x - 1$

9. $y = 3x + 4$ **10.** $y = 3x - 2$

Graph each equation. The domain is R.

11. $y = x + 4$ **12.** $y = 3x + 2$

13. $y = 2x - 4$ **14.** $y = 4 - x$

15. $y = 5 - 3x$ **16.** $y = -2x + 7$

Given the table of values, write an equation for each relation.

17.

x	y
-2	0
-1	1
0	2
1	3
2	4

18.

x	y
-2	2
-1	1
0	0
1	-1
2	-2

19.

x	y
-2	-6
-1	-5
0	-4
1	-3
2	-2

20.

x	y
-2	-6
-1	-3
0	0
1	3
2	6

Given the points on the grid,

a) write an equation to represent each relation

b) state the domain

21.

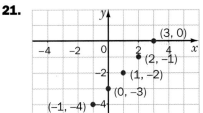

22.

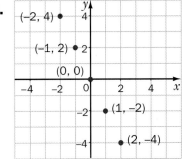

23.

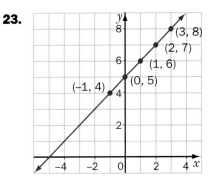

24.

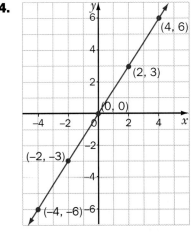

Applications and Problem Solving

B

25. Space probe The *Pioneer 10* space probe was launched in 1972 and recorded the first close-up images of Jupiter. *Pioneer 10* was the first space probe to leave our solar system. It now travels through space at 1000 km/min.

a) Copy and complete the table to show the distance travelled by the space probe in the specified lengths of time.

Time (min)	Distance (km)
0	
1	
2	
3	
4	
5	
6	

b) Plot distance versus time for this relation. Join the points.

c) The greatest east-west distance in Canada is 5514 km from Cape Spear, Newfoundland, to the Yukon-Alaska border. Use the graph to estimate how long it would take *Pioneer 10* to cover this distance.

d) Let d represent the distance, in kilometres, and t represent the time, in minutes. Write an equation for the relation.

26. Measurement One dimension of a rectangle is 6 cm. The table shows several different values for the other dimension.

Other dimension, x (cm)	2	4	6	8
Area, A (cm^2)				

a) Copy and complete the table.
b) Graph A versus x for the relation.
c) Write an equation for the relation.

27. Heart rates An adult's maximum heart rate, r beats/min, is given by the equation
$$r = 220 - a$$
where a is the person's age, in years.
a) Draw a graph of maximum heart rate versus age for adults from 20 to 60 years of age.
b) Use the graph to estimate the age at which a person's maximum heart rate is 178 beats/min.

28. Supersonic flight The distance travelled by a Concorde aircraft at cruising speed is given by the equation
$$d = 0.6t$$
where d is the distance travelled, in kilometres, and t is the time taken, in seconds.

a) Graph distance versus time for times up to 10 000 s by using a graphing calculator or by completing the table of values and plotting the points.

Time (s)	Distance (km)
0	
2 000	
4 000	
6 000	
8 000	
10 000	

b) The flying distance from Toronto to London, England, is 5735 km. Use the graph to estimate how long the Concorde would take to fly from Toronto to London, to the nearest hundred seconds; to the nearest tenth of an hour.

29. Numbers The difference between two real numbers, x and y, is 6. Graph this relation for
a) $y > x$ **b)** $x > y$

30. Graph the equation $y = 2x + 3$ for each given domain. State the range in each case.
a) the whole numbers from 0 to 5
b) the integers from -3 to 3
c) all real numbers, R

C

31. Running elk An elk can run at 20 m/s. If you drew a graph of distance travelled versus time for an elk running at this speed, would the graph be discrete or continuous? Explain.

32. Hopping kangaroo A kangaroo can cover a horizontal distance of 13 m in a single hop. If you drew a graph of distance travelled versus number of hops, would the graph be discrete or continuous? Explain.

5.5 Direct and Partial Variation

Because water expands when it freezes, the density of ice is less than the density of water. Therefore, ice floats on lakes and rivers, and icebergs float in the ocean.

Explore: Use the Data

The table shows the volume of ice produced when a given volume of water freezes. The graph of volume of ice versus volume of water shows the relation.

Volume of Water (cm³)	Volume of Ice (cm³)
100	109
200	218
300	327
400	436
500	545

a) Is the relation linear or non-linear?
b) For each ordered pair in the table, divide the volume of ice by the volume of water. How are the ratios related?

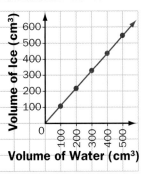

Inquire

1. Let I be the volume of ice and w be the volume of water. Write an equation of the form $I = \blacksquare w$ to describe the relation, where ■ represents a number.

2. Use the equation to find
a) the volume of ice formed when 800 cm³ of water freezes
b) the volume of water needed to form 1308 cm³ of ice

3. Large icebergs can be over 300 km long. Suppose that a large iceberg is 300 km long and 20 km wide. The height of the iceberg is 0.75 km, including the part under the water.
a) Calculate the volume of the iceberg, in cubic kilometres. What assumption have you made?
b) Calculate the volume of water produced when the iceberg melts, to the nearest cubic kilometre.

The table shows the distances travelled in different lengths of time by an albatross gliding at a constant speed of 10 m/s. If the time is doubled, the distance is doubled. If the time is tripled, the distance is tripled. If the time is halved, the distance is halved. We say that the distance *varies directly* as the time. This type of relation is known as a **direct variation**.

Time (s)	Distance (m)
1	10
2	20
3	30
4	40
5	50

In a direct variation, the ratio of corresponding values of the variables is a constant. In the case of the cruising albatross,

$$\frac{10}{1} = 10 \qquad \frac{20}{2} = 10 \qquad \frac{30}{3} = 10 \qquad \frac{40}{4} = 10 \qquad \frac{50}{5} = 10$$

So, if d is the distance and t is the time, $\frac{d}{t} = k$, or $d = kt$, where k is the **constant of variation**.

The graph of distance versus time is shown.

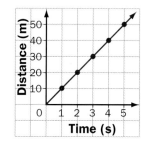

In general, if y varies directly as x,
• $y \propto x$ or $y = kx$ The symbol $\propto$ means "varies as."
• the graph is a straight line that passes through the origin

Example 1   Hourly Rates of Pay
Armin makes fruit baskets to sell at a market. He earns $8/h. How long must he work to earn $150?

Solution 1   Solving an Equation
Since Armin earns $8/h, the equation for the amount he earns is
$$A = 8t$$
where A is the amount, in dollars, and t is the time he works, in hours.
To find out how long Armin must work to earn $150, substitute 150 for A and solve the equation for t.

$$A = 8t$$

Substitute 150 for A: $150 = 8t$

Divide both sides by 8: $\dfrac{150}{8} = \dfrac{8t}{8}$

$$18.75 = t$$

Armin must work 18.75 h to earn $150.

Solution 2 Using a Graph

Method 1: Using Paper and Pencil
Complete a table of values and graph the relation.

Time Worked (h)	Amount Earned ($)
5	40
10	80
15	120
20	160

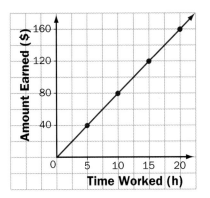

Interpolate to estimate how long Armin must work to earn $150. The exact answer is 18.75 h, but estimates may vary.
Armin must work about 19 h to earn $150.

Method 2: Using a Graphing Calculator
The equation that relates the amount Armin earns, A dollars, and the time he works, t hours, is

$$A = 8t$$

Graph the equation $y = 8x$ in a suitable viewing window using a graphing calculator.

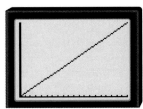

Use the TRACE instruction to interpolate from the graph.

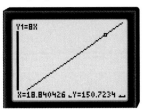

If necessary, zoom in and then trace to find a more accurate value.

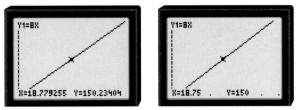

Armin must work 18.75 h to earn $150.

Note that, in Example 1, the algebraic method shown in Solution 1 gives the exact answer. The graphical methods shown in Solution 2 may not give the exact answer.

Example 2 Running Dogs
Whippets are fast-running dogs that look like small greyhounds. At top speed, a whippet can run 62 m in 4 s. At this speed, how far can it run in 10 s?

Solution 1   Using an Equation

For a constant speed, the distance run, d metres, varies directly as the time, t seconds,

$$\frac{d}{t} = k$$

where k is the constant of variation.

Substitute to find k:

$$\frac{62}{4} = k$$
$$15.5 = k$$

So, $\dfrac{d}{t} = 15.5$ or $d = 15.5t$

When $t = 10$ s, $d = 15.5(10)$
$$= 155$$

At top speed, a whippet can run 155 m in 10 s.

Solution 2   Solving a Proportion

Write a proportion.

Let d be the distance the whippet runs in 10 s.

$$\frac{62}{4} = \frac{d}{10}$$
$$10 \times \frac{62}{4} = 10 \times \frac{d}{10}$$
$$\frac{620}{4} = d$$
$$155 = d$$

At top speed, the whippet can run 155 m in 10 s.

Note that, in Solution 2, above, both sides of the proportion equal the constant of variation.

$$\frac{62}{4} = 15.5 \qquad \frac{155}{10} = 15.5$$

For this reason, the constant of variation is sometimes called the *constant of proportionality*. The distance the whippet runs can be described as *directly proportional* to the time taken.

The table shows the cost of a banquet. As the number of people increases, the cost increases. However, as the number of people is doubled, the cost is not doubled. So, this relation is not an example of a direct variation.

Number of People	Cost ($)
10	700
20	1200
30	1700
40	2200
50	2700

The graph of the relation is a straight line. However, extending the graph to the vertical axis shows that there is a fixed cost of $200 for every banquet. This amount covers such expenses as hydro and room rental, which do not change with the number of people at the banquet. We say that the cost *varies partially* as the number of people. This type of relation is known as a **partial variation**. An equation for the relation is

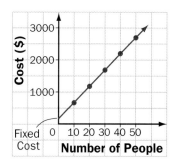

Though there must be a whole number of people, the points may be connected for convenience.

$$C = 50n + 200$$

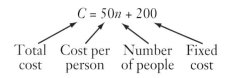

Total cost   Cost per person   Number of people   Fixed cost

In general, if y varies partially as x,
• the equation is of the form $y = kx + c$, $c \neq 0$
• the graph is a straight line that does not pass through the origin

Example 3 Base Salary Plus Commission
Olga sells clothing and shoes in a store. She earns \$400/week, plus a commission of 5% of her sales.
a) Write the partial variation equation.
b) Find Olga's earnings in a week when her sales total \$4600.

Solution
a) $E = 0.05S + 400$, where E represents earnings and S represents sales.
b) $E = 0.05S + 400$
$\quad = 0.05(4600) + 400$
$\quad = 230 + 400$
$\quad = 630$
Olga's earnings are \$630.

Estimate
$0.05 \times 5000 = 250$
$250 + 400 = 650$

You could graph $y = 0.05x + 400$ with a graphing calculator and use the Value operation.

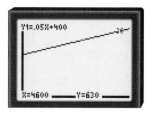

Example 4   Newspaper Advertisements
To place a 3-line ad in the classified section of a newspaper, there is a fixed cost of \$15, and a charge of \$10 for each day the ad is to be run.
a) Write the partial variation equation to show the cost of the ad in terms of the number of days it is run.
b) Graph the equation.
c) If you have an advertising budget of \$50, for how many days can you run the ad?
d) How would the graph from part b) change if the fixed cost changed to \$25 but the daily fee stayed at \$10?
e) How would the graph from part b) change if the fixed cost stayed at \$15 but the daily fee changed to \$14?

Solution
a) The equation is $C = 10n + 15$, where C is the cost of the ad, in dollars, and n is the number of days the ad is run.
b) Graph the equation using paper and pencil or a graphing calculator.

Number of Days	Cost ($)
1	25
2	35
3	45
4	55
5	65

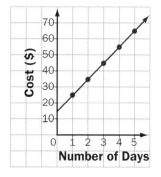

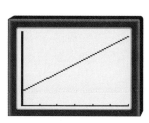

c) Interpolation from the graph indicates that, for $50, you can run the ad for 3.5 days. However, it is not possible to run an ad for part of a day. With an advertising budget of $50, you can run the ad for 3 days.

d) The new equation for the cost would be $C = 10n + 25$.

Number of Days	Cost ($)
1	35
2	45
3	55
4	65
5	75

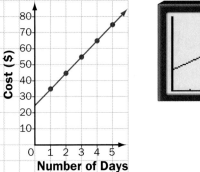

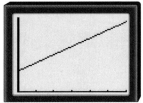

The graph would be parallel to the graph in part b), but each point would move up $10 on the vertical scale. The graph would meet the vertical axis at a fixed cost of $25, instead of the $15 fixed cost in part b).

e) The equation for the cost would now be $C = 14n + 15$.

Number of Days	Cost ($)
1	29
2	43
3	57
4	71
5	85

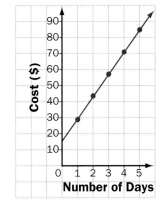

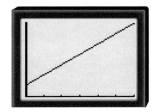

The graph would meet the vertical axis at a fixed cost of $15, as in part b). However, the graph would be steeper than in part b), since the daily fee has increased.

You may find it easier to compare the graphs of the three equations in Example 4 by displaying them on the same grid or in the same viewing window of a graphing calculator.

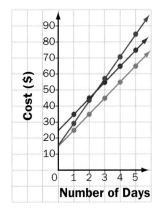

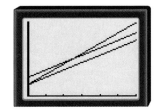

Practice

A

Given that y varies directly as x, copy and complete each table of values. Then, graph each relation.

1.

x	y
2	6
3	
4	
5	
6	

2.

x	y
3	
4	
5	−10
6	
7	

3.

x	y
	5
2	10
	15
	20
	25

Given that the first variable varies directly as the second, find
a) *the constant of variation*
b) *the equation that relates the variables*
4. when $p = 24$, $q = 8$ **5.** when $a = 10$, $b = 4$
6. when $s = 12$, $t = 20$ **7.** when $m = 11$, $n = 33$

8. If y varies directly as x, and $y = 24$ when $x = 3$, find y when $x = 7$.

9. If c varies directly as d, and $c = 12$ when $d = -3$, find c when $d = -10$.

10. If v varies directly as w, and $v = 4$ when $w = 8$, find w when $v = 16$.

11. If r varies directly as s, and $r = 39$ when $s = 26$, find s when $r = 21$.

12. a) Graph the equation $y = 2x$.
b) Is this equation a direct variation or a partial variation?

13. a) Graph the equation $y = 2x + 1$.
b) Is this equation a direct variation or a partial variation?

In each graph, y varies partially as x. State the equation that represents each relation.

14.

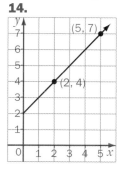

15.

16.

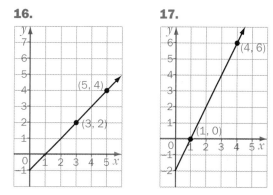

17.

Applications and Problem Solving

18. Hourly rates of pay Tom earns $12/h as a lifeguard at a wave pool.
a) Write a direct variation equation in the form $A = \blacksquare t$ to describe the relation, where A is the amount Tom earns, in dollars, and t is the time he works, in hours.
b) Graph the equation.
c) How many hours must Tom work to earn $270?

B

19. Walking tortoise A tortoise can walk at a speed of 4 m/min.
a) Write a direct variation equation in the form $d = \blacksquare t$ to describe this relation, where d is the distance the tortoise walks, in metres, and t is the time it walks, in minutes.
b) Graph the equation.
 c) Does the graph pass through the origin? Explain.
d) How far can a tortoise walk in 5.5 min?
e) How long does a tortoise take to walk 25 m?

20. Wages The amount that Anne-Marie earns varies directly as the number of hours she works. If she earns $132 in 8 h, how much does she earn in 15 h?

21. Radio station ads To run a 30-s ad in prime drive time, a radio station charges a fixed cost of $400, plus $200 for each day the ad is run.
a) Write the partial variation equation to show the cost of the ad in terms of the number of days it is run.
b) Graph the equation. Join the points for convenience.
c) For how many days could a company run the ad if the company could afford to spend $1000? $2500?
d) How would the graph from part b) change if the fixed cost was changed to $300 but the cost per day remained at $200?
e) How would the graph from part b) change if the fixed cost remained at $400 but the cost per day was changed to $100?

22. Salary plus commission Samantha works in a TV and audio store. She earns $300/week, plus a commission of 10% of her sales.
a) Write the partial variation equation to describe her earnings for one week.
b) Graph the equation.
c) Does the graph pass through the origin? Explain.
d) Find Samantha's earnings for a week in which her sales totalled $6500.
e) If Samantha aims to earn at least $825 a week, what is her minimum sales target for a week?

23. Fitness The amount of energy burned when skipping rope varies directly as the time spent skipping. Paulina burned 200 kJ of energy by skipping rope for 5 min.
a) Find the constant of variation and write the equation.
b) How much energy does Paulina burn if she skips rope for 3.5 min?
c) For how long would Paulina skip rope to burn 320 kJ of energy?

24. Pizza toppings A large tomato sauce and cheese pizza with one extra topping costs $13.50. With two extra toppings, the cost is $15.00. With three extra toppings, the cost is $16.50.
a) Graph the cost versus the number of extra toppings.
b) What is the cost of a large pizza with no extra toppings?
c) Write the equation for the partial variation.

25. Advertising There is a fixed cost of $500 to write and design an advertising flyer. It costs $0.15 to print a flyer.
a) Write the partial variation equation that relates the total cost to the number of flyers printed.
b) Find the total cost of producing 60 000 flyers.
c) How many flyers can be produced for a total cost of $12 500?

26. Sequence The E-shapes are made from asterisks.

```
                                    * * * * *
                                    *
                     * * * *        *
                     *              * * * *
    * * *            * * *          *
    * *              *              *
    * * *            * * * *        * * * * *
Diagram 1               2              3
```

a) How many asterisks are in the fourth diagram? the fifth diagram?
b) Plot the number of asterisks versus the diagram number for the first 5 diagrams.
c) Does the graph represent a direct variation or a partial variation?
d) Write an equation of the form $A = \blacksquare$ to represent the relation, where A is the number of asterisks in the nth diagram.
e) Use the equation to find the number of asterisks in the 55th diagram.

27. Service calls Rajiv is an electrician. The table shows how much he charges for service calls.

Cost ($)	Time (h)
110	1
160	2
210	3
260	4

a) Graph the cost versus the time.
b) What is the fixed cost?
c) Write the equation for the partial variation.
d) How much does Rajiv charge for a 7-h service call?
e) How long is a service call that costs $335?

28. Measurement What is the constant of variation for the direct variation of the circumference of a circle with
a) the diameter?   **b)** the radius?

C

29. Weight and mass The weight of an object is the force of gravity acting on the object. Weight is measured in newtons (N). The table shows the weights of objects of known masses on the Earth's surface.

Mass (kg)	Weight (N)
5	49
10	98
15	147
20	196
25	245

a) Graph weight versus mass.
b) Is the variation direct or partial?
c) Write the equation.
d) What is the weight of a 75-kg object on the surface of the Earth?
e) What is the mass of an object that weighs 539 N on the surface of the Earth?
f) Could you use the equation from part c) to determine the weight of a 30-kg object on the surface of the moon? Explain.

30. Field trip It costs a total of $550 to take 25 students to an art gallery. The fixed cost of the bus is $300.
a) Write the equation for the partial variation.
b) The total cost is divided equally among the students attending. What is the difference in the cost per student if 15 students attend instead of 25?
c) Explain why there is a difference in part b).
d) How much would it cost to take 15 students to the art gallery?

31. Planning a trip Maylin is saving for a trip to Europe. She puts away the same amount at the end of every month. After 3 months, she still needs to save $3150. After 7 months, she still needs to save $1750.
a) Graph the amount to be saved versus time.
b) Write the equation for the partial variation.
c) How much does Maylin need altogether for the trip?
d) How long will she take to save this amount?
e) If she decided at the beginning that she needed to save an extra $700 for the trip, how would the graph change?

PATTERN POWER

Write each sum as a power of 2.

$$2^1 + 2^1 = \blacksquare$$
$$2^2 + 2^2 = \blacksquare$$
$$2^3 + 2^3 = \blacksquare$$
$$2^4 + 2^4 = \blacksquare$$

a) Describe the pattern.
b) Explain why it works.
c) Use the pattern to predict $2^8 + 2^8$. Use a calculator to check your answer.
d) Can you write a similar pattern for powers with another base? Explain.

TECHNOLOGY

Finding the Equation of a Line

1 Direct Variations

1. Graph the points $(-4, -8)$, $(-2, -4)$, $(0, 0)$, $(2, 4)$, and $(4, 8)$ in the standard viewing window of a graphing calculator.

2. Graph each of the following equations, one at a time, in the standard viewing window. Display each graph and the graph from question 1 at the same time.
a) $y = x$ **b)** $y = 2x$ **c)** $y = 3x$ **d)** $y = 0.5x$

3. a) What is the equation of the line through the points from question 1?
b) Explain why the points lie on this line.

4. Determine graphically whether the equation of the line through the points $(-8, 4)$, $(-4, 2)$, $(0, 0)$, $(4, -2)$, and $(8, -4)$ is $y = -x$, $y = -2x$, $y = -0.5x$, or $y = -0.2x$.

5. Determine graphically the equation of the line through each of the following sets of points.
a) $(-2, 8)$, $(-1, 4)$, $(0, 0)$, $(1, -4)$, $(2, -8)$
b) $(-4, -1.2)$, $(-2, -0.6)$, $(0, 0)$, $(2, 0.6)$, $(4, 1.2)$

2 Partial Variations

1. Determine graphically whether the equation of the line through the points $(-3, -8)$, $(-1, -4)$, $(1, 0)$, and $(2, 2)$ is $y = 2x$, $y = 2x + 1$, $y = 2x - 1$, $y = 2x + 2$, or $y = 2x - 2$.

2. Determine graphically whether the equation of the line through the points $(-1, 8)$, $(1, 2)$, $(3, -4)$, and $(5, -10)$ is $y = 6 - 3x$, $y = 5 - 3x$, $y = 4 - 3x$, $y = 3 - 3x$, $y = 2 - 3x$, or $y = 1 - 3x$.

3. Determine graphically the equation of the line through each of the following sets of points.
a) $(-4, -1)$, $(-2, 0)$, $(0, 1)$, $(2, 2)$, $(4, 3)$
b) $(-3, 7)$, $(-1, 3)$, $(1, -1)$, $(3, -5)$, $(5, -9)$

3 Problem Solving

1. a) Determine graphically the equation of the line through the points $(-5, -1)$, $(-3, 0)$, $(-1, 1)$, $(1, 2)$, $(3, 3)$, and $(5, 4)$.
b) Describe how you can verify your answer using the linear regression instruction of your graphing calculator.

2. Aluminum The table shows the relation between the mass, m grams, and the volume, V millilitres, of some samples of aluminum.

Volume (mL)	Mass (g)
0.7	1.89
1.5	4.05
2.1	5.67
3.1	8.37

Determine graphically the equation of the form $m = \blacksquare V$ for this relation.

3. Walking home Sunita walked home from school quickly at a constant speed. Her distances, d kilometres, from home at different times, t minutes, after she left school are shown in the table.

Time (min)	Distance (km)
1	1
4	0.7
7	0.4
10	0.1

Determine graphically the equation of the form $d = \blacksquare$ for this relation.

5.6 Equations of Lines of Best Fit

In many cases, plotted data points do not lie on a straight line. However, the points may be close to a straight line.

Explore: Graph the Data

The table shows the approximate populations of 6 provinces at the time of a federal election, and the number of Members of Parliament (MPs) elected from each province.

Province	Population (millions)	Number of MPs
British Columbia	3.6	34
Manitoba	1.1	14
New Brunswick	0.7	10
Nova Scotia	0.9	11
Ontario	10.6	103
Québec	7.1	75

a) Draw a scatter plot of number of MPs versus population, in millions, manually on a grid, or in a suitable viewing window of a graphing calculator.
b) Draw the line of best fit.

Inquire

1. Use the graph to estimate the number of MPs elected from each of the following provinces. The approximate population at the time of the election is given.
a) Alberta; 2.7 million   **b)** Saskatchewan; 1 million
c) Prince Edward Island; 0.1 million

2. Use your research skills to find the actual numbers of MPs who are elected from Alberta, Saskatchewan, and Prince Edward Island. Compare the actual numbers with your estimates.

3. Use the graph to estimate the population of Newfoundland at the time of the election, if 7 MPs were elected from Newfoundland.

4. a) For each province in the table, divide the number of MPs by the population, in millions, to find the number of MPs per million people. Round each answer to the nearest tenth.
b) Are the numbers of MPs elected from different provinces fair? Explain.

5. a) Use your answers to question 4a) to estimate the equation of the line of best fit. Write the equation in the form $M = \blacksquare p$, where M is the number of MPs, p is the population, in millions, and $\blacksquare$ is a whole number.
b) Add the line with this equation to your graph. How close is this line to the line of best fit you drew above?

Example   Tall Buildings

The table gives the numbers of storeys and heights of 7 buildings in Canadian cities.

Building	City	Number of Storeys	Height (m)
First Canadian Place	Toronto	72	290
Manulife Place	Edmonton	36	146
Petro-Canada Centre, W Tower	Calgary	52	210
Place de Ville, Tower C	Ottawa	29	112
Royal Centre Tower	Vancouver	36	140
1100 Rue de la Gauchetière	Montréal	45	204
Toronto Dominion Centre	Winnipeg	33	126

a) Draw a scatter plot of height versus number of storeys. Draw the line of best fit.
b) How does the height of a building seem to be related to the number of storeys?
c) Use the relationship from part b) to write a possible equation for the line of best fit in the form $h = \blacksquare n$, where h is the height of the building, in metres, and n is the number of storeys.
d) Graph the equation from part c) on the same grid or in the same viewing window as the graph from part a).
e) Compare the graph of the equation with the line of best fit you drew in part a).

Solution 1   Graphing Manually

a) Plot the points on a grid and draw the line of best fit.

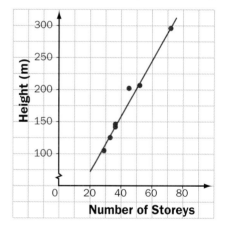

b) From the table, the height of a building, in metres, is about 4 times the number of storeys.
c) A possible equation is $h = 4n$.
d) Add the graph of the equation $h = 4n$ to the grid.

n	h
20	80
40	160
60	240
80	320

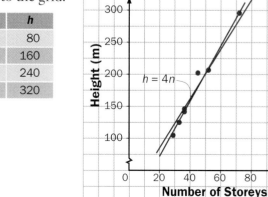

e) The graph of the equation $h = 4n$ is close to the line of best fit drawn in part a).

When graphing manually, we do not know which of the two lines is the more accurate line of best fit.

Solution 2   Using a Graphing Calculator

a) Graph the points in a suitable viewing window. Use the linear regression instruction to draw the line of best fit.

b) From the table, the height of a building, in metres, is about 4 times the number of storeys.
c) A possible equation is $h = 4n$.
d) Add the graph of the equation $y = 4x$ to the same viewing window.

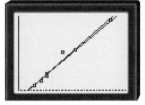

e) The graph of the equation $h = 4n$ is close to the line of best fit drawn in part a).

We expect that the line drawn using the linear regression instruction in part a) is the more accurate line of best fit.

Note that the linear regression instruction of a graphing calculator draws a very accurate line of best fit through a set of points and also gives the equation of the line. For Solution 2 of the example, the equation found by linear regression is as shown in the screen display to the right. The equation is approximately $y = 4.2x - 5.9$ or $h = 4.2n - 5.9$.

Practice

A

1. a) Graph the data and draw the line of best fit.
b) Use the graph to find the value of y when $x = 25$; when $x = 60$.
c) Use the graph to find the value of x when $y = 45$; when $y = 75$.

x	y
10	19
20	42
30	57
40	81
50	96

2. a) Graph the data and draw the line of best fit.
b) Use the graph to find the value of y when $x = -40$; when $x = 35$.
c) Use the graph to find the value of x when $y = 70$; when $y = -30$.

x	y
-50	-39
-30	-20
-10	3
10	18
30	41
50	59

3. a) Graph the data and draw the line of best fit.

b) Use the data in the table to write a possible equation for the line of best fit in the form $y = x +$ ■, where ■ represents a number.

c) Graph the equation from part b) on the same grid or in the same viewing window as the graph from part a).

d) Compare the graph of the equation with the line of best fit you drew in part a). If necessary, try other equations until you find one whose graph is close to the line of best fit.

x	y
1	5
4	7
5	7
7	9
10	13

4. a) Graph the data and draw the line of best fit.

b) Use the data in the table to write a possible equation for the line of best fit in the form $y = x -$ ■, where ■ represents a number.

c) Graph the equation from part b) on the same grid or in the same viewing window as the graph from part a).

d) Compare the graph of the equation with the line of best fit you drew in part a). If necessary, try other equations until you find one whose graph is close to the line of best fit.

x	y
–5	–10
–2	–6
0	–3
1	–3
3	0
5	1

5. a) Graph the data and draw the line of best fit.

b) Use the data in the table to write a possible equation for the line of best fit in the form $y =$ ■x, where ■ represents a number.

c) Graph the equation from part b) on the same grid or in the same viewing window as the graph from part a).

d) Compare the graph of the equation with the line of best fit you drew in part a). If necessary, try other equations until you find one whose graph is close to the line of best fit.

x	y
–5	4
–3	4
–1	0
2	–2
4	–4
5	–6

6. a) Graph the data and draw the line of best fit.

b) Use the data in the table to write a possible equation for the line of best fit in the form $y =$ ■x, where ■ represents a number.

c) Graph the equation from part b) on the same grid or in the same viewing window as the graph from part a).

d) Compare the graph of the equation with the line of best fit you drew in part a). If necessary, try other equations until you find one whose graph is close to the line of best fit.

x	y
–6	–10
–2	–3
0	0
3	4
5	8
6	9

Applications and Problem Solving

B

7. Baseball and softball The table gives the horizontal distances a baseball and a softball travel through the air when launched at different speeds at an angle of about 40°.

Speed (km/h)	Distance (m)	
	Baseball	Softball
130	88	75
145	104	87
160	119	98
175	133	109

a) Graph distance versus speed for these data. Draw the line of best fit for each type of ball.

b) A good major league pitcher throws a baseball at 150 km/h. Use the graph to estimate how far a pitcher could throw a baseball.

c) A major league baseball player can hit a ball at a speed of 190 km/h. When hit at this speed, what is the distance travelled by a baseball? a softball?

d) How does the distance travelled by a baseball seem to be related to the speed at which it is launched?

e) How does the distance travelled by a softball seem to be related to the speed at which it is launched?

f) Use the relationship from part d) to write a possible equation for the line of best fit for a baseball.

g) Use the relationship from part e) to write a possible equation for the line of best fit for a softball.

h) Graph the equations from parts f) and g) on the same grid or in the same viewing window as the graphs from part a).

i) Compare the graphs of the equations with the lines of best fit you drew in part a). If necessary, try other equations until you find ones whose graphs are close to the lines of best fit.

C

8. Populations The table includes the populations of some South American countries in 1995 and the estimated populations in 2025. All data are rounded to the nearest million.

Country	Population (millions)	
	1995	2025
Argentina	36	47
Bolivia	8	13
Chile	15	20
Colombia	37	53
Ecuador	12	18
Paraguay	5	9
Peru	24	36
Venezuela	23	35

a) Graph the population in 2025 versus the population in 1995. Draw the line of best fit.

b) Determine an equation for the line of best fit in the form $p = \blacksquare n + \blacktriangle$, where p is the population in 2025, n is the population in 1995, and $\blacksquare$ and $\blacktriangle$ are numbers.

c) The population of Brazil was 163 million in 1995. Predict the population of Brazil in 2025.

d) The population of Portugal was 10 million in 1995. Should the line of best fit be used to predict the population of Portugal in 2025? Explain.

9. Education levels The table shows the percent of Canadians over the age of 15 with less than a grade 9 education, and the percent with a university degree, in different years. In the second column of the table, 1976 is taken as year 0, 1981 as year 5, and so on.

Year	Years From 1976	Percent of the Population	
		Less Than Grade 9	University Degree
1976	0	25.4	6.4
1981	5	20.7	8.0
1986	10	17.7	9.6
1991	15	14.3	11.4
1996	20	12.4	13.3

a) Graph the percent of the population with a university degree versus the years from 1976. Draw the line of best fit.

b) Determine an equation for the line of best fit from part a).

c) Graph the percent of the population with less than a grade 9 education versus the years from 1976. Draw the line of best fit.

d) Determine an equation for the line of best fit from part c).

e) Predict the percent of Canadians over the age of 15 who will have less than a grade 9 education in 2011.

f) Predict the percent of Canadians over the age of 15 who will have a university degree in 2016.

g) Estimate the year in which the percent of Canadians over the age of 15 with a university degree equalled the percent with less than a grade 9 education.

h) How would drawing the graphs from parts a) and c) on the same grid or in the same viewing window help you to answer part g)? Explain and justify your reasoning.

i) Graph the percent of the population with a university degree versus the percent of the population with a grade 9 education. Draw the line of best fit.

j) Determine an equation for the line of best fit from part i).

10. Education spending research a) Make a table of values listing the amount, in billions of dollars, spent per year on education in Canada at 5-year intervals from 1971 to the most recent year possible.
b) Taking 1971 as year 0, 1976 as year 5, and so on, graph the amount spent versus the year. Draw the line of best fit.
c) Determine an equation for the line of best fit.
d) Use the equation to predict the amount that will be spent on education in the year 50 years after the most recent year in the table.

11. Medical research Make a table of values listing the current population of each province and the number of medical doctors who practise there.
a) Graph the number of doctors versus the population and draw the line of best fit.
b) How is the number of doctors related to the population?
c) Determine an equation for the line of best fit.

12. Physiology experiment a) Measure, in centimetres, the width of the hand span and the length of the forearm for several classmates. Record the data in a table.
b) Plot the length of the forearm versus the width of the hand span. Draw the line of best fit.
c) How is the length of the forearm related to the width of the hand span?
d) Determine an equation for the line of best fit.

13. "The wave" experiment Fans in the stands at spectator sports sometimes perform "the wave." The fans in a column stand, raise their arms, cheer, lower their arms, and sit down. As these fans are sitting down, the fans in the column to their right begin to stand, and then they raise their arms, cheer, and sit down. The process continues along the rows in the stands.
a) Predict how long it would take 200 people sitting in a row to do the wave.
b) For different numbers of classmates sitting in a row, determine the time, in seconds, it takes to

complete the wave. Copy and complete the table.

Number of Students	2	4	6	8	10	12
Time Taken (s)						

c) Graph the time taken versus the number of students. Draw the line of best fit.
d) How is the time taken related to the number of students?
e) Let the time taken be t seconds and the number of students be n. Determine an equation for the line of best fit.
f) Use the equation to predict how long it would take 200 people to do the wave.
g) Compare your answer in part f) to your prediction in part a). Give possible reasons for any difference.

14. Bouncing ball experiment a) Use a tennis ball or some other suitable ball for this experiment, if you did not complete it on page 220. Drop the ball several times from different heights. Make a hypothesis about the relationship between the rebound height of the ball and the height from which it is dropped.
b) Drop the ball from 10 different heights. Each time the ball is dropped, measure and record the height from which the ball is dropped and the rebound height. Record the data in a table like the one shown.

Height of Ball (cm)	Rebound Height (cm)

c) How is the rebound height related to the height from which the ball is dropped?
d) How does the relationship between the rebound height and the height from which the ball is dropped compare with your hypothesis?
e) Graph the rebound height versus the height from which the ball is dropped. Draw the line of best fit.
f) Determine an equation for the line of best fit.
g) Predict whether the relationship between the rebound height and the height from which the ball is dropped depends on the type of ball used. Explain your reasoning.
h) Test your prediction from part g) and communicate your results.

5.7 Non-Linear Relations

Non-linear relations are relations whose graphs are not straight lines.

Explore: Interpret the Graph

The Leaning Tower of Pisa was built in the twelfth century. The graph shows the relationship between the angle of tilt of the tower and the year.

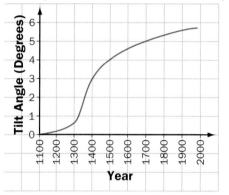

a) What was the tilt angle in 1700?

b) In what year was the tilt angle about 3°?

Inquire

1. During what time period did the tilt angle increase at the fastest rate?

2. Does the tower appear to have stopped leaning further? Explain.

3. Do you think Pisans want the tower pushed upright?

4. If the tower suddenly fell over tomorrow, how would you show this change on the graph?

When drawing the graphs of some relations, you will need to draw a curve through the points. This curve is known as the **curve of best fit.**

Example 1   Speeds of Runners

The table shows the average speeds of runners for races of different lengths.

a) Plot speed versus length of race on a grid, and draw a smooth curve through the points.

b) Use the graph to find the speed for a 1000-m race.

c) Use the graph to find the speed for a 2000-m race.

d) Why is the 200-m race run at the fastest speed?

Length of Race (m)	Speed (km/h)
100	36
200	37
400	33
800	28
1500	25

Solution

a)

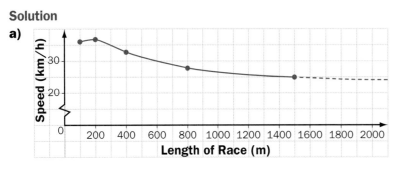

b) About 27 km/h.

c) Extending the graph to the right gives a speed of about 24 km/h for a 2000-m race.

d) In a 200-m race, the runners are at top speed for a greater distance than the runners in a 100-m race. In races longer than 200 m, runners can reach top speed but cannot maintain it over the greater distances.

Example 2   Graphing an Equation
Graph the equation $y = x^2 + 3$. The domain is R.

Solution 1   Using Paper and Pencil
Complete a table of values.

x	$x^2 + 3$	y	(x, y)
0	$0^2 + 3$	3	(0, 3)
1	$1^2 + 3$	4	(1, 4)
−1	$(-1)^2 + 3$	4	(−1, 4)
2	$2^2 + 3$	7	(2, 7)
−2	$(-2)^2 + 3$	7	(−2, 7)
3	$3^2 + 3$	12	(3, 12)
−3	$(-3)^2 + 3$	12	(−3, 12)

Plot the points and join them with a smooth curve.

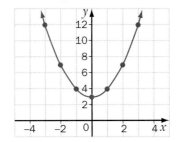

Solution 2   Using a Graphing Calculator
Set the viewing window to suitable values. Then, use your calculator to graph the equation $y = x^2 + 3$, without calculating a table of values.

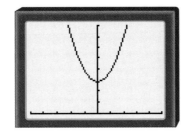

Practice

A

Plot the points on a grid and draw a smooth curve through the points.

1.

x	y
0	10
1	11
2	14
3	19
4	26
5	35

2.

x	y
0	30
1	29
2	26
3	21
4	14
5	5

Graph each equation using a graphing calculator, or complete the table of values for each equation and draw its graph on a grid. The domain is R.

3. $y = x^2 + 1$

x	y
-3	
-2	
-1	
0	
1	
2	
3	

4. $y = x^2 - 4$

x	y
-3	
-2	
-1	
0	
1	
2	
3	

Applications and Problem Solving

5. a) Measurement Copy and complete the table for squares of the given side lengths.

Side Length	Area	Perimeter
0	0	0
1		
2		
3		
4		
5		

b) Plot perimeter versus area on a grid and draw a smooth curve through the points.

c) Use the graph to find the area of a square with a perimeter of 14 units.

d) Use the graph to find the perimeter of a square with an area of 20 square units.

6. Cube volumes a) Copy and complete the table for cubes with the given edge lengths.

Edge Length (cm)	1	2	3	4
Volume (cm³)	1	8		

b) Plot the volume versus the edge length and draw a smooth curve of best fit.

c) Use the graph to find the approximate volume of a cube with an edge length of 1.5 cm; 2.5 cm.

d) Solve part c) by a different method. Which method do you prefer? Explain.

7. Stopping distance The stopping distance of a car is related to the car's speed. The table gives the minimum stopping distance on dry, level concrete. This distance includes the distance travelled during the reaction time the driver takes to apply the brakes.

Speed (km/h)	Stopping Distance (m)
0	0
20	10
40	18
60	32
80	55
100	85

a) Plot stopping distance versus speed on a grid and draw a smooth curve through the points.

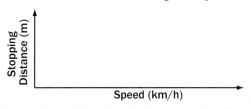

b) From the graph, what is the stopping distance at a speed of 50 km/h? 70 km/h?

c) A soccer field is 100 m long. How fast would a car be travelling if it took the length of the soccer field to stop?

8. Prism volumes The volume of a rectangular prism is found using the formula $V = B \times h$, where B is the area of the base and h is the height of the prism.

a) A rectangular prism has a height of 2 cm and a square base. The side length of the base is s. Copy and complete the table for the given values of s.

Side Length of Base (cm)	Area of Base (cm²)	Volume (cm³)
1		
2		
3		
4		
5		

b) Plot the volume versus the side length of the base and draw a smooth curve of best fit.

c) Use the graph to find the approximate volume of the prism with a height of 2 cm and a square base of side length 2.5 cm; 3.5 cm.

B

9. Paper-cutting experiment A large sheet of paper is cut in half, and one of the pieces is placed on top of the other. The two pieces are then cut in half, the resulting pieces are placed on top of each other, and so on.

a) Copy and complete the table to show the number of pieces there are after each number of cuts.

Number of Cuts	1	2	3	4	5	6
Number of Pieces	2	4				

b) Plot the number of pieces versus the number of cuts and draw the curve of best fit.

c) How many pieces will there be after 7 cuts? 8 cuts?

10. a) On the same set of axes, sketch the graphs of $y = x^2$, $y = x^2 + 1$, $y = x^2 + 4$, $y = x^2 - 1$, and $y = x^2 - 4$ for a domain of the real numbers from -3 to 3. Alternatively, graph these relations in the same viewing window of a graphing calculator.

b) Describe how the graphs are the same and how they are different.

11. Farming research The percent of Canadians who live on farms has changed since data were first collected in 1931.

a) Use your research skills to make a table of values listing the percent of Canadians living on farms at 10-year intervals, from 1931 to the most recent year possible.

b) Plot the percent versus the year and draw the curve of best fit.

c) Predict the percent of Canadians living on farms 10 years after the most recent year in the table.

12. Book research Books that are still available from the publisher are known as books in print. To find the total number of books in print at any time, each book in print with an International Standard Book Number (ISBN) is counted exactly once. No account is taken of the number of copies of the book that have been printed.

a) Use your research skills to make a table showing the total number of books in print in Canada and the United States each year over the past 10 years.

b) Graph the number versus the year and draw the curve of best fit.

c) Use the curve to predict the number of books in print 10 years from now.

13. Wood bison research The wood bison, also called the wood buffalo, is found only in Canada. In 1800, it was estimated that there were about 186 000 wood bison.

a) Draw a graph to show how the number of wood bison has changed from 1800 to the present.

b) Use your graph to predict the number of wood bison 100 years from now.

C

14. Measurement A rectangle has a width of w units and a length of $2w$ units.
a) Write an equation for the area, A, in terms of the width, w.
b) Graph the equation.
c) Which quadrant(s) did you use for the graph? Explain.
d) If the rectangle has an area of 12.5 cm^2, what is its width, in centimetres?

15. Falling objects By dropping objects from the Leaning Tower of Pisa, Galileo showed that different

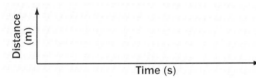

Time (s)	Distance (m)
0	0
1	4.9
2	19.6
3	44.1
4	78.4

objects fall at the same rate. The table gives the total distance travelled by a baseball dropped from a tower after different lengths of time.

a) Plot distance versus time on a grid and draw a smooth curve through the points.

b) Acapulco cliff divers dive from a height of 36 m. How long does it take them to hit the water?
c) Using the data in the table, write an equation of the form $d = \blacksquare t^2$, where d represents the distance, in metres, t represents the time, in seconds, and $\blacksquare$ represents a number.
d) In the equation from part c), replace d with y and replace t with x.
e) Graph the equation from part d) using positive and negative values of x.
f) Compare the graphs from parts a) and e). How are they the same? How are they different?
g) Explain the differences in the two graphs.

16. Pattern Each large square is made with red border squares and blue interior squares.

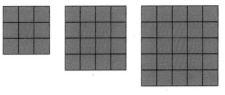

Copy and complete the table.

Side Length of Large Square (s)	Number of Blue Squares (b)
3	1
4	
5	
6	
7	

a) Plot the number of blue squares versus the side length of the large square. Draw the curve of best fit.
b) Write an equation in the form $b = \blacksquare$ to express the number of blue squares, b, in terms of the side length of the large square, s.
c) How many blue squares are there if the side length of the large square is 12? 50?
d) What is the side length of the large square if there are 529 blue squares? 1936 blue squares?
e) Is it possible to have a large square with 408 blue squares? Explain.

17. Counting experiment a) Estimate how long you would take to count the whole numbers from 1 to 1000. When making your estimate, consider the time it takes to say one-digit numbers, two-digit numbers, and three-digit numbers.
b) Measure the time it takes to say numbers with from 1 to 6 digits. Record the data.
c) Plot the time versus the number of digits.
d) Calculate the time you would take to count from 1 to 1000. Compare the result with your estimate from part a).
e) Use the data to predict how long you would take to count from 1 to 1 000 000. Describe and justify your procedure, and communicate your solution.

INVESTIGATING MATH

Finite Differences

In a table of values with evenly-spaced x-coordinates, the x-coordinate increases or decreases by the same number from one row to the next. **Finite differences** are differences between consecutive y-values in tables with evenly-spaced x-coordinates. Tables of values and first difference calculations for the equations $y = 3x$ and $y = x^2$ are as shown.

$y = 3x$

x	y	First Differences
0	0	
		$3 - 0 = 3$
1	3	
		$6 - 3 = 3$
2	6	
		$9 - 6 = 3$
3	9	
		$12 - 9 = 3$
4	12	
		$15 - 12 = 3$
5	15	

$y = x^2$

x	y	First Differences
0	0	
		$1 - 0 = 1$
1	1	
		$4 - 1 = 3$
2	4	
		$9 - 4 = 5$
3	9	
		$16 - 9 = 7$
4	16	
		$25 - 16 = 9$
5	25	

By calculating finite differences from a table of values, you can determine whether a graph of a relation is linear or non-linear.

1 Exploring Finite Differences

1. Copy and complete the table of values shown and calculate the first differences for each of the following relations.

a) $y = 2x$ **b)** $y = x^2 + 3$
c) $y = 3x - 1$ **d)** $y = 2^x$

x	y	First Differences
0		
1		
2		
3		
4		

2. Plot the points for each relation from question 1. For the linear relations, join the points with a straight line. For the non-linear relations, join the points with a smooth curve.

3. Which of the four graphs are linear?

4. What do the first differences of the linear relations have in common?

5. Which of the four graphs are non-linear?

6. How do the first differences of non-linear relations differ from the first differences of linear relations?

7. Write a rule for using first differences to determine whether a relation is linear or non-linear.

2 Using First Differences

1. Use first differences to determine whether each relation is linear or non-linear.

a)

x	y
0	2
1	3
2	4
3	5
4	6

b)

x	y
0	0
1	2
2	8
3	18
4	32

c)

x	y
0	5
1	7
2	9
3	11
4	13

d)

x	y
0	-2
1	-1
2	2
3	7
4	14

e)

x	y
0	4
1	1
2	-2
3	-5
4	-8

f)

x	y
0	0
1	1
2	8
3	27
4	64

g)

x	y
0	5
2	3
4	1
6	-1
8	-3

h)

x	y
-2	4
-1	2
0	0
1	-2
2	-4

i)

x	y
-4	-17
-3	-10
-2	-5
-1	-2
0	-1

2. Gravity The table shows the height above the ground, after different lengths of time, for an object dropped from the top of the Skylon tower in Niagara Falls, Ontario.

Time (s)	Height (m)
0	236
1	231
2	216
3	191
4	156

Without graphing height versus time, determine whether this relation is linear or non-linear.

3. Caribou At top speed, caribou can run at 14 m/s.

a) Copy and complete the table by determining the distances covered in different lengths of time by caribou running at top speed.

Time (s)	Distance (m)
1	
2	
3	
4	
5	

b) Without graphing distance versus time, determine whether this relation is linear or non-linear.

4. Pattern The first figure consists of one pentagon with equal sides and a perimeter of 5 units. The second figure consists of two connected pentagons and has a perimeter of 8 units.

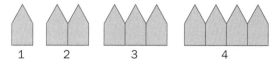

a) Complete a table of values showing the number of pentagons and the perimeter for each of the first five figures in the pattern.

b) Without graphing perimeter versus number of pentagons, determine whether this relation is linear or non-linear.

5. Pattern The first five diagrams in a pattern are shown. Each square has an area of 1 square unit.

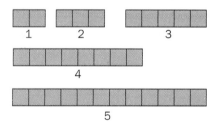

a) Complete a table of values showing the diagram number and the area for each diagram.

b) Without graphing area versus diagram number, determine whether the relation is linear or non-linear.

c) Would the graph of area versus number of squares be linear or non-linear? Explain.

d) If the area of each square was 2 square units, would your answers to parts b) and c) change? Explain.

5.8 General Relations

The 110-m hurdles race is one of the most exciting events in track. In 1992, Mark McKoy became the second Canadian to win an Olympic gold medal in this event. The first was Earl Thomson who won gold in 1920.

Explore: Study the Graph

The graph shows an imaginary race between Mark McKoy and Earl Thomson, using their winning times at the Olympics.

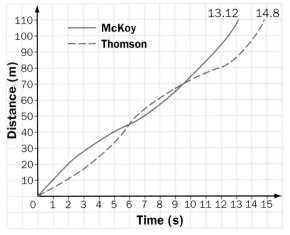

a) Who won the race? What was his time?

b) What was the loser's time?

Inquire

1. Who took the lead at the start of the race?

2. After how many seconds was the leader passed?

3. At what distance from the finish did the winner take the lead?

4. Draw a graph of an imaginary 110-m hurdles race between 3 runners. Have the lead change 3 times. Have one of the runners fall, then get up and complete the race. Compare your graph with a classmate's.

Example   Height of Water in a Spa

The diagram shows the side view of a personal spa. Your job as the spa tester is to run water into the spa up to the red mark, get into the spa, test the jets, get out of the spa, and then drain the spa. Sketch a graph of the height of the water in the deep end of the spa versus time from when you start to fill the spa to when it is empty.

Solution

From A to B, the height increases quickly as water fills only the deep end.

From B to C, the height increases more slowly as water fills the deep and shallow ends.

From C to D, the height increases rapidly when you get in.

From D to E, the height stays constant while you stay in.

From E to F, the height decreases rapidly when you get out.

From F to G, the height decreases slowly as you drain the top part of the spa.

From G to H, the height decreases rapidly as you drain the deep end.

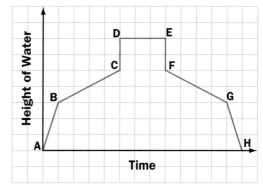

Applications and Problem Solving

A

1. Water-skiing The graph shows the distance a water-skier is from a dock versus time.

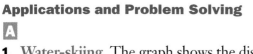

a) Describe what the water-skier did.
b) Draw a diagram to show the skier's possible path on the lake.

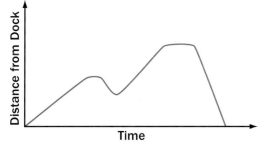

2. Measurement Sketch each of the following graphs.
a) perimeter of a square versus its side length
b) area of a square versus its side length

B

3. Modelling math Each graph shows distance from school versus time. Describe a situation that could be modelled by each graph.

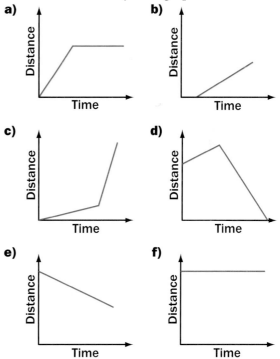

4. Bicycle trips State which of the following graphs can represent a trip taken by a student on a bicycle and which ones cannot. Give reasons for your decisions.

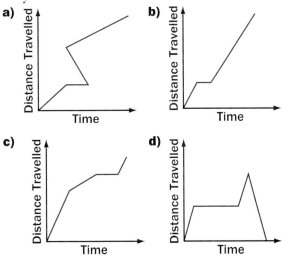

a)
b)
c)
d)

5. Whale watching The graph shows the distance from port versus time for three boats taking people to watch whales. The boats stop when whales are sighted.

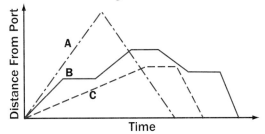

a) Describe what each boat did.
b) Which boat spent the most time stopped?
c) From which boat were no whales sighted?

6. Montréal metro In the Montréal metro, you can ride a subway train anywhere on the system for the cost of one ticket. All tickets are the same price.
a) Sketch a graph of the cost versus the distance travelled for one trip on the metro.
b) Sketch a graph of the cost versus the number of metro trips. Is the graph discrete or continuous?

7. Cross-country skiing The picture shows the elevation of a cross-country ski trail.

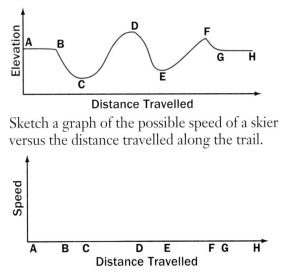

Sketch a graph of the possible speed of a skier versus the distance travelled along the trail.

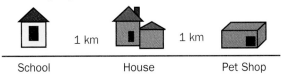

8. Shopping trip Josette leaves school and rides her bike 2 km to a pet shop to buy food for her dog. She passes her house on her way to the store. After buying the food, she rides 1 km to her house.

School   1 km   House   1 km   Pet Shop

a) Sketch a graph of the distance Josette rides versus time, starting when she leaves school.
b) Sketch a graph of the distance Josette is from her house versus time, starting when she leaves school.
c) Sketch a graph of the distance Josette is from school versus time, starting when she leaves school.
d) Sketch a graph of the distance Josette is from the pet shop versus time, starting when she leaves school.

9. Modelling math Sketch each of the following graphs.
a) the temperature of boiling water versus the time for which it boils
b) the average daily temperature in your town versus the date for a year beginning on April 1
c) the height of the average person versus the person's age

10. Tourist site An observatory overlooks a waterfall. A path leads from the observatory to a restaurant 500 m from the observatory. The path passes the waterfall 200 m from the observatory.

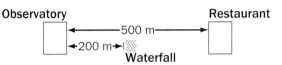

The graph shows the actions of 4 tourists during a 12-min period, starting at 09:00.

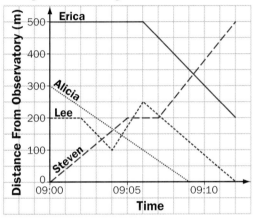

Describe what the 4 tourists did between 09:00 and 09:12. Include:
- where they were at 09:00
- the directions and distances they walked between 09:00 and 09:12
- the people each of them met or passed on the path during the 12-min period

C

11. Go-kart track A test track for new go-karts is shown. Drivers drive at top speed on the straight parts and slow down for the corners.

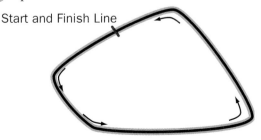

a) Sketch a graph of speed versus time from the start to the end of the first lap.

b) Sketch a graph of speed versus time from the start of the second lap to the end of the third lap.

c) For the second lap, sketch a graph of distance from the start line versus the time.

12. Modelling math Describe a practical situation that could be represented by each graph.

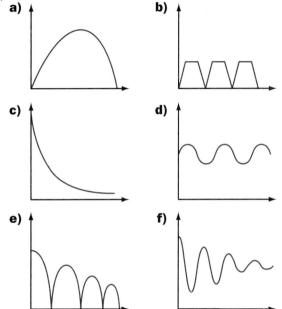

13. Modelling math Sketch a graph similar to the one in question 5. Have a classmate describe the scene.

14. Swimming race Canadian swimmer Anne Ottenbrite won an Olympic gold medal in the 200-m breaststroke in a time of 2 min 30.38 s. Another Canadian, Lisa Flood, won a Commonwealth Games bronze medal in the 200-m breaststroke in 2 min 31.85 s.

a) Draw a graph of distance swum versus time for an imaginary race between these two swimmers. Use the times given and remember that, in a 200-m race, the swimmers turn after 50 m, 100 m, and 150 m. Have a classmate interpret your graph to describe the race.

b) For this imaginary race, how would the graph be different if you plotted distance from the start versus time, instead of distance swum versus time? Explain and justify your reasoning.

CAREER CONNECTION

The Environment

Many people have careers that are related to the environment. Some are scientists studying subjects such as rain forest destruction, acid rain, or the extinction of plant and animal species. Others work in jobs that have a direct environmental impact, including garbage disposal, sewage treatment, or recycling programs.

A team of Canadian scientists, including professors Donna Mergler and Marc Lucotte of the University of Québec, has done environmental research in Brazil. The team has studied mercury pollution along the Tapajos River, a tributary of the Amazon.

There are two sources of mercury pollution in the Tapajos. The first is gold mining, in which liquid mercury is used to extract gold from sediments dredged from the river. The resulting amalgam is caught in wooden sluices and heated to evaporate the mercury, leaving the gold behind. Half of the mercury ends up in the river. The second source of mercury in the river is deforestation, which causes the release of naturally occurring mercury in the soil.

The Canadian team has found that villagers who eat the fish from the river are beginning to show signs of mercury poisoning.

1 Gold Mining

1. The graph shows the relationship between the mass of gold extracted and the mass of mercury used in Brazil's gold mining industry.

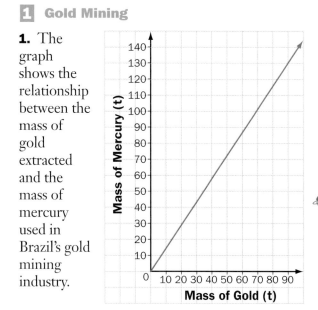

Mass of Gold (t)

a) Brazil produces about 90 t of gold per year. Use the graph to estimate the mass of mercury used per year.
b) What mass of mercury, to the nearest tenth of a tonne, is used in extracting each tonne of gold?

2. By redesigning the sluices, gold miners could boost gold production by 50% and reclaim 95% of the mercury. If the sluices were redesigned,
a) what mass of gold, in tonnes, would Brazil produce per year?
b) what mass of mercury, to the nearest tenth of a tonne, would be lost per year?

3. Use your results from question 2 to plot a graph of mass of mercury lost versus mass of gold for the redesigned sluices.

2 Locating Information

1. Where would you look to find information about an environmental career or an environmental issue that interests you?

2. Find information about mercury contamination of fish in Canada's North. What causes the mercury pollution? Which people are most affected by it?

3. Mercury poisoning is sometimes called Minamata disease. Find out why, and describe the symptoms of mercury poisoning.

Summer Olympics

Use the *Olympics* database, from the Computer Data Bank to complete the following.

1 Timed Events

There are over 250 Summer Olympics events, many of which have taken place at each Summer Olympics since 1896. The 20 Summer Olympics events that are in this database are timed events where winning times are less than two minutes.

1. Find the winning time in 1996 that is over 60.00 s. For which event is it?

2. Find the *Swimming* records, and sort them from fastest to slowest time. What is the fastest time? For which event and in which year is it? Who is the winning athlete?

3. Repeat question 2 for *Track and Field* records.

2 Canadian Winners

1. Find all the records where Canada is the winning country. How many records are displayed?

2. Canadians have won 45 gold medals at Summer Olympics from 1896 to 1996. What fraction of those are in this database?

3. In which events are Canada's most recent wins? Who are the athletes?

4. In which event and year was Canada's first win? Who was the athlete?

3 World Records

The *World Record, s* field tells what the world record was going into the Olympic event.

1. Find all the records for which *World Record, s* is available.

2. Do winning Olympic times usually beat world records? Explain.

4 Finding Trends

1. Display the following fields together.

Event   Year   Winning Time, s

2. Find all the records for *100-m Backstroke, Men*, and sort them by year.

3. Copy and paste those records onto a spreadsheet. Then, create a graph of winning time versus year.

4. Describe any trends you observe.

5. Write a problem about your graph. Have a classmate solve your problem.

6. Repeat questions 2 to 5 for the following.
a) 100-m Freestyle, Women
b) 110-m Hurdles, Men
c) 4×100-m Relay, Women

5 Female and Male Athletes

There are usually separate competitions for female and male athletes. In the past, men's Olympic times have been faster than women's.

1. Work with classmates to compare men's and women's winning times in at least six events. Are women's winning times getting closer to men's winning times? Explain.

2. If the trend continues in each event from question 1, will the women's winning time ever be faster than the men's winning time? If so, estimate the first year in which the women's winning time will be faster.

3. Do you think that the trends found in question 1 will actually continue? Explain.

MODELLING MATH — SPORTS

5.9 How Can We Model the Flight of an Object?

The flight of an object that follows a curved path was introduced on page 235 at the beginning of this chapter. Use the following mathematical models to analyze the flight of a punted football.

1 **Modelling the Flight of a Football Punted Nose First**

The graph models the flight of a football punted nose first at about 90 km/h when there is no wind. The graph shows the relationship between the following three variables.
• the angle at which the ball is kicked
• the distance it travels
• the time it spends in the air
For a ball punted at an angle of 30°, locate 30° on the graph. Read horizontally from 30° to find the distance the ball travels, which is about 55 m. Read vertically to find the time in the air, which is about 2.7 s.

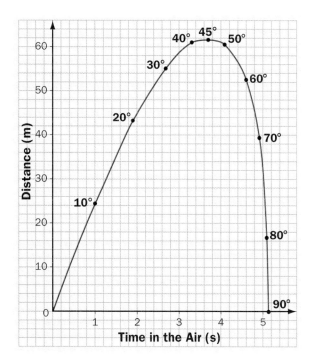

1. What are the distance and the time in the air for a ball punted at an angle of 20°? 60°?

2. If you wanted to punt a ball 30 m, what punt angles could you use? What would be the time in the air for each punt?

3. If the time in the air is 3 s, what are the punt angle and the distance for the punt?

4. What punt angle gives the maximum distance? What is the time in the air for this punt?

5. What punt angle gives the maximum time in the air? What is the distance for this punt?

2 Modelling the Flight of a Football Punted End-Over-End

The graph models the flight of a football punted end-over-end at a speed of about 90 km/h.

1. What are the distance and the time in the air for a ball punted at an angle of 20°? 60°?

2. If the time in the air is 4 s, what are the punt angle and the distance of the punt?

3. What punt angle gives the maximum distance? What is the time in the air for this punt?

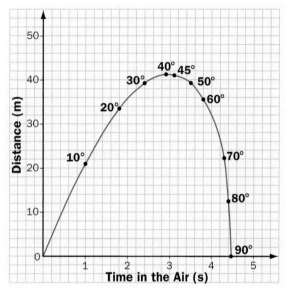

4. What punt angle gives the maximum time in the air? What is the distance for this punt?

3 Comparing the Models

1. What is the difference in the maximum distances for the punts that are nose first and those that are end-over-end?

2. What is the difference in the maximum times in the air for the punts that are nose first and those that are end-over-end?

3. a) What percent of the maximum distance for a nose-first punt is the maximum distance for an end-over-end punt, to the nearest percent?
b) What percent of the maximum time in the air for a nose-first punt is the maximum time in the air for an end-over-end punt, to the nearest percent?
c) Why are the percents so different?

4. Why does a football punted nose first travel farther and stay in the air longer than a football punted end-over-end?

Review

5.1 *Use each of the following equations.*
✏ **a)** *Describe the relation in words.*
b) *Complete a table of values for the domain* {–2, –1, 0, 1, 2}.
c) *Write the relation as a set of ordered pairs.*
d) *State the range.*

1. $x + y = 8$ **2.** $x - y = 0$
3. $y = x + 2$ **4.** $y = 2x + 5$

Find 5 ordered pairs for each relation.

5. $x + y = 6$ **6.** $x - y = 4$
7. $y = 3 - x$ **8.** $y = 2x - 3$

Write an equation that describes each relation.

9.

x	y
–1	3
0	2
1	1
2	0

10.

x	y
–2	–8
–1	–4
0	0
1	4

5.2 **11. a)** Plot the points A(–3, 6), B(2, 6), and C(–3, –2) on a grid.
b) Write the coordinates of the fourth point needed to form a rectangle.
c) What are the dimensions of this rectangle?

For each graph,
a) *express the relation as a set of ordered pairs*
b) *write the domain and range*

12. 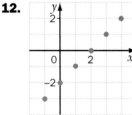   **13.**

5.3 **14. Grizzly bear** Over short distances, a grizzly bear has a top speed of about 13 m/s.
a) Copy and complete the table of values for a grizzly bear at top speed.

Time (s)	Distance (m)
0	
1	
2	
3	
4	

b) Use the ordered pairs to plot a graph of distance versus time.
c) Use the graph to estimate the distances a grizzly bear can cover in 2.6 s; in 4.8 s.

15. Screening movies This graph shows the relation between the width of the image on a movie screen and the distance of the projector from the screen.

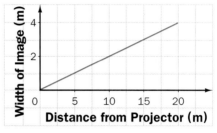

a) How wide is the image if the projector is 12.5 m from the screen?
b) How far is the projector from the screen if the width of the image is 3.5 m?

5.4 **16.** Graph the equation $y = 3x - 1$ for each of the following domains.
a) {2, 1, 0, –1, –2}
b) the real numbers, R

Given the points on the grid, write an equation to represent each relation.

17.   **18.**

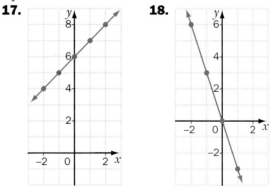

5.5 a) *Graph each of the following relations.*
b) *State whether each relation is a direct variation or a partial variation.*
19. $y = 4x + 1$
20. $y = -2x$

21. Wages Romie earns \$12/h as a security guard. How long must she work to earn \$285?

22. Pattern a) For this pattern, how many dots are in the fourth diagram? the fifth diagram?

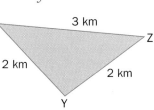

1	2	3

b) Plot the number of dots versus the diagram number for the first 5 diagrams.
c) Write a partial variation equation in the form $d = \blacksquare$ to express the number of dots, d, in terms of the diagram number, n.
d) Use the equation to find the number of dots in the 100th diagram.

5.6 **a)** *Graph the data and draw the line of best fit.*
b) *Determine an equation for the line of best fit.*

23.

x	y
–20	–15
–10	–6
0	4
10	15
20	24
30	36

24.

x	y
–20	–56
–10	–33
0	–3
10	27
20	64
30	89

5.7 *Graph each relation using a graphing calculator, or complete a table of values for each relation and draw the graph on a grid. The domain is R.*

25. $y = x^2 + 2$ **26.** $y = x^2 - 3$

5.8 **27. Sailboat race** A triangular race course for sailboats is shown, with the starting buoy marked S and the other buoys marked Y and Z. A boat sailed from S to Y to Z and back to S. Sketch a graph of
a) the boat's distance from S versus time
b) the boat's distance from Y versus time
c) the boat's distance from Z versus time

S — 3 km — Z
2 km
2 km
Y

Exploring Math

The Game of Pong Hau K'i

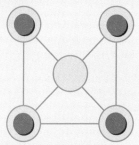

A board game for two players is called Pong Hau K'i in China and Ou-moul-ko-no in Korea. The game board is made up of five circles joined by seven line segments. One player has two red counters placed on the upper circles. The other player has two blue counters placed on the lower circles.

One player moves a counter along a line segment to an adjacent empty circle. The other player then moves a counter along a line segment to an adjacent empty circle. The players continue to take turns.

The object of the game is to block your opponent's counters, so that your opponent does not have a move.

1. a) Play the game several times, taking turns to make the first move.
b) Is there a winning strategy for the player who makes the first move? Explain.
c) Is it better to have the red counters or the blue counters? Explain.

2. a) Modify the game by placing the counters on any four of the five circles at the start. Decide which colour each of you will play and who will place the first counter. After the first counter is placed, the other player places a counter. The players, in the same order, then each place their second counters. Decide who will make the first move. Play the modified game several times.
b) Is it better to be the first player or the second player to place a counter? Explain.
c) Is it better to make the first move or the second move? Explain.

Chapter Check

Use each of the following equations.
a) *Describe the relation in words.*
b) *Complete a table of values for the domain {–2, –1, 0, 1, 2}.*
c) *Write the relation as a set of ordered pairs.*
d) *State the range.*

1. $x + y = -2$ **2.** $y = 2x - 1$

3. Write 5 ordered pairs for the relation $y = 3x + 4$.

Write an equation that describes each relation.

4.

x	y
–2	1
–1	2
0	3
1	4
2	5

5.

x	y
–2	–10
–1	–5
0	0
1	5
2	10

6. Plot and join each set of points in order. Join the last point to the first point in each set to form a closed figure. Identify each figure.
a) P(6, 1), Q(2, –3), R(5, –2)
b) A(–5, 3), B(–4, –1), C(4, –1), D(3, 3)
c) P(0, –3), Q(–5, –3), R(–5, –2), S(0, –2)

For each graph,
a) *express the relation as a set of ordered pairs*
b) *write the domain and range*
c) *describe the relation in words*
d) *write an equation for the relation*

7.   **8.**

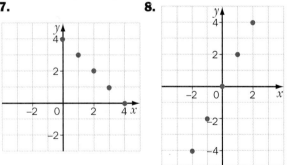

9. a) Graph the equation $y = 3x + 2$.
b) Is this equation a direct variation or a partial variation?

10. **Train travel** This graph shows the distance a train travels over time.

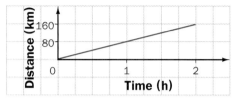

a) About how far does the train travel in 1.25 h?
b) About how long does the train take to travel 20 km?

11. **Keyboarding** The number of words input varies directly as the time spent keyboarding. Janos can input 240 words in 5 min.
a) Find the constant of variation and write the equation.
b) How many words can Janos input in 12 min?
c) How long will it take him to input a 3000-word short story?

12. **Track and field**
Ahmad ran in a 10 000-m race. The table shows the approximate distances he ran in different lengths of time.

Time (min)	Distance (m)
5	1600
10	3100
15	4700
20	6400
25	8000
30	9700

a) Draw a scatter plot of distance versus time. Draw the line of best fit.
b) Determine an equation for the line of best fit.
c) Estimate, to the nearest tenth of a minute, the time Ahmad took to run the first 7000 m; to finish the race.

Graph each relation using a graphing calculator, or complete a table of values for each relation and draw the graph on a grid. The domain is R.
13. $y = x^2 + 5$ **14.** $y = x^2 - 1$

15. **Walking the dog**
The diagram shows the route Rosa travelled from her home, H, when she took her dog for a walk. Sketch a graph of Rosa's distance from home versus time for the walk.

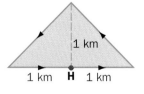

Using the Strategies

1. Measurement The squares are exactly the same size. The total area of the figure is 384 cm^2. What is the perimeter of the figure?

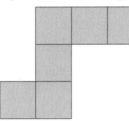

2. Dividing grids The diagram shows two ways to divide the grid into two congruent pieces using line segments that connect grid points.

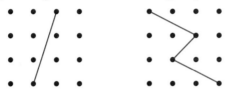

How many other ways are there, if rotations are reflections are not permitted?

3. Grouping numbers In how many different ways can you place the numbers 1, 2, 3, 4, 5, 6, 7, 8, and 9 into groups so that the sum of the numbers in each group is 15?

4. Estimating distances About how many kilometres will you travel on school property this school year?

5. Eating habits Estimate the number of ice cream cones the high school students in Ontario eat in one year.

6. Seating arrangements Justine, Chris, and Meelang plan to travel together in a van. They will all sit in the front seat. In how many different arrangements can they sit in each of the following situations?
a) all three can drive
b) only Chris and Meelang can drive
c) only Justine can drive

7. Pattern If the pattern continues, find the following product.

$$\left(1 - \frac{1}{2}\right)\left(1 - \frac{1}{3}\right)\left(1 - \frac{1}{4}\right)\cdots\left(1 - \frac{1}{24}\right)$$

8. Car trip The graph shows the speed of a car for 10 min. Write a story to explain the graph.

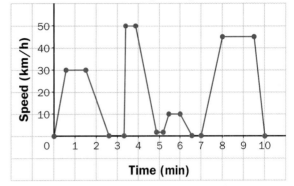

9. Calendar math If two months in a row have a Friday the 13th, what months are they? Explain.

10. Even numbers Six consecutive even numbers are written on a piece of paper. If the sum of the first three numbers is 60, what is the sum of the last three?

11. Difference of squares The number 16 can be written as the difference of two squares.

$$16 = 25 - 9$$
$$= 5^2 - 3^2$$

What other whole numbers between 10 and 20 can be written as the difference of two squares?

12. Plane trip A plane left Calgary at 16:00 and flew to Montréal at a speed of 700 km/h. What time was it in Montréal when the plane landed?

13. Migration For a recent 10-year period, determine
a) the total number of immigrants who moved to Canada
b) the total number of emigrants who left Canada
c) the quotient of immigrants divided by emigrants, to the nearest tenth

CHAPTER 6

Algebra

How Can We Model Readability?

The term *readability* refers to all the factors that affect success in reading. One factor is reading speed. People who read too slowly may give up before they complete and understand what they are reading. Reading speed is calculated in words per minute.

1. Suppose a book has the following characteristics.
Total number of pages: 235
Average number of words per page: 228
Average number of lines per page: 25
a) What is the total number of words in the book?
b) What is the total number of lines in the book?
c) What is the average number of words per line?

2. Suppose you read 9 pages and 6 lines of the book from question 1 in 10 min.
a) How many words did you read, to the nearest ten?
d) How many words did you read per minute?

3. For a book you are currently reading, determine your reading speed, in words per minute.

4. Other factors that affect success in reading are the interest of the reader in what is being read and the quality of the lighting that the reader uses. List three other factors that affect success in reading.

In Modelling Math — English on pages 331 to 333, you will explore ways of modelling the readability of a mystery novel and other pieces of writing.

Using Patterns

1 Patterns in Tables

The patterns in the tables are found in the columns. Copy and complete the tables. Write the rules for completing each table.

1.

1	4	7	9	12	9		
3	3	4	5	4	7	9	
4	7	11			16	20	
3	12	28					72

2.

1	4	6	9	11			
2	8	12			14		30
4	16	24				20	
7	28	42					

3.

1	4	6	9	3		
30	77	91			99	96
6	11	13		8		12
5	7	7	1	5	2	9

4.

15	14	12			36	40
3	2	3		3	4	
5	7	4	6	9		20
2	5	1	2			

5.

3	5	6	4		7	5
24	45	42		16	28	25
35	59	55				
8	9	7	5	8		

6.

2	3	5	4			10
6	9	15		18		
7	10	16			25	
13	19	31				

2 Stamp Patterns

Two stamps can be attached to form two rectangular shapes.

1. In how many ways can 12 stamps be attached to form rectangular shapes? Sketch your solutions.

2. How many rectangular shapes can be made with 10 attached stamps?

3. How many rectangular shapes can be made with 24 attached stamps?

4. Without drawing the stamps, how can you determine how many rectangular shapes can be made with 100 attached stamps? Explain and justify your reasoning.

3 Tile Patterns

A floor is being tiled using the pattern shown. Each grey tile is surrounded by orange tiles.

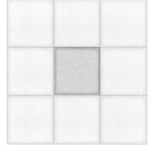

How many tiles of each colour do you need to tile each of the following areas?

1. 3 tiles by 3 tiles
2. 5 tiles by 3 tiles
3. 5 tiles by 5 tiles
4. 7 tiles by 3 tiles
5. 7 tiles by 5 tiles
6. 7 tiles by 7 tiles

Warm Up

1. Evaluate $5x$ for each value of x.
a) 2   **b)** -5
c) 0   **d)** -4

2. Evaluate $3y + 1$ for each value of y.
a) 0   **b)** 1
c) 5   **d)** -3

3. Evaluate $2z - 1$ for each value of z.
a) -1 **b)** 2
c) -5 **d)** 10

4. Evaluate for $x = -2$.
a) $x + 3$ **b)** $3x + 2$
c) $2x - 6$ **d)** $8 - 2x$

5. Evaluate for $x = 2$, $y = 3$, and $z = -4$.
a) $x + y + z$ **b)** xyz
c) $x + 2z$ **d)** $xy - z$

6. Evaluate for $a = 1.5$, $b = 2.5$, and $c = 3.5$.
a) $a + b + c$ **b)** $ab - 0.75$
c) $5a - 3b$ **d)** $1.2a + 3.2b$
e) $5.65 - ab$ **f)** $2.4b - a$
g) $ac - 2b$ **h)** $ab - bc - ca$

7. Evaluate for $a = 3$, $b = 2$, and $c = 4$.
a) $a^2 + b^2 + c^2$ **b)** $2ab^2 - 4c$
c) $2c^2 - a^3 + b^3$ **d)** $7 - 2ab + b^4$
e) $7ac - 3b^4$ **f)** $1 - a^2 + b^2 - c^2$

8. Evaluate for $x = -2$, $y = -3$, and $z = -1$.
a) $x^2 - y^2 - 3z$ **b)** $x^3 + z^3$
c) $2x^2 - 3yz$ **d)** $3xyz + 2xy - y^2$
e) $3x^2y - 2y^2z$ **f)** $z^5 + y^3 - 4x$

9. Evaluate for $x = -2.1$, $y = -1.4$, and $z = 2$.
Round answers to the nearest tenth, if necessary.
a) $2x + y + 5$ **b)** $2xz - 3y$
c) $2.3x - 4z$ **d)** $-0.5xyz$
e) $x^2 + y^2 + z$ **f)** $4z^2 - 2xy$
g) $x^3 + y^3$ **h)** $z^4 - x^2 - y^2$

Mental Math

Order of Operations

Calculate.

1. $2(3) + 4$ **2.** $3(-1) - 2$
3. $2(-3) + 3(2)$ **4.** $4(6 - 2)$
5. $-2(4 - 1)$ **6.** $-3(2 - 4)$
7. $3(4 - 1) - 1$ **8.** $5(1 - 2) + 3$

Calculate.

9. $2(4)^2$ **10.** $3(3 - 1)^3$
11. $3^2 - 2(3)$ **12.** $-2(2)^2 + 2$
13. $4(3)^2 - 2(3)$ **14.** $2(-2)^2 + 3(-2)$
15. $5(1)^2 + 2(1) - 3$ **16.** $-3(-1)^2 + 4(-1) + 5$

Multiplying Two Numbers That Differ by 2

To determine 16×14, first square their average, 15. Then, subtract 1.

$15^2 = 225$
$225 - 1 = 224$
So, $16 \times 14 = 224$.

Calculate.

1. 13×11 **2.** 14×12 **3.** 19×21
4. 29×31 **5.** 24×26 **6.** 41×39
7. 101×99 **8.** 59×61 **9.** 999×1001

To calculate 1.6×1.4 or 160×140, think 16×14. Then, place the decimal point.

$1.6 \times 1.4 = 2.24$
$160 \times 140 = 22\ 400$

Calculate.

10. 1.2×1.4 **11.** 1.5×1.3 **12.** 260×240
13. 290×310 **14.** 10.1×9.9 **15.** 130×110
16. 590×6.1 **17.** 39×0.41 **18.** 510×49
19. 180×1.6 **20.** 89×910 **21.** 0.69×0.71

22. Describe a method for multiplying two numbers that differ by 4. Use your method to evaluate each of the following.
a) 11×15 **b)** 22×18 **c)** 17×13
d) 32×28 **e)** 27×23 **f)** 98×102

6.1 Collecting Like Terms

The three dogs are *like* each other. The two cats are *like* each other. A dog and a cat are *unlike* each other. The words *like* and *unlike* are also used in mathematics.

Explore: Use a Diagram

The tangram square is made up of 7 pieces. The square is placed on a 4 by 4 grid. Copy the diagram into your notebook. Label the pieces with letters, starting at A. Use the same letter to label pieces with equal areas.

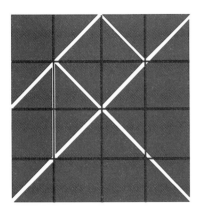

Inquire

1. What is the total number of pieces that make up the square?
2. Which of the pieces have areas that are identical or *like*?
3. Which of the pieces have areas that are not identical or are *unlike*?
4. Write two different expressions that represent the area of the tangram square.
5. Which of the two expressions in question 4 is simpler?

A **variable** is a letter that represents one or more numbers. A **term** is a number or a variable, or the product or quotient of numbers and variables. Some examples of terms are x^2, $4a$, and $\frac{b}{2}$.

Expressions that include numbers and variables, such as $3x + 2y + 10$, are called **algebraic expressions**. The algebraic expression $3x + 2y + 10$ has three terms.

Like terms have exactly the same variables raised to exactly the same exponents. For example, x, $3x$, and $7x$ are like terms. Another set of like terms is $2a^2$, $-5a^2$, and $9a^2$.

Unlike terms have different variables, or the same variable but different exponents. For example, $7b$, $3b^2$, $10q$, $3x$, and 7 are unlike terms.

If a term includes a variable, the numerical factor is called the **coefficient**. A term that does not include a variable is called a **constant term**. To identify the coefficients in the expression $x - 3y + 7$, the expression can be rewritten as $1x - 3y + 7$.

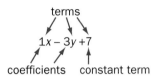

The coefficient of y is –3, not 3.

Since $8x$ and $3x$ are like terms, the expressions $8x + 3x$ and $8x - 3x$ can be simplified as shown.

$$8x + 3x = 11x \qquad 8x - 3x = 5x$$

The expression $8x + 3x$ and the expression $11x$ are called **equivalent expressions**, because they are equal for all values of the variable.

An expression is in **simplest form** when there are no like terms. For example, the expression $5x$ is in simplest form, but the expression $8x - 3x$ is not.

Example 1 **Expressions With One Variable**

Simplify.

a) $x + 2x$ **b)** $3b - b$ **c)** $2a - 5a$ **d)** $2y + y - 4$

Solution

Collect like terms.

a) $x + 2x = 3x$ **b)** $3b - b = 2b$

c) $2a - 5a = -3a$ **d)** $2y + y - 4 = 3y - 4$

Example 2 **Expressions With More Than One Variable**

Simplify.

a) $5x - 6y - 2x + 2y + 1$

b) $-11 + a - 2c + 16 + 3a - b - 5c$

Solution

a) $5x - 6y - 2x + 2y + 1 = 5x - 2x - 6y + 2y + 1$
$$= 3x - 4y + 1$$

b) $-11 + a - 2c + 16 + 3a - b - 5c = a + 3a - b - 2c - 5c - 11 + 16$
$$= 4a - b - 7c + 5$$

Example 3   Simplifying and Evaluating

a) Simplify $3x^2 - 5x + 4x - x^2$.

b) Evaluate for $x = -3$.

Solution

a) $3x^2 - 5x + 4x - x^2 = 3x^2 - x^2 - 5x + 4x$

$$= 2x^2 - x$$

b) For $x = -3$, $2x^2 - x = 2(-3)^2 - (-3)$

$$= 18 + 3$$

$$= 21$$

Practice

A

State the number of terms in each expression.

1. $a + b$ **2.** $2s + t - 5$

3. $x^2 - x + 4$ **4.** $jkl + mn$

State the coefficient(s) and the constant term in each expression.

5. $2y + 1$ **6.** $n - 4$

7. $3x^2 - 2x + 5$ **8.** $3 + w - 5w^4$

Simplify.

9. $3x + 5x$ **10.** $15p - 9p$

11. $-21s + 12s$ **12.** $-13a - 10a$

Simplify.

13. $6r + 4r - r$ **14.** $9p - p - 6p$

15. $-w + 6w - w$ **16.** $11a - 10a - 5a$

17. $-8q - 9q + 10q$ **18.** $16n + n - 17n$

Simplify.

19. $3t + 5a - 2t$ **20.** $2x - 5x - 7$

21. $2a - b + 3a$ **22.** $-4x + y - 6x$

23. $-9p - 10q + 8p$ **24.** $-j + 7k - 3j$

Simplify.

25. $5c + d - 2c - d$

26. $7p - q + p - 2q$

27. $3j + k - 5j - 2k$

28. $8a - 2b - 6a - 3b$

29. $-r + s + 2r - 2s$

30. $-5x + 5y + 5x - y$

Simplify.

31. $5x + 10 + 5y - 3x + 1$

32. $3a - 4b - 5 + a - b$

33. $-7t + 2 + 8r + 9r - 8t$

34. $-8 - 3z + 9x - 11 - 6z$

35. $8r - 11 - 18q + 5p + 7q$

36. $-4w + 7c - 8x - 9w - 3c$

37. $13j - 18d - 5d + 2j + 2c$

38. $-q + 7q + 11n + 11p - 8q$

Simplify.

39. $-p + 5q - 8r - q + 3p + 9r + 1$

40. $-2z + 3y - 10x - 4y + 4z - 3x$

41. $5q - 9s - 8r + 8q - 7r + 13s$

42. $-10 - a + 6c - 11 - 9c + 8a - d$

Simplify.

43. $2x^2 + x + x^2 + 4x$

44. $a^2 - 4a - 5a + 3a^2$

45. $y^2 + 2y^3 + y^3 - 5y^2$

46. $3 + 4t^2 - 5t - t^2 - 7$

Simplify, and then evaluate.

47. $2a + 8a$, when $a = 2$

48. $7t - 3t$, when $t = 3$

49. $-6k - 8k$, when $k = -2$

50. $-6y - 9y - y$, when $y = -3$

51. $3 + 4x - 2x$, when $x = 0.5$

52. $-5p - 3p + 1 - 6$, when $p = -1.5$

Simplify, and then evaluate.

53. $2x^2 - 3x^2$, when $x = 4$

54. $n^2 - n + 2n^2 - n$, when $n = -1$

55. $-3m^2 - m + 3m - m^2$, when $m = 0.5$

56. $-2d^3 + 5 + 4d^3 - 3.75$, when $d = -0.5$

Applications and Problem Solving

B

57. Measurement Write an expression for each perimeter in 2 different ways.

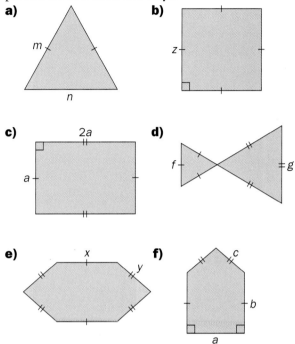

a)

b)

c) 2a

d)

e) x y

f) c b a

58. Measurement Write and simplify an expression for each perimeter.

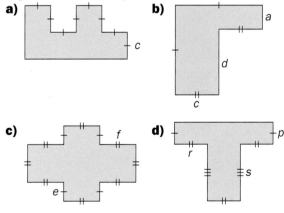

a) c

b) a d c

c) f e

d) p r s

C

59. a) Evaluate each of the following expressions for $x = 1$.

$$2x - 3 \qquad 2x^2 - 3x$$

b) Are the two expressions in part a) equivalent? Explain and justify your reasoning.

60. What is wrong with this sign?

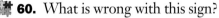

SMITHVILLE	
Population	460
Established	1830
Elevation	750
Sum	3040

61. Measurement Work with a partner to calculate the perimeter of this figure. Describe the simplest method you can find.

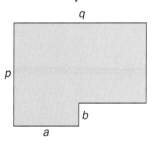

q p b a

NUMBER POWER

Place the digits from 1 to 9 in the boxes to make the statements true. Use the order of operations.

$$\blacksquare + \blacksquare - \blacksquare = 10$$

$$\blacksquare \div \blacksquare + \blacksquare = 10$$

$$\blacksquare - \blacksquare + \blacksquare = 10$$

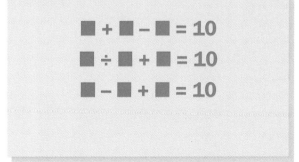

INVESTIGATING MATH

Modelling With Algebra Tiles

Each red tile represents +1.
Each white tile represents −1.

Each long green tile represents +x or x.
Each long white tile represents −x.

Each square green tile represents +x^2 or x^2.
Each square white tile represents −x^2.

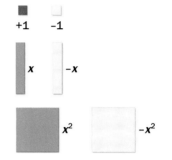

+1   -1

x   -x

x^2 -x^2

1 Representing Variables With Tiles

1. Write the expression represented by each group of tiles,
and then evaluate each expression for $x = 2$ and $x = -3$.

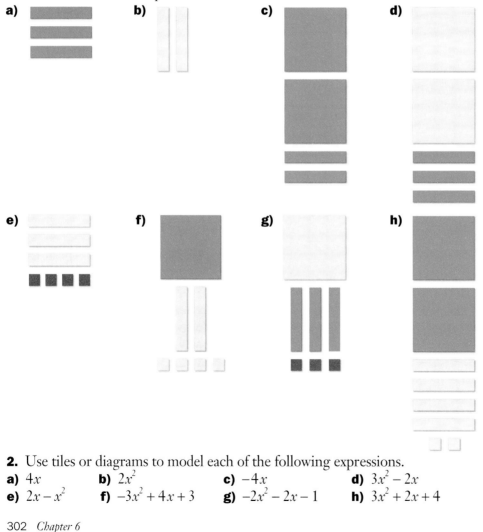

a)

b)

c)

d)

e)

f)

g)

h)

2. Use tiles or diagrams to model each of the following expressions.
a) $4x$
b) $2x^2$
c) $-4x$
d) $3x^2 - 2x$
e) $2x - x^2$
f) $-3x^2 + 4x + 3$
g) $-2x^2 - 2x - 1$
h) $3x^2 + 2x + 4$

Each pair represents zero.

1. Copy and complete the table. The first row has been done for you.

Tile Display	Simplified Form	Expression	Substituting $x = 3$ and $x = -2$
		$2x$	When $x = 3$, $2x = 6$ When $x = -2$, $2x = -4$

2. What is the smallest number of tiles you can add to each group to make zero? Explain.

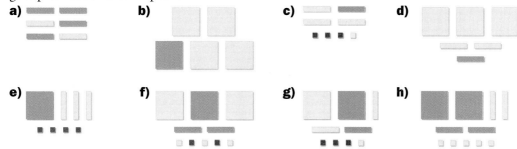

6.2 Polynomials

The Olympic biathlon consists of two events. The events are cross-country skiing and shooting. At the Winter Olympics in Lillehammer, Norway, Canada's Myriam Bédard won two gold medals in the biathlon.

Just like combination Olympic events, algebraic expressions have special names. A **monomial** is a number or variable or the product of numbers and variables. A **polynomial** is a monomial or the sum of monomials. A polynomial with two terms is called a **binomial**. A polynomial with three terms is called a **trinomial**.

Explore: Use the Diagrams

Copy the diagrams into your notebook.

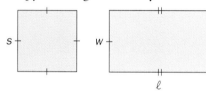

Write the expressions for the perimeter and area of each figure. Combine like terms, where possible.

Inquire

1. Which expressions are monomials?
2. Which expression is a binomial?
3. Which expression is a trinomial?
4. Explain why it is appropriate to call expressions with one, two, and three terms, monomials, binomials, and trinomials.

Example 1   Classifying Polynomials

Classify each of the following as a monomial, binomial, or trinomial.

a) $a - 2b$ **b)** $x^2 + y^2 + z^2$ **c)** 10

Solution

a) The expression $a - 2b$ is a binomial because it contains two terms.
b) The expression $x^2 + y^2 + z^2$ is a trinomial because it contains three terms.
c) The number 10 is a monomial because it contains one term.

The **degree of a monomial** is the sum of the exponents of its variables.

Monomial	Degree
$4x^3$	3
$3xy$	$1 + 1 = 2$
$5a^2b^3c$	$2 + 3 + 1 = 6$

The **degree of a polynomial in one variable** is the highest power of the variable in any one term.

Polynomial	Degree
$6x^2 + 3x$	2
$x^5 + 7x^2 - 3$	5

The **degree of a polynomial in two variables or more** is the greatest sum of the exponents in any one term.

Polynomial	Degree
$3x^3t^4 + 7xy^3 - 2xy$	7
$x^2y^3 + xy^4 + xy^5$	6

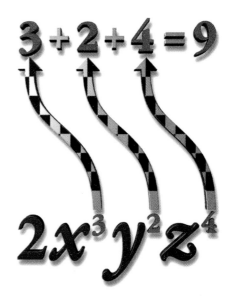

Example 2   Degree of a Polynomial
Classify each polynomial and state its degree.

a) $3abc$ **b)** $2x^2 + x$ **c)** $3xy + 5x^2y^2 - 3$

Solution
a) $3abc$ is a monomial, because it has one term.
The sum of the exponents is $1 + 1 + 1 = 3$.
$3abc$ is a third-degree polynomial.

b) $2x^2 + x$ is a binomial, because it has two terms.
The highest power, 2, is contained in the term $2x^2$.
$2x^2 + x$ is a second-degree polynomial.

c) $3xy + 5x^2y^2 - 3$ is a trinomial, because it has three terms.
The greatest exponent sum is contained in the term $5x^2y^2$.
$3xy + 5x^2y^2 - 3$ is a fourth-degree polynomial.

The terms of a polynomial are usually arranged so that the powers of one variable are in either descending order or ascending order.

Descending Order	Ascending Order
$x^3 + 2x^2 - 5x + 7$	$7 - 5x + 2x^2 + x^3$
(in x) $5x^2 + 7xy + 3y^2$	(in x) $3y^2 + 7xy + 5x^2$

Practice

A

Identify as a monomial, binomial, or trinomial.

1. $5xyz$ **2.** $x + 2y$ **3.** $a - 2b + 3c$
4. $x^2 + y^2$ **5.** 23 **6.** $x - y + 2$

State the degree of each monomial.

7. $25x$ **8.** $25x^2y^2$ **9.** 17
10. $2x^2y^3$ **11.** $-5x^3y^4$ **12.** $-6xy^4z$

State the degree of each polynomial.

13. $5x^2y^2 + 3xy^3$
14. $3x + 2y - 5z$
15. $x^4 + 2x^3 + 3x^2 + 4$
16. $4x^4y^2 + 2x^3y^5 - 23$
17. $3x - 2y + z^2$
18. $25m^3n + 36m^3n^3$
19. $-5x^4y^2z + 2x^2y^2z^2$

Arrange the terms in each polynomial in descending powers of x.

20. $1 + x^3 + x^2 + x^5$

21. $5 - 3x^3 + 2x$

22. $5y^2 + 2xy - x^2$

23. $25xy^2 - 5x^2y + 3x^3y^3 - 4x^4$

24. $5ax + 7b^2x^4 - 3x^3 + 4abx^2$

Arrange the terms in each polynomial in ascending powers of x.

25. $3x^2 - 2x^3 + 5x^4 + x - 2$

26. $4x^4 + x^2 - 3x^3 + 5 - x$

27. $4xy^2 - 2x^2y^2 - 3x^4 + 2x^3y$

28. $5x^2yz^2 + 2xy^4z + 3x^3y^4z^2 - 3$

29. $z - xy + x^2$

30. $x^2 - 2xy - 3x^3 + 16$

31. $2x^3y + 3xy - x^5$

32. $3x^3y^2 + x^4y + xy - 1$

Applications and Problem Solving

33. Classify each polynomial.

a) $\dfrac{4\pi r^3}{3}$ **b)** $\pi r^2 + 2\pi rh$ **c)** $4\pi r$

B

34. Measurement a) Calculate the area of each face of this box.

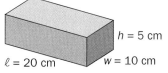
$h = 5$ cm $\ell = 20$ cm $w = 10$ cm

b) What is the total area of the box?
c) Write a polynomial that can be used to calculate the answer you gave in part b).

35. Measurement What type of polynomial is represented by the perimeter of each of these figures?

a)
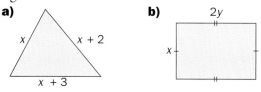
x $x + 2$ $x + 3$

b)
$2y$ x

c)
x y z

d)
$2x$ x

36. Jewellery box The formula for the volume of a rectangular jewellery box is *lwh*. Its dimensions are 25 cm × 18 cm × 17 cm. It has 2-cm thick walls. What is the volume of the interior of the box? Explain your solution. Include clear reasons for the steps you used.

C

37. Write a problem that can be solved with a polynomial. Have a classmate solve your problem.

LOGIC POWER

In the diagram, a locomotive, L, is on the main track. Two boxcars, A and B, are on sidings that meet and that end at P. Where the sidings meet, there is room on the track for one boxcar but not the locomotive.

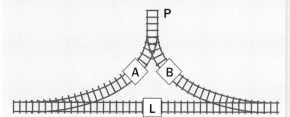

The locomotive can push or pull the boxcars. It can push or pull two at a time. It can go between them and push one and pull the other. The problem is to switch the positions of the two boxcars and leave the locomotive in its original position. *Hint*: Draw the diagram and use different coins for the locomotive and the boxcars.

6.3 Adding Polynomials

Cootes Paradise is a large wetland in Hamilton on the Lake Ontario shoreline. For centuries, it has been an important stopover for waterfowl during fall migration.

Following the start of a program to clean up the pollution in the area, the number of birds stopping at Cootes Paradise has increased. To determine the increase in the number of birds, birdwatchers count them during October and November. The table shows the counts for three species of birds in one year.

	Number of Birds		
Species	October	November	Total
Mallard Duck	653	742	1395
Mute Swan	45	67	112
Tundra Swan	59	73	132

To find the totals, birdwatchers add the numbers of birds of the same species, which can be thought of as *like* birds. Two or more polynomials can be added in a similar way.

To model polynomials, we can use x^2-tiles, x-tiles, and 1-tiles.
When the x^2- or x-tile is green side up, it means x^2 or x.
When the x^2- or x-tile is white side up, it means $-x^2$ or $-x$.
When the 1-tile is red side up, it means $+1$.
When the 1-tile is white side up, it means -1.

Explore: Use a Model

Two algebraic expressions have been modelled using the x^2-tiles, x-tiles, and 1-tiles in Set A and Set B.

a) How many x^2-tiles, x-tiles, and 1-tiles are in Set A? in Set B?
b) Write an algebraic expression to represent Set A; Set B.

Inquire

1. If the tiles in Set A and Set B are combined into one set, what algebraic expression represents the combined set?

2. Combine each of the following pairs of expressions and write the algebraic sum.

a) $x^2 + 2x + 3$
$2x^2 + 3x + 2$

b) $x^2 - 2x + 6$
$3x^2 + 5x - 2$

c) $3x^2 + 4x - 2$
$5x^2 - 2x + 3$

3. Write a rule for adding polynomials.

Example 1   Collecting Like Terms

Add $(x^2 + 4x + 3) + (2x^2 + 5x + 1)$.

Solution

Remove the brackets, collect like terms, and add.

$$\begin{aligned}
(x^2 + 4x + 3) + (2x^2 + 5x + 1) &= x^2 + 4x + 3 + 2x^2 + 5x + 1 \\
&= x^2 + 2x^2 + 4x + 5x + 3 + 1 \\
&= 3x^2 + 9x + 4
\end{aligned}$$

The answer $3x^2 + 9x + 4$ is in simplest form.

Example 2   Using Column Form

Use column form to add these polynomials.

a) $(5x^2 - 3x + 5) + (2x^2 - 7x - 10)$ **b)** $(3y^3 - 3y + 2y^2 + 8) + (-5 - 6y^2 + 2y)$

Solution

a) Write the like terms of the polynomials in columns, and then add.

$$\begin{array}{r}
5x^2 - \ 3x + \ \ 5 \\
+\ 2x^2 - \ 7x - 10 \\
\hline
7x^2 - 10x - \ \ 5
\end{array}$$

b) Rewrite the terms in descending powers of y before arranging them in columns and adding.

$$\begin{array}{l}
3y^3 - 3y + 2y^2 + 8 \ \rightarrow \\
-5 - 6y^2 + 2y \ \ \ \ \ \ \ \ \rightarrow
\end{array}
\quad
\begin{array}{r}
3y^3 + 2y^2 - 3y + 8 \\
- 6y^2 + 2y - 5 \\
\hline
3y^3 - 4y^2 - \ \ y + 3
\end{array}$$

Practice

A

Find the sums of the expressions, A and B, represented by the algebra tiles.

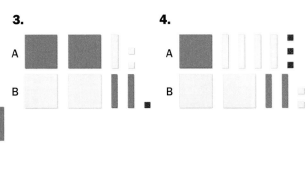

1.

A

B

2.

A

B

3.

A

B

4.

A

B

Identify the like terms in each expression.
5. $2x + 3y - 4xy + 5x - 2y + 6xy$
6. $2a + 5a - 6b + 8b - 2c + 3c$
7. $3s^2 + 5s - 2 + 7s^2 + s - 3$

Add.
8. $(3x + 1) + (4x - 2)$
9. $(3x^2 + 5x - 4) + (x^2 - 7x + 2)$
10. $(-y^2 + 7y - 5) + (2y^2 + 7y - 4)$
11. $(2y^3 - 3y^2 - 1) + (-5y^2 - 4y^3 + 3)$

Add.

12.
$$\begin{array}{r} x + 7 \\ + 5x + 2 \\ \hline \end{array}$$

13.
$$\begin{array}{r} 3y^2 + 2y + 8 \\ + 4y^2 + 7y + 11 \\ \hline \end{array}$$

14.
$$\begin{array}{r} 5x - 2y + 6 \\ + 3x - 6y + 9 \\ \hline \end{array}$$

15.
$$\begin{array}{r} 5x^2 - 3x + 7 \\ + 2x^2 - 5x - 12 \\ \hline \end{array}$$

16.
$$\begin{array}{r} 5x^2 + 7x - 9 \\ + 4x^2 - 8x + 11 \\ \hline \end{array}$$

17.
$$\begin{array}{r} 3y^2 - 8y + 3 \\ + 2y^2 + 8y - 9 \\ \hline \end{array}$$

Simplify.
18. $(5z + 6 - 3z^2) + (4 - 7z + 2z^2)$
19. $(3x^2 + 2y^2 - 5) + (4x^2 + 3y^2 - 11)$
20. $(2x^4 + 7x - 5x^2 + 3) + (2x^3 - 7)$

Add.
21. $(5x^2 + 7x - 7) + (4x^2 - 8x + 12)$
22. $(2y^2 - 3y + 2) + (4y^2 + 6y - 1)$
23. $(m^3 + 5m^2 + 3) + (4m^2 + 7)$
24. $(x^2 + x + 3) + (x^2 - 6) + (x^2 - 2x - 3)$

Simplify.
25. $(4x^2 + 3xy - 2y^2) + (-x^2 - 5xy + 7y^2)$
26. $(5y^2 + 3y - 7) + (-2y^2 - 5y + 8)$
27. $(3x^2y - 2xy + 4y^2) + (x^2y + y^2)$

Applications and Problem Solving

28. Measurement a) Write
an expression in simplest form
for the perimeter of the figure.
b) If $x = 4$ cm, what is the
perimeter?

B

29. Measurement
a) Write an expression in
simplest form for the
perimeter of the figure.
b) If $x = 7$ cm, what is the
perimeter?

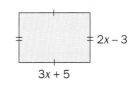

30. Fort York The lengths of the sides of
historic Fort York can be represented by the
expressions x, $x + 171$, and $x + 156$.
a) What geometric shape is the perimeter of
Fort York?
b) If $x = 153$ m, what is the perimeter?

31. Measurement Write a
monomial that describes the
perimeter of this figure.

C

32. Add $(3x^2 + x - 1) + (x^2 - 3x - 2)$. How can
you use $x = 1$ to check your solution?

PATTERN POWER

a) Evaluate the following differences in the
squares of consecutive whole numbers.
$$1^2 - 0^2 = \blacksquare$$
$$2^2 - 1^2 = \blacksquare$$
$$3^2 - 2^2 = \blacksquare$$
$$4^2 - 3^2 = \blacksquare$$
$$5^2 - 4^2 = \blacksquare$$
b) Describe the pattern.
c) Use the pattern to evaluate mentally
$245^2 - 244^2$.

6.4 Subtracting Polynomials

The Imperial Palace in Beijing, China, is the largest palace in the world. The area of its rectangular base can be represented by the expression $x^2 - 10\ 000$. The palace is surrounded by a moat, which has the same width on all sides of the palace. The total area of the palace and the moat can be represented by the expression $x^2 + 200x$.

Explore: Use a Model

Two algebraic expressions have been modelled using the x^2-tiles, x-tiles, and 1-tiles in Set A and Set B.

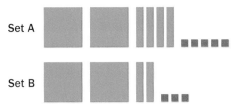

a) How many x^2-tiles, x-tiles, and 1-tiles are in Set A? in Set B?

b) Write an algebraic expression to represent Set A; Set B.

Inquire

1. If the x^2-tiles, x-tiles, and 1-tiles in Set B are subtracted from those in Set A, how many of each type of tile are left?

2. If Set B is turned over to make its opposite, the result is as shown.

Write the sum of Set A and the opposite of Set B. Compare the result with your answer in question 1.

3. Use algebra tiles or diagrams to represent each pair of expressions.

a) $x^2 + 5x - 7$
$ - 2x + 3$

b) $3x^2 - 4x + 3$
$ x^2 + 3x - 5$

c) $-2x^2 + 4x - 5$
$ -x^2 + x - 3$

4. For each pair in question 3, use algebra tiles or diagrams to add the opposite of the second polynomial to the first polynomial.

5. Write a rule for subtracting polynomials.

6. Subtract the expression $x^2 - 10\ 000$ from the expression $x^2 + 200x$ to find an expression that represents the area of the moat around the Imperial Palace.

7. If $x = 850$ m, what is the area of the moat, in square metres?

Example 1   Using Column Form

Use column form to subtract $-2x^2 + 2x + 5$ from $5x^2 - 7x + 4$.

Solution

To subtract one polynomial from another, add the opposite of the polynomial that is being subtracted.

The opposite of $-2x^2 + 2x + 5$ is $2x^2 - 2x - 5$.

$$\begin{array}{r} 5x^2 - 7x + 4 \\ + 2x^2 - 2x - 5 \\ \hline 7x^2 - 9x - 1 \end{array}$$

In Example 1, how can you check your answer by addition?

Example 2   Adding the Opposite

Simplify $(4x^2 - 5x + 7) - (3x^2 + 2x - 5)$.

Solution

Write the opposite of $3x^2 + 2x - 5$ and add.

$$\begin{aligned} (4x^2 - 5x + 7) - (3x^2 + 2x - 5) &= (4x^2 - 5x + 7) + (-3x^2 - 2x + 5) \\ &= 4x^2 - 5x + 7 - 3x^2 - 2x + 5 \\ &= 4x^2 - 3x^2 - 5x - 2x + 7 + 5 \\ &= x^2 - 7x + 12 \end{aligned}$$

Practice

A

Write the opposite.

1. $x^2 + 4x + 1$

2. $x^2 - 2x - 3$

3. $2x^2 + x - 5$

4. $-3x^2 - 7x + 2$

Subtract.

5. $(3x - 5) - (x + 2)$

6. $(x + 5) - (3x - 1)$

7. $(x + 4) - (-x - 3)$

8. $(3x - 5) - (x + 4)$

Subtract.

9. $5x^2 + 3x - 5$
    $2x^2 - 5x - 4$

10. $-3x^2 + 5x - 7$
    $2x^2 + 3x - 3$

11. $-4x^2 - 4x + 3$
    $-3x^2 + 4x - 8$

12. $x^2 - 5x + 1$
    $x^2 - 5x + 6$

13. $x^2 + 7x - 1$
    $x^2 + 4x + 1$

14. $12x^3 + 3x^2 - 5x$
    $9x^3 + 4x^2 - 4x$

Subtract.

15. $(2y^2 + 3y - 5) - (2y^2 + 4y + 6)$

16. $(4s^2 + s - 2) - (-3s^2 + s - 5)$

17. $(y^2 - 5y + 3) - (-2y^2 + 7y + 5)$

Subtract.

18. $3x^2 + 7x - 3$ from $2x^2 - 2x + 3$

19. $5y^2 + 7y - 5$ from $-2y^2 + 3y - 2$

20. $-t^2 + 5t - 1$ from $2t^2 + 3t + 6$

Simplify.

21. $(-5n^2 - n - 8) - (-2n^2 + 7n - 3)$

22. $(4 + 2x - x^2) - (3 - 7x^2 + 5x)$

23. $(-t^2 + 4t - 7) - (3t^2 + 4t - 2)$

24. $(x^2 + 5x + 3) - (-x^2 - 7x + 11)$

25. $(3m^2 + 7m - 8) - (-m^2 + m - 1)$

26. $(-5y^2 + 7y - 12) - (-3y^2 + 4y - 2)$

Applications and Problem Solving

27. Measurement Find the length of PQ.

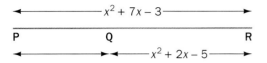
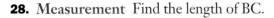
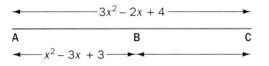

28. Measurement Find the length of BC.

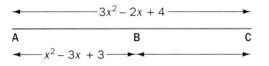

B

29. Measurement Given the perimeter, P, of a figure and two or three sides, find the missing side length.

a)

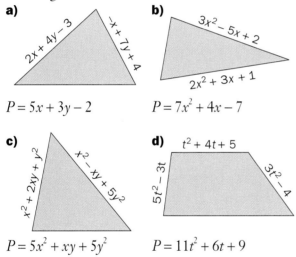

$2x + 4y - 3$
$-x + 7y + 4$

$P = 5x + 3y - 2$

b)

$3x^2 - 5x + 2$
$2x^2 + 3x + 1$

$P = 7x^2 + 4x - 7$

c)

$x^2 + 2xy + y^2$
$x^2 - xy + 5y^2$

$P = 5x^2 + xy + 5y^2$

d)

$t^2 + 4t + 5$
$5t^2 - 3t$
$3t^2 - 4$

$P = 11t^2 + 6t + 9$

30. Measurement The area of the large rectangle is $4x^2 + 9x + 2$. What is the area of the shaded region?

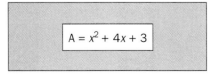

$A = x^2 + 4x + 3$

31. Royal Palace The Royal Palace in Madrid, Spain, is colossal, containing 2800 rooms. The walls are 4 m thick. The area of the rectangular base of the palace can be represented by the algebraic expression $x^2 + 50x - 5000$. The palace sits in the middle of a courtyard. The palace and the courtyard occupy a rectangular lot with an area that can be represented by the expression $3x^2 + 100x$.

a) Write an expression that represents the area of the courtyard.

b) If $x = 200$ m, what is the area of the courtyard, in square metres?

C

32. What is the result of adding a polynomial and its opposite? Explain why.

33. a) If you add two polynomials, A and B, does it matter if you add A + B or B + A? Explain and give an example.

b) If you subtract two polynomials, A and B, does it matter if you subtract A − B or B − A? Explain and give an example.

LOGIC POWER

Four students entered a problem solving contest. Each student represented a different zone of the town. Use the clues to determine which zone each student represented and in which order the students finished.

1. David came second, just behind the student from the west zone.

2. Petra represented neither the east nor the west zone.

3. The student from the north zone finished second last, just ahead of Frank.

4. David and Jarvi represented opposite zones in the town.

6.5 The Distributive Property

Curling became an Olympic sport for the first time when the Winter Games were held in Nagano, Japan. The Canadian women's team won a gold medal, and the Canadian men's team won a silver medal.

The diagram shows one sheet of a curling rink. The distance from a back line to the first hog line is about 8 m. The variable x represents the distance from the first hog line to the far back line.

Explore: Use a Model

An x-tile has a length of x units, a width of 1 unit, and an area of x square units. A 1-tile has a side length of 1 unit and an area of 1 square unit.

The following three rectangles have been modelled using x-tiles and 1-tiles.

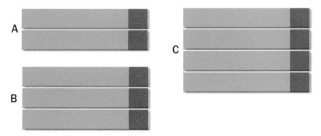

Use the models of the rectangles to copy and complete the table.

Rectangle	Area	Length	Width
A			
B			
C			

Inquire

1. Describe a method for multiplying the length by the width to give the area of each rectangle.

2. From the diagram of one sheet of a curling rink, what is
a) the width? **b)** the length between the back lines?

3. Use the method from question 1 to write an expression for the area of the sheet between the back lines.

4. If $x = 30$ m, what is the area of the sheet between the back lines, in square metres?

To expand an expression means to remove the brackets and simplify. To do this, we use the **distributive property**.
$a(b + c) = ab + ac$

Example 1   Expanding Expressions
Expand using the distributive property.
a) $3(x + 5)$ **b)** $-(2 - x)$ **c)** $4(3x - 2y + 7)$

Solution
Multiply each term inside the brackets by the term outside the brackets.

a) $3(x + 5) = 3(x + 5)$
$= 3(x) + 3(5)$
$= 3x + 15$

b) $-(2 - x) = -1(2 - x)$
$= -1(2) - 1(-x)$
$= -2 + x$

c) $4(3x - 2y + 7) = 4(3x - 2y + 7)$
$= 12x - 8y + 28$

Example 2   Expanding and Simplifying
Expand and simplify $-2(x + 3) - (x - 5)$.

Solution
$-2(x + 3) - (x - 5) = -2(x + 3) - 1(x - 5)$
$= -2x - 6 - x + 5$
$= -2x - x - 6 + 5$
$= -3x - 1$

Practice

A

Expand.
1. $5(x + 1)$
3. $4(x + 2)$

2. $3(x - 2)$
4. $2(x - 3)$

5. $7(x - 1)$
7. $2(n + 6)$
9. $7(t + 3)$
11. $10(d + 2)$
13. $0.5(x + 2)$

6. $5(x + 3)$
8. $4(m - 5)$
10. $3(x - 4)$
12. $9(y - 3)$
14. $4\left(a - \dfrac{1}{2}\right)$

Expand.

15. $2(3x+2)$ **16.** $3(3x+1)$
17. $5(2x+1)$ **18.** $4(2x+3)$
19. $6(2y-1)$ **20.** $5(3z-2)$
21. $7(2x+1)$ **22.** $6(3y+2)$

Expand.

23. $-3(x+2)$ **24.** $-4(2x+1)$
25. $-2(5y-2)$ **26.** $-3(3p-2)$
27. $-5(2x-1)$ **28.** $-2(5r-3)$
29. $-4(x+5)$ **30.** $-(2x-1)$
31. $-\dfrac{1}{2}(2x+3)$ **32.** $-0.2(3x-5)$

Expand.

33. $-2(3x-2y)$ **34.** $-3(5x+3y)$
35. $-4(5a+2b)$ **36.** $-(2x+y)$
37. $-5(-x+y)$ **38.** $-7(x-3y)$
39. $-2(3x+7y)$ **40.** $-4(2m-n)$

Expand.

41. $-4(2x+3y+z)$ **42.** $3(5x-2y+2)$
43. $6(-x+3y+4)$ **44.** $-(2c-3d+5)$

Expand and simplify.

45. $4(y-3)+2(y+4)$
46. $2(5x-1)-(3x+2)$
47. $4(x+7)-(3x+2)$
48. $3(2w-3)-3(2w-5)$
49. $3(2g-5)+3(2g+1)$
50. $4(-x+3)-2(3x+1)$
51. $-2(x-3y+2)-3(x-2y)$

Applications and Problem Solving

B

Expand and simplify.

52. $3(x^2+4x-3)+2(x^2+5)$
53. $2(3x^2+7x-3)+4(x-3)$
54. $5(y^2+3y-4)+2(y^2-4y+1)$
55. $-(2x+3y-5)+5(2x-3y+6)$
56. $-(2a+3)+3(a-1)-4(a-2)$
57. $(2t+1)-4(2t-3)+2(3t-1)$

Expand and simplify.

58. $4(4x-3y+2)-(2x+5y-4)$
59. $-(3x-2y+7)+4(x+y-2)$
60. $2(x^2+y^2)-3x^2+4y^2+7$
61. $4(x^2+2x-3)-2(x^2+4y-1)$
62. $5(2y^2+3y-2)-2(y^2-4y+1)$

63. Measurement For each large rectangle, find the length and width, and then state the area in expanded form.

a)   **b)**

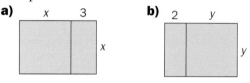

64. Measurement Write the area of the shaded rectangle in expanded form.

a)   **b)**

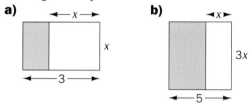

65. Earning interest The money you deposit in a bank is called the principal, P. After your money earns interest, the new principal is given by the expression $P(1+rt)$, where r is the interest rate and t is the length of time your money was deposited.
a) Expand the expression $P(1+rt)$.
b) Evaluate the expression for $P=\$300$, $r=0.05$, and $t=2$ years.

C

66. In the following equations, x is the variable, and A, B, C, D, E, and F are constants.
a) If $-3(Cx+D)=-6x+15$, what are the values of C and D?
b) If $2(Ax+B)=3x+8$, what are the values of A and B?
c) If $-4(Ex+F)=-6x-10$, what are the values of E and F?

6.6 Multiplying Monomials by Monomials

The Olympeion, which is in Athens, Greece, was built around 174 B.C. The base of the Olympeion is a rectangle. Its length can be represented by the monomial $11x$, and its width by the monomial $4x$.

Explore: Use a Model

Six x^2-tiles have been arranged to form a rectangle, as shown.

Write a monomial that represents each of the following.
a) the area of the rectangle
b) the length of the rectangle
c) the width of the rectangle

Inquire

1. How can you multiply the expressions from b) and c), above, to obtain the expression from a)?

2. Write the product of each of the following pairs of monomials.
a) $3x \times 4x$ **b)** $5x \times 6x$ **c)** $7x \times x$

3. Write a rule for multiplying a monomial by a monomial.

4. a) Use the length and width of the base of the Olympeion to write an expression for the area of the base.
b) If $x = 10$ m, what is the area of the base of the Olympeion, in square metres?

Example 1   Multiplying Monomials
Find the product.
a) $(30x)(4y)$ **b)** $-5x^2(-3yz)$

Solution
a) $(30x)(4y) = 30 \times x \times 4 \times y$
$\qquad\qquad\quad = 30 \times 4 \times x \times y$
$\qquad\qquad\quad = 120xy$

b) $-5x^2(-3yz) = -5 \times x^2 \times (-3) \times y \times z$
$\qquad\qquad\quad\ = -5 \times (-3) \times x^2 \times y \times z$
$\qquad\qquad\quad\ = 15x^2yz$

Practice

A

Multiply.
1. $4x \times 2x$
2. $2y \times 5y$
3. $n \times 8n$
4. $5x \times 3y$
5. $2m \times 3n$
6. $5s \times 7t$
7. $4a \times 6b$
8. $3x^2 \times 2y$
9. $4a \times 5b^2$
10. $4b \times 3c$
11. $3a \times 2b^2$
12. $6s \times 3t$

Multiply.
13. $(3x)(2y)$
14. $(3a)(4b)$
15. $(5x^2)(2y^2)$
16. $(5ab)(3c)$
17. $(4x)(3y)$
18. $(6xy)(5z)$
19. $(2a^2)(3b^2)$
20. $(3a)(3b)$
21. $(7a)(5b)$

Multiply.
22. $(3x^2)(-5y^2)$
23. $-2t^3(-4a)$
24. $(6ab)(-2c^2)$
25. $-8a^2(3y^2)$
26. $(5x)(5yz)$
27. $-12x^2(4y^2)$

Multiply.
28. $(-2xy)(-7xy)$
29. $-5m^2(-2mn)$
30. $4s^2t^3(-3st)$
31. $-3abx(-2a^2b^4y)$
32. $-2s^2t^3(-5s^4t^2)$
33. $-5x^2y^2(4c^2x^3y^8)$

Multiply.
34. $-3x^2yz(5yz)$
35. $-2x^2(-3cy^2z^3)$
36. $-2x^2(-2y^2)(z)$
37. $-5x^2(-7y)(-2z)$
38. $-5x(-7y)(-2z)$
39. $-6xy(-5z^2)(3t^2)$

Multiply.
40. $(4a^2x^3z)(-2x^3y^2z^2)$
41. $(2b^2xy^4z^2)(-3xyz)$
42. $-5a^2b^3(-2a^2b^2)$

Multiply.
43. $(3abc)(-4abc)(2abc)$
44. $(-x^2yz)(2xy^2z)(-2xyz^2)$
45. $(-2jkl)(-3jkl)(-4jkl)$

Applications and Problem Solving

46. Measurement Write an expression for the volume, V, of each prism, where $V = l \times w \times h$.

a)

b)

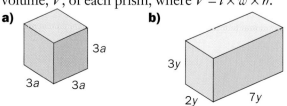

47. Measurement Find the area of each figure.

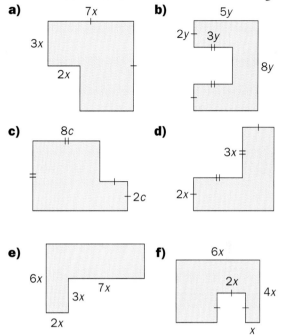

a) 7x, 3x, 2x, 2x
b) 5y, 2y, 3y, 8y
c) 8c, 2c
d) 3x, 2x
e) 6x, 3x, 7x, 2x
f) 6x, 2x, 4x, x

48. Manufacturing a) If x is the time, in minutes, needed to make a hat, and y is the cost of production, in dollars per minute, what does the expression $24xy$ mean?
b) Use $x = 3$ and $y = 0.5$ to evaluate your expression in part a).

C

49. Measurement What is the edge length of a cube that has the same volume as this rectangular solid? Explain and justify your reasoning.

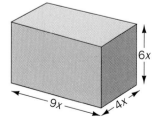

6.7 Powers of Monomials

Not all ancient pyramids were built in Egypt. Many were built in Central America. In fact, the world's largest pyramid is the Quetzalcóatl Pyramid, 100 km southeast of Mexico City. The area of the square base of this pyramid can be written as a power of a monomial, s^2, where s is the side length of the square.

Explore: Look for a Pattern

The following cubes have been built from interlocking cubes.

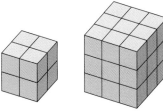

Copy and complete the table. Consider each interlocking cube to have an edge length of 1 unit.

Edge Length of Large Cube	Total Number of Interlocking Cubes
2	
3	
4	
5	
10	
100	

Inquire

1. To what exponent is the edge length of each cube raised to express the volume?

2. What algebraic expression represents the volume of a cube with edge length x?

3. What algebraic expression represents the volume of a cube with edge length $2x$?

4. a) The volume of a cube with edge length $2x$ can also be found by multiplying the lengths of the edges. Find the volume by this method.
b) How does the resulting expression compare with the expression you wrote in question 3?

5. Write a rule for finding powers of monomials.

The edge lengths of a cube puzzle are represented by the monomial $2a^2b$. We can find the volume of the cube from the formula $V = s^3$, where s is the edge length.

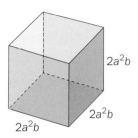

2a²b

2a²b

2a²b

For the given cube, the volume is
$$V = (2a^2b)^3$$
$$= (2a^2b)(2a^2b)(2a^2b)$$
$$= (2 \times 2 \times 2)(a^2 \times a^2 \times a^2)(b \times b \times b)$$
$$= 8a^6b^3$$

We obtain the same result by finding the third power of each factor in the monomial.
$$(2a^2b)^3 = (2)^3(a^2)^3(b)^3$$
$$= 8a^6b^3$$

In general, $(x^m y^n)^a = x^{am} y^{an}$

Example 1   Monomials With One Variable
Simplify.

a) $(x^3)^2$

b) $(y^3)^4$

Solution

a) $(x^3)^2 = x^{3 \times 2}$
$$= x^6$$

b) $(y^3)^4 = y^{3 \times 4}$
$$= y^{12}$$

Example 2   Monomials With Two Variables
Simplify.

a) $(5x^2y^4)^3$ **b)** $(-2x^3y)^4$ **c)** $(3x^4y^2)(-x^2y^3)^2$

Solution

a) $(5x^2y^4)^3$
$$= (5)^3(x^2)^3(y^4)^3$$
$$= 125x^6y^{12}$$

b) $(-2x^3y)^4$
$$= (-2)^4(x^3)^4(y)^4$$
$$= 16x^{12}y^4$$

c) $(3x^4y^2)(-x^2y^3)^2$
$$= (3x^4y^2)(-1)^2(x^2)^2(y^3)^2$$
$$= (3x^4y^2)(1)(x^4)(y^6)$$
$$= (3 \times 1)(x^{4+4})(y^{2+6})$$
$$= 3x^8y^8$$

Practice

A

Simplify.

1. $(x)^2$ **2.** $(a)^3$ **3.** $(p)^5$

4. $(n^2)^2$ **5.** $(-t^3)^2$ **6.** $(-y^2)^3$

Simplify.

7. $(x^2)^3$ **8.** $(y^3)^2$ **9.** $(m^2)^2$

10. $(n^3)^4$ **11.** $(x^3)^3$ **12.** $(y^2)^3$

13. $(z^4)^3$ **14.** $(m^4)^5$ **15.** $(p^{18})^2$

16. $(-s^{10})^2$ **17.** $(-x)^{31}$ **18.** $-(-b^0)^3$

Simplify.

19. $(xy)^2$ **20.** $(ab)^3$ **21.** $(-xy)^2$

22. $(mn)^4$ **23.** $(pq)^3$ **24.** $(-2xt)^2$

25. $(4xy)^2$ **26.** $(-2ax)^3$ **27.** $-(3rs)^3$

Simplify.

28. $(x^2y^2)^3$ **29.** $(x^2y^3)^2$ **30.** $(a^2b)^3$

31. $(ab^3)^2$ **32.** $(mn)^3$ **33.** $(-ab^2)^2$

34. $(-c^3d^4)^2$ **35.** $(x^2y)^2$ **36.** $-(s^3t^2)^0$

Simplify.

37. $(2x^2)^3$ **38.** $(3y^3)^2$

39. $(4x^4)^2$ **40.** $(5y^2)^2$

41. $(-m^2)^2$ **42.** $(-n^2)^3$

43. $(-2n^2)^3$ **44.** $(-3y^2)^2$

45. $(3pqr)^2$ **46.** $(-3yz)^3$

47. $(-4x^2y^3)^3$ **48.** $-(3xy^0)^2$

49. $\left(\dfrac{1}{2}abc\right)^3$ **50.** $\left(-\dfrac{1}{2}xy^2\right)^4$

Simplify.

51. $(2x^2y^3)^2(x^2y)$

52. $(-3xy)(-2xy)^2$

53. $(2xy^2)^3(3x^2y^2)$

54. $(2a^4b^3)(-3ab)^3(10a^2b^2)$

55. $(10abc)^2(-2a^2bc)$

56. $(0.25mn^2)(2mn)^2$

Applications and Problem Solving

57. Measurement Write and simplify an expression for the area of each square.

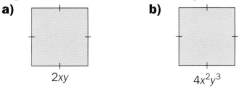

a) 2xy   **b)** $4x^2y^3$

58. Measurement Write and simplify an expression for the volume of each cube.

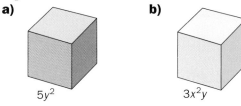

a) $5y^2$ **b)** $3x^2y$

B

59. Measurement Find the volume of this cube if $a = 1$, $b = 2$, and $c = 3$.

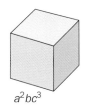

a^2bc^3

C

60. Does replacing the variables by their opposites, x by $-x$ and y by $-y$, result in the opposite of each monomial? Explain.

a) $(3x^2y^3)^2$ **b)** $(3x^2y^3)^3$

6.8 Multiplying a Polynomial by a Monomial

Northern Dancer was one of the fastest thoroughbred horses that ever raced. He was born, raised, and trained at Windfields Farm in Oshawa. Windfields Farm contains many different sizes and shapes of rectangular fields attached to each other, like the rectangles shown below.

Explore: Use a Diagram

Copy the diagram.

In simplest form, write the area of
a) the square
b) the rectangle attached to the square

Inquire

1. Write the sum of the areas for the square and the rectangle.
2. Consider the larger rectangle that includes the square.
a) What is the length of the larger rectangle?
b) What is the width of the larger rectangle?
c) Use your answers to parts a) and b) to write an expression for the area.
d) How can you multiply the monomial in your expression by the binomial in your expression to arrive at the answer you gave in question 1?
3. Write a rule for multiplying a polynomial by a monomial.

Example 1   Expanding Expressions
Expand $2x(x^2 - 2x + 5)$.

Solution
Expand using the distributive property.

$$2x(x^2 - 2x + 5) = 2x(x^2 - 2x + 5)$$
$$= 2x^3 - 4x^2 + 10x$$

Example 2   Expanding and Simplifying
Expand and simplify.
a) $4x(x - 3) - 2(x + 3)$
b) $2(3x^2 - 4x + 5) - 2x(x - 3)$

Solution
Use the distributive property to expand each expression.

a) $4x(x-3) - 2(x+3) = 4x(x-3) - 2(x+3)$
$$= 4x^2 - 12x - 2x - 6$$
$$= 4x^2 - 14x - 6$$

b) $2(3x^2 - 4x + 5) - 2x(x-3) = 2(3x^2 - 4x + 5) - 2x(x-3)$
$$= 6x^2 - 8x + 10 - 2x^2 + 6x$$
$$= 4x^2 - 2x + 10$$

Practice

A

Expand.

1. $x(x+2)$ **2.** $x(x-3)$ **3.** $a(a+1)$
4. $t(t-1)$ **5.** $y(y+4)$ **6.** $m(m+5)$
7. $x(x-5)$ **8.** $y(y-7)$ **9.** $a(a-10)$

Expand.

10. $3x(x+2)$ **11.** $4b(b-11)$
12. $5t(t+3)$ **13.** $2x(3+x)$
14. $7y(y-5)$ **15.** $-2x(x+4)$
16. $-x(x+2)$ **17.** $-y(y-3)$

Expand and simplify.

18. $x(x+3) - x(x-2)$
19. $y(2+y) + y(y-1)$
20. $m(m-1) + m(m-1)$
21. $x(x+2) - (2x-2)$
22. $y(y-4) - y(3-2y)$
23. $a(2a-1) + a(a+1)$
24. $x(x-2) - x(x+1)$

Expand and simplify.

25. $3x(x+2) + 2x(x+5)$
26. $2x(x-3) - x(x-5)$
27. $3x(2x+1) + x(3x+2)$
28. $-2y(y-3) - y(y+1)$
29. $2a(a+3) + 3a(a-2)$
30. $-x(3x-4) - 2x(1-x)$
31. $4x(x+2) + 2x(7-2x)$

Expand.

32. $x(x^2 + 2x + 3)$ **33.** $3(x^2 + 2x - 5)$
34. $5x(x^2 + 2x - 7)$ **35.** $-(x^2 - 3x - 1)$
36. $4m(m^2 - 5m + 6)$ **37.** $3y(2y^2 - 4y + 3)$
38. $-3b(3b^2 - 5b + 1)$ **39.** $-5z(z^2 - 2z - 5)$

Applications and Problem Solving

B

Expand and simplify.

40. $3(x^2 + 2x - 5) - x(x+1)$
41. $5(x^2 + 2x - 7) + 3x(x+1)$
42. $-(x^2 - 3x - 1) + x(3x+2)$
43. $4(2x+3) + 3x(x^2 - x + 3)$
44. $3m(m-2) + 4(m^2 - 5m + 6)$
45. $5y(1-y) + 3(2y^2 - 4y + 3)$
46. $-3x(x+2) + 2x(2x-1)$

C

47. Measurement Write, expand, and simplify an expression for the area of each figure.

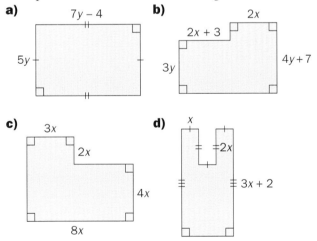

a) $7y - 4$, $5y$ **b)** $2x$, $2x + 3$, $3y$, $4y + 7$

c) $3x$, $2x$, $4x$, $8x$ **d)** x, $2x$, $3x + 2$

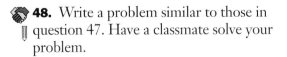

48. Write a problem similar to those in question 47. Have a classmate solve your problem.

6.9 Dividing Monomials by Monomials

The 12.9-km Confederation Bridge joins Prince Edward Island and New Brunswick. The opening under the navigation span, which allows ships to sail under the bridge, is a rectangle. The height of the rectangle can be represented by x, and the area by $4x^2$.

$A = 4x^2$ x

Dividing the area by the height to find an expression for the width of the rectangle involves the division of a monomial by a monomial.

Recall that for the multiplication statement $3 \times 2 = 6$, there are two division statements.

$$6 \div 2 = 3 \qquad 6 \div 3 = 2$$

Explore: Discover the Relationship

Copy and complete.

a) $2a \times 3b$ **b)** $3x \times 5x$ **c)** $4x^2 \times 2x$

Inquire

1. Write two division statements for each multiplication statement above.

2. Write two division statements for each of the following.

a) $3m \times 4n = 12mn$ **b)** $5y \times 2y^2 = 10y^3$

c) $2x \times 3y = 6xy$ **d)** $x^2 \times 2y^3 = 2x^2y^3$

3. Write a rule for dividing monomials by monomials.

4. a) Use division to write an expression for the width of the navigation span of the Confederation Bridge.

b) If $x = 60$ m, what are the height and width of the span?

Example   Dividing Monomials by Monomials

Divide.   **a)** $\dfrac{-8x^6y^7}{4x^5y^5}$ **b)** $\dfrac{60a^4b^3c^2}{30a^2b^2c^2}$ **c)** $10x^3y^4 \div 2y^3$

Solution

a) $\dfrac{-8x^6y^7}{4x^5y^5}$

$= \left(\dfrac{-8}{4}\right)\left(\dfrac{x^6}{x^5}\right)\left(\dfrac{y^7}{y^5}\right)$

$= -2xy^2$

b) $\dfrac{60a^4b^3c^2}{30a^2b^2c^2}$

$= \left(\dfrac{60}{30}\right)\left(\dfrac{a^4}{a^2}\right)\left(\dfrac{b^3}{b^2}\right)\left(\dfrac{c^2}{c^2}\right)$

$= 2a^2b$

c) $10x^3y^4 \div 2y^3$

$= \dfrac{10x^3y^4}{2y^3}$

$= \left(\dfrac{10}{2}\right)\left(\dfrac{x^3}{1}\right)\left(\dfrac{y^4}{y^3}\right)$

$= 5x^3y$

Practice

Divide.

1. $\dfrac{6x}{3}$ **2.** $\dfrac{-15a}{5}$ **3.** $\dfrac{24y}{8}$

4. $\dfrac{36m}{9}$ **5.** $\dfrac{-30x}{6}$ **6.** $\dfrac{-25y}{5}$

7. $\dfrac{12x}{4x}$ **8.** $\dfrac{-18y}{3y}$ **9.** $\dfrac{24a}{24a}$

10. $\dfrac{-32b}{-b}$ **11.** $\dfrac{-40x}{40x}$ **12.** $\dfrac{-32m}{-8}$

Divide.

13. $\dfrac{15xyz}{5xy}$ **14.** $\dfrac{-18ab}{6a}$ **15.** $\dfrac{12pqr}{4pqr}$

16. $\dfrac{36abc}{-4a}$ **17.** $\dfrac{28xy}{7y}$ **18.** $\dfrac{-15rst}{3rt}$

Divide.

19. $25xy \div 5xy$ **20.** $22ab \div 11ab$
21. $21xyz \div 3xyz$ **22.** $9amn \div amn$
23. $36rst \div 3rs$ **24.** $39jkl \div 13kl$
25. $52pqrs \div 13ps$ **26.** $51defg \div 3eg$

Simplify.

27. $5x^4y^2 \div x^3y$ **28.** $-3a^3b^4 \div ab$
29. $18m^7n^7 \div (-9m^4)$ **30.** $-20x^5y^{15} \div 4x^2y$
31. $7a^3b^2c \div (-7ab)$ **32.** $-8x^2y^9 \div (-2xy^8)$

Simplify.

33. $\dfrac{10a^6b^3}{5a^4b^2}$ **34.** $\dfrac{-15x^6y^8}{-5x^5y^7}$ **35.** $\dfrac{-12m^6n^2}{4m^3n^2}$

36. $\dfrac{22x^2y^4z^3}{11xy^3z}$ **37.** $\dfrac{20a^4b^6c}{15a^4b^6c}$ **38.** $\dfrac{-18x^5y^8}{12x^3y^6}$

Simplify.

39. $\dfrac{10x^5y^3}{5x^3y^{-1}}$ **40.** $\dfrac{-12a^4b^{-3}}{3a^2b^{-5}}$ **41.** $\dfrac{-16m^8n^3}{4m^7n^3}$

42. $\dfrac{-9x^4y^3}{-3x^{-5}y^2}$ **43.** $\dfrac{-24x^{-5}y^{-2}}{18x^{-6}y^{-3}}$ **44.** $\dfrac{9p^5q^{15}}{p^2q^3r^2}$

Applications and Problem Solving

45. Measurement Find the missing dimension in each rectangle.

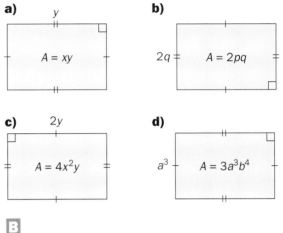

a) y $A = xy$

b) $2q$ $A = 2pq$

c) $2y$ $A = 4x^2y$

d) a^3 $A = 3a^3b^4$

46. Measurement What are the dimensions of each rectangle if each area is 160 cm^2?

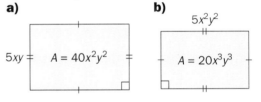

a) $5xy$ $A = 40x^2y^2$

b) $5x^2y^2$ $A = 20x^3y^3$

47. Cubic box Find the quotient of the volume of this box divided by its surface area.

48. A and B represent monomials. When you multiply $A \times B$, the result is A. When you divide $A \div B$, the result is A. What is the monomial B?

49. Write a problem similar to problem 46. Have a classmate solve your problem.

NUMBER POWER

On what day in which month and year will you have lived for at least 1 billion seconds?

Personal Fitness Training

Physical activity contributes to our overall health and well-being. However, according to the first National Health Survey from Statistics Canada, only 17% of Canadians over the age of 15 are physically active, with teenagers the most active.

Some people consult a personal fitness trainer at a recreation centre or a fitness club to increase their level of physical activity. A personal trainer assesses fitness levels, and designs and monitors programs to improve fitness levels. Fitness assessments include measures of cardiorespiratory fitness, muscle strength, flexibility, and endurance.

Most personal trainers study physical education and exercise science at university or college. Many are certified by the Canadian Association of Sports Science as fitness appraisers.

1 Cardiorespiratory Assessment

One index of cardiorespiratory fitness involves three 30-s heartbeat measurements taken at precise intervals after a timed step exercise. This index is found by substituting the duration of the exercise, d seconds, and the sum of the three heartbeat measurements, s beats, into the expression $\dfrac{100d}{2s}$.

The index is interpreted using this scale.

Index	Fitness Level
< 55	poor
55 – 64	low average
65 – 79	average
80 – 89	good
> 90	excellent

1. Write the expression $\dfrac{100d}{2s}$ in simplest form.

2. Find, and interpret, the cardiorespiratory fitness of each person.
a) 5 min of exercise and heartbeat measurements of 91, 88, and 83 beats
b) 4 min of exercise and heartbeat measurements of 52, 49, and 45 beats
c) 5 min of exercise and heartbeat measurements of 70, 66, and 59 beats

2 Burning Energy

The amount of energy you burn depends on how active you are. The energy, in kilojoules, a person burns during an activity can be found using the expression mdr. In this expression, m kilograms is the person's mass, d minutes is the duration of the activity, and r kilojoules per minute per kilogram is the rate. The table shows the rates for some activities.

Activity	Rate (kJ/min/kg)
Aerobic Dancing	0.567
Free Weights	0.361
Running (7.2 min/km)	0.567
Running (5.0 min/km)	0.874
Running (3.7 min/km)	1.058
Swimming	0.655
Walking	0.336
Word Processing	0.113

1. Find the energy burned, to the nearest tenth of a kilojoule, in each situation.
a) a 53.5-kg person lifting free weights for 30 min
b) a 66-kg person word processing for 2 h
c) a 72.5-kg person running at 7.2 min/km for 45 min

2. Which burns more energy for a specific person, walking for 1 h or aerobic dancing for 30 min? How much more energy is burned?

6.10 Common Factors and the GCF

On the average, Montreal has blowing snow on 12 days of the year, and Halifax has blowing snow on 14 days of the year. The number 12 has 6 factors: 1, 2, 3, 4, 6, and 12. The number 14 has 4 factors: 1, 2, 7, and 14. The **greatest common factor** (GCF) of 12 and 14 is 2.

Explore: Discover the Relationship
Write all the factors of each number.
a) 6   **b)** 18   **c)** 24

Inquire
1. Which prime factors are common to all three numbers?
2. What is the GCF of the three numbers?
3. Write a rule for finding the GCF of a set of numbers from their prime factors.
4. Write three different numbers that have a GCF of
a) 3   **b)** 8   **c)** 10   **d)** 12

Example 1   Finding Greatest Common Factors
Determine the GCF of each pair of numbers.
a) 24 and 48   **b)** 36 and 42

Solution
a) Write each number as a product of its prime factors.

$24 = 2 \times 2 \times 2 \times 3$
$48 = 2 \times 2 \times 2 \times 2 \times 3$

Multiply the common factors to calculate the GCF.
The GCF of 24 and 48 is $2 \times 2 \times 2 \times 3$ or 24.

b) $36 = 2 \times 2 \times 3 \times 3$
$42 = 2 \times 3 \times 7$

The GCF of 36 and 42 is 2×3 or 6.

Example 2   Monomials With One Variable
a) Determine the common factors of the monomials $2x^2$ and $4x$.
b) Write their GCF.

Solution
For algebraic expressions, the variable must also be factored.
Write each expression as a product. Write the factors common to both.
a) $2x^2 = 2 \times x \times x$
$4x = 2 \times 2 \times x$

The common factors of $2x^2$ and $4x$ are 2 and x.
b) The GCF of $2x^2$ and $4x$ is $2x$.

Example 3   Monomials With Two Variables

Find the GCF of $2x^3y$, $4x^2y^2$, and $2x^2y$.

Solution

$2x^3y = 2 \times x \times x \times x \times y$

$4x^2y^2 = 2 \times 2 \times x \times x \times y \times y$

$2x^2y = 2 \times x \times x \times y$

The GCF of $2x^3y$, $4x^2y^2$, and $2x^2y$ is $2 \times x \times x \times y$ or $2x^2y$.

Practice

A

Write each number as the product of its prime factors.

1. 12   **2.** 16

3. 28   **4.** 63

5. 144   **6.** 225

Factor fully.

7. $4xy^2$ **8.** $18a^2b^3$

9. $36x^2yz^2$ **10.** $10x^2y$

11. $54x^5$ **12.** $125a^4b^2$

Determine the GCF of each pair.

13. 15, 20   **14.** 16, 24

15. 27, 36   **16.** 28, 42

17. 48, 72   **18.** 64, 63

Determine the GCF of each pair.

19. $4a$, $6a$ **20.** $2x^2$, $3x$

21. $12m^3$, $10m^2$ **22.** $12abc$, $3abc$

23. $2x$, $4y$ **24.** $14a$, $7b$

25. $5x^2$, $10x$ **26.** $4xy$, $5xy$

27. $9mn^2$, $8mn$ **28.** $2a^3$, $8a^2$

29. $15bc$, $25b^2c$ **30.** $6x^2y^2$, $9xy$

Determine the GCF of each set.

31. $5xyz$, $10abc$, $25pqr$

32. $20x$, $10x^3$, $8x^2$

33. $12abc$, $18ab$, $6ac$

34. $10x^2y$, $15xy^2$, $25xyz$

35. $12xy$, $16x^2y$, $20xyz$

36. $56abc$, $64a^2b$, $36ab^2c$

37. $21a^2b$, $35a^2b^2c$, $49ab^2c$

Find the GCF.

38. x^2y^2, x^2y^3, x^3y^4

39. $2x^3y$, $4x^2y^4$, $2x^2y^4$

40. $3x^2y^3$, $3x^3y^2$, $6xy^2$

41. $4a^3b^3$, $8a^2b^3$, $16ab^3$

42. $10s^4t^5$, $5s^5t^4$, $15s^3t^4$

Applications and Problem Solving

43. Weather Edmonton has 210 days with frost in a year, whereas Ottawa has 165. What is the GCF of these numbers?

C

44. Getting to school Suppose students can get to school by walking at 5 km/h, riding a bike at 10 km/h, or being driven in a car at 30 km/h. Bob rides a bike, as does Karin. Bob lives the same distance from the

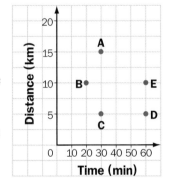

school as Collette, who walks. Gustav and Shirley come by car. Karin and Gustav live the same distance from school. The graph gives the times the five students take to get to school one day.

a) Which person does each point represent? Give clear reasons for your answers.

b) Draw a map of the area, showing where each student could live. Compare your map with a classmate's.

6.11 Factoring Expressions With Common Factors

The world's narrowest commercial building is in Vancouver. The Jack Chow building is 30 m long by 1.8 m wide. In how many ways can you determine the perimeter?

Explore: Discover the Relationship
Examine the diagram of an x-tile.

1 [   ]
x

What is the sum of the length and width of the tile?

Inquire
1. Write an expression for twice the sum of the length and width of the x-tile. Do not expand.

2. Add the sides of the x-tile to find the perimeter. Collect like terms.

3. How do the quantities represented in questions 1 and 2 compare?

4. Write a rule for removing a common factor from the terms in a polynomial.

5. Use your rule to remove a common factor from each of the following.
a) $5x + 5$ **b)** $3x + 6$ **c)** $2x - 8$

Example   Factoring Expressions
a) Factor the expression $6x^2 - 14x$.
b) Check your answer by expanding.

Solution
a) Determine the GCF of both terms. Then, divide both terms by the GCF.
$6x^2 = 2 \times 3 \times x \times x$
$14x = 2 \times 7 \times x$
The GCF is $2x$.

The second factor is $\dfrac{6x^2}{2x} - \dfrac{14x}{2x}$ or $3x - 7$.

The factors of $6x^2 - 14x$ are $2x$ and $3x - 7$.
Therefore, $6x^2 - 14x = 2x(3x - 7)$.

b) $2x(3x - 7) = 2x(3x - 7)$
$\qquad\qquad\quad = 6x^2 - 14x$

Practice

A

State the missing factor.

1. $12x + 18y = (\blacksquare)(2x + 3y)$

2. $3x^2 - 5x = (\blacksquare)(3x - 5)$

3. $4ab + 3ac = (\blacksquare)(4b + 3c)$

4. $5x^2 + 10x = (\blacksquare)(x + 2)$

5. $8abc - 12ab = (\blacksquare)(2c - 3)$

Copy and complete.

6. $3y^2 + 18y = 3y(y + \blacksquare)$

7. $14a - 12b = 2(\blacksquare - 6b)$

8. $4a^3 - 8a^2 = 4a^2(\blacksquare - 2)$

9. $10x^3 - 5x^2 + 15x = 5x(2x^2 - \blacksquare + \blacksquare)$

Copy and complete.

10. $33ab - 22b = 11b(\blacksquare - \blacksquare)$

11. $4a^3 - 10a^2 + 6a = 2a(\blacksquare - \blacksquare + \blacksquare)$

12. $27a^2b^2 - 18ab + 9b = 9b(\blacksquare - \blacksquare + \blacksquare)$

13. $6x^2y - 4xy^2 = 2xy(\blacksquare - \blacksquare)$

14. $9a^3b - 12ab^4 = 3ab(\blacksquare - \blacksquare)$

Factor each binomial.

15. $10x + 15$

16. $28y - 14$

17. $2mn - n$

18. $5x^2 + 10x$

19. $8x^2 + 4x^3$

20. $9a^3b^2 - 6a^2b$

21. $4x^2y^2 - 6xy^2z^2$

22. $14a^2b^4 - 21b^2c^2$

23. $6x^2y^3z + 12xy^2z$

24. $15a^3b^5 - 9b^4c^5$

Applications and Problem Solving

B

Factor each trinomial.

25. $9a - 6b + 3$

26. $4a - 8b + 16$

27. $12x^3 - 6x^2 + 24x$

28. $10x^3 - 5x^2 + 15x$

29. $24x^4y - 18x^3y + 12x^2y^2$

30. $8a^2b + 16ab - 24a$

31. $25m^3n - 15m^2n^2 + 5mn^3$

32. Measurement a) Write the perimeter of the rectangle as the sum of two different products and as the product of a number and a sum.

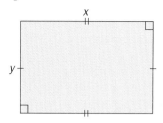

b) Which of the two forms in part a) is the factored form?

33. Gravity If you stood on the Earth and could jump up at 5 m/s, your approximate height in metres above the ground after t seconds would be given by the expression $5t - 5t^2$.

a) Factor the binomial.

b) Evaluate for $t = 0.4$ s.

LOGIC POWER

A container made of interlocking cubes has outside dimensions $5 \times 5 \times 5$. The walls and the base of the container are all 1 cube thick. How many cubes were used to make the container?

TECHNOLOGY

Polynomials and the Graphing Calculator

Complete the following with a graphing calculator that has the capability to work with polynomials.

1 Adding and Subtracting Polynomials

Simplify.

1. $(x^2 + x + 1) + (2x^2 - 2x + 5)$

2. $(2y^3 - 5y^2 + 3y - 2) + (y^3 + 5y^2 - y + 1)$

3. $(4a^2 - 7a - 6) - (2a^2 + a - 4)$

4. $(5x^3 - 2x + 8) - (3x^3 - 2x^2 - 4x + 5)$

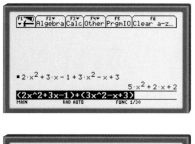

2 Multiplying and Dividing Monomials

Simplify.

1. $(3xy^3)(4x^2y)$ **2.** $(5a^3b^3)(-2ab^2)$

3. $(3x^2yz)^2$ **4.** $(-2.5m^2n)^3$

5. $(8p^5q^4) \div (2p^2q^3)$ **6.** $(-12a^4b^3c^3) \div (3ac^3)$

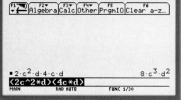

3 Expanding Expressions

Use the expand function, or its equivalent, to expand each of the following.

1. $3(2x^2 + x - 4)$ **2.** $-2y(y^2 - 5y + 3)$

Expand and simplify.

3. $4(a - 2) + 5a(2a - 1)$ **4.** $2(x^2 - 5) - 4(2x^2 + x + 1)$

5. $-(3z^2 - 2z - 4) + 2(2z^2 + z - 5)$ **6.** $3x(2x + 5) - 2x(4x - 3)$

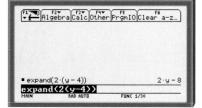

4 Factoring Expressions

Use the factor function, or its equivalent, to factor each of the following.

1. 280   **2.** 468

3. $6x + 15y$ **4.** $16t^2 - 40t$

5. $14m^2n^3 + 35mn^2$ **6.** $60a^2b^2 - 8ab^2$

5 Evaluating Polynomials

Evaluate each of the following.

1. $4x^2 + 3x + 2$ for $x = 5$ **2.** $2x^2 - 6x - 4$ for $x = -3$

3. $x^3 + 3x - 4$ for $x = 6$ **4.** $3x^3 - x^2 - 2x + 9$ for $x = -4$

5. $3x^2 + 7x - 2$ for $x = 2.5$ **6.** $x^3 - 3x^2 + 2x - 4$ for $x = -0.5$

This example evaluates $2x^3 + 4x - 1$ for $x = 3$.

6.12 How Can We Model Readability?

1 Modelling Readability

Readability statistics are one way to determine how well a piece of writing communicates with a reader. The Flesch-Kincaid formula puts a reading grade level on a piece of writing. The formula for determining the reading grade level, G, is

$$G = 0.39w + 11.8s - 15.59$$

where w represents the average number of words per sentence, and s represents the average number of syllables per word.

The steps used to calculate the reading level are as follows.

1. Select a 100-word passage at random. Start counting at the first word of the first complete sentence.

2. Count the number of syllables and divide by 100 to find the average number of syllables per word, to the nearest hundredth. (You know there are at least 100 syllables in a 100-word passage, so just count the extra syllables in words with more than one syllable and add 100). Use the following rules for counting syllables.
• Count one syllable for each vowel sound.
Track, coil, jet, and rough each have one syllable.
Turnip, thorough, and science each have two syllables.
• Do not count a silent e as a syllable.
Rope has one syllable.
Wildlife has two syllables.
• When endings such as -y, -le, and -ed are sounded at the end of a word, count them as a syllable.
Baby, rattle, and dropped each have two syllables.
• Count abbreviations, such as "Corp." and "Blvd.," as one-syllable words.

3. Find the number of sentences, to the nearest hundredth. For example, suppose that 95 of the 100 words take up 10 sentences, and the remaining 5 words form part of a 12-word sentence. The total number of sentences is $10 + \dfrac{5}{12} \doteq 10.42$.

4. Divide 100 by the number of sentences to find the average number of words per sentence, to the nearest hundredth.

5. Repeat steps 1 to 4 for two other 100-word passages. Average the three values for the number of syllables per word, to the nearest hundredth. Also, average the three values for the number of words per sentence, to the nearest hundredth.

6. Substitute the values from step 5 into the formula.

A different way to model readability is the Flesch Reading Ease score, which is on a scale from 0 to 100. The lower the score, the more difficult the writing is to read. The formula to calculate the score, F, is

$$F = 206.84 - 1.02w - 85s$$

where w and s have the same meanings as before.

The table shows how to interpret the score.

Score	Reading Difficulty
90 – 100	Very easy (grade 4)
80 – 90	Easy (grade 5)
70 – 80	Fairly easy (grade 6)
60 – 70	Standard (grades 7, 8)
50 – 60	Fairly difficult (some high school)
30 – 50	Difficult (high school – college)
0 – 30	Difficult (college and up)

The following are three excerpts from the book *Deadly Appearances*, a Joanne Kilbourn mystery written by Canadian writer Gail Bowen. Use these excerpts to determine the reading grade level and the reading ease score for the book.

(Page 1) There was, and still is, something surreal about that moment: the famous face looming up out of nowhere. He was pulling himself up the portable metal staircase that was propped against the back of the truck bed. His body appeared in stages over the metal floor: head, shoulders and arms, torso, belly, legs, feet. He seemed huge. He was climbing those steps as if his life depended on it, and his face was shiny and red with exertion. The heat on the floor of the stage was unbearable. I could smell it. I remember thinking very clearly, a big man like that could die in this heat, then I turned and scrambled toward Andy.

(Page 174) A tiny young woman in a trench coat came in carrying a medical bag. She went not to Eve, but to me. She slid her fingers around my wrist, positioned her face close to mine.

"Shock," she said, still holding my wrist in her hand. Then there was a swab and a pinprick sensation at the crease of my elbow, and I felt warm and weary. "You'll be all right now. You're Joanne Kilbourn, aren't you? Well, Joanne, someone will get you some tea. Plenty of sugar," she said over her shoulder. "Hang in there, Joanne," and then, smooth as silk, she moved along.

(Page 201) The next morning I woke up in my own bed in the house on Eastlake Avenue. The room was full of light, and as I lay there, I could hear in the distance the mournful cries of geese flying south. I got out of bed, opened the window and curled up in the window seat to watch. The air that came into the room was fresh and cold and smelled of the north. I hugged my knees for warmth and looked out. There were no clouds. The sky was clear, hard blue. It was a flawless October day.

Suddenly the air was black with geese, hundreds, then thousands of them.

2 Applying the Models

1. Calculate the reading grade level and the reading ease score for
a) the editorials in your local newspaper
b) articles in the sports or entertainment section in your local newspaper

2. Is there a difference in the readability of the editorials and the sports or entertainment articles? Explain.

3. a) Calculate the reading grade level and the reading ease score for something you have written.
b) Rewrite some of the material in a way that you think would make it easier to read.
c) Calculate the reading grade level and the reading ease score for the rewritten material. Did you make it easier to read? Explain.

4. Why do writers and editors of popular fiction novels concern themselves with the readability of the novels?

Review

6.1 *Simplify.*

1. $7x + 10 + 7y - 4x + 1$
2. $2a - 3b - 5 + a - b$
3. $-q + 4q - 9r - q + 2r + 1$
4. $2x^2 + 3x - x^2 - 7x$
5. $y^2 - 2y + 5y - 4 + 3y^2 - y$

6. **a)** Simplify $2t^2 - 3t + 5t - 1 - t^2 + 4t$.
   b) Evaluate for $t = -2$.

7. **Measurement** Write and simplify an expression for the perimeter.

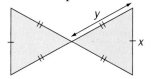

6.2 *Classify each polynomial and state its degree.*

8. xyz
9. $3x^2y^3$
10. $5xy^2 - 5xy$
11. $x^2 + y$
12. $ab^3 + b^2 + 1$
13. $3m^2n^3 + 5mn$
14. $x^6 + 2x^4 + 5x^2$
15. $3x^3 - 5x + 3$
16. $x^2yz + 2yz$
17. $b^2x^3 - 2x^3 - 4xy^2$

Arrange each polynomial with its powers in descending order.

18. $x^2 + 3x - 5x^3$
19. $5 + 2y^2 - 3y + y^4$
20. $2m + 6 - 3m^2 - m^4 + 6m^3$
21. $3 + x + x^2 + x^3 + x^4$
22. $y^5 - 2y^7 + 3y - 4y^2 + 5y^6$

6.3 *Add.*

23. $(m^2 + 3m - 5) + (2m^2 - 5m + 7)$
24. $(5a + 3a^2 - 2) + (a^2 + 3a + 4)$
25. $(b + 5 - 2b^2) + (1 - 2b + b^2)$

Add.

26. $2x^3 - 3x^2 + 5x$
    $\underline{\quad\ -x^2 + 3x}$
27. $3x^2 - 7x + 5$
    $\underline{-x^2 - \ x - 3}$
28. $-5a^2 - 2a - 7$
    $\underline{6a^2 + 4a + 3}$
29. $7t^2 + \ 8t - 9$
    $\underline{2t^2 - 10t - 5}$

6.4 *Subtract.*

30. $(5a^2 - 3a + 6) - (2a^2 + 3a + 7)$
31. $(3m^2 + 5m + 1) - (5m^2 + 2m - 1)$
32. $(3x^2 + 2x - 5) - (x^2 + x + 1)$

Subtract.

33. $5x^2 - 3x + 2$
    $\underline{-x^2 - 2x + 4}$
34. $4x^2 - 7x + 5$
    $\underline{7x^2 - 9x + 3}$
35. $\ 2x^2 + \ 8x - \ 4$
    $\underline{-3x^2 + 13x - 11}$
36. $8x^2 - 2x - 1$
    $\underline{3x^2 + \ x + 7}$

6.5 *Expand and simplify.*

37. $2(3x + 1) + 3(x + 4)$
38. $4(a + 5) + 3(a - 2)$
39. $2(4x - 1) - 4(2x - 3)$
40. $5(2y + 6) - (3y - 7)$
41. $2(x^2 - x - 7) - 3(x^2 + 5x - 1)$
42. $-3(y^2 - 2y + 5) - 4(2y^2 + y + 2)$

6.6 *Multiply.*

43. $(10x)(4y)$
44. $(-30y)(5xy)$
45. $(3ax)(4bx)$
46. $(-2ap)(-5ab)$
47. $(3xy)(-5xy)$
48. $-4a^2(-ab)$
49. $4x^2(-2xy^2z)$
50. $-s^2t^2(3s^3t^3)$

51. **Measurement** Find the area of the figure.

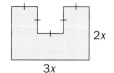

6.7 *Simplify.*

52. $(x^3)^2$
53. $(y^4)^3$
54. $(xy)^3$
55. $(3y^3)^2$
56. $(x^2y^3z)^2$
57. $(-r^3s^4t^2)^3$
58. $(-2x^2y^3)^3$
59. $(-5x^2y^2)^2$

Simplify.

60. $(2x^2yz^2)(x^2y^2z^2)^3$
61. $(3a^3b)^3(-a^3bx^4)$
62. $(-2k^3l^2m^2)^3(-k^2l^3m^3)$
63. $(a^4b^3)(-2ab)^3(5a^2b^2)$
64. $(-abc)^2(-a^2b^3c^3)(-a^2b^2c)$

334   *Chapter 6*

6.8 *Expand and simplify.*

65. $3y(2y - 7) + 2(y - 5)$

66. $2(m + 1) - m(m + 1)$

67. $-z(2z + 3) - (z - 5)$

68. $5x(2x - 7) - 3x(3x - 5)$

Expand.

69. $2y(-y^2 + 3y - 7)$

70. $-3t(1 - 2t - t^2)$

71. $4m(m^2 + 2m - 3)$

72. $-3x(2x^2 - 4x + 2)$

6.9 *Divide.*

73. $\dfrac{20x^5 y^8}{5x^4 y^6}$

74. $\dfrac{36x^3 y^4}{4x^2 y^3}$

75. $\dfrac{45a^3 b^6}{9ab^4}$

76. $\dfrac{-20a^4 b^4}{10a^3 b^{-3} c^2}$

77. Measurement Find the missing dimension of the rectangle.

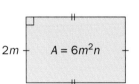

$2m$ $A = 6m^2 n$

6.10 **78.** Write the GCF of each pair.

a) 35, 40   **b)** 21, 28

c) 34, 51   **d)** 120, 96

e) $10a^2, 5a$ **f)** $16xy, 12xz$

g) $10ab^2, 18ab$ **h)** $15xy, 25x^2 y^2$

79. Write the GCF of each set.

a) $21x^2 y, 15xy^2, 9x^2 y^2$

b) $24x^2, 16xy, 32y^2$

c) $18xy^2, 27x^2 y^2, 36x^2 y$

6.11 *Factor.*

80. $5x - 15$ **81.** $6x^2 - 18x$

82. $5ab + 10ac$ **83.** $7a^2 + 35a^3$

84. $8abc - 12bc$ **85.** $3x^2 + 9y^2$

86. $3a^2 - 6ab + a$ **87.** $2x + 6y - 10z$

Exploring Math

Tiling Squares With L-Shaped Triominoes

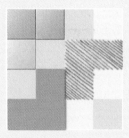

An L-shaped triomino is made up of 3 squares. You can make triominoes out of paper or linking cubes, or you can use a pencil to mark triominoes on a grid. A 4 by 4 grid cannot be tiled with triominoes, because it has 16 squares. The grid can be tiled if one of the squares is removed, so that there are only 15 squares to be covered.

1. Copy the 4 by 4 grid, from which the indicated square has been removed. Tile the grid with 5 L-shaped triominoes. Show your solution by drawing the triomino shapes on your copy of the grid.

2. a) Are there locations from which a square can be removed from the 4 by 4 grid so that the grid cannot be tiled with 5 L-shaped triominoes?

b) To answer part a), what was the minimum number of locations you needed to try? Explain.

3. Using a 5 by 5 grid with one square removed and 8 L-shaped triominoes, find

a) the locations of the shaded square so that the grid can be tiled

b) the locations of the shaded square so that the grid cannot be tiled

c) the minimum number of locations you needed to try in order to answer parts a) and b)

4. Is it possible to tile a 3 by 3 grid with L-shaped triominoes? Explain.

Chapter Check

Collect like terms and simplify.

1. $3x - 2y - 3x + 3y + 2$

2. $-15 + 2a - 3c + 10 + 4a - b - 7c$

3. $y^2 - 3y + 4y^2 - 5y - 11$

Classify each polynomial and state its degree.

4. $x^2 + 3x + 7$ **5.** $3x^3 + x^2$ **6.** $3x^2y$

Arrange the terms in each polynomial in descending powers of x.

7. $1 + x^3 + x^5 + x^4$

8. $5x^3 + 2xy - yx^4$

9. $x^3y - 3x^4 - 2x^2y + 10xy^2$

10. $3ax - 5b^2x^3 - 1 + 5abx^2$

Simplify.

11. $(5a^2 - x + 9) + (a^2 + x - 13)$

12. $(b^3 + b^2 - 2y + 7) + (3y - 8 - 2b^2)$

Simplify.

13. $(6y^2 - 6x + 3) - (y^2 + 6x - 3)$

14. $(-8t^2 + 4t - 1) - (4 - 7t^2 + 5t)$

Simplify.

15. $(10x^2 - 3x + 8) + (-11x^2 - 4x - 2)$

16. $(8y^2 + 6y - 1) - (3y^2 - 8y - 2)$

Add.

17. $\begin{array}{r} 3x^2 + 2x - 7 \\ +5x^2 - 11x - 5 \\ \hline \end{array}$ **18.** $\begin{array}{r} 10x^2 + 4x - 5 \\ -12x^2 + 6x + 6 \\ \hline \end{array}$

Multiply.

19. $-10x(5y)$ **20.** $(-15x^2y)(-3xy^2)$

21. $-2x^5(3b^2yz)$ **22.** $3x^3yz(-5xyz^2)$

Simplify.

23. $(-3x^4y^3)^3$ **24.** $(-ab^2c^2)^5$

25. $(x^2y^2z)(xy)^3$ **26.** $(x^2y^4)(-3x^3y^2)^2$

Expand and simplify.

27. $2(3y - 4) + 5(2y + 3)$

28. $4(2x - 7) - (3x + 1)$

29. $2x(x - 2) + 3(x + 3)$

30. $4x(x + 1) - 5x(x - 1)$

31. $-3x(x^2 - 2x + 1)$

32. $2m(2m^2 - 6m - 10)$

Divide.

33. $\dfrac{-6a^8b^5}{3a^5b^3}$ **34.** $\dfrac{-39p^7q^5r^5}{-13p^5q^4r^3}$

35. Write the GCF of each pair.

a) $20, 24$ **b)** $12a, 6b$

c) $25ab^2, 20a^2b$ **d)** $2xy, 3xy$

36. Write the GCF of each set.

a) $10xy, 15x^2y, 20xy^2$

b) $24ab^2c, 28a^2b^2c^2, 36ab^2c$

Factor.

37. $20x - 5$

38. $4t^2 - 12t$

39. $18a^2b^3 + 27a^3b - 9a^2b$

40. Measurement Write and simplify an expression for the volume of the cube.

$3ab^2$

41. Measurement Write, expand, and simplify an expression for the area of the figure.

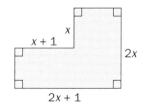

Using the Strategies

1. Lifeguards There are 12 h of lifeguard work available for the weekend. Three lifeguards have each agreed to work a whole number of hours. In how many different ways can the 12 h be divided so that each person works at least 2 h?

2. Geometry This is a 4 by 4 square.

One way to separate it into two congruent shapes, made up of smaller squares, is shown.

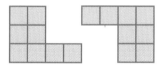

Find at least five other ways.

3. Train trip Your train leaves at 08:15. The bus trip to the train station takes 25 min. The bus stop is a 5-min walk from your place. You should get to the train station to buy your ticket 15 min before the train leaves. It will take you 55 min to get dressed, eat breakfast, and pack. For what time should you set your alarm clock?

4. Coins How many different combinations of coins have a value of $0.28? Copy and complete the table to find out.

Combinations	$0.25	$0.10	$0.05	$0.01
1	1	0	0	3
2	0	1	2	8
3				

5. Chores Kim has two chores at home. Every 4 days, she must clean the gerbil cage. Every 6 days, she must clean the canary cage. Last Monday, she did both jobs. On what day of the week will she next do both jobs?

6. Coin collection In a collection of coins, the numbers of dimes and nickels add to 5. The numbers of dimes and quarters add to 7. The numbers of nickels and quarters add to 8. How many of each type of coin are there?

7. Pop machine Students are allowed into the school at 08:00. Classes start at 09:00. There are 15-min breaks that begin at 10:30 and 14:30. Lunch is from 12:00 to 13:00. School is dismissed at 16:00. Students must leave the building by 17:00. Students are allowed to use the pop machine in the school cafeteria before and after school and during their breaks and lunch hour. The machine is filled twice a day, at 07:00 and 14:00. Sketch a graph of the number of cans in the machine versus time on a hot Monday in September.

8. Factors The number 9 has three different factors, 1, 3, and 9. Find all the positive integers less than 50 that have an odd number of different factors.

9. Fence posts The sides of a triangular field are 40 m, 44 m, and 52 m. A fence is to be built around the field with a post in each corner and the posts 4 m apart. How many fence posts are needed?

10. Library books For all the books in your school library, estimate the total number of words.

11. Canadian provinces Which two provinces are closest to each other in area? Which province is larger and by how much?

12. Canadian cities The Canadian city with the greatest elevation is 561 m higher than Saskatoon. What is the elevation of Saskatoon?

CHAPTER 7

Equations

How Can We Identify People?

One way to identify people is a device that scans and recognizes the patterns in the iris, which is the coloured part of a person's eye.

The iris controls the amount of light that enters the pupil. The iris consists of two muscles and elastic fibres. The fibres form into a pattern before a person is born. No two iris fibre patterns are the same. In fact, your left eye and right eye have different fibre patterns.

You will soon be able to access automatic banking machines by glancing at a camera. To use this system, you will have one iris photographed. Then, a digital code will be created, based on the fibre pattern in the iris. The pattern will be stored in a database. When you look in the camera at a banking machine, the system will search the database of iris codes and identify you. The system will search 100 000 iris codes in one second.

1. How long would it take the machine to scan the iris codes of all Canadians?

2. How long would it take the machine to scan the iris codes of all the people in the world?

3. What other methods are used to identify people?

In Modelling Math — Criminology on pages 382 and 383, you will learn how fingerprints are modelled to identify people.

GETTING STARTED

Balancing Acts

1 Balancing Act One

Suppose you have masses of 1 kg, 3 kg, and 9 kg, and you want to measure 13 kg of sand. Place the 1 kg, 3 kg, and 9 kg masses on one side of the balance scale. Pour sand into the pan on the other side until the scale balances.

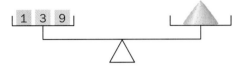

To measure 6 kg of sand, place the 9 kg mass on one side and the 3 kg mass on the other. Now, add sand until the scale balances.

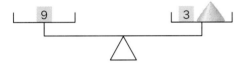

Draw balance scales to show how you can measure any unit mass of sand from 1 kg to 12 kg using the 1 kg, 3 kg, and 9 kg masses.

2 Balancing Act Two

Suppose you have masses of 1 kg, 3 kg, 9 kg, and 27 kg available to you.

To measure 30 kg of sand, put the 27 kg mass and the 3 kg mass on one side of the balance scale. Now, pour sand until the scale balances.

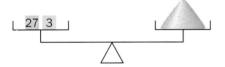

To measure 24 kg of sand, place the 27 kg mass on one side and the 3 kg mass on the other. Pour sand until the scale balances. Why is there 24 kg of sand on the scale?

You saw above how 1 kg, 3 kg, and 9 kg masses let you measure unit masses of sand from 1 kg to 13 kg. Using the 27 kg mass as well as the 1 kg, 3 kg, and 9 kg masses, draw balance scales to show how you can measure any unit mass of sand from 14 kg to 40 kg.

Warm Up

Simplify.
1. $3x + 4x$
2. $5x - 2x$
3. $6m - 2m + 5m$
4. $6t - 7t + 5t + 2t$
5. $2a - 3a - 4a$
6. $-5n + 2n - 3n$
7. $8s - 4s - 7s + 5s$
8. $3y + 6y - 10y + 2y$

Simplify.
9. $3x + 2y - 2x + 5y$
10. $3a - 4a - 2b + 5b$
11. $4x - 7 + 3x - 6$
12. $-7t + 4s - 5s - 8t$
13. $3x - 4y + 5 - 6x + 2$
14. $-3a - 2b - 7b + 5a$
15. $10 - 7x - 8x + 5y - 11y$

Expand.
16. $2(x + 7)$
17. $5(2x - 5)$
18. $3(6x - 1)$
19. $7(5x - 4)$
20. $4(2a - 3b)$
21. $6(2p - q)$
22. $-2(3y - 7)$
23. $-(4x - 9)$
24. $-5(2x - 3y - 4)$
25. $-(4x + 5y - 1)$

Evaluate for x = –2 and y = 3.
26. $x + y$
27. $4x + 5y$
28. $x - y$
29. $y - x$
30. $4y - 3x - 7$
31. $-4 - 2x - 4y$
32. $3xy - 4y - 3x$
33. $-5xy - 5x - 11$
34. $y - 2xy - x$
35. $10 - y - x - xy$

Evaluate for x = 3 and y = –2.
36. $x + 2y$
37. $7x - 4y$
38. $2x + y$
39. $y - 3x$
40. $2y - 3x - 1$
41. $5 - y - x - 6$
42. $5 - y - x + xy$
43. $-2xy + 12 - x$
44. $x - 5xy - 2y$
45. $y - x - xy - 1$

Mental Math
Expressions and Equations

Evaluate for the indicated value of the variable.
1. $3x - 5$ for $x = -1$
2. $9 - 2a$ for $a = 5$
3. $4(n + 1)$ for $n = 1.5$
4. $2(5 - y)$ for $y = -2$
5. $6x + 4x$ for $x = -0.5$
6. $4t - 7t + 5t$ for $t = 3$

Solve by inspection.
7. $x + 4 = 11$
8. $x - 5 = 9$
9. $5x = 20$
10. $2y = -10$
11. $m - 3 = 0$
12. $z + 1 = 0$
13. $4w = 24$
14. $p - 3 = 8$
15. $5 + x = 12$
16. $3q = 21$

Multiplying by Multiples of 9
To multiply a number by 9, first multiply the number by 10. Then, subtract the number.
For 23×9,
multiply by 10: $23 \times 10 = 230$
subtract 23: $230 - 23 = 207$
So, $23 \times 9 = 207$

Calculate.
1. 19×9
2. 28×9
3. 55×9
4. 88×9
5. 110×9
6. 125×9
7. 4.5×9
8. 2.6×9
9. 5.7×9

To multiply by 0.9, 90, 900, and so on, first multiply by 9, as shown above. Then, place the decimal point.
Thus, $23 \times 0.9 = 20.7$, and $23 \times 90 = 2070$.

Calculate.
10. 13×90
11. 27×90
12. 41×90
13. 15×900
14. 37×900
15. 35×900
16. 4.9×90
17. 6.4×90
18. 10.5×90
19. 16×0.9
20. 38×0.9
21. 42×0.9

22. Explain why the rule for multiplying by 9 works.

23. Modify the rule for multiplying by 9 to write a rule for multiplying by 11.

Calculate using your rule from question 23.
24. 36×11
25. 48×11
26. 53×1.1
27. 85×1.1
28. 21×110
29. 66×110

7.1 Solving Equations Using Addition and Subtraction

Canada won 3 gold medals at the Summer Olympic Games in Atlanta. This number was 5 less than the number of bronze medals Canada won.

If we let x represent the number of bronze medals Canada won, the above information can be represented by the equation $x - 5 = 3$.

Explore: Use a Model

The equation $x - 5 = 3$ is modelled on the balanced scale. Recall that each red tile represents +1, and each white tile represents −1. A red tile and a white tile together represent 0. The green tile represents the variable $+x$ or x.

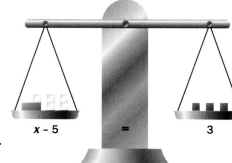

$x - 5$ =   3

a) How many red 1-tiles must be added to the left side of the scale so that only the value of the x-tile remains?
b) What must be done to the right side of the scale to keep it balanced?

Inquire

1. What is the value of x?
2. How many bronze medals did Canada win?
3. Use the above method to solve the following equations.
a) $x - 2 = 5$ **b)** $x - 1 = 2$
c) $x - 4 = -1$ **d)** $x - 6 = -2$
4. Write a rule for solving equations by addition.

When the same tiles are added to both sides of a balanced scale, the scale remains balanced. This process models the **addition property of equality**, which can be stated as follows.

For any numbers a, b, and c, if $a = b$, then $a + c = b + c$.

The number c can be positive or negative.
Since $7 = 7$
then $7 + 5 = 7 + 5$
and $7 + (-5) = 7 + (-5)$

If the same number is added to both sides of an equation, the result is an equation that is *equivalent* to the original equation. **Equivalent equations** are equations that have the same solution.

To solve an equation, isolate the variable on one side of the equation.

Example 1   Solving by Addition
Solve the equation $x - 2 = 6$.

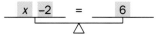

Solution
To isolate the variable, add 2 to both sides of the equation.

Write the equation: $\qquad\qquad x - 2 = 6$
Add 2 to both sides: $\quad x - 2 \boxed{+2} = 6 \boxed{+2}$
Simplify: $\qquad\qquad\qquad x = 8$
The solution is $x = 8$.

Example 2   Adding Negative Integers
Solve $x + 7 = -2$.

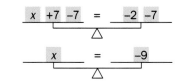

Solution
To isolate the variable, add -7 to both sides of the equation.

Write the equation: $\qquad\qquad x + 7 = -2$
Add -7 to both sides: $\quad x + 7 \boxed{+(-7)} = -2 \boxed{+(-7)}$
Simplify: $\qquad\qquad\qquad x = -9$
The solution is $x = -9$.

In Example 2, subtracting 7 from both sides of the equation would give the same result as adding -7 to both sides.

Write the equation: $\qquad\qquad\qquad x + 7 = -2$
Subtract 7 from both sides: $\quad x + 7 \boxed{-7} = -2 \boxed{-7}$
Simplify: $\qquad\qquad\qquad\qquad x = -9$

Subtracting the same number from both sides of an equation produces an equivalent equation. This property is called the **subtraction property of equality**, which can be stated as follows.

For any numbers a, b, and c, if $a = b$, then $a - c = b - c$.

Example 3 Solving by Subtraction

Solve and check $3 + x = -4$.

Solution

To isolate the variable, subtract 3 from both sides of the equation.

Write the equation: $\qquad\qquad 3 + x = -4$

Subtract 3 from both sides: $\quad 3 + x - 3 = -4 - 3$

Simplify: $\qquad\qquad\qquad\qquad\quad x = -7$

Substitute -7 for x in the equation.
The solution is correct if the value of the left side equals the value of the right side.

Check.

L.S. $= 3 + x \qquad$ **R.S.** $= -4$
$\qquad = 3 + (-7)$
$\qquad = 3 - 7$
$\qquad = -4$

Since L.S. = R.S., the solution is $x = -7$.

Example 4 Using Rational Numbers

Solve $x - 3.2 = 1.7$.

Solution

To isolate the variable, add 3.2 to both sides of the equation.

Write the equation: $\qquad\qquad x - 3.2 = 1.7$

Add 3.2 to both sides: $\quad x - 3.2 + 3.2 = 1.7 + 3.2$

Simplify: $\qquad\qquad\qquad\qquad\quad x = 4.9$

The solution is $x = 4.9$.

Practice

A

Write and solve the equations shown by the tiles.

1.   **2.**

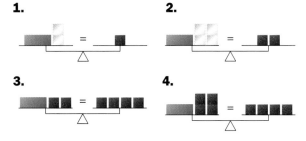

3.   **4.**

What number would you add to both sides to solve each equation?

5. $x - 3 = 11$ **6.** $x - 1 = 5$

7. $n - 7 = -8$ **8.** $-8 = -4 + m$

9. $3 = y - 10$ **10.** $z - 5 = -11$

What number would you subtract from both sides to solve each equation?

11. $x + 6 = 13$ **12.** $8 = x + 1$

13. $y + 2 = -7$ **14.** $m + 5 = -5$

15. $x + 3 = 9$ **16.** $-10 = 7 + z$

Solve and check.

17. $m - 5 = -4$ **18.** $2 = -3 + n$
19. $p - 7 = -3$ **20.** $r + 7 = -9$
21. $-3 = s + 5$ **22.** $t - 8 = 10$
23. $2 + x = -4$ **24.** $7 = x - 5$
25. $x + 4 = -8$ **26.** $-11 = t - 1$

Applications and Problem Solving

Solve and check.

27. $x + 1.5 = 3.5$ **28.** $m - 3.2 = 4.8$
29. $4.6 = t - 1.4$ **30.** $5.7 = r + 3.6$
31. $4.3 + m = 1.3$ **32.** $y - 2.4 = -1.4$
33. $9 = 8.2 + x$ **34.** $3.7 + t = 6.4$
35. $-1.4 + q = 4.4$ **36.** $10.3 = x - 5.4$
37. $-8.8 = w - 1.1$ **38.** $x + 15.7 = -18.1$

Estimate. Then, use a calculator to solve.

39. $17.89 + y = 43.01$
40. $-32.49 = s - 21.65$
41. $x + 0.234 = 5.922$
42. $n - 0.346 = -0.156$

B

In questions 43–45, find the equation that represents the problem and solve it.

43. Numbers Three more than a number, x, is eight. What is the number?
a) $x - 3 = 8$ **b)** $x + 8 = 3$
c) $x + 3 = 8$ **d)** $x - 8 = 3$

44. Unloading boxes How many boxes are left to unload if there are 195 boxes in a shipment and 72 boxes have been unloaded?
a) $x + 72 = 195$ **b)** $x + 195 = 72$
c) $x - 72 = 195$ **d)** $x - 195 = 72$

45. Measurement In a triangle, the sum of the sides is 9.7 cm. The lengths of two of the sides are 3.2 cm and 4.5 cm. What is the length of the unknown side?
a) $x - 4.5 = 9.7 - 3.2$
b) $9.7 - x = 4.5 - 3.2$
c) $4.5 + x - 3.2 = 9.7$
d) $x + 3.2 + 4.5 = 9.7$

Solve by adding or subtracting.

46. $y - \dfrac{1}{7} = \dfrac{5}{7}$ **47.** $x + \dfrac{1}{2} = \dfrac{3}{4}$

48. $\dfrac{1}{4} + t = -\dfrac{3}{8}$ **49.** $\dfrac{7}{12} = m - \dfrac{1}{6}$

50. $\dfrac{3}{4} = s + \dfrac{2}{3}$ **51.** $w - \dfrac{1}{2} = -\dfrac{3}{5}$

52. $x - 4\dfrac{1}{2} = 1\dfrac{1}{3}$ **53.** $y + 3 = 1\dfrac{5}{8}$

54. Uranus The number of moons around Uranus is 5 more than the number of rings. Uranus has 15 moons. Solve the equation $r + 5 = 15$ to find the number of rings.

55. Walking distances A nurse walks about 6.3 km a day, which is 0.8 km less than a letter carrier walks. Solve the equation $x - 0.8 = 6.3$ to find out how far a letter carrier walks in a day.

C

56. What is the result if you add 0 to both sides of an equation?

57. Find two solutions for each equation.
a) $x^2 - 1.8 = 7.2$ **b)** $t^2 + 18.2 = 82.2$

58. Write one equation that can be solved by addition and one equation that can be solved by subtraction. Each equation should have $x = -3$ as its solution. Have a classmate solve your equations.

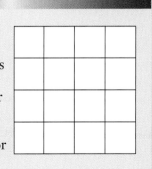

LOGIC POWER

Copy the diagram. Place 4 As, 3 Bs, 3Cs, 3 Ds, and 3 Es in the squares so that the same letter does not appear more than once in any row, column, or diagonal.

7.2 Solving Equations Using Division and Multiplication

The second time the Summer Olympics were held in Los Angeles, Canada won 10 gold medals. This was 5 times the number of gold medals that Canada won in 1932, the first time the Games were held in Los Angeles.

If we let x represent the number of gold medals Canada won in 1932, the above information can be represented by the equation $5x = 10$.

Explore: Use a Model

The equation $5x = 10$ is modelled on the balanced scale.
a) How many x-tiles are shown?
b) How many pairs of 1-tiles are shown?
c) How many 1-tiles does an x-tile represent?

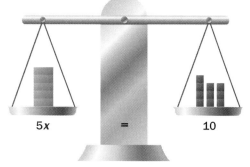

5x   =   10

Inquire

1. How many gold medals did Canada win in 1932?

2. Divide both sides of the equation $5x = 10$ by 5.

3. How does your answer to question 2 compare with your answer to question 1?

4. Use the above method to solve the following equations.
a) $2x = 8$ **b)** $3x = 6$
c) $2x = -4$ **d)** $4x = -8$

5. Write a rule for solving equations by division.

When both sides of an equation are divided by the same number, the result is an equation that is equivalent to the original equation. This property is called the **division property of equality**, which can be stated as follows.

For any numbers a, b, and c, if $a = b$, and $c \neq 0$, then $\dfrac{a}{c} = \dfrac{b}{c}$.

The number c can be positive or negative.

Since $\quad 12 = 12$

then $\quad \dfrac{12}{2} = \dfrac{12}{2}$

and $\quad \dfrac{12}{-2} = \dfrac{12}{-2}$

Example 1   Solving by Division

Solve the equation $3x = 15$.

Solution

Divide both sides of the equation by 3.

Write the equation: $\qquad 3x = 15$

Divide both sides by 3: $\quad \dfrac{3x}{3} = \dfrac{15}{3}$

Simplify: $\qquad\qquad\qquad x = 5$

The solution is $x = 5$.

In Example 1, multiplying both sides of the equation by $\dfrac{1}{3}$ would give the same result as dividing both sides by 3.

Write the equation: $\qquad\qquad 3x = 15$

Multiply both sides by $\dfrac{1}{3}$: $\quad \dfrac{1}{3} \times 3x = \dfrac{1}{3} \times 15$

Simplify: $\qquad\qquad\qquad\qquad x = 5$

Multiplying both sides of an equation by the same number produces an equivalent equation. This property is called the **multiplication property of equality**, which can be stated as follows.

For any numbers a, b, and c, if $a = b$, then $ac = bc$.

Example 2   Solving by Multiplication

Solve the equation $\dfrac{x}{2} = -5$.

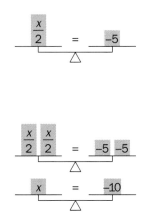

Solution
Multiply both sides of the equation by 2.

Write the equation: $\dfrac{x}{2} = -5$

Multiply both sides by 2: $2 \times \dfrac{x}{2} = 2 \times -5$

Simplify: $x = -10$

The solution is $x = -10$.

Example 3   Using Rational Numbers
Solve and check $-2x = 18.4$.

Solution
Divide both sides of the equation by -2.

Write the equation: $-2x = 18.4$

Divide both sides by -2: $\dfrac{-2x}{-2} = \dfrac{18.4}{-2}$

Simplify: $x = -9.2$

Check.

L.S. $= -2x$ **R.S.** $= 18.4$
$= -2(-9.2)$
$= 18.4$

Since L.S. = R.S., the solution is $x = -9.2$.

Practice

A

Write and solve the equation represented by each balanced scale.

1.   **2.**

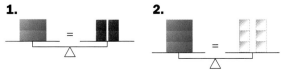

By what number would you divide both sides to solve each equation?

3. $6x = 12$ **4.** $2x = -8$

5. $7z = -14$ **6.** $11r = 22$

7. $6n = -18$ **8.** $8y = 64$

By what number would you multiply both sides to solve each equation?

9. $\dfrac{x}{3} = 9$ **10.** $\dfrac{x}{2} = -4$

11. $\dfrac{y}{7} = 4$ **12.** $\dfrac{m}{5} = -6$

13. $\dfrac{t}{4} = -1$ **14.** $\dfrac{x}{6} = 0$

Solve.

15. $3x = 15$ **16.** $2y = -12$

17. $-8x = 16$ **18.** $-15 = 5p$

19. $-6t = -24$ **20.** $12 = 3s$

21. $2x = 24$ **22.** $-25 = 5j$

23. $-7x = -21$

Solve.

24. $\dfrac{x}{2} = 2$　　　　**25.** $\dfrac{y}{2} = -4$

26. $\dfrac{x}{3} = 7$　　　　**27.** $-4 = \dfrac{p}{3}$

28. $\dfrac{m}{4} = 8$　　　　**29.** $-3 = \dfrac{n}{5}$

30. $\dfrac{s}{10} = 5$　　　　**31.** $-2 = \dfrac{t}{12}$

32. $\dfrac{u}{11} = 4$

Solve and check.

33. $2x = 8.4$　　　　**34.** $3m = -6.3$

35. $\dfrac{x}{5} = 2.4$　　　　**36.** $\dfrac{x}{2} = -1.5$

37. $-4x = -2.8$　　　　**38.** $1.6x = 4.8$

39. $4 = \dfrac{m}{1.5}$　　　　**40.** $-8.4 = 0.2x$

Applications and Problem Solving

Estimate. Then, use a calculator to solve.

41. $-2.35x = 3.384$　　　　**42.** $\dfrac{t}{7.1} = -0.96$

43. $371w = -36\,358$　　　　**44.** $\dfrac{-s}{452} = 14$

B

In questions 45 and 46, find the equation that represents the problem and solve it.

45. Money Six dollars is to be divided equally among three people. How much money does each person receive?

a) $3x = 6$　　　　**b)** $6x = 3$

c) $\dfrac{x}{3} = 6$　　　　**d)** $\dfrac{x}{6} = 3$

46. Measurement One third of the sum of the side lengths of an equilateral triangle is 4.2 cm. What is the sum?

a) $3x = 4.2$　　　　**b)** $\dfrac{1}{3}x = 4.2$

c) $\dfrac{1}{3}x + 4.2 = 0$　　　　**d)** $x = \dfrac{1}{3}(4.2)$

47. Snowfall The average annual snowfall in Vancouver is about one sixth of the average annual snowfall in St. John's. Vancouver averages 60 cm of snow a year. Solve the equation $\dfrac{s}{6} = 60$ to find the average annual snowfall in St. John's.

48. Animal masses The mass of a white-tailed deer is 1.4 times the mass of a cougar. White-tailed deer average 98 kg in mass. Solve the equation $1.4x = 98$ to find the mass of a cougar.

C

49. What is the result if you multiply both sides of an equation by 0?

50. Describe the solutions to these equations.
a) $3x = 0$　　　　**b)** $0y = 2$

51. Find 2 solutions to each equation.
a) $2x^2 = 72$　　　　**b)** $\dfrac{m^2}{4} = 1$

52. Write one equation that can be solved by division and one that can be solved by multiplication. Each equation should have $x = 7$ as its solution. Have a classmate solve your equations.

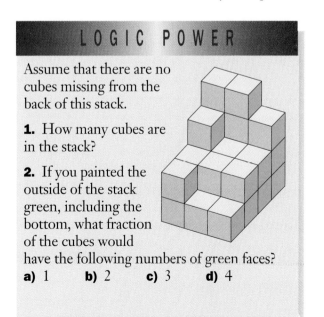

LOGIC POWER

Assume that there are no cubes missing from the back of this stack.

1. How many cubes are in the stack?

2. If you painted the outside of the stack green, including the bottom, what fraction of the cubes would have the following numbers of green faces?
a) 1　　**b)** 2　　**c)** 3　　**d)** 4

7.3 Solving Multi-Step Equations

A cow sleeps 7 h a day. This is 1 h less than twice the amount an elephant sleeps a day. If we let the hours that an elephant sleeps be x, we can represent this information with the equation $2x - 1 = 7$.

Explore: Use a Model

The equation $2x - 1 = 7$ is modelled on the balanced scale.

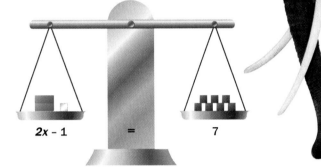

a) How many red 1-tiles must be added to both sides of the scale so that only the value of the 2 x-tiles remains on the left?
b) How many red 1-tiles does an x-tile represent?

Inquire

1. For how many hours does an elephant sleep each day?

2. Use the above method to solve the following equations.
a) $3x + 2 = 8$ **b)** $4x - 1 = 11$
c) $2x + 3 = -9$ **d)** $5x - 1 = -11$

3. Write the steps for solving each equation in question 2.

4. The flow charts show the order of the steps to solve the equation $5x + 2 = 17$. First, the term containing x is isolated on the left side. Then, x itself is isolated.

Left Side   START → 5x + 2 → Subtract 2 → Divide by 5 → x → STOP

Then, the same steps are applied to the right side.

Right Side   START → 17 → Subtract 2 → Divide by 5 → 3 → STOP

Use flow charts to solve these equations.
a) $2x + 3 = 11$ **b)** $3x - 1 = 17$

Example 1   Solving Multi-Step Equations
Solve the equation $5x + 4 = -16$.

Solution

Write the equation:	$5x + 4 = -16$
Subtract 4 from both sides:	$5x + 4 - 4 = -16 - 4$
Simplify:	$5x = -20$
Divide both sides by 5:	$\dfrac{5x}{5} = -\dfrac{20}{5}$
Simplify:	$x = -4$

The solution is $x = -4$.

Example 2   Equations With Decimals
Solve and check $7.2 = 3x - 4.2$.

Solution

Write the equation:	$7.2 = 3x - 4.2$
Add 4.2 to both sides:	$7.2 + 4.2 = 3x - 4.2 + 4.2$
Simplify:	$11.4 = 3x$
Divide both sides by 3:	$\dfrac{11.4}{3} = \dfrac{3x}{3}$
Simplify:	$3.8 = x$

Substitute $x = 3.8$.
Check.

$$\textbf{L.S.} = 7.2 \qquad \textbf{R.S.} = 3(3.8) - 4.2$$
$$= 11.4 - 4.2$$
$$= 7.2$$

Since L.S. = R.S., the solution is $x = 3.8$.

Example 3   Equations With Fractions
Solve and check $\dfrac{9x}{2} - 6 = 21$.

Solution

Write the equation:	$\dfrac{9x}{2} - 6 = 21$
Add 6 to both sides:	$\dfrac{9x}{2} - 6 + 6 = 21 + 6$
Simplify:	$\dfrac{9x}{2} = 27$
Multiply both sides by 2:	$2 \times \dfrac{9x}{2} = 2 \times 27$
Simplify:	$9x = 54$
Divide both sides by 9:	$\dfrac{9x}{9} = \dfrac{54}{9}$
Simplify:	$x = 6$

Substitute $x = 6$.
Check.

L.S. $= \dfrac{9x}{2} - 6$ **R.S.** $= 21$

$\quad = \dfrac{9(6)}{2} - 6$

$\quad = \dfrac{54}{2} - 6$

$\quad = 27 - 6$

$\quad = 21$

Since L.S. = R.S., the solution is $x = 6$.

Example 4   Simplifying and Solving
Solve the equation $7x - 9x - 6 = 21 - 5$.

Solution
Simplify both sides of the equation.
Then, apply the rules for solving equations.

Write the equation: $\quad 7x - 9x - 6 = 21 - 5$
Simplify: $\quad\quad\quad\quad -2x - 6 = 16$
Add 6 to both sides: $\quad -2x - 6 + 6 = 16 + 6$
Simplify: $\quad\quad\quad\quad\quad -2x = 22$
Divide both sides by -2: $\quad \dfrac{-2x}{-2} = \dfrac{22}{-2}$
Simplify: $\quad\quad\quad\quad\quad\quad x = -11$

The solution is $x = -11$.

Example 5   Approximate Solutions
Solve $3x - 2 = 5$. Round your answer to the nearest tenth.

Solution
Write the equation: $\quad 3x - 2 = 5$
Add 2 to both sides: $\quad 3x - 2 + 2 = 5 + 2$
Simplify: $\quad\quad\quad\quad 3x = 7$
Divide both sides by 3:– $\quad \dfrac{3x}{3} = \dfrac{7}{3}$
Evaluate: $\quad\quad\quad\quad x \doteq 2.3$

The solution is $x = 2.3$, to the nearest tenth.

Practice

A

Draw flow charts to show the solution steps for each equation.

1. $5x + 2 = 22$ **2.** $2x + 5 = 25$

Solve.

3. $3x = 11 + 1$ **4.** $2y - 5 = 9$
5. $5n + 2n = -14$ **6.** $3m + 7 = 19$
7. $4x + 2x = -18$ **8.** $4y - 9y = 35$
9. $5w + w = 7 + 23$ **10.** $6n + 3n = -18$

Solve and check.

11. $3y - 5y = 4$ **12.** $3t + 7t = -30$
13. $3x + 2x = -20$ **14.** $5 + 11 = 4y$
15. $15 = 2n + 3n$ **16.** $5 + n = -15$
17. $3 + m = -7$ **18.** $4 + x = 20$

Solve and check.

19. $\dfrac{x}{3} = 4 + 2$ **20.** $\dfrac{y}{2} = 6 - 3$

21. $\dfrac{n}{3} + 3 = 5$ **22.** $\dfrac{m}{5} - 5 = -9$

23. $4 + \dfrac{x}{3} = -7$ **24.** $\dfrac{y}{2} + 5 = 3$

25. $\dfrac{x}{4} - \dfrac{1}{4} = -\dfrac{3}{4}$ **26.** $\dfrac{y}{2} + \dfrac{1}{4} = \dfrac{3}{4}$

Solve and check.

27. $4x + 3x + 7 = 21$
28. $2y - 5y - 5 = 13$
29. $4t + 7t = 15 - 4$
30. $6s + 2s + s = 18$
31. $4t - 7t = 8 + 4$
32. $3y = 10 - 6 - 7$
33. $4 + 3t = -6 - 2$
34. $x + 2x = -15 - 6$

Solve and check.

35. $5n + 3n - 2n = 17 - 2 + 9$
36. $2m + 5m + m = -10 - 5 - 1$
37. $3x + 5x + 1 = 11 - 2$
38. $4 + 3t - 5t = 12$
39. $2s + 3s - 5 = 18 + 12$
40. $4y - 7 + 2y = -24 - 1$

Solve.

41. $2x + 1.4 = 7.8$ **42.** $5t - 2.1 = 8.9$
43. $1.4m - 3.6 = 3.4$ **44.** $9.2 = 1.5t + 1.7$
45. $6 - 1.2x = 8.4$ **46.** $9.3 + 2.5k = 1.3$
47. $2 - 1.8r = 11$ **48.** $4.2 + 0.5y = 8.1$

Solve. Round your answer to the nearest tenth.

49. $7x + 5 = -3$ **50.** $2.4n - 3.8 = 1.1$
51. $3 = 3y + 8$ **52.** $4 = -6z + 14$

Applications and Problem Solving

B

53. Measurement The equation $2x + 3x + 5x = 180$ represents the sum of the interior angles of the triangle. Find the degree measure of each interior angle.

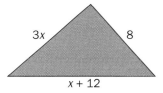

54. Measurement The equation $(x + 12) + 3x + 8 = 40$ represents the perimeter of the triangle. Find the lengths of the sides.

55. Prime Ministers Pierre Trudeau was Prime Minister of Canada for 15 years. This was 3 years longer than twice the number of years that John Diefenbaker was Prime Minister. Solve the equation $2y + 3 = 15$ to find out how long John Diefenbaker was Prime Minister.

C

56. a) Solve the equation $2x + 5 = 11$, using the division rule first.
b) Is the result the same when you use the subtraction rule first?
c) Is one method better than the other? Explain.

57. Write an equation in which the solution requires at least 2 steps and is $x = -15$. Have a classmate solve your equation.

7.4 Solving Equations With the Variable on Both Sides

The Group of Seven was formed in 1920 by seven artists who took on the task of capturing the beauty and power of the Canadian North in their paintings. Today, the Group's work is exhibited in every major gallery in Canada.

Between 1920 and 1933, when the Group disbanded, the members met formally a few times a year to plan exhibitions and the addition of new members. If x represents the total number of members of the Group, we can write the equation $x + 4 = 24 - x$. This is an example of an equation with the variable on both sides.

National Gallery of Canada, Ottawa

Explore: Use a Model

The equation $5x = 3x + 8$, which has the variable on both sides, is modelled by the balanced scale.

a) Solve the equation for x.

b) Describe and justify your method.

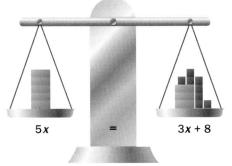

$5x$ $=$ $3x + 8$

Inquire

1. Solve the equation $x + 7 = 2x + 3$ by isolating the variable on the right side of the equation.

2. Solve the equation $x + 7 = 2x + 3$ by isolating the variable on the left side of the equation.

3. Compare the results from questions 1 and 2.

4. Write the steps for solving equations with the variable on both sides.

5. Solve the equation $x + 4 = 24 - x$ to find the total number of members of the Group of Seven.

6. Use your research skills to name the members of the Group of Seven.

Example 1   Variable on Both Sides

Solve the equation $5x - 8x = x + 8$.

Solution

Simplify before solving.

Write the equation:	$5x - 8x = x + 8$
Simplify:	$-3x = x + 8$
Subtract x from both sides:	$-3x - x = x + 8 - x$
Simplify:	$-4x = 8$
Divide both sides by -4:	$\dfrac{-4x}{-4} = \dfrac{8}{-4}$
Simplify:	$x = -2$

The solution is $x = -2$.

Practice

A

Write and solve the equations shown by the tiles.

1.

2.

Solve.

3. $5x = 4x + 7$

4. $6y = 7y - 4$

5. $3m = m + 4$

6. $7n = 4n - 6$

7. $9t = 5t - 8$

8. $4s = 2s + 10$

9. $8x = -2x - 10$

10. $3y = -2y + 15$

Solve and check.

11. $2x = -30 + 5x$

12. $7y = 20 + 3y$

13. $3t = -12 + 7t$

14. $12s = -36 + 6s$

15. $2a = 0.35 - 5a$

16. $4n = 3.6 - 2n$

Solve.

17. $2x + 3x = 8x - 3$

18. $5x - 4x = -x + 6$

19. $3y + y = 2y - 8$

20. $5a - 3a = 6 - a$

21. $6s + 4s = 20 + 5s$

22. $3t + 3t = -9 + 9t$

23. $6r + 4r = 16 + 2r$

24. $7x - 4x = x - 10$

Solve and check.

25. $5x - 3x = 4x - 2$

26. $7x - 4x = x + 6$

27. $3y + 5y = 5y - 6$

28. $4t - 7t = -7 - 2t$

29. $3s - 5s = 4s + 6$

30. $6j - 7j = 3j + 12$

31. $5a - 2a = 5a - 8$

32. $8y = 5y + y + 14$

Solve.

33. $15x - 7x = -52 - 5x$

34. $21y = -205 + 75 + 47y$

35. $7t + 53 = 14 - 6t$

36. $m = 26.8 - 6.8 + 3m$

37. $2x = -8.4 - 3.6 - 4x$

38. $7y = 0.3 + 2.7 + 4y$

39. $3n = 10.1 + 9.9 - 2n$

Solve and check.

40. $2x + 10 = 9 + 11 - 3x$

41. $11s + 25 = 54 + 25 + 2s$

42. $65 + n = 85 - 16 + 3n$

Applications and Problem Solving

43. Baseball cards Bill has x baseball cards. Abbas has $4x$ baseball cards. The number of cards Abbas has is equal to the number of cards Bill has plus 60. Solve the equation $x + 60 = 4x$ to find the number of cards Bill has.

44. Ringette Marlene scored y ringette goals. Lia scored $3y$ goals. The number of goals that Marlene scored equals the number of goals Lia scored minus 12. Solve the equation $y = 3y - 12$ to find the number of goals Marlene scored.

45. Wind speeds The average wind speed in Bonavista, Newfoundland, is twice the average wind speed in Whitehorse, Yukon Territory. The difference between the wind speeds is 14 km/h. Solve the equation $2x - 14 = x$ to find the average wind speed in Whitehorse.

46. States The number of states in India is 1 more than 4 times the number of states in Australia. There are 19 more states in India than in Australia. Solve the equation $x + 19 = 4x + 1$ to find the number of states in Australia.

C

47. Solve for x. Assume the letters a, b, c, and y represent non-zero integers.

a) $x + a = b + c + y$

b) $a + x - b = c - y$

c) $ax + b = c - y$

d) $a(x - b) + y = c$

e) $b + y = cx - a$

f) $\dfrac{x}{a} + b - y = -c$

48. Write an equation with a variable on both sides and a solution of $x = -2$. Have a classmate solve your equation.

PATTERN POWER

There are x cars in a bumper-to-bumper lineup. The car's bumpers are touching. How many bumpers are touching?

7.5 Solving Equations With Brackets

Canada became a country in 1867. If we take the number of provinces in Canada at that time, add 1, and double the sum, the result is Canada's present number of provinces Thus, we can find the number of provinces in 1867 by solving the equation $2(x + 1) = 10$.

Explore: Solve an Equation

a) Expand to remove the brackets in the equation $2(x + 1) = 10$.
b) Solve the equation.

Inquire

1. Solve these equations.
a) $3(x - 1) = 12$ **b)** $-2(x + 1) = 6$
c) $2(x + 3) = -4$ **d)** $-(x + 1) = -7$
2. Write a rule for solving equations with brackets.
3. How many provinces were there in 1867?
4. Use your research skills to list Canada's provinces in 1867.

Example 1   Solving Equations With Brackets
Solve the equation $2(x + 2) = -6$ and check.

Solution
Expand, and then solve.

Write the equation:	$2(x + 2) = -6$
Expand:	$2x + 4 = -6$
Subtract 4 from both sides:	$2x + 4 - 4 = -6 - 4$
Simplify:	$2x = -10$
Divide both sides by 2:	$\dfrac{2x}{2} = \dfrac{-10}{2}$
Simplify:	$x = -5$

Substitute $x = -5$.
Check.
L.S. $= 2(x + 2)$ **R.S.** $= -6$
$\quad = 2(-5 + 2)$
$\quad = 2(-3)$
$\quad = -6$
Since L.S. = R.S., the solution is $x = -5$.

Example 2 Variable on Both Sides

Solve the equation $2(x-3)-5=13-4x$ and check.

Solution

To follow the order of operations, first expand to remove the brackets.

$$2(x-3)-5=13-4x$$
$$2x-6-5=13-4x$$
$$2x-11=13-4x$$
$$2x-11+11=13-4x+11$$
$$2x=24-4x$$
$$2x+4x=24-4x+4x$$
$$6x=24$$
$$\frac{6x}{6}=\frac{24}{6}$$
$$x=4$$

Substitute $x=4$.

Check.

L.S. $=2(x-3)-5$	**R.S.** $=13-4x$
$=2(4-3)-5$	$=13-4(4)$
$=2(1)-5$	$=13-16$
$=2-5$	$=-3$
$=-3$	

Since L.S. $=$ R.S., the solution is $x=4$.

Example 3 Variable and Brackets on Both Sides

Solve and check.

$$3(2x-5)-(x+3)=2(x+1)+4$$

Solution

$$3(2x-5)-(x+3)=2(x+1)+4$$
$$6x-15-x-3=2x+2+4$$
$$6x-x-15-3=2x+6$$
$$5x-18=2x+6$$
$$5x-2x=6+18$$
$$3x=24$$
$$x=8$$

Check.

L.S. $=3(2x-5)-(x+3)$	**R.S.** $=2(x+1)+4$
$=3[2(8)-5]-(8+3)$	$=2(8+1)+4$
$=3(16-5)-(11)$	$=2(9)+4$
$=3(11)-11$	$=18+4$
$=33-11$	$=22$
$=22$	

Since L.S. $=$ R.S., the solution is $x=8$.

Practice

A

Solve.

1. $2(x+1)=4$ **2.** $2(x-3)=2$
3. $3(x+1)=6$ **4.** $2(x+3)=-6$
5. $3(x+2)=-9$ **6.** $2(x+5)=-4$

Solve and check.

7. $2(3x+4)=14$ **8.** $14=2(3x-2)$
9. $3(x+5)=18$ **10.** $3(2x+3)=-3$
11. $-24=4(x+3)$ **12.** $5(2x+3)=-15$

Solve.

13. $2(x+3)-3=8-3x$
14. $3(x+1)+10=8-2x$
15. $8-3x=4(x-3)+6$
16. $5(2x-3)+6=-35-3x$

Solve.

17. $5(2x-3)=2(x-2)+5$
18. $2(x+1)=(3x-2)+1$
19. $3(y+4)=5(y-3)+23$
20. $4(n+7)=-44+2(n+6)$
21. $5(2x-3)=2(x+7)+11$

Solve and check.

22. $2(x-3)+(x+3)=6x$
23. $5(x+4)-(x+2)=8x+2$
24. $4(m-2)-(m+3)=m-1$
25. $4(n-7)-2(n+3)=-15n$
26. $4(y+2)-5(y+1)=y-1$

Solve.

27. $3(2x+1)-(x-2)=2(x+4)$
28. $12(s-1)-4(2s-1)=2(s+1)$
29. $2(x-8)-(x-4)=3(x+5)+3$
30. $7(x-1)-2(x-6)=2(x-5)+6$
31. $3(4n-1)=4(2n+9)-7$

Applications and Problem Solving

32. Measurement The equation $5(x+1)=20$ represents the area of the rectangle.
a) Solve the equation.
b) Find the width of the rectangle.

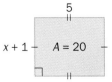

B

33. Measurement The equation $2(3x+2)+2(x+4)=36$ represents the perimeter of the rectangle.

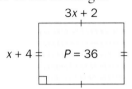

a) Solve the equation. Explain each step of your solution.
b) Calculate the dimensions of the rectangle.

34. Oceans The Pacific Ocean accounts for 46% of the area of the water on the Earth's surface. If we take the percent that the Atlantic Ocean accounts for, subtract 1, and double the difference, the result is the percent that the Pacific Ocean accounts for. Solve the equation $2(x-1)=46$ to find the percent that the Atlantic Ocean accounts for.

C

35. Write an equation that has 1 bracketed expression on its left side and 1 bracketed expression plus a number on its right side. The equation should have a solution of $x=-2$. Have a classmate solve your equation.

NUMBER POWER

Find the missing sum.

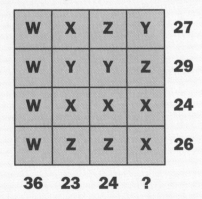

358 *Chapter 7*

7.6 Solving Equations With Fractions and Decimals

One year, a survey of Canadian households found that the percent with camcorders was 1.4% less than one half the percent with home computers. The percent of households with camcorders was 16.7%. If x represents the percent of households with home computers, we can find this percent by writing and solving the equation $0.5x - 1.4 = 16.7$.

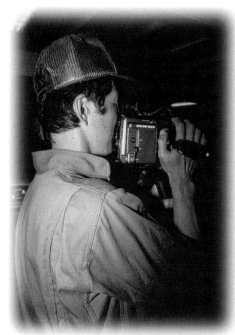

Explore: Solve the Equations

Solve these equations.
a) $1.2x - 0.4 = 2$ **b)** $0.25x - 5 = 2.75$
c) $3.14n + 2 = 12.99$ **d)** $2.3t - 1.47 = 6.85 + 0.7t$

Inquire

1. Multiply the terms in the equations a) to d) by a power of 10 to produce an equation with whole-number coefficients.
2. Solve each equation you wrote in question 1.
3. Compare the two solution methods you used. Which method do you prefer? Explain.
4. Solve the equation $0.5x - 1.4 = 16.7$ to find the percent of Canadian households with home computers in the year the survey was taken.
5. Use your research skills to find the percent of Canadian households with home computers today. Compare your findings with your answer to question 4.

Example 1   Equations With Decimals
Solve the equation $5.84 - 2.2y = 18.6$.

Solution 1
The number 5.84 has the greatest number of decimal places.
To obtain whole-number coefficients, multiply each term by 100.

Write the equation:	$5.84 - 2.2y = 18.6$
Multiply both sides by 100:	$100 \times (5.84 - 2.2y) = 100 \times 18.6$
Expand:	$100 \times 5.84 - 100 \times 2.2y = 100 \times 18.6$
Simplify:	$584 - 220y = 1860$
Subtract 584 from both sides:	$-220y = 1276$
Divide both sides by -220:	$y = -5.8$

The solution is $y = -5.8$.

Estimate
$$1200 \div (-200) = -6$$

Solution 2
Keep the decimals and solve with a calculator.

Write the equation:	$5.84 - 2.2y = 18.6$
Subtract 5.84 from both sides:	$-2.2y = 18.6 - 5.84$
Simplify:	$-2.2y = 12.76$
Divide both sides by -2.2:	$y = -5.8$

The solution is $y = -5.8$.

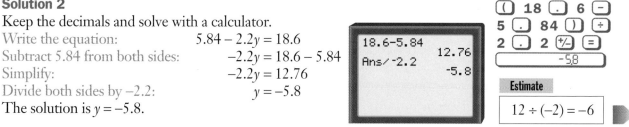

Estimate
$$12 \div (-2) = -6$$

Example 2   Equations With Fractions

Solve $\dfrac{x}{3} - \dfrac{3x}{2} = \dfrac{1}{6} - x$.

Solution

To eliminate the fractions, multiply each term in the equation by
the lowest common denominator, 6.

Write the equation:
$$\frac{x}{3} - \frac{3x}{2} = \frac{1}{6} - x$$

Multiply both sides by 6:
$$6 \times \left(\frac{x}{3}\right) - 6 \times \left(\frac{3x}{2}\right) = 6 \times \left(\frac{1}{6}\right) - 6 \times x$$

Simplify:
$$2x - 9x = 1 - 6x$$

Simplify:
$$-7x = 1 - 6x$$

Add $6x$ to both sides:
$$-7x + 6x = 1 - 6x + 6x$$

Simplify:
$$-x = 1$$

Divide both sides by –1:
$$x = -1$$

The solution is $x = -1$.

Example 3   Using Brackets

Solve and check $\dfrac{x-2}{4} - \dfrac{x-7}{3} = 1$.

Solution

Multiply all terms by the lowest common denominator, 12.

Write the equation:
$$\frac{x-2}{4} - \frac{x-7}{3} = 1$$

Multiply both sides by 12:
$$12 \times \frac{(x-2)}{4} - 12 \times \frac{(x-7)}{3} = 12 \times 1$$

The division bar is a grouping symbol. It acts like a bracket.

Simplify:
$$3(x-2) - 4(x-7) = 12$$

Expand:
$$3x - 6 - 4x + 28 = 12$$

Simplify:
$$-x + 22 = 12$$

Subtract 22 from both sides:
$$-x = -10$$

Multiply both sides by –1:
$$x = 10$$

Check.

L.S. $= \dfrac{x-2}{4} - \dfrac{x-7}{3}$ **R.S.** $= 1$

$\quad = \dfrac{10-2}{4} - \dfrac{10-7}{3}$

$\quad = \dfrac{8}{4} - \dfrac{3}{3}$

$\quad = 2 - 1$

$\quad = 1$

Since L.S. = R.S., the solution is $x = 10$.

Practice

A

Solve.

1. $x + 0.2 = 0.8$ **2.** $y - 0.5 = 1.2$
3. $s + 1.2 = 1.5$ **4.** $t + 4.5 = -3$
5. $m + 5.2 = 2.2$ **6.** $-2.3 = 4.6 + n$

Solve.

7. $0.3x = 0.3$ **8.** $-5 = 0.5y$
9. $1.2m = -3.6$ **10.** $0.3n = 1.2$
11. $4.8 = 2n$ **12.** $1.1s = -4.4$

Solve and check.

13. $3x - 0.4 = 0.8$ **14.** $3.64 = 2m + 4.7$
15. $4y + 0.88 = 5.24$ **16.** $2.5 = 3.7 + 0.2x$
17. $0.3r + 0.54 = -3$ **18.** $1.2s + 3.6 = 4.8$

Solve.

19. $\dfrac{x}{4} = \dfrac{1}{2}$ **20.** $\dfrac{y}{12} = \dfrac{1}{3}$

21. $\dfrac{8}{10} = \dfrac{n}{5}$ **22.** $\dfrac{m}{6} = -\dfrac{1}{3}$

23. $-\dfrac{1}{9} = \dfrac{y}{27}$ **24.** $\dfrac{x}{8} = -\dfrac{1}{4}$

Solve and check.

25. $\dfrac{y}{2} = \dfrac{y}{3} - 1$ **26.** $\dfrac{y}{4} = \dfrac{y}{5} + 1$

27. $\dfrac{5n}{2} = \dfrac{4n}{3} - \dfrac{7}{6}$ **28.** $\dfrac{p}{2} - \dfrac{3p}{4} = \dfrac{3}{4} - p$

29. $\dfrac{n}{3} + 2 = \dfrac{n}{5} + 4$ **30.** $\dfrac{(x+1)}{3} = \dfrac{(x-1)}{5}$

31. $\dfrac{(3-y)}{5} = \dfrac{(-2-3y)}{4}$

32. $\dfrac{(2x-3)}{2} = \dfrac{(-x-1)}{4}$

B

Solve and check.

33. $\dfrac{x-1}{3} + \dfrac{x+2}{6} = 7$

34. $\dfrac{x+1}{2} - \dfrac{x-7}{6} = 3$

35. $\dfrac{n+5}{2} - \dfrac{n}{3} = 1$

36. $\dfrac{4x+5}{3} - \dfrac{3x}{2} = -x$

37. $4 = \dfrac{k+1}{3} + \dfrac{k+5}{5}$

38. $\dfrac{1-x}{4} - \dfrac{x}{2} = 7$

39. $\dfrac{x+1}{3} + \dfrac{2-3x}{2} = -1$

40. $\dfrac{z+1}{3} + \dfrac{z-2}{7} = 1$

Applications and Problem Solving

41. Animal masses On the average, the mass of a raccoon is 1 kg more than $\dfrac{1}{4}$ of the mass of a coyote. The mass of a raccoon is 9.5 kg. To find the mass of a coyote, solve the equation

$$\dfrac{m}{4} + 1 = 9.5.$$

42. Spending time On the average, a Canadian adult spends 35% or 0.35 of the time sleeping. Solve the equation $9t - 0.01 = 0.35$ to find the fraction of the time spent shopping.

C

43. Comparing methods Solving equations using **systematic trial** involves substituting different values of the variable until you find the solution. For example, to solve $7x + 13 = 55$, you might try substituting 5 for x. However $7(5) + 13 = 48$, not 55. Substituting 6 for x gives the true statement $7(6) + 13 = 55$, so the solution is $x = 6$. Solve each of the following equations using systematic trial. Then, solve each equation by isolating the variable. Which method do you prefer? Why?

a) $6x - 14 = 40$ **b)** $3.5y + 2.4 = 8$

c) $2.5(x + 3.4) = -12$ **d)** $\dfrac{t-6}{3} - \dfrac{5t}{6} = -6$

7.7 Writing Equations

The Canadian Coast Guard patrols Canada's rivers and coastline. The Coast Guard has three branches — Search and Rescue, Boating Safety, and Environmental Response.

Explore: Study the Information

A Coast Guard boat that travels at a speed of 15 km/h in still water was patrolling up a river with a current of 6 km/h. The boat's actual speed, s kilometres per hour relative to the river bank, was given by the equation $s = 15 - 6$.

When it patrolled down the river, the boat's actual speed, s kilometres per hour relative to the river bank, was given by the equation $s = 15 + 6$.

Inquire

1. Let the speed of the boat in still water be x kilometres per hour. Write an equation to find x if the boat patrols up a river where
a) the current is 6 km/h and the boat's actual speed is 11 km/h
b) the current is 4 km/h and the boat's actual speed is 10 km/h
2. Write an equation to find x if the boat patrols down a river where
a) the current is 5 km/h and the boat's actual speed is 17 km/h
b) the current is 7 km/h and the boat's actual speed is 20 km/h

Example 1   Movie Costs
It costs 4 times as much to go to the movie theatre as it does to rent a movie. Together, both ways of seeing a movie cost $10. Write an equation to find each cost.

Solution
Let the smaller cost, a movie rental, be represented by x.
Then, the cost of going to a movie theatre is $4x$.
Together, both ways cost $10.
The total cost of both ways equals the sum of x and $4x$.
$$x + 4x = 10$$
$$5x = 10$$

Example 2   Great Lakes
Lake Ontario is 77 km shorter than Lake Erie. The lengths of the two lakes total 699 km. Write an equation to find the length of Lake Ontario.

Solution
Let the length of Lake Ontario be represented by x.
Then, the length of Lake Erie is $x + 77$.
The sum of x and $x + 77$ is equal to 699.
$$x + (x + 77) = 699$$
$$2x + 77 = 699 \qquad \text{The equation models the situation described in the example.}$$

Practice

A

Match each sentence with the correct equation.
1. Three times a number is equal to eighteen.
2. A number decreased by six is four.
3. Kim's age in four years will be eighteen.
4. Shuji's age four years ago was ten.
5. A number divided by four is eighteen.

$x - 4 = 10$

$3x = 18$

$\dfrac{m}{4} = 18$

$y - 6 = 4$

$x + 4 = 18$

Write an equation to model each sentence.
6. Four times a number is twenty.
7. A number divided by two equals five.
8. Six more than a number is fifteen.
9. A number increased by five is twelve.
10. A number decreased by six is ten.
11. Four less than a number is seven.
12. The square of a number is twenty-five.
13. Ten decreased by a number is two.
14. Three more than a number is eighteen.
15. Five less than a number is nine.
16. A number increased by four is twenty-one.
17. A number multiplied by three is nine.
18. A number divided by five is ten.
19. A number decreased by six is negative eight.

Applications and Problem Solving

Write an equation to model the situations in questions 20–24.
20. Piano keys There are 16 more white keys than black keys on a full-sized piano keyboard. There are 88 keys on a piano.
21. Money Brad has $12 more than Pietro. Together they have $84.
22. Ages Mike is seven years older than Ayla. The sum of their ages is 29.
23. Oceans The area of the Pacific Ocean is twice the area of the Atlantic. The sum of their areas is 250 000 000 km².

24. Populations The population of Japan is about 4.2 times the population of Canada. The sum of the populations is about 155 000 000.

B

25. Measurement The perimeter of each rectangle is 36 cm. Write an equation to find the dimensions of each rectangle.

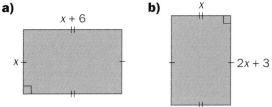

a)   **b)**

26. Measurement The perimeter of each triangle is 39 m. Write an equation to find the dimensions of each triangle.

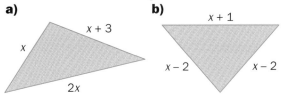

a)   **b)**

27. Decide whether each of the following situations could be modelled by the equation $2x - 1 = 9$. Explain.
a) One less than twice a number is nine.
b) Leroy and Malia have a total of $9. Leroy has $1 less than Malia.

C

28. Niagara Falls Niagara Falls has 2 parts. The American Falls are 2 m higher than the Horseshoe Falls. Their average height is 58 m. Use this information to write an equation.

29. Describe a situation that could be modelled by each equation. Compare your descriptions with a classmate's.
a) $x + 8 = 12$ **b)** $y - 5 = 11$
c) $4m = 20$ **d)** $\dfrac{n}{3} = 7$
e) $2x + 3 = 13$ **f)** $3t - 1 = 14$

7.8 Using Equations to Solve Problems

The ground speed of a jet depends on its air
speed and the speed of the headwind or tailwind.

Explore: Use the Information

The equation for the ground speed, g, of a jet flying at an air
speed of 760 km/h with a headwind, h kilometres per hour, is
$$g = 760 - h$$
If there is a tailwind, t kilometres per hour, the equation is
$$g = 760 + t$$

What is the ground speed when there is
a) a headwind of 50 km/h?
b) a tailwind of 80 km/h?

Inquire

1. What is the headwind if the ground speed is 720 km/h?
2. What is the tailwind if the ground speed is 825 km/h?
3. a) Write an equation to find the air speed, a, of an aircraft
when the ground speed is 800 km/h and there is a headwind,
h kilometres per hour.
b) What is the air speed when the headwind is 70 km/h?
4. a) Write an equation to find the air speed, a, of an aircraft when the
ground speed is 800 km/h and there is a tailwind, t kilometres per hour.
b) What is the air speed when the tailwind is 45 km/h?

Example 1   Purchase Prices
A compact disc player costs $75 more than a tape deck.
Together, they cost $725. How much does each cost?

Solution
Let the cost of the tape deck be x dollars.
Then, the cost of the compact disc player is $(x + 75)$ dollars.
The sum of the costs is $725.
Write the equation: $\qquad x + (x + 75) = 725$
Simplify: $\qquad\qquad\qquad 2x + 75 = 725$
Subtract 75 from both sides: $\qquad 2x = 725 - 75$
Simplify: $\qquad\qquad\qquad\qquad 2x = 650$
Divide both sides by 2: $\qquad\qquad x = 325$
The cost of the tape deck is $325.
The cost of the compact disc player is $325 + $75 or $400.

Check.
$325 + $400 = $725

Example 2   Perimeter of a Triangle

The sides of a triangle are 3 consecutive whole numbers of centimetres.
The perimeter of the triangle is 48 cm. How long is each side?

Solution

Let x represent the length of the shortest side, in centimetres.
Then, the lengths of the other two sides are $x + 1$ and $x + 2$.
The sum of the three sides is 48 cm.

Write the equation: $\qquad x + (x + 1) + (x + 2) = 48$
Simplify: $\qquad\qquad\quad x + x + x + 1 + 2 = 48$
$\qquad\qquad\qquad\qquad\qquad 3x + 3 = 48$
Subtract 3 from both sides: $\qquad\quad 3x = 45$
Divide both sides by 3: $\qquad\qquad x = 15$

If $x = 15$, then $x + 1 = 16$, and $x + 2 = 17$.
The lengths of the sides are 15 cm, 16 cm, and 17 cm.
Check.
The numbers 15, 16, and 17 are consecutive whole numbers,
and $P = 15$ cm + 16 cm + 17 cm or 48 cm.

Example 3   Coins

A parking meter contains $27.05 in quarters and dimes.
There are 146 coins. How many quarters are there?

Solution

Let x represent the number of quarters.
Then, $(146 - x)$ is the number of dimes.
The value of the quarters is $25x$ cents.
The value of the dimes is $10(146 - x)$ cents.
The total value of the coins is $27.05 or 2705 cents.

Write the equation: $\qquad 10(146 - x) + 25x = 2705$
Expand: $\qquad\qquad\quad 1460 - 10x + 25x = 2705$
Simplify: $\qquad\qquad\qquad 1460 + 15x = 2705$
Subtract 1460 from both sides: $\qquad 15x = 1245$
Divide both sides by 15: $\qquad\qquad x = 83$
The number of quarters is 83.

Estimate

$1200 \div 15 = 80$

Check.
The number of dimes is $146 - 83$ or 63.
The value of the coins, in dollars, is
$(0.25)(83) + (0.10)(63)$ or $27.05.

Example 4   Right Triangle

In right triangle ABC, find the length of BC, to the nearest tenth
of a centimetre.

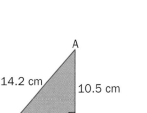

Solution

Use the Pythagorean Theorem.

Let the length of BC be x centimetres.

Write the equation: $x^2 + 10.5^2 = 14.2^2$

Subtract 10.5^2 from both sides: $x^2 = 14.2^2 - 10.5^2$

Take the square root of both sides: $x = \sqrt{14.2^2 - 10.5^2}$

Evaluate x. $x \doteq 9.6$

Because the length of BC is positive, consider only the positive root.

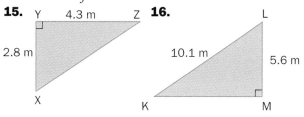

The length of BC is 9.6 cm, to the nearest tenth of a centimetre.

Practice

A

Each statement has two unknowns. Represent both in terms of x.

1. The sum of two numbers is 35.
2. There are 50 nickels and dimes.
3. There are 125 quarters and dimes.
4. The length and width of a rectangle total 36 cm.
5. There is a total of 32 males and females in the class.
6. The cafeteria sold 738 hamburgers and hot dogs.
7. Jim and Tosha sold 468 kg of cheese.
8. The parking meter has 246 coins in quarters and dimes.

Find the length of each side.

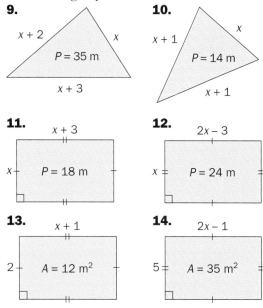

9. $x + 2$, x, $x + 3$, $P = 35$ m
10. $x + 1$, x, $x + 1$, $P = 14$ m
11. $x + 3$, x, $P = 18$ m
12. $2x - 3$, x, $P = 24$ m
13. $x + 1$, 2, $A = 12$ m^2
14. $2x - 1$, 5, $A = 35$ m^2

Find the unknown side length in each triangle, to the nearest tenth of a metre.

15. Y — 4.3 m — Z, 2.8 m, X

16. L, 10.1 m, 5.6 m, K, M

Applications and Problem Solving

17. Numbers The sum of 2 numbers is 46. One number is 12 more than the other. What are the numbers?

18. Canadian rivers The Mackenzie River is 1183 km longer than the St. Lawrence. The sum of their lengths is 7299 km. How long is each river?

B

19. Measurement The length of a rectangle is 5 m more than its width. Its perimeter is 90 m. What are its dimensions?

20. Numbers The sum of 3 consecutive whole numbers is 105. Find the numbers.

21. Weather The number of frost-free days per year in Quebec City is 18 less than the number in Halifax. The total number in both cities is 292. How many frost-free days are there per year in Halifax?

22. Life spans The maximum life span of a brown bear is 10 times the maximum life span of a mouse. The sum of their maximum life spans is 33 years. What is the maximum life span of a mouse?

23. Women's hockey When Canada won the Women's World Hockey Championships, the Canadian team scored 35 more goals than were scored against it. The total number of goals scored in the games that Canada played was 41.
a) How many goals were scored against Canada?
b) How many goals did Canada score?

24. Weather There are 2.25 times as many days of fog per year in Vancouver as in Winnipeg. The total number of days of fog in both cities is 65. How many days of fog does Winnipeg have per year?

25. Measurement One of the equal sides of an isosceles triangle is 3 m less than twice its base. The perimeter is 44 m. Find the lengths of the sides.

26. Pens and pencils The cost of a pen is 3 times the cost of a pencil. The cost of 4 pencils and 3 pens is $9.75. What is the cost of a pencil?

27. Coins Sally has twice as many dimes as nickels. The total value is $3.50. How many nickels does she have?

28. Coins Aretha has $0.85 in nickels and dimes. She has 2 more nickels than dimes. How many nickels and dimes does she have?

29. Basketball court A basketball court is a rectangle with dimensions 26 m by 14 m. What is the length of a diagonal, to the nearest metre?

30. Coins A box contains 140 dimes and nickels. The total value is $11.15. How many dimes and how many nickels are there?

31. Numbers The sum of two numbers is 39. Twice the first number plus 3 times the second number is 101.
a) Find the numbers using guess and check.
b) Find the numbers by writing and solving an equation.
c) Which method do you prefer? Why?

32. Numbers One number is 5 more than another number. Three times the first plus twice the second is 30. Find the numbers.

33. Coins A jar contains $18.50 in dimes and quarters. There are 110 coins in the jar.
a) Use guess and check to find the number of quarters in the jar.
b) Find the number of quarters in the jar by writing and solving an equation.
c) Which method do you prefer? Why?

34. Pizza sales Large pizzas cost $12.50 and small pizzas cost $9.00. The pizza parlour sold 38 pizzas with a total value of $415.50. How many of each type did the pizza parlour sell? Explain how you used a mathematical model to solve the problem.

35. Concert tickets Tickets to the concert cost $9.00 for adults and $6.50 for students. A total of 950 people paid $7675.00 to attend. How many students attended the concert?

36. Egyptian pyramid The pyramid of Menkaure at Giza, Egypt, has a square base. The length of the diagonal of the base is 154 m. Find the side length of the base, to the nearest metre.

C

37. Picture A picture is 5 cm longer than it is wide. The perimeter of the picture is 90 cm.
a) What is the width of the picture?
b) The picture is surrounded by a 6-cm wide border. What are the outside dimensions of the border?

38. Garden A garden is 20 m by 25 m. It is surrounded by a walkway. The outside perimeter of the walkway is 114 m. What is the width of the walkway? Explain and justify the steps in your solution.

39. Picture frame A picture measures 40 cm by 30 cm. The outside perimeter of the frame around the picture is 156 cm.
a) What is the width of the frame?
b) What is the area of the frame?

40. Write a problem that can be solved using an equation. Have a classmate solve your problem.

7.9 Working With Formulas

A squid has 8 arms and 2 tentacles. The arms and the ends of the tentacles are covered with tooth-rimmed suction pods. The squid uses its tentacles to pull prey into its arms. Giant squids prey on sharks and, in turn, are preyed upon by sperm whales.

Explore: Use the Formula

Scientists can determine the length of a giant squid by measuring the diameter of the suction-pod scars left on its prey. The formula $l = 180d$ gives the length of a squid, in centimetres, from the diameter of its suction pods, in centimetres. How long is a squid whose suction pods have a diameter of 0.5 cm?

Inquire

1. Squids found off the coast of Newfoundland have suction pods with diameters of 5 cm. How long are these squids, in metres?

2. The longest squid, to date, was found in New Zealand. The suction pods were 5.4 cm in diameter. How long was this squid, in metres?

3. A sperm whale was found with suction-pod scars that measured 35 cm in diameter. How many metres long was the squid that made these scars?

Example 1 Using a Formula

The perimeter of a rectangle is given by the formula $P = 2(l + w)$, where l is the length and w is the width. Evaluate w for $P = 35.6$ cm and $l = 12.5$ cm.

Solution 1 Solving Before Substituting

Since we want the value of w, isolate this variable.

Write the formula:	$P = 2(l + w)$
Expand:	$P = 2l + 2w$
Subtract $2l$ from both sides:	$P - 2l = 2l + 2w - 2l$
Simplify:	$P - 2l = 2w$
Divide both sides by 2:	$\dfrac{P - 2l}{2} = \dfrac{2w}{2}$
Simplify:	$\dfrac{P - 2l}{2} = w$

Substitute $P = 35.6$ and $l = 12.5$ into the formula.

$$w = \frac{P - 2l}{2}$$

$$= \frac{35.6 - 2(12.5)}{2}$$

$$= \frac{10.6}{2}$$

$$= 5.3$$

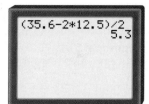

So, $w = 5.3$ cm.

Solution 2   Substituting Before Solving

Substitute $P = 35.6$ and $l = 12.5$ into the formula.
Then, solve for w.

Write the formula:	$P = 2(l + w)$
Substitute known values:	$35.6 = 2(12.5 + w)$
Expand:	$35.6 = 25 + 2w$
Subtract 25 from both sides:	$10.6 = 2w$
Divide both sides by 2:	$5.3 = w$

So, $w = 5.3$ cm.

Check.
Substitute into $P = 2(l + w)$.
$$35.6 = 2(12.5 + 5.3)$$
$$35.6 = 2(17.8)$$
$$35.6 = 35.6$$

Practice

A

1. For the formula $A = lw$,
a) find A if $l = 8$ cm and $w = 5$ cm
b) find w if $A = 40$ m^2 and $l = 10$ m
c) find l if $A = 238$ m^2 and $w = 14$ m

2. Assume $\pi = 3.14$. For the formula $C = 2\pi r$,
a) find C if $r = 10$ cm
b) find r if $C = 628$ cm

3. For the formula $A = \frac{1}{2}bh$,
a) find A if $b = 6$ cm and $h = 8$ cm
b) find h if $A = 40$ cm^2 and $b = 4$ cm
c) find b if $A = 61.5$ m^2 and $h = 20.5$ m

4. For the formula $P = 2(l + w)$,
a) find P if $l = 9$ m and $w = 6$ m
b) find w if $P = 60$ m and $l = 16$ m
c) find l if $P = 84.2$ m and $w = 5.4$ m

Solve each formula for the indicated variable.
5. $A = lw$ for w

6. $A = \frac{1}{2}bh$ for b

7. $I = Prt$ for P
8. $C = 2\pi r$ for r
9. $E = mc^2$ for m
10. $A = \frac{1}{2}h(a + b)$ for b

Applications and Problem Solving

B

11. Spaceships The distance travelled by a spaceship is given by the formula
$$d = 40\ 000t$$
where d is the distance, in kilometres, and t is the time, in hours.

a) How far does a spaceship travel in 12 h? in 17.5 h?

b) How long does it take a spaceship to travel 130 000 km?

12. Water resistance Whales, sharks, and dolphins have shapes that minimize water resistance. The ideal shape for minimum water resistance is a torpedo shape, with a width that is one quarter of the length. The following equations show how the width, w, of a blue whale, a shark, or a dolphin is related to its length, l.

Blue Whale	$w = 0.21l$
Shark	$w = 0.26l$
Dolphin	$w = 0.25l$

a) About how wide is a shark that is 18 m long?

b) The blue whale is the world's largest mammal. Is a 30-m long blue whale wider than your classroom?

c) The average width of a dolphin is about 0.6 m. What is the average length of a dolphin?

13. Pulse rates The maximum desirable pulse rate for a person exercising can be found using the formula
$$m = 0.8(220 - a)$$
where m is the pulse rate, in beats per minute, and a is the person's age, in years.

a) Copy and complete the table.

Age (years)	Maximum Desirable Pulse Rate (beats/min)
20	
30	
40	
50	
60	

b) To what ages do these maximum desirable pulse rates correspond?

140   132   148

14. Food energy The amount of food energy required per day by military personnel on active duty is given by the formula
$$E = -125T + 15\ 250$$
where E is the amount of food energy, in kilojoules (kJ), and T is the outside temperature, in degrees Celsius.

a) Copy and complete the table.

Temperature (°C)	Energy (kJ)
40	
23	
0	
–10	
–45	

b) At what temperature is 14 000 kJ of food energy required per day?

C

15. Band concert Shawna is at an outdoor concert in Vancouver. She is sitting 100 m from the band. The formula that gives the length of time for the band's sound to reach her is
$$t = \frac{d}{330}$$
where t is the time, in seconds, and d is Shawna's distance from the band, in metres.

Pablo is listening to the same concert on a radio in Halifax. The formula that gives the length of time for the band's sound to reach him is
$$t = \frac{d}{300\ 000}$$
where t is the time, in seconds, and d is the distance from Halifax to Vancouver, in kilometres. Who hears each sound first, Shawna or Pablo? Explain how you know that your answer is reasonable.

7.10 Developing Formulas

The *Bluenose* was Canada's most famous sailing ship. It was launched in Lunenberg, Nova Scotia, in 1921. It was the fastest racing schooner of its time, winning many championships until its last race in 1938.

Explore: Study the Information

In the early days of sailing ships, navigators estimated the speed of their ship by tying a rope to a log and tossing the log into the water behind the ship. After 30 s, the length of the rope was measured, showing how far the ship had travelled in this amount of time.
If the length of the rope after 30 s was 90 m, what was the speed of the ship in metres per second?

Inquire

1. Let the length of the rope after 30 s be *l*. Write a formula for the speed of the ship in metres per second.
2. If the length of the rope after 30 s was 60 m, what was the speed of the ship, in metres per second?
3. Use the formula to calculate the speed of the ship if the length of the rope after 30 s was 120 m.
4. Rewrite the formula to calculate the speed of the ship in kilometres per hour.

Example   Speed of a Galleon

Many early navigators also estimated the speed of a ship by measuring the number of seconds it took a piece of wood to float from one end of the ship to the other.
a) Write a formula to estimate the speed of a galleon, in metres per second.
b) Use the formula to find the speed of a 40-m long galleon if $t = 8$ s.

Solution

a) Let the time, in seconds, be *t*. Let the speed, in metres per second, be *s*.
The distance travelled in metres is the length of the galleon, *l*.

$$\text{Speed} = \frac{\text{Distance}}{\text{Time}}$$

$$s = \frac{l}{t}$$

b) $s = \frac{40}{8}$
$= 5$

The speed of the galleon was 5 m/s.

Practice

Complete the table and state a rule for each pattern.

1.

a	1	2	3	4	5	6	7
b	3	6	9	12			

2.

m	2	4	6	8			
n	5	7	9	11	13	15	17

3.

t	25	24	23	22			
u	100	96	92	88	84	80	76

Complete the table. Then, use the variables to write a formula for each pattern.

4.

Number of Books (n)	1	2	3	4
Cost (c)		40	80	120

5.

Hours (h)	5	10	15	20
Wages (w)	52.50	105.00	157.50	

6.

Selling Price (s)	300	400	500	600
Profit (p)	60	80	100	

Applications and Problem Solving

7. Bus rental The cost to rent a bus is $100, plus a certain amount per kilometre. The table gives the cost of 3 bus trips. Write a formula to calculate the cost of a bus trip in terms of distance.

Trip	Distance, d (km)	Cost, C ($)
1	50	250
2	100	400
3	150	550

8. Taxi ride This table shows the cost of a taxi ride. Write a formula that relates the cost of the ride, C dollars, to the distance driven, d kilometres.

d (km)	0	5	10	15	20
C ($)	3.00	10.50	18.00	25.50	33.00

9. Making maps The map shows an area where there are 6 towns, 9 roads, and 4 regions.

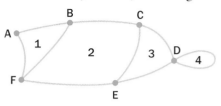

Roads start and end at a town. If roads cross, there is a town where they cross. A road can connect a town to itself. Regions are completely surrounded by roads. Each town is connected to at least 1 other town. In such maps, there is a relationship between the numbers of towns, regions, and roads.

a) Make at least 5 maps, each with 4 regions. Complete a table like the one shown.

Map	Regions	Towns	Roads
1	4		
2	4		
3	4		
4	4		
5	4		

Look for a pattern in the Towns and Roads columns.
Write a formula that lets you determine the number of regions if you know the numbers of towns and roads.
Regions = ▨
Test your formula on another map.

b) Make at least 5 maps, each with 6 towns. Complete a table like the one in part a). Write a formula that lets you determine the number of towns if you know the numbers of roads and regions. Test your formula on another map.

c) Make at least 5 maps, each with 6 roads. Complete a table like the one in part a). Write a formula that lets you determine the number of roads if you know the numbers of towns and regions. Test your formula on another map.

Meteorology

In January, 1998, parts of Ontario, Québec, and the Maritimes experienced the most destructive winter storm in Canadian history. An ice storm deposited up to 10 cm of ice. Over 1000 power transmission towers collapsed from the weight of the ice, and over 1.5 million people were without electricity. About 100 000 people moved into shelters.

Predicting the weather and its effects is the work of meteorologists, most of whom are employed by the Atmospheric Environment Service (AES) of the federal government. Meteorologists prepare weather forecasts to meet the needs of various users, including the news media, and the aviation and shipping industries.

Satellite pictures, surface observations, and information from weather balloons are used in preparing forecasts. Regional computers provide up-to-date information on fluctuations. Computers at the national analysis centre in Montréal make long-range predictions.

Several Canadian universities offer meteorology programs. Meteorology students study mathematics and physics, as well as atmospheric science.

1 Precipitation in Canada

Each year about 5.5 trillion tonnes of precipitation, in the form of rain, snow, or hail, fall on Canada.

1. a) Estimate the mass of precipitation that falls on Ontario in a year. What are your assumptions?
b) Do you think that your estimate is reasonable? Explain.

2. About 36% of Canada's annual precipitation falls as snow. This is about one septillion or 1×10^{24} snowflakes.
a) What mass of snow, in tonnes, falls on Canada in a year?
b) What is the average mass of one snowflake, to the nearest thousandth of a milligram?

2 Greatest Precipitation

The greatest amount of precipitation to fall on Canada in a 24-h period was recorded at Ucluelet, British Columbia, where about 489.6 mm of rain fell.

1. Solve the equation $489.6 = 24r$ to find the average rate, r millimetres per hour, at which rain fell at Ucluelet.

2. The total precipitation in Toronto in a year is equivalent to about 780 mm of rain. If this amount of rain fell at the rate you found in question 1, how long would it take to fall, to the nearest hour?

3. If rain continued falling at the rate you found in question 1, and none of it drained away, how long would it take to reach the height of your classroom, to the nearest day?

INVESTIGATING MATH

Developing Pick's Formula for Area

1 No Points in the Interior

For each polygon in the grid, points are marked where grid lines cross. Each polygon has been constructed so that there are no points in its interior.

1. Construct the polygons on grid paper or on a geoboard.

2. Copy and complete this table. The first line has been completed for you.

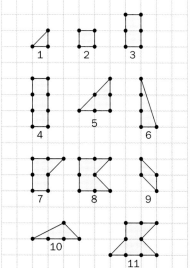

Polygon	Points on the Perimeter (P)	Area (square units)
1	3	$\frac{1}{2}$
2		
3		
4		
5		
6		
7		
8		
9		
10		
11		

3. If 2 figures have the same number of points on the perimeter, what can you say about their areas?

4. List the areas from least to greatest. Do not repeat areas. The first two are:
3 points, 0.5 square units
4 points, 1 square unit

5. Predict the area of a figure with 10 points on the perimeter and no points in its interior. Check your prediction by making 2 such shapes and finding their areas.

6. Use the pattern in the table to write a formula for the area of a polygon with no points in the interior if you know the number of perimeter points.

7. Draw 3 different figures with no interior points. Verify your formula.

8. Use your formula to determine the area of a figure with 99 points on the perimeter and no interior points.

2 Points in the Interior

Each polygon has 10 points on the perimeter. The number of points in the interior, I, increases from 0 to 6.

1. Find the area of each polygon.

2. Copy and complete the table.

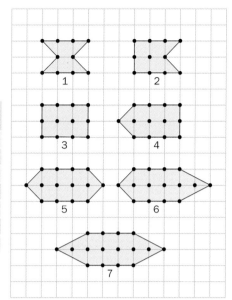

Polygon	Points on the Perimeter (P)	Interior Points (I)	Area (square units)
1	10		
2	10		
3	10		
4	10		
5	10		
6	10		
7	10		

3. What happens to the area of the polygon as the number of interior points increases by 1?

4. Predict the areas of figures with 10 points on the perimeter and 7 and 8 points in the interior. Check your predictions by making 2 such shapes and finding their areas.

5. Use the pattern in the table and the formula for area you found in Exploration 1. Write a formula for the area of a polygon if you know the number of perimeter points and interior points. This formula is called **Pick's formula**, after the mathematician who discovered it.

6. Draw 3 different figures with points in the interior. Verify your formula.

7. Use your formula to determine the areas of the following figures.

a)

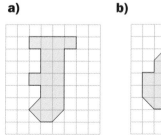

b)

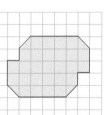

c)

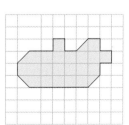

7.11 Uniform Motion Problems

Problems involving uniform motion are those in which the speeds of the objects do not change. The formula $D = r \times t$ is used to solve these problems, where D is the distance, r is the rate of speed, and t is the time.

Explore: Use the Information

A Canadian Coast Guard boat left Halifax at 08:00 to assist a disabled ship. The boat travelled at 30 km/h. One hour later, a Canadian Navy frigate left Halifax at a speed of 40 km/h to assist in the operation.

a) Let x be the time, in hours, the Coast Guard boat travelled before the frigate caught up. Write an expression for the distance, in kilometres, travelled by the Coast Guard boat in x hours.

b) If x hours is the time the Coast Guard boat travelled, write an expression in terms of x for the time the frigate travelled, in hours, before catching up with the Coast Guard boat.

c) Use the expression from b) to write an expression for the distance the frigate travelled, in kilometres.

Inquire

1. When the frigate caught up with the Coast Guard boat, the distances they had travelled were the same. Use the expressions from b) and c), above, to write an equation stating that the two distances were equal.

2. Solve the equation for x.

3. a) How long had the Coast Guard boat been travelling when the frigate caught up?

b) How long had the frigate been travelling?

Example 1   Flying Times

A plane left Montréal for Calgary, a distance of 3000 km, travelling at 800 km/h. At the same time, a plane left Calgary for Montréal travelling at 700 km/h. How long after takeoff did the planes pass each other?

Solution

Set up a table and let x be the time from takeoff until the planes passed. Write expressions for D using r and t. The sum of the distances is 3000 km.

	t (h)	r (km/h)	D (km)
Montréal to Calgary	x	800	800x
Calgary to Montréal	x	700	700x

Write the equation: $800x + 700x = 3000$
Simplify: $1500x = 3000$
Divide both sides by 1500: $x = 2$
The planes passed each other 2 h after takeoff.

Check.
In 3 h, the plane from Montréal flew 3×550 or 1650 km.
In 3 h, the plane from Calgary flew 3×450 or 1350 km.
1650 km + 1350 km = 3000 km

Practice

A

Calculate the distance travelled.
1. 3 h at 60 km/h
2. 2 h at 85 km/h
3. $\frac{1}{2}$ h at 90 km/h
4. $\frac{3}{4}$ h at 60 km/h

How long does each trip take?
5. 40 km at 80 km/h
6. 400 km at 50 km/h
7. 20 km at 100 km/h
8. 360 km at 80 km/h

Calculate each speed.
9. 300 km in 3 h
10. 400 km in 5 h
11. 360 km in 4 h
12. 40 km in $\frac{1}{2}$ h

Copy and complete the table.

	Distance (km)	Rate (km/h)	Time (h)
13.	450	100	
14.		65	3
15.	600		8
16.		80	x
17.		90	$x + 1$
18.		85	$x - 1$
19.	200	x	
20.	400		x
21.		r	t
22.	D	r	
23.	D		t

Applications and Problem Solving

B

24. Sailing times A cruise ship left Halifax for Bermuda at 20 km/h. A private boat left for Bermuda 1 h later and travelled at 25 km/h. After how long did the private boat overtake the cruise ship?

25. Driving times Two cars left a service centre at the same time. One car travelled in one direction at 75 km/h. The other car travelled in the opposite direction at 85 km/h. After how long were they 600 km apart? Explain your solution, giving clear reasons for the steps you used.

C

26. Driving times Two friends, Elsa in Winnipeg and Gina in Edmonton, decided to meet on the Trans-Canada Highway. The distance from Edmonton to Winnipeg is 1360 km. They both left home at 08:00, Winnipeg time. Elsa drove at 80 km/h, and Gina drove at 90 km/h.
a) Make a table showing the total distance driven by each person by 09:00, 10:00, and so on, Winnipeg time. Use the table to find how many hours the friends drove until they met.
b) Find the number of hours they drove by writing and solving an equation.
c) Which problem solving method do you prefer? Explain.

27. Flying times A plane left Vancouver for Los Angeles at 08:30 and flew at 600 km/h. Fifteen minutes later, another plane left Vancouver for Los Angeles and flew at 700 km/h.
a) How long did it take the second plane to overtake the first one?
b) At what time did it happen?

28. Driving times A car left a garage on the highway at 80 km/h. Fifteen minutes later, a second car left the same garage at 100 km/h and travelled in the same direction. How long did it take the second car to catch up with the first?

29. Write a problem involving uniform motion and ask a classmate to solve it.

TECHNOLOGY

Solving Equations Using a Graphing Calculator

Complete the following with a graphing calculator that has the capability to solve equations algebraically.

1 Solving Equations

- Enter the equation $7x - 3 = 5x + 11$.
- To subtract $5x$ from both sides, enter $-5x$.
- To add 3 to both sides, enter $+3$.
- To divide both sides by 2, enter $\div 2$.

The solution is $x = 7$.

Use the above method to solve each of the following equations.

1. $5x + 7 = 2x - 26$

2. $2x - 7 = 6x + 5$

3. $7 + 8y = 13y + 24$

4. $0.2x - 1.8 = 2.6 - 0.6x$

5. $4.1a - 9.7 = 3.5a + 5.9$

6. $11.8 + 0.1x = 23.4 + 0.2x$

2 Solving Equations With Fractions

1. Enter the equation $\dfrac{x}{2} + \dfrac{x}{3} = 1$.

a) Did the calculator do any steps for you? Explain.

b) Solve the resulting equation.

2. Enter the equation $\dfrac{x-3}{3} + \dfrac{x+7}{4} = 6$.

a) Did the calculator do any steps for you? Explain.

b) Solve the resulting equation.

Solve each of the following equations.

3. $\dfrac{x}{4} - \dfrac{x}{5} = 2$

4. $\dfrac{x}{6} + \dfrac{x}{8} = 14$

5. $\dfrac{2x}{3} - \dfrac{3x}{5} = -1$

6. $\dfrac{x}{4} = \dfrac{5x}{6} + 2$

7. $\dfrac{x-2}{3} - \dfrac{x+4}{4} = 5$

8. $\dfrac{n+3}{8} + \dfrac{n-1}{3} = 1$

9. $\dfrac{y+1}{2} + \dfrac{y-3}{3} = 4$

10. $\dfrac{z+6}{3} - \dfrac{z-2}{5} = 2$

11. $\dfrac{x+3}{5} = \dfrac{x-2}{4} + 1$

3 Using the Solve Function

Complete each of the following with a graphing calculator that has a Solve function. This function solves equations without displaying the steps.

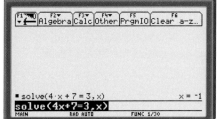

Solve.

1. $2x + 1 = 7$ **2.** $4a - 5 = 2$ **3.** $\dfrac{y}{2} + 4 = 1$

4. $\dfrac{2t}{3} - 1 = 3$ **5.** $1.8x - 4 = 2.3$ **6.** $2.8 = 4.5 + 0.2m$

Solve.

7. $3x + 4x = 5x - 3$ **8.** $9y + 2 = 4y - 8$

9. $2.5 - 0.5x = 2x - 3$ **10.** $\dfrac{n}{2} + 1 = \dfrac{n}{3} - 1$

Solve.

11. $2(p + 2) = 5(p - 1)$ **12.** $3(1 - x) = 2(x + 5)$
13. $2(2z + 3) = 3(z - 2) + 8$ **14.** $4(g + 1) + 3(2g - 3) = 5(g - 1) + 2$

Solve.

15. $\dfrac{x}{3} - \dfrac{x}{4} = -1$ **16.** $\dfrac{y + 3}{2} - \dfrac{y - 1}{3} = -1$

17. $\dfrac{w - 1}{4} - \dfrac{4w - 3}{2} = 3$ **18.** $\dfrac{x + 1}{2} + \dfrac{x + 2}{3} = \dfrac{x}{4}$

4 Solving Formulas

Solve for the indicated variables.
1. $I = Prt$ for t **2.** $y = 4x + 1$ for x
3. $a = 2(b - c)$ for c **4.** $w = xy + yz$ for y

5 Problem Solving

1. Coastlines The total length of the coastline of Canada and the United States is about 265 000 km. The Canadian coastline is about 5000 km longer than 12 times the length of the U.S. coastline. Find the approximate length of the Canadian coastline.

2. Ontario lakes Subtracting 108 km² from the area of Lake Nipigon and multiplying the result by 4 gives the area of Lake Ontario. The total area of the two lakes is 23 808 km². What is the area of Lake Nipigon? Explain how you used a mathematical model to solve the problem.

Healthy Eating

To achieve a balanced diet, *Canada's Food Guide to Healthy Eating* recommends different numbers of servings per day from the four food groups.

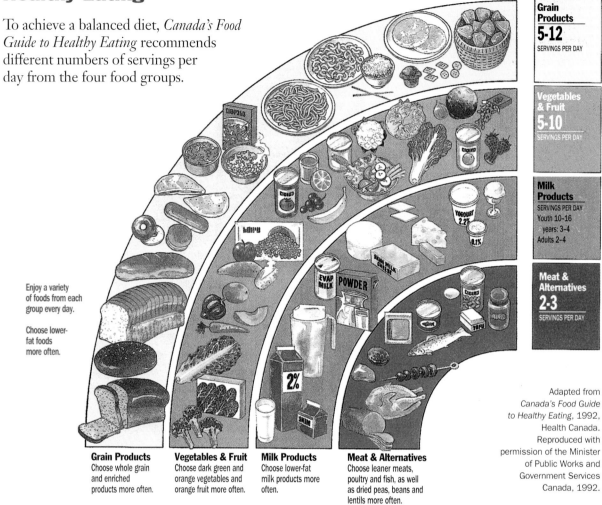

Grain Products
5-12
SERVINGS PER DAY

Vegetables & Fruit
5-10
SERVINGS PER DAY

Milk Products
SERVINGS PER DAY
Youth 10-16 years: 3-4
Adults 2-4

Meat & Alternatives
2-3
SERVINGS PER DAY

Enjoy a variety of foods from each group every day.

Choose lower-fat foods more often.

Grain Products
Choose whole grain and enriched products more often.

Vegetables & Fruit
Choose dark green and orange vegetables and orange fruit more often.

Milk Products
Choose lower-fat milk products more often.

Meat & Alternatives
Choose leaner meats, poultry and fish, as well as dried peas, beans and lentils more often.

Adapted from *Canada's Food Guide to Healthy Eating*, 1992, Health Canada. Reproduced with permission of the Minister of Public Works and Government Services Canada, 1992.

Health Canada recommends that no more than 30% of our daily food energy should come from fat, and health professionals recommend eating at least 25 g to 30 g of fibre a day.

Use the *Nutrition* database, from the Computer Data Bank to complete the following.

1 Fat and Fibre

1. Display the following fields together in this order for all records.

Food   Type   Serving   Energy, kJ   Fat, g   Fibre, g

2. Find the record for *Ice cream, vanilla, rich*. What is the mass of fat in a serving?

3. a) Find all the records for which one serving contains more fat than one serving of rich vanilla ice cream. How many records are displayed?
b) Are you surprised by any of the foods you found in part a)? Explain.
c) What do you notice about the fibre content of the foods you found in part a)?

4. Sort all the records from greatest to least fibre content. What do you notice about the fat content of foods with high fibre content?

5. a) Find the record for *Potato chips*. What are the masses of fat and fibre in a serving?
b) Compare the serving size with the amount that you think of as a "normal portion." What are the masses of fat and fibre in your idea of a "normal portion"?

6. Repeat question 5 for these foods.
a) Eclair, chocolate, custard filled
b) Strawberries, raw
c) Pizza, cheese
d) Cookies, peanut butter

2 Energy From Fat

One gram of fat provides about 38 kJ of energy. For a food, the percent of energy from fat, p, is given by the formula $p = \dfrac{38f}{e} \times 100$, where f is the mass of fat, in grams, and e is the energy from the food, in kilojoules.

1. Add a calculated field for the percent of energy from fat, rounding the percents to 1 decimal place.

2. Move through the records. Explain why some percents are greater than 100%.

3 Planning Meals

1. Sort all the records alphabetically by type, and, within each type, alphabetically by food.

2. Move through the records and identify foods you would eat for one breakfast. Remember to include such items as added butter and sugar. Also, increase serving sizes to your idea of a "normal portion," if appropriate.

3. What are the total energy, total mass of fat, and total mass of fibre?

4. What is the percent of energy from fat, rounded to 1 decimal place, using the total fat and total energy values from question 3?

5. What might you add to the meal to increase the mass of fibre without increasing the mass of fat?

6. Repeat questions 2 to 5 for a lunch.

4 Planning a Day's Menu

1. Repeat questions 2 to 5 from *Planning Meals* once again. This time identify all the foods you would eat in a day. Remember to include snacks.

2. The typical Canadian gets 40% or more of energy from fat and eats 15 g or less of fibre in a day. Is your menu typical? Explain.

3. If your menu does not have 30% or less of energy from fat and 25 g to 30 g of fibre, adjust it to meet these recommendations.

4. Which is easier for you — eating enough fibre or not eating too much fat? Explain.

7.12 How Can We Identify People?

Because your fingerprints never change and are different from everyone else's, they can be used to identify you. There are 3 different patterns of fingerprints, known as arches, whorls, and loops.

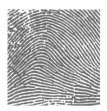

Plain Arch
The ridge lines enter on one side and curve up and exit on the other side.

Tented Arch
The ridge lines are the same as a plain arch, except that they make a sharp point or tent in the middle.

Whorl
The ridge lines are circles or ovals.

Loop
The ridge lines enter on one side of the print, curve, and exit on the same side. An **ulnar loop** slants toward the ulna bone in the wrist. A **radial loop** slants toward the radius bone in the wrist.

Right-hand ulnar loop or left-hand radial loop.

Right-hand radial loop or left-hand ulnar loop.

Traditionally, fingerprint identification has been used by law enforcement agencies. Applications are being developed for use in such fields as banking and home security.

Law enforcement agencies receive many sets of fingerprints, with requests to identify the people they belong to. To avoid checking the prints against all the prints on file, the agencies first classify the prints using fractions. Prints can then be checked against only those prints with the same classification.

1 Modelling Fingerprints

The primary fingerprint classification is based on the number of whorls.
Prints are assigned the following values.
Whorl = 1   Arch = 0   Loop = 0

These values are substituted into the following expression.

$$\frac{(Rt\ Index) \times 16 + (Rt\ Ring) \times 8 + (Lt\ Thumb) \times 4 + (Lt\ Middle) \times 2 + (Lt\ Little) \times 1 + 1}{(Rt\ Thumb) \times 16 + (Rt\ Middle) \times 8 + (Rt\ Little) \times 4 + (Lt\ Index) \times 2 + (Lt\ Ring) \times 1 + 1}$$

For example, Yoshiko has whorls on her left thumb, left little finger, and right thumb.
All her other prints are arches and loops. Her primary classification is as follows.

$$\frac{(0) \times 16 + (0) \times 8 + (1) \times 4 + (0) \times 2 + (1) \times 1 + 1}{(1) \times 16 + (0) \times 8 + (0) \times 4 + (0) \times 2 + (0) \times 1 + 1} = \frac{0+0+4+0+1+1}{16+0+0+0+0+1}$$

$$= \frac{6}{17}$$

Her primary classification is $\frac{6}{17}$.

1. Identify each of your fingerprints as an arch, a loop, or a whorl.

2. What is your primary classification?

3. How many different primary classifications are there in your class?

4. How many different primary classifications are possible?

2 Extending the Model

The secondary classification is a fraction made up of letters based on the prints on the index fingers.

The fraction is $\dfrac{right\ index\ finger}{left\ index\ finger}$.

The letters are A for plain arch, T for tented arch, W for whorl, U for ulnar loop, and R for radial loop. If the right index finger is a plain arch and the left index finger is a radial loop, the secondary classification is $\dfrac{A}{R}$.

1. What is your secondary classification?

2. How many different secondary classifications are there in your class?

3. How many different secondary classifications are possible?

4. The combined classification of a set of prints is written in the form $\dfrac{6\ \ A}{17\ \ R}$.
What is your combined classification?

5. How many different combined classifications are there in your class?

Review

7.1 *Solve.*

1. $y + 7 = 12$ **2.** $2 = -4 + s$
3. $3 + z = 7$ **4.** $x + 1 = -2$

7.2 *Solve.*

5. $3n = -21$ **6.** $-24 = 12x$
7. $5p = 3.0$ **8.** $7z = -2.8$
9. $\dfrac{x}{2} = 5$ **10.** $\dfrac{y}{2} = -5$
11. $\dfrac{b}{3} = -3$ **12.** $\dfrac{z}{4} = 6$

7.3 *Solve.*

13. $3x - 17 = 13$ **14.** $56 = 5y + 11$
15. $2x + 3.1 = 1.1$ **16.** $5m + 25 = -65$
17. $3y + 10 = 82$ **18.** $0.3x + 2.6 = 4.4$
19. $-39 = 25 + 4a$ **20.** $-54 = 6z - 18$
21. $-33 + 7t = -61$ **22.** $8q - 42 = -26$

Solve.

23. $6a - 3a + 2a = 10 - 2 + 7$
24. $2p + 3p - p = 9 - 15 - 6$
25. $10j - 5j - 8j = -6 + 15 + 12$
26. $12k - 8k - 6k = -18 + 20 - 6$

7.4 *Solve and check.*

27. $2x + 7 = 5x + 13$ **28.** $5y - 12 = y - 4$
29. $3x - 4 = 8 - x$ **30.** $6x - 6 = 4x - 10$
31. $7 - x = -7 + 6x$ **32.** $4 + x = 36 - 7x$
33. $2 + 3j = 5j - 24$ **34.** $-3 + 2r = -30 - 7r$

Solve.

35. $5x + 6x - 2x = 3x - 18 + 12 - 6$
36. $2x + 15 = -12 - 13 - 3x$
37. $b - 17 = 15 + 3b + 18$
38. $21 + 4q = q + 13 + 17$

7.5 *Solve and check.*

39. $7 + 5(x - 3) = 3(x + 2)$
40. $4(y - 4) + 3(y + 7) = -30$
41. $-38 = 5(2y - 1) + y$
42. $6(3x - 4) - (1 - 3x) = -67$

7.6 *Solve.*

43. $9m - 0.8 = 7m + 4.8$
44. $5y + 0.4 - 3y = -6$

45. $1.6m - 2.4 + 0.1m = 0.1m + 0.8$
46. $8.4x - 0.8 = 4.4x - 4$
47. $12.2x + 0.3 = 20.7 + 5.4x$

Solve.

48. $\dfrac{y}{2} - \dfrac{1}{2} = \dfrac{1}{2}$ **49.** $\dfrac{y}{3} + \dfrac{1}{3} = -\dfrac{2}{3}$
50. $\dfrac{y}{2} + \dfrac{y}{3} = \dfrac{5}{6}$ **51.** $\dfrac{5y}{4} - \dfrac{y}{2} = -\dfrac{3}{4}$
52. $\dfrac{2y + 1}{3} = -5$ **53.** $\dfrac{x - 2}{6} = \dfrac{x + 2}{2}$
54. $\dfrac{x - 2}{4} = \dfrac{2x - 5}{2}$ **55.** $\dfrac{x - 2}{2} - \dfrac{x}{6} = -2$

Solve and check.

56. $\dfrac{n}{2} - \dfrac{1 + n}{5} = -\dfrac{1}{2}$ **57.** $\dfrac{2x - 1}{3} - \dfrac{x + 2}{4} = -5$
58. $\dfrac{3y + 5}{3} - \dfrac{y - 3}{6} = -2$ **59.** $\dfrac{2y + 1}{3} - \dfrac{y + 4}{5} = 7$

7.7 *In questions 60–64, write an equation for each statement.*

60. Eight more than a number is twenty.
61. A number multiplied by six is seventy-two.
62. Hadib is eight years older than Cam. The sum of their ages is twenty-four.
63. Sonya has ten dollars less than Paula. Together they have ninety dollars.
64. Karl has three times as many stamps as Tim. Together they have 2400 stamps.

65. Measurement The perimeter of each figure is 64 m. Write an equation to find the dimensions of each figure.

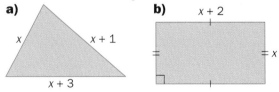

7.8 *Solve.*

66. Measurement The length of a rectangle is 3 m greater than the width. The perimeter is 26 m. What are the dimensions of the rectangle?
67. Numbers The sum of three consecutive numbers is 183. Find the numbers.

68. Coins In a pile of coins, there are 15 more quarters than loonies. The total value of the coins is $21.25. How many quarters are there?

69. Measurement Calculate the length of MN, to the nearest tenth of a centimetre.

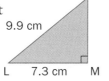

9.9 cm

L   7.3 cm   M

N

7.9 **70. Water tank** A hot water tank holds 200 L of water. When the tap is opened, the water drains at a rate of 15 L/min. The amount of water left in the tank after t minutes is given by $A = 200 - 15t$.
a) How much water will be in the tank after 5 min? 10 min?
b) How long, to the nearest minute, will it take to drain the tank?

71. Perimeter The formula for the perimeter of a rectangle is $P = 2(l + w)$. Solve for l.

7.10 **72. Tutoring** Shandra is a math tutor. She charges $20 a visit plus $25/h.
a) Write a formula that determines her earnings from the hours she tutors on a visit.
b) How much will she earn if she tutors for 3 h? 2.5 h?

7.11 **73. Jogging** Marie started jogging at 08:30 at 9 km/h. Heather started jogging 15 min later in the same direction. Heather jogged at 12 km/h.
a) How long did it take Heather to catch up to Marie?
b) At what time did she catch up to her?

74. Driving Two cars left the same highway restaurant at the same time but drove in opposite directions. One travelled at 65 km/h, the other at 55 km/h. After how long were they 600 km apart?

75. Flying times A plane left Darwin for Beijing, a distance of 6000 km, travelling at 700 km/h. At the same time, a plane left Beijing for Darwin travelling at 800 km/h. How long after takeoff did the planes pass each other?

Exploring Math

The Locker Problem

A high school has a very long hallway, with 1000 lockers along one side. They are numbered from 1 to 1000.

On April Fools' Day, each of the school's 1000 students walks down the hallway to leave the school. Every student walks in the same direction, past locker 1 first and locker 1000 last.

The first student closes every locker door. The second student opens every second locker door. The third student changes the state of every third locker door. This means that, if the locker door is open, the student closes it. If the locker door is closed, the student opens it. The fourth student changes the state of every fourth locker door.

This pattern continues until the thousandth student leaves and changes the state of the thousandth locker door.

What are the numbers of the lockers that are closed after the last student leaves?

Hint: Solve a simpler problem. You may want to make a table to show the states of some locker doors after the first few students walk down the hall. Use the table to predict which of the 1000 doors are closed after 1000 students leave. Another way is to use cards or counters as lockers and act out the problem.

		Locker Number									
		1	2	3	4	5	6	7	8	9	10
Student	1	C	C	C	C	C	C	C	C	C	C
	2		O		O		O		O		O
	3			O			C			O	
	4										
	5										

Chapter Check

Solve and check.
1. $x - 12 = -4$
2. $x + 15 = 12$
3. $x + 2 = 8$
4. $x - 10 = -19$
5. $5 = x - 3$
6. $15 - x = -5$

Solve.
7. $6x = -54$
8. $4x = 44$
9. $\dfrac{x}{5} = 7$
10. $\dfrac{x}{3} = 4$

Solve.
11. $5x + 8 = 3x + 2$
12. $5x + 12 = 7x + 16$
13. $6z + 8 = 9z - 7$
14. $2y - 6 = 10 + 11y + 2$

Solve.
15. $3(2x - 4) = 9x + 3$
16. $5(2x - 1) + 9 = 2(x - 2)$

Solve.
17. $10x - 0.4 = 2x - 3.6$
18. $7.6x - 0.7 = 5.6x - 6.5$

Solve.
19. $\dfrac{2x}{3} = -6$
20. $\dfrac{y}{3} + \dfrac{1}{3} = -\dfrac{2}{3}$
21. $\dfrac{y}{3} - \dfrac{5y}{6} = -\dfrac{1}{2}$
22. $\dfrac{3y + 1}{2} = 5$
23. $\dfrac{x + 2}{2} = \dfrac{x - 1}{5}$
24. $\dfrac{x + 2}{2} + \dfrac{x - 2}{5} = 2$

25. **Ages** Bilal is four years older than Anna, and the sum of their ages is 36. Write an equation to find their ages.

26. **Numbers** When 47 is subtracted from a certain number, the result is 34. Find the number.

27. **Measurement** The length of a rectangle is 15 m more than the width. The perimeter of the rectangle is 74 m. Find the length and width.

28. **Measurement** The lengths of the sides of a triangle are 3 consecutive whole numbers. The perimeter of the triangle is 102 m. Find the lengths of the sides.

29. **Coins** A jar contains \$36.25 in dimes and quarters. There are 250 coins in the jar. How many quarters are in the jar?

30. **Measurement** The formula for the perimeter of a rectangle is $P = 2(l + w)$. Find w if $P = 200$ m and $l = 56$ m.

31. **Area** The formula for the area of a triangle is $A = \dfrac{1}{2}bh$. Solve for h.

32. **Shipping** A cargo ship left Montréal for Halifax at 15 km/h. One hour later, a patrol boat left Montréal at 20 km/h, trying to overtake the cargo ship. After how long did the patrol boat overtake the cargo ship?

33. **Service calls** Dana is an electrician. She charges \$50 for a service call, plus \$40/h.
a) Write a formula that determines the total charge from the length of a service call.
b) Calculate the total charge for a 4-h service call.

34. **Driving times** Mark lived 350 km from his agent. Mark had to sign a contract his agent had. Mark and his agent left their apartments at the same time in their cars and drove along the same road toward each other. Mark drove at 65 km/h and his agent drove at 75 km/h. After how long did they meet?

Einstein as a boy.

Using the Strategies

1. Whole numbers Find 5 consecutive whole numbers whose sum is 405.

2. Bulletin board To hang a picture on a bulletin board, Masao uses 4 thumbtacks, 1 in each corner. For two pictures of the same size, Masao can overlap the corners and hang both pictures with only 6 tacks.

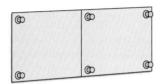

a) What is the minimum number of tacks Masao needs to hang 6 pictures of the same size in a row?
b) Write an expression for finding the number of tacks needed to hang any number of pictures in a row.

3. Squares What is the total number of squares in this diagram?

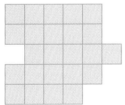

4. Bus schedules The Beach bus leaves every 20 min, and the Sand bus leaves every 45 min. If they leave together at noon, when is the next time that they will leave together?

5. Making change List the different ways you can make change for a dollar using only quarters and nickels.

6. Averages The average of two numbers is 21. When a third number is included, the average of the three numbers is 23. What is the third number?

7. Measurement The perimeter of the figure is 12 units.

Sketch your answers to the following.
a) Remove 1 square and keep the perimeter the same.
b) Remove 2 squares and keep the perimeter the same.
c) Remove 1 square and increase the perimeter by 2.
d) Remove 2 squares and increase the perimeter by 2.
e) Remove 2 squares and increase the perimeter by 4.

8. Coffee shop A coffee shop on the corner of a busy intersection is open 24 h a day. Sketch a graph of the number of customers in the shop versus the time of day.

9. Piano tuners About how many piano tuners are there in Canada?

10. Numbers Use any of the arithmetic operations and brackets, if necessary, to combine each set of numbers so that they equal the number in brackets.
a) 4, 5, 12   [8]
b) 3, 7, 14   [10]
c) 4, 6, 7, 8   [15]
d) 3, 5, 6, 11   [19]

11. Countries About what percent of the countries in the world are in the Northern Hemisphere?

CHAPTER 8

Analytic Geometry

How Can We Model Slopes on the Earth?

The source of the St. Lawrence River is Lake Ontario. The St. Lawrence flows to the Gulf of St. Lawrence, meeting it at Anticosti Island.

The source of the Mississippi River is Lake Itasca in Minnesota. The Mississippi flows to the Gulf of Mexico, entering it near New Orleans, Louisiana.

1. The elevation of Lake Itasca is 446 m. When the Mississippi passes through Minneapolis, the river has an elevation of about 214 m. The length of the river between Lake Itasca and Minneapolis is about 960 km. On average, how many centimetres does the river drop for every kilometre of its length between these two locations?

2. The length of the Mississippi between Minneapolis and the Gulf of Mexico is about 2810 km. On average, how many centimetres does the river drop for every kilometre of its length between these two locations?

3. On average over the whole length of the Mississippi, how many centimetres does the river drop for every kilometre of its length?

4. The elevation of Lake Ontario is 75 m. The length of the St. Lawrence is 3060 km. On average over the whole length of the St. Lawrence, how many centimetres does the river drop for every kilometre of its length?

5. On average over its whole length, which river is steeper — the Mississippi or the St. Lawrence? Explain.

In Modelling Math — Geography on pages 442 and 443, you will learn how topographical maps are used to model slopes on the Earth.

GETTING STARTED

Slope

1 Surfaces That Slope

There are many examples of surfaces that slope, including wheelchair ramps and playground slides. The roofs of most houses are sloped, so that rain and melting snow will run off. In nature, the outer shape of a pine tree appears sloped.

1. List three other examples of sloped surfaces that people build. Give a reason why each is sloped.

2. List three other examples of sloped surfaces found in nature. Give a reason why each is sloped.

2 Describing Slope

1. Ladder A ladder is leaning against a wall. The base of the ladder is 1 m from the bottom of the wall.
a) What happens to the steepness of the ladder if you move the base so that its distance from the wall is 1.5 m? 2 m?

← 1 m →

b) What happens to the steepness of the ladder if you continue moving the base away from the wall until the ladder is flat on the ground? Is the ladder still sloped? Explain.
c) Suppose the base of the ladder is again 1 m from the wall. What happens to the steepness of the ladder if you move the base so that its distance from the wall is 0.5 m?
d) What happens to the steepness of the ladder if you continue moving the base toward the wall until the ladder is flat against the wall? Is the ladder still sloped? Explain.

2. Ski hills Some ski hills are described as beginner, intermediate, or expert hills. How do you think these descriptions are related to the slopes of the hills?

3. Road signs Some road signs describe slopes. Where and why are these signs used?

Warm Up

Evaluate.

1. $4 + (-8)$ **2.** $-11 + 13.5$

3. $-7.2 + (-6.3)$ **4.** $7 - 9$

5. $-8.1 - 3.6$ **6.** $-2 - (-2)$

7. $7 \times (-4)$ **8.** -3×11

9. $-5.2 \times (-3.5)$ **10.** $-12 \div 4$

11. $36.4 \div (-9.1)$ **12.** $-20.5 \div (-5)$

Evaluate.

13. $\dfrac{15-1}{5-3}$ **14.** $\dfrac{2-(-2)}{1-(-1)}$ **15.** $\dfrac{1.8-19.8}{5-2}$

16. $\dfrac{8-(-7)}{2.5-4}$ **17.** $\dfrac{25-5.4}{3-(-1)}$ **18.** $\dfrac{-1-9}{-6-(-2)}$

For each equation, complete a table of values using the domain $\{-2, -1, 0, 1, 2\}$.

19. $y = 2x - 5$ **20.** $y = \dfrac{x}{2} + \dfrac{1}{2}$

21. $x + y = 1$ **22.** $x - y = 3$

Expand.

23. $3(x + 2)$ **24.** $2(3x - 1)$ **25.** $-4(5x - 2)$

Expand and simplify.

26. $2(2x + 1) + 3$ **27.** $-(3x - 2) - 4$

Solve.

28. $3x + 2 = -1$ **29.** $\dfrac{x}{2} - 1 = 3$

Express as a unit rate.

30. walking 10 km in 2 h

31. printing 48 pages in 6 min

32. $112 for 8 h of house painting

33. $1.50 for 6 bagels

34. $9.30 for a 15-min long-distance phone call

35. Hockey One season, Pavel Bure scored 51 goals out of 331 shots on goal. Express the fraction of his shots that scored goals as
a) a decimal, to the nearest thousandth
b) a percent, to the nearest tenth

36. Planet Neptune spins once about its axis every 16 h. Find the rate at which it spins
a) in degrees per hour
b) in degrees per Earth day

Mental Math

Operations With Integers

Evaluate.

1. $-3 + 9$ **2.** $2 + (-5)$ **3.** $-3 - 5$

4. $6 - (-9)$ **5.** -3×9 **6.** $-8 \times (-2)$

7. $-12 \div (-6)$ **8.** $22 \div (-11)$ **9.** $-35 \div 7$

Evaluate.

10. $\dfrac{6-2}{3-1}$ **11.** $\dfrac{10-1}{2-5}$ **12.** $\dfrac{5-(-1)}{8-2}$

13. $\dfrac{1-9}{2-4}$ **14.** $\dfrac{5-(-1)}{-3-(-1)}$ **15.** $\dfrac{-3-(-2)}{-2-(-1)}$

Adding Using Compatible Numbers

Compatible numbers are numbers that you can compute mentally. Suppose that you are adding two numbers, and one of them is just below a multiple of 10. The mental addition is easier if you round this number up to a multiple of 10, then add, then subtract the number you added when rounding.

For $79 + 64$, think $79 + 1 + 64 = 80 + 64$
$$= 144$$

and $144 - 1 = 143$

So, $79 + 64 = 143$

Calculate.

1. $47 + 34$ **2.** $59 + 53$ **3.** $34 + 78$

4. $127 + 79$ **5.** $114 + 167$ **6.** $235 + 148$

Adapt the method to calculate the following. Describe how you adapted the method.

7. $1.8 + 2.3$ **8.** $3.4 + 1.9$ **9.** $7.8 + 4.5$

10. $8.4 + 3.9$ **11.** $12.7 + 6.5$ **12.** $120 + 190$

13. $240 + 180$ **14.** $150 + 270$ **15.** $660 + 450$

16. a) Complete the following additions, where x, y, n, m, and b represent whole numbers.
$(10x + y) + (10n + m)$
$(10x + y + b) + (10n + m) - b$
b) Explain how these additions are related to the method shown above.
c) For the method to work as shown, what is the value of $y + b$?

INVESTIGATING MATH

Lengths of Horizontal and Vertical Line Segments

1 Lengths on a Number Line

1. The lengths of line segments are always positive. Count units to find the length of each line segment shown on the number lines.

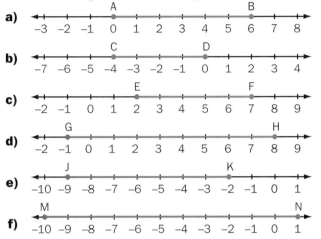

2. Write a rule for finding the length of a line segment on a number line without counting units.

3. Use your rule to find the length of the line segment joining each of the following pairs of points.

a) P(8) and Q(15)   **b)** R(−5) and S(7)
c) T(−12) and U(−3)   **d)** V(−6) and W(8)

2 Lengths of Horizontal Line Segments

1. Find the length of each horizontal line segment by counting units.

2. Describe how the lengths can be found from the coordinates of the endpoints of the line segments.

3. Find the length of the horizontal line segment joining each of the following pairs of points.

a) S(4, 3) and T(10, 3)   **b)** P(−3, 1) and Q(2, 1)
c) K(−7, −3) and L(−4, −3)   **d)** V(−6, 5) and W(4, 5)

3 Lengths of Vertical Line Segments

1. Find the length of each vertical line segment by counting units.

📎 **2.** Describe how the lengths can be found from the coordinates of the endpoints of the line segments.

3. Find the length of the vertical line segment joining each of the following pairs of points.

a) R(4, 6) and S(4, 1) **b)** P(1, 2) and Q(1, –4)
c) V(–2, –7) and W(–2, –3) **d)** T(–4, 0) and U(–4, –3)

4 Problem Solving

1. Measurement Plot the points and make a quadrilateral by joining them in the order A, B, C, D, A. Identify the type of quadrilateral, and find its perimeter and area.
a) A(2, 3), B(2, 7), C(6, 7), D(6, 3)
b) A(–3, 2), B(2, 2), C(2, –3), D(–3, –3)
c) A(1, 1), B(4, 1), C(4, 9), D(1, 9)
d) A(5, –2), B(5, –5), C(–1, –5), D(–1, –2)

2. Three vertices of rectangle WXYZ are W(4, 3), X(–1, 3), and Y(–1, –1). What are the coordinates of Z?

3. Two adjacent vertices of a square have coordinates (–1, –3) and (–1, 0). What are the possible coordinates of the other two vertices?

4. Measurement Rectangle QRST has an area of 6 square units, and Q is at the origin. R lies on the x-axis, T lies on the y-axis, and the coordinates of the vertices are whole numbers. What are the possible sets of coordinates for the vertices of the rectangle?

8.1 Slope

The **slope** of a line is the measure of the steepness of the line. The slope also describes the direction of the line.

Diagram 1 shows the steepness of two objects as you move up them. Line I represents the height of a triangular face of the Great Pyramid of Cheops. Line II represents Russian Hill, which is a street in San Francisco.

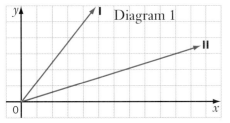

Diagram 1

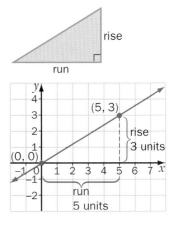

To study the shape of a line, look at the line from *left to right*, the direction in which we read in English. In Diagram 1, the lines *rise* from left to right. They have *positive* slopes.

Diagram 2 shows the steepness of the same two objects as you move down them. Line III shows the steepness of the face of the pyramid. Line IV shows the steepness of the street.

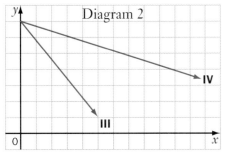

Diagram 2

In Diagram 2, the lines *fall* from left to right. They have *negative* slopes.

The slope of a line, m, is found by dividing the vertical change, called the **rise** (or fall), by the horizontal change, called the **run**, from one point to a second point on the line.

The graph shows the line that passes through the origin and the point (5, 3).

$$\text{slope}(m) = \frac{\text{rise(change in } y)}{\text{run (change in } x)}$$

$$= \frac{3}{5}$$

Explore: Develop a Method

Count units to determine the rise and run for each line segment. Copy and complete the table.

a)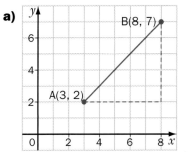

b)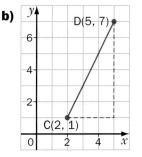

c)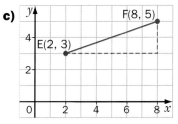

Line Segment	Rise	Run	Slope
AB			
CD			
EF			

Inquire

1. Which line segment is the steepest?

2. Which line segment has the greatest slope?

3. How can the rise of each line segment be calculated using the y-coordinates of the endpoints?

4. How can the run of each line segment be determined using the x-coordinates of the endpoints?

5. If you are given the coordinates of the endpoints of a line segment, describe a method for finding the slope without plotting the points.

6. Which has the greater slope — the face of the Great Pyramid or Russian Hill? Explain.

Example 1   Slopes of Line Segments

The coordinates of three points on a line are shown.
a) Calculate the slopes of segments AB, BC, and AC.
b) How are the slopes related?

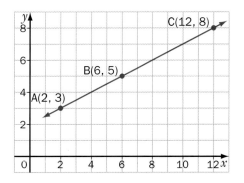

Solution

a) Find the rise and run for each segment.

For segment AB,
rise = 2
run = 4

$$\text{slope} = \frac{2}{4}$$
$$= \frac{1}{2}$$

For segment BC,
rise = 3
run = 6

$$\text{slope} = \frac{3}{6}$$
$$= \frac{1}{2}$$

For segment AC,
rise = 5
run = 10

$$\text{slope} = \frac{5}{10}$$
$$= \frac{1}{2}$$

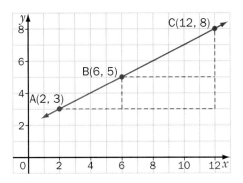

b) The slopes are equal.

As Example 1 suggests, the slopes of all segments on a line are equal. Therefore, the slope of a line can be found using any two points on the line. Points that lie on the same line are called **collinear points**.

The slope, m, of a line containing the points $P(x_1, y_1)$ and $Q(x_2, y_2)$ is

$$m = \frac{\text{vertical change}}{\text{horizontal change}} \text{ or } \frac{\text{rise}}{\text{run}}$$

$$= \frac{y_2 - y_1}{x_2 - x_1}, \; x_2 \neq x_1$$

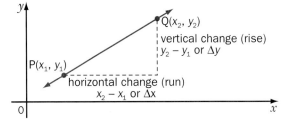

Another common formula for slope is

$$m = \frac{\Delta y}{\Delta x}$$

Δy is read as "delta y."
Δx is read as "delta x."

Δy means the change in the y-coordinates or $y_2 - y_1$.
Δx means the change in the x-coordinates or $x_2 - x_1$.

Example 2   Line with a Positive Slope

Find the slope of the line that passes through the points S(2, 1) and T(6, 8).

Solution

Let $(x_1, y_1) = S(2, 1)$ and $(x_2, y_2) = T(6, 8)$.

Write the formula:

$$m_{ST} = \frac{y_2 - y_1}{x_2 - x_1}$$

Substitute known values:

$$= \frac{8 - 1}{6 - 2}$$

Simplify:

$$= \frac{7}{4}$$

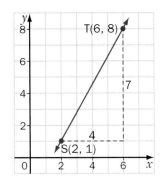

The slope of the line that passes through the points S and T is $\frac{7}{4}$.

Note that, if a line rises from left to right, its slope is a positive number. The slope of $\frac{7}{4}$ means that, for every increase of 4 in the x-coordinate, the y-coordinate increases by 7.

Example 3   Line with a Negative Slope

Find the slope of the line that passes through the points E(–5, 4) and F(3, –1).

Solution

Let $(x_1, y_1) = $ E(–5, 4) and $(x_2, y_2) = $ F(3, –1).

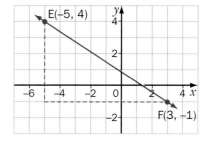

Write the formula:
$$m_{EF} = \frac{y_2 - y_1}{x_2 - x_1}$$

Substitute known values:
$$= \frac{-1 - 4}{3 - (-5)}$$

Simplify:
$$= -\frac{5}{8}$$

The slope of the line that passes through the points E and F is $-\frac{5}{8}$.

Note that, if a line falls from left to right, its slope is a negative number.

The slope of $-\frac{5}{8}$ means that, for every increase of 8 in the x-coordinate, the y-coordinate decreases by 5.

Example 4   Slope of a Horizontal Line

Find the slope of the line that passes through the points J(–5, 4) and K(2, 4).

Solution

Write the formula:
$$m_{JK} = \frac{\Delta y}{\Delta x}$$

Substitute known values:
$$= \frac{4 - 4}{2 - (-5)}$$

Simplify:
$$= \frac{0}{7}$$
$$= 0$$

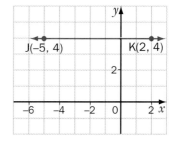

The slope of the line that passes through the points J and K is 0.

Note that the slope of a horizontal line is zero.

The slope of 0 means that, when the x-coordinate increases or decreases, the y-coordinate does not change.

Example 5 Slope of a Vertical Line

Find the slope of the line that passes through the points V(3, 5) and W(3, −4).

Solution

Let (x_1, y_1) = V(3, 5) and (x_2, y_2) = W(3, −4).

Write the formula:

$$m_{VW} = \frac{\Delta y}{\Delta x}$$

Substitute known values:

$$= \frac{-4-5}{3-3}$$

Simplify:

$$= \frac{-9}{0}$$

Since division by zero is undefined, the slope of the line that passes through V and W is not defined by a real number.

Note that the slope of a vertical line is undefined.

For a vertical line, when the y-coordinate increases or decreases, the x-coordinate does not change.

The slopes of lines can be summarized as follows.

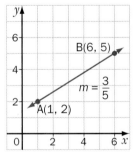

A line that rises from left to right has a positive slope.

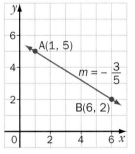

A line that falls from left to right has a negative slope.

The slope of a horizontal line is zero.

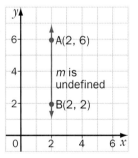

The slope of a vertical line is undefined.

Example 6 Drawing a Line

Draw the line through the point (2, 2) with slope $\frac{3}{4}$.

Solution

Plot the point (2, 2).

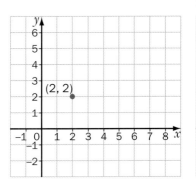

Use the slope $\frac{3}{4}$ to find another point.

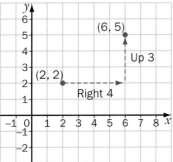

Draw a line through the points.

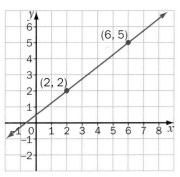

Practice

A

1. State whether each slope is positive or negative.

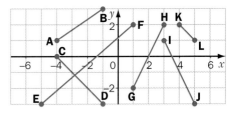

2. State the slope of each line segment.

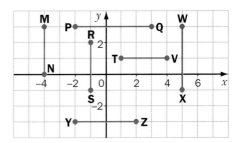

a) *Without calculating the slope, state whether the slope of each line is positive, negative, zero, or undefined.*
b) *State the rise.*
c) *State the run.*
d) *Calculate the slope, where possible.*

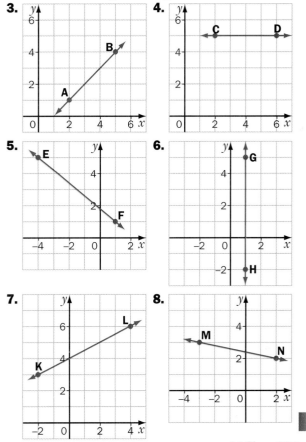

Find the slope of the line passing through the points.
9. (0, 0) and (2, 3) **10.** (0, 0) and (−2, −4)
11. (1, 3) and (2, 7) **12.** (−4, 5) and (6, 5)
13. (5, −2) and (−3, 4) **14.** (0, 6) and (4, 0)
15. (−5, 7) and (−4, −2) **16.** (−2, 5) and (0, 8)
17. (−6, −5) and (0, 0) **18.** (−8, −7) and (−4, −3)
19. (5, 7) and (5, −3) **20.** (−6, −1) and (−2, 5)

Find the slope of the line passing through the points.
21. A(3.4, 1.6) and B(5.4, 2.2)
22. C(0, −1.7) and D(0.3, −3.8)
23. E(11.9, −2.3) and F(15.4, 8.2)
24. G$\left(\dfrac{1}{2}, 4\right)$ and H(2, −6)
25. J$\left(\dfrac{1}{3}, 1\dfrac{1}{2}\right)$ and K$\left(2, 3\dfrac{1}{2}\right)$

Write the coordinates of two points on a line that satisfies the given condition.
26. The line rises from left to right.
27. The line is horizontal.
28. The line falls from left to right.
29. The line is vertical.

Draw the line through the given point with the given slope.
30. A(2, 3), $m = 2$ **31.** B(−1, 1), $m = 3$
32. C(0, 4), $m = -2$ **33.** D(−3, 0), $m = \dfrac{1}{2}$
34. E(−3, −2), $m = \dfrac{2}{3}$ **35.** F(−3, 4), $m = -\dfrac{4}{3}$
36. G(4, −1), $m = 0$
37. H(−4, 5), m is undefined

Applications and Problem Solving
B

38. Given the point A(2, 2), find the coordinates of a point B so that the slope of AB is
a) 1 **b)** −1 **c)** 2 **d)** −2
e) 0 **f)** $\dfrac{1}{2}$ **g)** undefined
h) 7 **i)** −4 **j)** $-\dfrac{1}{3}$ **k)** $\dfrac{5}{2}$

39. A line passes through the point A(1, −3). State the coordinates of one other point on the line so that the slope of the line is
a) 0 **b)** 4 **c)** undefined
d) −1 **e)** $\dfrac{3}{4}$ **f)** $-\dfrac{1}{2}$ **g)** $\dfrac{5}{4}$
h) −8 **i)** 12 **j)** $\dfrac{7}{5}$ **k)** $-\dfrac{8}{3}$

40. Quadrants
The quadrants on a coordinate grid are named as follows.

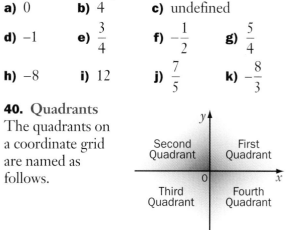

Point 1 and Point 2 lie on a line. Write the coordinates of the points so that the following conditions are satisfied.

Location of Points		
Point 1	Point 2	Slope of Line
a) in 1st quadrant	in 1st quadrant	negative
b) in 2nd quadrant	in 3rd quadrant	positive
c) in 2nd quadrant	in 3rd quadrant	negative
d) in 3rd quadrant	in 4th quadrant	negative
e) in 3rd quadrant	in 4th quadrant	positive
f) in 4th quadrant	in 3rd quadrant	zero
g) in 3rd quadrant	on x-axis	negative
h) in 3rd quadrant	on x-axis	positive
i) on y-axis	on x-axis	positive
j) on y-axis	on x-axis	negative
k) in 1st quadrant	in 2nd quadrant	$\dfrac{1}{2}$
l) in 1st quadrant	in 2nd quadrant	$-\dfrac{1}{2}$
m) in 4th quadrant	in 3rd quadrant	$\dfrac{2}{3}$
n) in 4th quadrant	in 3rd quadrant	$-\dfrac{2}{3}$
o) in 3rd quadrant	in 2nd quadrant	$\dfrac{3}{2}$
p) in 3rd quadrant	in 2nd quadrant	$-\dfrac{3}{2}$

41. Equations Given the equation of each line, find two points on the line and calculate the slope.
a) $x + y = 4$ **b)** $y = x + 2$
c) $x - y = 1$ **d)** $y = 5 - 2x$

42. Highway grade A sign on a highway indicates that the next hill has a grade of 10%. What is the slope of the hill?

43. Measurement Line segments AB and AC intersect at point A. The slope of AB is 0. The slope of AC is undefined. What is the measure of $\angle$BAC?

44. Find the coordinates of the vertices of a triangle so that the slopes of all three sides are positive.

45. Find the coordinates of the vertices of a quadrilateral so that the slopes of all four sides are negative.

46. The slope of a line is 3. The line passes through $(2, k)$ and $(4, 1)$. Find the value of k.

47. The slope of a line is -2. The line passes through $(t, -1)$ and $(-4, 9)$. Find the value of t.

C

48. Cycling The graph shows how far Danzel cycled in 3 h.

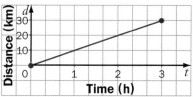

a) About how far did he travel in 2 h 45 min?
b) About how long did it take him to cycle 15 km?
c) What does the value of the slope of this line tell you?

49. a) On the same grid, draw a line through A(1, 4) and B(−2, 2) and a line through P(−1, −1) and Q(2, 1).
b) Calculate the slope of each line in part a).
c) Use your answer to part b) to explain why these lines are parallel.

50. a) Plot the points P(−4, 2), Q(−1, −2), R(4, −2), and S(1, 2). Join PQ, QR, RS, and SP.
b) Draw diagonals PR and QS.
c) The diagonals PR and QS are perpendicular to each other. Find the slope of each diagonal. How are the slopes related?
d) Is this relationship true for any pair of perpendicular lines? Explain.

51. Ski slopes The lengths of two ski slopes are 625 m and 760 m. The horizontal distance from the start of the run to the end of the run for both slopes is 500 m.
a) What is the height of the higher ski slope, to the nearest metre?
b) Which of the two ski slopes is steeper? Explain and justify your reasoning.

52. Three or more points are collinear if they lie on the same straight line.
a) Use slopes to determine whether the points A(6, 7), B(2, 1), and C(−2, −5) are collinear.
b) Use slopes to determine whether the points P(−2, 5), Q(1, 3), and R(5, 1) are collinear.
c) Give the coordinates of three collinear points if one point is in the first quadrant, one is in the second quadrant, and one is in the fourth quadrant.
d) If the points D(−2, −1), E(1, 1), and F(7, k) are collinear, find the value of k.

53. The equal sides of isosceles triangle ABC meet at A(5, 0). Vertices B and C lie on the y-axis. The slope of AB is 2. Find
a) the coordinates of B
b) the coordinates of C
c) the slope of AC

54. Stairways For comfortable stairways, the slope $\frac{3}{4}$ is often used. This is the maximum slope permitted by many building codes.
a) Why do building codes specify a maximum slope for stairways?
b) What is the slope of the stairways in your school?

INVESTIGATING MATH

Finite Differences and Slopes of Linear Relations

Recall that, for tables of values with evenly spaced x-coordinates, finite differences are the differences between consecutive y-values. The graph of a linear relation is a straight line. The first difference for a linear relation is a constant.

1 Comparing First Differences and Slopes

For each table of values for a linear relation,
a) *calculate the slope of the line using any two given points*
b) *calculate the difference between successive x-coordinates*
c) *calculate the first difference*
d) *describe how the first difference and the difference between successive x-coordinates can be used to determine the slope of the line*

1. x	y		2. x	y		3. x	y		4. x	y		5. x	y
0	1		0	4		0	1		0	0		0	−1
1	3		1	1		2	4		3	2		2	−2
2	5		2	−2		4	7		6	4		4	−3
3	7		3	−5		6	10		9	6		6	−4
4	9		4	−8		8	13		12	8		8	−5
5	11		5	−11		10	16		15	10		10	−6

6. Write a rule for determining the slope of a linear relation from its table of values, without graphing the relation.

2 Calculating Slopes

Use first differences to determine the slope of the graph of each of the following linear relations. Check each solution by using $m = \dfrac{y_2 - y_1}{x_2 - x_1}$.

1. x	y		2. x	y		3. x	y		4. x	y		5. x	y
0	1		0	−4		0	3		−2	5		0	2
1	4		1	−2		1	2		−1	1		2	3
2	7		2	0		2	1		0	−3		4	4
3	10		3	2		3	0		1	−7		6	5
4	13		4	4		4	−1		2	−11		8	6

6. x	y		7. x	y		8. x	y		9. x	y		10. x	y
0	−1		0	0		0	−2		−3	2		−4	−10
3	0		4	−3		5	−5		−1	1		−2	−5
6	1		8	−6		10	−8		1	0		0	0
9	2		12	−9		15	−11		3	−1		2	5
12	3		16	−12		20	−14		5	−2		4	10

Alpine Skiing in Canada

Use the *Skiing* database, from the Computer Data Bank, to complete the following.

1 Vertical Drop

1. Find all the records for which the summit and base elevations are available.

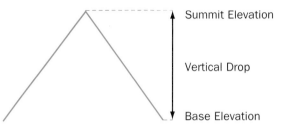

2. Add a calculated field for vertical drop, in metres.

3. Sort the records from greatest to least vertical drop. In which province is the ski area with the greatest vertical drop?

2 Finding Slope

1. Find the records from those above for which longest trail, in kilometres, is also available.

2. Add a calculated field for longest trail, in metres.

3. Outline a plan to calculate the slope of the longest trail using the two calculated fields. Describe any other calculation fields you would add. What assumptions are you making?

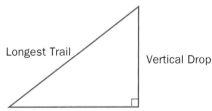

4. Compare your plan with the plans of your classmates. Revise your plan, if necessary.

5. Carry out your plan.

6. Sort the records from greatest to least slope of the longest trail. For which ski area does the longest trail have the greatest slope?

7. Explain, in terms of the assumptions you made, why the longest trail for that ski area might not actually have the greatest slope.

3 Ski Vacations

1. Consider the information provided in this database. What else would alpine skiers want to know about the ski areas when planning ski vacations? What fields would you add so that the database could be used to plan alpine ski vacations?

8.2 Slope as Rate of Change

Canada's Catriona LeMay Doan won the gold medal in the 500-m long-track speed skating event at the Winter Olympics in Nagano, Japan. She skated the 500 m in 38.21 s.

To find her average rate, or average speed, divide the distance by the time.

$$\text{Average rate} = \frac{500}{38.21}$$
$$\doteq 13.1$$

Catriona's average rate was about 13.1 m/s. This rate describes how the total distance she skated changed with time, so we can say that her average *rate of change* was 13.1 m/s. On the average, she moved forward 13.1 m per second of the race.

The slope of a line is the rate of change between any two points on the line.

$$\text{slope} = \frac{\text{change in } y}{\text{change in } x}$$

The slope of the line shown is 2.

The slope describes how much the vertical measure changes with respect to each unit change in the horizontal measure. For the line shown, the vertical measure increases by 2 units for each 1-unit increase in the horizontal measure.

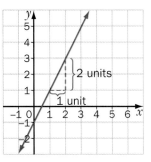

In applied problems, the slope of a line describes a constant or average rate of change.

Explore: Interpret the Graph

Marnie McBean and Kathleen Heddle won Olympic gold medals for Canada in the women's pairs rowing event at both the Barcelona and the Atlanta games. The graph shows their approximate times at the 500-m and 1500-m marks of their gold medal race in Atlanta. All Olympic rowing events are 2000 m long.

Find the slope of the graph, to the nearest tenth.

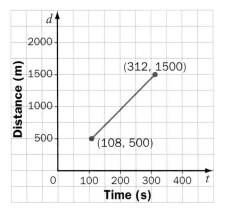

Inquire

1. The slope of the graph represents the average speed from the 500-m mark to the 1500-m mark. State the speed and the units in which it should be expressed. How do you know the units?

2. a) Would you expect that the average speed for the first 500 m of the race was higher or lower than the speed in question 1? Explain.
b) Determine the average speed for the first 500 m of the race.

3. On the same grid, which is steeper — a slope that represents a higher speed or a slope that represents a lower speed? Explain.

Example 1   Altitudes of Aircraft

An aircraft flying at an altitude of 7600 m is instructed to climb to 10 000 m. The graph shows the relationship between the average altitude of the aircraft and the time for which it climbs.
a) Find the average rate of change of altitude.
b) What does the average rate of change mean?

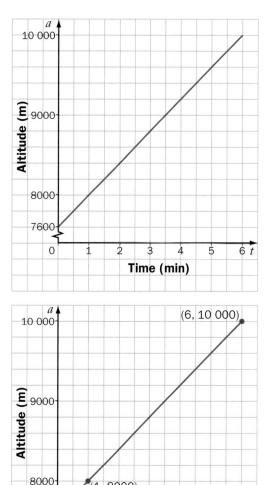

Solution

a) Determine the slope of the line, which is the rate of change. Choose any two points with convenient coordinates, for example, (1, 8000) and (6, 10 000).

$$m = \frac{y_2 - y_1}{x_2 - x_1}$$
$$= \frac{10\ 000 - 8000}{6 - 1}$$
$$= \frac{2000}{5}$$
$$= 400$$

The average rate of change of altitude is 400 m/min.

b) The aircraft climbs an average of 400 m each minute.

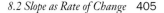

Example 2   Parachuting

The graph shows the relationship between the height of a parachutist, in metres, and the time of descent, in seconds.
a) Find the average rate of change in height.
b) Explain the meaning of the average rate of change.

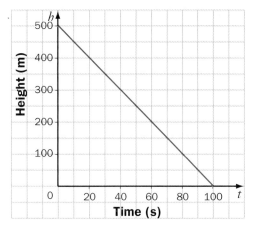

Solution

a) Determine the slope using two convenient points, such as (0, 500) and (100, 0).

$$m = \frac{y_2 - y_1}{x_2 - x_1}$$
$$= \frac{0 - 500}{100 - 0}$$
$$= \frac{-500}{100}$$
$$= -5$$

The average rate of change in height is −5 m/s.

b) The parachutist descends an average of 5 m each second.

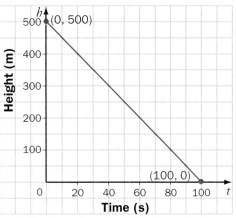

Example 3   Internet Access

Christina's Internet provider charges a flat fee for the first 10 h of Internet access per month, plus an hourly rate for additional access. One month, Christina was on-line for 15 h and paid $18.75. The next month, she was on-line for 27 h and paid $39.75. What is the hourly rate for hours above 10 h/month?

Solution

a) The hourly rate is the slope of the graph of cost versus time.

$$m = \frac{y_2 - y_1}{x_2 - x_1}$$
$$m = \frac{39.75 - 18.75}{27 - 15}$$
$$= 1.75$$

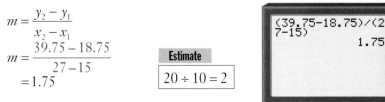

Estimate

$20 \div 10 = 2$

The rate for hours above 10 h/month is $1.75/h.

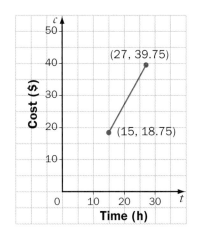

Applications and Problem Solving

A

Determine each rate of change.

1. Blue whale At birth, a blue whale is about 7 m long. After 7 months, it is about 15 m long.

2. Sleeping A 5 year-old sleeps an average of 11 h a night, whereas a 25 year-old sleeps an average of 8 h a night.

3. Bird migration Flocks of up to two million sandpipers feed on mudflats in the Bay of Fundy before their 4200-km, 89-h non-stop flight over open water to South America.

For each graph,
a) *determine the rate of change*
b) *explain the meaning of the rate of change*

4.

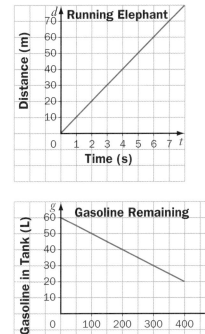

5.

6. Video recording The length of tape in a T-120 videocassette is 246 m.

a) In the SP mode, the tape will record 120 min of programs. What is the rate of change, in metres per minute?

b) What does the rate of change mean?

c) In the LP mode, the tape will record 240 min of programs. What is the rate of change, in metres per minute?

d) In the EP mode, the tape will record 360 min of programs. What is the rate of change, to the nearest hundredth of a metre per minute?

B

7. University students In 1971, there were 323 000 full-time university students in Canada. In 1997, there were 544 000. Find the average rate of change, to the nearest hundred students per year.

8. Televisions In 1970, 12.1% of Canadian households had colour televisions. In 1997, the figure was 98.7%. Find the average rate of change, to the nearest tenth of a percent per year.

9. Railways In 1947, Canadian railways logged 9 570 000 000 passenger-kilometres. In 1996, they logged 1 520 000 000 passenger-kilometres. Find the average rate of change, to the nearest million passenger-kilometres per year.

10. LP record sales The table shows LP record sales in Canada, in millions of units, over a 20-year period.

Year	1971	1981	1991
Sales (millions)	26.4	54.4	0

a) Calculate the average rate of change from 1971 to 1981; from 1981 to 1991; from 1971 to 1991.

b) Does the average rate of change from 1971 to 1991 give a true picture of the changes in LP record sales over the 20-year period? Explain.

11. Running Bill jogged for 5 min, and then sprinted 400 m in 64 s.

a) At what rate did he sprint?

b) Can you use the rate from part a) to find how far Bill jogged? Explain and justify your reasoning.

12. Thunderstorms Because light travels much faster than sound, you see lightning before you hear a thunderclap. If the storm is 960 m from you, the time interval between the flash and the thunderclap is 2.8 s. If the storm is 1680 m from you, the time interval is 4.9 s.
a) Determine the rate of change, to the nearest metre per second.
b) Describe the rate of change in words.
c) If the time interval is 3.7 s, determine your distance from the storm, to the nearest ten metres.
d) If you are 2500 m from the storm, what is the time interval, to the nearest tenth of a second?

13. Commission Hariko is paid a base salary plus commission for selling kitchen appliances. One week, her sales totalled $3800, and she earned $594. In a busier week, her sales totalled $5750, and she earned $652.50.
a) What rate of commission is Hariko paid? Express your answer as a percent.
b) What is her weekly base salary?
c) How much would she earn in a week if her sales totalled $4325?

C

14. National debt In 1940, Canada's national debt was $3 271 000 000. In 1990, the national debt was $357 811 000 000.
a) Determine the rate of change in the national debt over this 50-year period.
b) Use your research skills to determine the national debt today.
c) Determine the rate of change in the national debt from 1990 until today.
d) Compare the rates of change from parts a) and c).

15. Taxes Tax freedom day is the first day of the year on which average Canadians keep the money they earn. Before that day, everything they earn is paid in taxes to various levels of government. In 1961, tax freedom day was May 3. In 1998, tax freedom day was June 27.

a) Find the average rate of change in the tax freedom day, to the nearest tenth of a day per year.
b) Is there a limit to how long this average rate of change can continue? Explain.

16. Canada's population In 1871, Canada's population was 3 690 000. In 1996, it was 29 670 000.
a) Find the average rate of change, to the nearest thousand people per year.
b) Predict the year in which Canada's population reached 20 000 000. Then, use your research skills to check your prediction.
c) Predict the year in which Canada's population will reach 50 000 000.
d) Do you think that your prediction from part c) is valid? Explain.

17. a) On a graph of *y* versus *x* using data you make up, is it possible to have a slope of 0? a positive slope? a negative slope? an undefined slope?
b) On a graph of distance travelled versus time, using real-world data, is it possible to have a slope of 0? a positive slope? a negative slope? an undefined slope? Explain.

18. Give three examples of rates of change that you use in your everyday life, and describe how you use them. Compare your examples with a classmate's.

PATTERN POWER

If the pattern continues, how many toothpicks make 9 triangles?

Oceanography

Oceans and seas, with a total surface area of 3.6×10^8 km^2, cover about 70% of the Earth's surface. Their properties, such as saltiness, temperature, and the movement of water, are studied by oceanographers. The numbers and lives of plants and animals of the oceans are also the concern of oceanographers.

1 Antarctic Ice

International teams of oceanographers study the waters of Antarctica. This continent is covered with frozen fresh water that is thousands of metres thick. Around its perimeter, there is another type of ice, called sea ice, which is formed from salty ocean water.

The graph shows how the area of sea ice increases and decreases during a year.

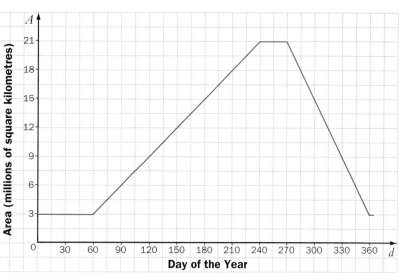

1. What is the area of the sea ice, in square kilometres, for the first 60 days of the year?

2. a) By how much does the area of the sea ice increase between day 60 and day 240?
b) How does this increase compare with the area of Canada?

3. a) What is the slope of the line segment between day 60 and day 240?
b) What rate of increase does the slope represent?
c) How fast does the area of the sea ice increase each hour? each minute?

4. What happens to the sea ice between day 240 and day 270?

5. What happens to the sea ice between day 270 and day 360?

6. a) What is the slope of the line segment between day 270 and day 360?
b) What rate of decrease does the slope represent?
c) How fast does the area of the sea ice decrease each hour? each minute?

7. How does the slope you found in question 6 compare with the slope you found in question 3?

2 Antarctic Krill

Krill are crustaceans that grow under the Antarctic sea ice. They feed the millions of penguins, millions of seals, and thousands of whales in the Antarctic. The total mass of krill is estimated to be 1.5 billion tonnes.

1. Estimate the total mass, in tonnes, of all the humans on Earth.

2. How does the total mass of krill compare with the total mass of humans?

3 Locating Information

Use your research skills to find information about the education needed for a career in oceanography. Share your information with your classmates.

TECHNOLOGY

Programming a Graphing Calculator

1 Slope of a Line

The graphing calculator program shows how to calculate the slope of the line that passes through the two points with coordinates (x_1, y_1) and (x_2, y_2).

PROGRAM:SLOPE
:ClrHome
:Disp "X1="
:Input A
:Disp "Y1="
:Input B
:Disp "X2="
:Input C
:Disp "Y2="
:Input D
:(D − B)/(C − A)→S
:Disp "SLOPE"
:Disp "IS"
:Disp S

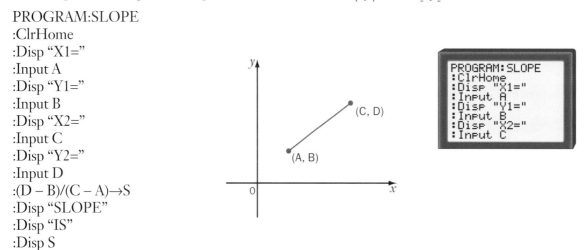

1. Describe what each line of the program does.

2. Enter the program into your graphing calculator. Use the program to find the slope of the line that passes through each of the following pairs of points.
a) (8, 14) and (2, 4)   **b)** (4, −1) and (16, −4)
c) (1.7, −3.8) and (−4.3, 9.7)

2 Problem Solving

1. A line passes through the point (−1, 6) and has a slope of −3. Find one other point on the line. Use the slope program to check your answer.

2. Human heart The human heart pumps 18 L of blood in 3.6 min and 37.5 L in 7.5 min.
a) Determine the rate at which the heart pumps blood.
b) Determine the volume of blood the heart pumps in a day.

3. Pulse rates As the human heart grows, it beats more slowly. At one year of age, a person's normal pulse rate is 115 beats/min. At age 20, the normal rate is 75 beats/min.
a) Determine the average rate of change.
b) Predict the pulse rate at age 16.
c) Predict the age at which the pulse rate is 102 beats/min.
d) Predict the pulse rate of a newborn baby.
e) The pulse rate of a newborn is actually 140 beats/min. Does the rate of change you found in part a) apply before age 1? Explain.

Characteristics of Linear and Non-Linear Equations

To graph equations using a graphing calculator, you must input them in the form $y = \blacksquare$. For example, to graph $x + 2y - 3 = 0$, first solve the equation for y using pencil and paper or a suitable graphing calculator.

$$x + 2y - 3 = 0$$

Add 3 to both sides: $\qquad x + 2y = 3$

Subtract x from both sides: $\qquad 2y = 3 - x$

Divide both sides by 2: $\qquad y = \dfrac{3 - x}{2}$

Entering the equation and graphing it in the standard viewing window gives the graph shown.

1 Characteristics of Equations

Recall that the graphs of linear equations are straight lines. The graphs of non-linear equations are not straight lines.

Use a graphing calculator to graph the following equations. In your notebook, complete a table by writing each equation in a column headed "Linear Equation" or a column headed "Non-Linear Equation."

1. $y = x + 4$ **2.** $y = x^2$ **3.** $y = 2x + 3$ **4.** $y = 3 - x$

5. $y = x^3$ **6.** $y = 2^x$ **7.** $y = x^2 + x$ **8.** $y - x + 6 = 0$

9. $2x^2 + y = 4$ **10.** $y = 4$ **11.** $x^3 + y - 2 = 0$ **12.** $x + 3y - 5 = 0$

13. $y = \dfrac{1}{x}$ **14.** $y + x^4 - 3 = 0$ **15.** $y = \dfrac{2}{x}$ **16.** $2x - y = 6$

17. $3x + 4y + 12 = 0$ **18.** $y = 3^x$ **19.** $y = 0.5x - 4$ **20.** $y - x^2 - 5 = 0$

21. Use your table to list the characteristics of equations whose graphs are straight lines.

22. Use your table to list characteristics of equations whose graphs are not straight lines.

2 Selecting Linear Equations

Use your results from Exploration 1 to predict which of the following equations have straight lines as their graphs. Check your predictions by graphing the equations.

1. $y = 3x^2$ **2.** $y = 3x - 5$ **3.** $y - x - 4 = 0$ **4.** $y = 4^x$

5. $x^3 + y + 3 = 0$ **6.** $4x + y + 1 = 0$ **7.** $y = -3$ **8.** $y = 2x^4$

9. $y = x^2 + 7$ **10.** $y - x = 0$ **11.** $2x + 3y - 6 = 0$ **12.** $y = 6$

13. $y = \dfrac{3}{x}$ **14.** $y = 3x^2 - x$ **15.** $y - 5^x - 3 = 0$ **16.** $y = 1 - 0.2x$

8.3 Linear Equations: Point-Slope Form

One way to find the age of a tree is to count the rings in the trunk. However, for a living tree, this method means cutting the tree down. For many types of trees, except for palms, firs, yews, horse chestnuts, and redwoods, the circumference of a tree gives its approximate age.

Explore: Develop a Method

The graph of the circumference of a tree, in centimetres, versus its age, in years, is linear.
One point on the line is (0, 0).
The slope of the line is 2.5.
Let (x, y) represent any other point on the line.

a) Use the points (0, 0) and (x, y) to write and simplify an expression for the slope in the form $m = \dfrac{\blacksquare}{\blacksquare}$.

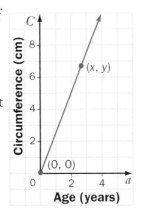

b) Substitute the given value of the slope for m.

Inquire

1. a) Write the equation from b), above, in the form $y = \blacksquare\, x$, where $\blacksquare$ is a number.
b) How does the value of $\blacksquare$ compare with the slope?

2. Use the equation to find the circumference of a tree with an age of
a) 20 years   **b)** 85 years

3. Use the equation to find the age of a tree with a circumference of
a) 80 cm   **b)** 175 cm

4. Rewrite the equation in the form $\blacktriangle\, x + \bullet\, y = 0$, where $\blacktriangle$ and $\bullet$ are integers.

When the equation of a line is written in the form $Ax + By + C = 0$, the equation is in **standard form**. For an equation in standard form, A, B, and C are integers, A and B are not both zero, and variables x and y represent real numbers.

The equation $2x + 3y - 7 = 0$ is in standard form.

The definition of slope can be used to find the equation of a line, given a point on the line and the slope of the line.

Example 1 Finding an Equation Given a Point and the Slope

a) Find an equation of the line that passes through $D(1, 4)$ with slope $m = 3$.
b) Write the equation in standard form.
c) State the values of A, B, and C.

Solution

a) To find an equation that satisfies the given conditions, let $P(x, y)$ be any point on the line, other than $D(1, 4)$. The slope of the line is 3.

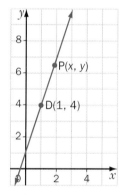

$$\frac{y_2 - y_1}{x_2 - x_1} = m_{PD}$$

Substitute known values: $\dfrac{y - 4}{x - 1} = 3$

Multiply both sides by $x - 1$: $(x - 1) \times \dfrac{y - 4}{x - 1} = (x - 1) \times 3$

Simplify: $y - 4 = 3(x - 1)$

b) Simplify the equation by removing the brackets.
$$y - 4 = 3(x - 1)$$
Expand: $y - 4 = 3x - 3$
Add 3 to both sides: $y - 4 + 3 = 3x - 3 + 3$
Simplify: $y - 1 = 3x$
Subtract $3x$ from both sides: $y - 1 - 3x = 3x - 3x$
Simplify: $-3x + y - 1 = 0$
or $3x - y + 1 = 0$

For an equation in standard form, the value of A is usually not negative.

c) In the equation $3x - y + 1 = 0$, $A = 3$, $B = -1$, and $C = 1$.

In general, an equation for a line through (x_1, y_1) with slope m can be found as follows.

Let (x, y) be any point on the line, other than (x_1, y_1).

Then $\dfrac{y - y_1}{x - x_1} = m$

so $\quad y - y_1 = m(x - x_1)$

Therefore, given a point on a line, (x_1, y_1), and the slope, m, an equation of the line may be expressed as $y - y_1 = m(x - x_1)$

This equation is written in **point-slope form**. The solution to Example 1a), $y - 4 = 3(x - 1)$, is written in point-slope form.

Example 2   Using Point-Slope Form

Write an equation in standard form for the line through A(−4, −2) with slope $\dfrac{2}{3}$.

Solution

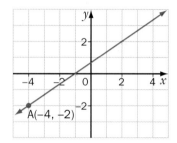

Use the point-slope form: $\qquad\qquad y - y_1 = m(x - x_1)$

$(x_1, y_1) = (-4, -2)$ and $m = \dfrac{2}{3}$

Substitute known values: $\qquad y - (-2) = \dfrac{2}{3}(x - (-4))$

$$y + 2 = \dfrac{2}{3}(x + 4)$$

Expand: $\qquad\qquad\qquad\qquad y + 2 = \dfrac{2}{3}x + \dfrac{8}{3}$

Multiply both sides by 3: $\quad 3 \times (y + 2) = 3 \times \left(\dfrac{2}{3}x + \dfrac{8}{3}\right)$

Expand: $\qquad\qquad\qquad\qquad\quad 3y + 6 = 2x + 8$
Subtract 6 from both sides: $\quad 3y + 6 - 6 = 2x + 8 - 6$
Simplify: $\qquad\qquad\qquad\qquad\quad 3y = 2x + 2$
Subtract 3y from both sides: $\quad 3y - 3y = 2x + 2 - 3y$
Simplify: $\qquad\qquad\qquad\qquad\quad 0 = 2x - 3y + 2$

An equation of the line through A(−4, −2) with slope $\dfrac{2}{3}$ is $2x - 3y + 2 = 0$.

Example 3   Finding an Equation, Given Two Points

a) Write an equation in standard form for the line that passes through the points F(–2, 3) and G(2, –5).
b) Use the equation to find two other points on the line. Check the solutions.

Solution 1   Using Paper and Pencil

a) To use the point-slope form to write the equation of a line, you need a point on the line and the slope.
Two points on the line are given. Use the two points to find the slope of the line.

$$m_{FG} = \frac{y_2 - y_1}{x_2 - x_1}$$
$$= \frac{-5 - 3}{2 - (-2)}$$
$$= \frac{-8}{4}$$
$$= -2$$

Use the point-slope form and either of the known points for (x_1, y_1).

Method 1
Using the point F(–2, 3) for (x_1, y_1),
$$y - y_1 = m(x - x_1)$$
$$y - 3 = -2(x - (-2))$$
$$y - 3 = -2(x + 2)$$
$$y - 3 = -2x - 4$$
$$2x + y + 1 = 0$$

Method 2
Using the point G(2, –5) for (x_1, y_1),
$$y - y_1 = m(x - x_1)$$
$$y - (-5) = -2(x - 2)$$
$$y + 5 = -2x + 4$$
$$2x + y + 1 = 0$$

An equation in standard form for the line through the points (–2, 3) and (2, –5) is $2x + y + 1 = 0$.

b) To find two other points on the line, it is convenient to solve the equation for *y*.
$$2x + y + 1 = 0$$
$$y = -2x - 1$$
When $x = 0$, $y = -2(0) - 1$
$$= -1$$
When $x = 1$, $y = -2(1) - 1$
$$= -2 - 1$$
$$= -3$$
Two other points on the line are (0, –1) and (1, –3).

Solution 2 Using a Graphing Calculator

a) Input the coordinates of the two given points. Use the linear regression instruction to find an equation for the line.

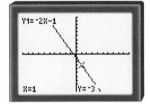

The calculator gives the equation as $y = -2x - 1$. So, an equation in standard form for the line is $2x + y + 1 = 0$.

b) Use the equation $Y_1 = -2X - 1$ in the Y= editor.

Method 1: Using a table of values
Display the table of values and choose any two points.

Method 2: Using the Value operation
Graph the equation and use the Value operation to find the values of y for any two values of x.

Two other points on the line are $(0, -1)$ and $(1, -3)$.

Check for Solution 1 and Solution 2.
Substitute the coordinates of the points into the equation $2x + y + 1 = 0$.

For $x = 0$ and $y = -1$,
L.S. $= 2x + y + 1$ **R.S.** $= 0$
$\quad = 2(0) + (-1) + 1$
$\quad = 0$

For $x = 1$ and $y = -3$,
L.S. $= 2x + y + 1$ **R.S.** $= 0$
$\quad = 2(1) + (-3) + 1$
$\quad = 0$

Example 4 Horizontal Lines

Write an equation in standard form for the horizontal line that passes through the point $(-6, 2)$.

Solution
Horizontal lines have slope 0.
Use the point-slope form.
$y - y_1 = m(x - x_1)$
$y - 2 = 0(x - (-6))$
$y - 2 = 0$

For any two points on the line, such as $(-6, 2)$ and $(-5, 2)$, the linear regression instruction of a graphing calculator finds the equation.

```
LinReg
 y=ax+b
 a=0
 b=2
```

An equation in standard form for the horizontal line that passes through $(-6, 2)$ is $y - 2 = 0$.

An equation of this type is often written as $y = 2$.

The vertical line shown passes through the points (4, –2) and (4, 5). The slope of a vertical line is not defined, so the point-slope form cannot be used to find an equation of the line. However, the coordinates of points on the line can be used to write an equation.

For the vertical line shown, an equation is $x = 4$, since the x-coordinate of every point on the line is 4. In standard form, an equation for the vertical line is $x - 4 = 0$.

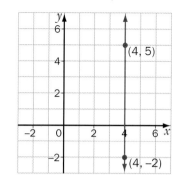

Example 5 Equation of a Line of Best Fit

Humans and dogs age differently. The table shows how dog years and human years are related for small breeds of dogs.

a) Plot human years versus dog years and draw the line of best fit.

b) Write an equation of the line of best fit in standard form.

c) Use the equation to find how many human years are equivalent to 11 dog years.

Dog Years	Human Years
1	15
2	24
3	28
4	32
5	37
6	42
7	47

Solution

a) Draw the scatter plot. Then, draw the line of best fit.

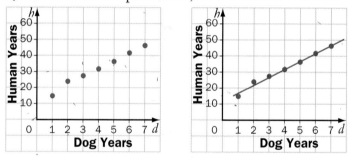

b) Choose two points that are on or close to the line of best fit. Two points are (4, 32) and (6, 42).

Use the two points to find the slope of the line.

$$m = \frac{y_2 - y_1}{x_2 - x_1}$$

$$= \frac{42 - 32}{6 - 4}$$

$$= \frac{10}{2}$$

$$= 5$$

Use the point-slope form and the point $(4, 32)$ for (x_1, y_1).

$$y - y_1 = m(x - x_1)$$
$$h - 32 = 5(d - 4)$$
$$h - 32 = 5d - 20$$
$$-5d + h - 12 = 0$$
$$5d - h + 12 = 0$$

An equation of the line of best fit is $5d - h + 12 = 0$.

c) To find how many human years are equivalent to 11 dog years, solve the equation for h.

$$5d - h + 12 = 0$$
$$-h = -5d - 12$$
$$h = 5d + 12$$

When $d = 11$,

$$h = 5(11) + 12$$
$$= 67$$

So, 67 human years are equivalent to 11 dog years.

Practice

A

Write an equation in point-slope form for the line that passes through the given point and has the given slope.

1. $(1, 2)$; $m = 5$

2. $(4, 3)$; $m = 6$

3. $(-4, 1)$; $m = 1$

4. $(5, -6)$; $m = -7$

5. $(-3, -2)$; $m = -3$

6. $(9, -1)$; $m = 0$

7. $(2, -3)$; $m = \dfrac{1}{2}$

8. $(-6, 8)$; $m = -\dfrac{3}{4}$

Write each equation in standard form.

9. $y + 6 = 2(x + 7)$

10. $y - 3 = -5(x + 1)$

11. $y - 2 = -3(x - 8)$

12. $y + 4 = 4(x + 1.5)$

13. $y + 1 = \dfrac{1}{3}(x - 2)$

14. $y - 1 = \dfrac{3}{2}(x - 1)$

Write an equation of the line that passes through the given point and has the given slope. Express the equation in standard form.

15. $(2, 3)$; $m = 4$ **16.** $(1, 4)$; $m = 3$

17. $(-5, 2)$; $m = 2$ **18.** $(3, -6)$; $m = -3$

19. $(-5, -1)$; $m = -2$ **20.** $(0, 7)$; $m = -1$

21. $(-6, 0)$; $m = 5$ **22.** $(5, 4)$; $m = 0$

23. $(1, -3)$; $m = 0$ **24.** $(2, 4)$; m is undefined

25. $(-3, 4)$; $m = \dfrac{1}{2}$ **26.** $\left(-\dfrac{1}{2}, -5\right)$; $m = -\dfrac{1}{2}$

27. $\left(\dfrac{1}{2}, 6\right)$; $m = \dfrac{4}{3}$ **28.** $(-2, 1)$; $m = -1.5$

Write an equation of the line that passes through the given point and has the given slope. Use the equation to find two other points on the line. Check your solutions.

29. $(1, 5)$; $m = 1$

30. $(-2, 2)$; $m = 3$

31. $(4, 3)$; $m = -1$

32. $(3, -1)$; $m = -4$

Write an equation of the line that passes through the given points. Express the equation in standard form.

33. A(3, 4) and B(4, 6)

34. C(–2, –4) and D(0, 6)

35. E(3, 2) and F(6, –7)

36. G(–5, –8) and H(–7, –9)

37. J(–1, –2) and K(3, 0)

38. L(3, –1) and M(9, –5)

39. N(–1, 4) and P(3, 9)

40. Q(8, –7) and R(–6, –7)

41. S(0, 4) and T(–5, 0)

42. U(5, 2) and V(5, –7)

43. W(0.3, 0.4) and X(0.5, 0.7)

44. Y(3.4, –7.2) and Z(2.2, –5.4)

45. $A\left(\frac{2}{3}, \frac{1}{4}\right)$ and $B\left(\frac{1}{3}, \frac{1}{3}\right)$

Write an equation of the line that passes through the given points. Use the equation to find two other points on the line. Check your solutions.

46. (1, 4) and (3, 10)   **47.** (3, –3) and (–6, 6)

48. (1, –4) and (–3, 12) **49.** (0, –1) and (2, –2)

Given the graph of a line, determine an equation of the line.

50.   **51.**

52.   **53.**

54.   **55.**

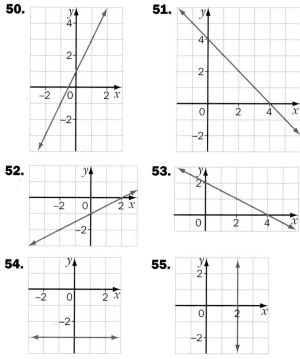

56. a) Plot the points (–2, 1), (–1, 3), (1, 3), (2, 5), (3, 7), (4, 6), and (5, 8) on a grid. Draw the line of best fit.
b) Write an equation for the line of best fit in standard form.

57. a) Plot the points (–4, 7), (–2, 5), (–2, 3), (1, 1), (1, –1), (3, –3), and (3, –5) on a grid. Draw the line of best fit.
b) Write an equation for the line of best fit in standard form.

Applications and Problem Solving

B

58. Aviation The Strato 2C aircraft was built so that scientists could study the ozone layer. The number of hours the aircraft can fly depends on its altitude. The plane can cruise for 18 h at an altitude of 24 000 m, or for 48 h at an altitude of 18 000 m.
a) Plot a graph of time, in hours, versus altitude, in thousands of metres, for this relation.
b) Using a for altitude and t for time, find an equation of the line.
c) Use the equation to find the time for which the plane can fly at 20 000 m; at 26 000 m.

59. Find an equation of the line through $(a, 0)$ and $(0, b)$.

60. What do x_1 and y_1 represent in the point-slope form of an equation?

61. Compare and contrast the graphs of $x = 5$ and $y = 5$.

62. Show that the point (7, 3) is on the line through the points (3, 4) and (–5, 6).

63. Geometry The three lines shown on the grid intersect to form triangle RST. Write the equation for each line in standard form.

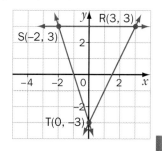

64. Geometry A rectangle has vertices K(2, 4), L(2, −6), M(−1, −6), and N(−1, 4). Write an equation in standard form for each diagonal of the rectangle.

65. The Mariana Trench The Mariana Trench in the Pacific Ocean is the deepest spot on Earth. The bottom of the trench is 11 000 m below the surface of the ocean. A winged submersible, called *Deep Flight*, allows scientists to explore the trench for the first time. Conventional submersibles rely on ballast to sink. *Deep Flight* is powered by thrusters to move it through the water. The ordered pairs (15, 1830) and (55, 6710) give the time, in minutes, that *Deep Flight* has been diving and its depth, in metres.
a) Calculate the slope of the line.
b) What rate of change does the slope represent?
c) Find an equation of the line.
d) Use the equation to determine how long it will take *Deep Flight* to reach the bottom of the Mariana Trench.

66. Space debris NASA scientists are worried about the amount of debris being put into Earth orbit, because collisions with particles as small as a paint chip can damage a space shuttle. The collisions happen at a speed of 35 000 km/h. The table gives the mass of space debris, in millions of kilograms, put into Earth orbit each year for four years.

Year	Mass Added (millions of kilograms)
1994	0.98
1995	1.02
1996	1.06
1997	1.1

a) Let 1994 = 1, 1995 = 2, and so on. Write the ordered pairs in the form (*y*, *d*), where *y* is the year and *d* is the mass of debris added in the year.
b) Calculate the slope of the line.
c) What rate of change does the slope represent?
d) Find an equation of the line.
e) Use the equation to predict the mass of debris that will be put into orbit in the year 2010.

67. Temperature in the Earth The average temperature on the Earth's surface is 15°C. For every kilometre you go down into the Earth's crust, the temperature increases by 3.5°C.
a) Graph this relation.
b) Find an equation of the line.

68. Cats Humans age differently than cats. The table shows how cat years and human years are related.

Cat Years	Human Years
1	15
2	27
3	31
4	41
7	51
10	61

a) Plot human years versus cat years and draw the line of best fit.
b) Write an equation of the line of best fit in standard form.
c) Use the equation to find how many human years are equivalent to 15 cat years.

69. a) Can the point-slope form be used to write an equation of the vertical line through the point (1, 3)? Explain.
b) Write an equation of the line in standard form.

70. Technology Try to use the linear regression instruction of a graphing calculator to find an equation of the line through the points (1, −1) and (1, 5). Describe and explain your findings.

C

71. Algebra An equation of a line is $kx − 5y + 6 = 0$. If the line passes through (2, 4), what is the value of k?

72. Algebra An equation of a line is $8x + ky − 6 = 0$. If the line passes through (1, −2), what is the value of k?

73. Algebra For the line $3x − 2y + 10 = 0$, find the coordinates of a point for which
a) the *x*-coordinate is 4 times the *y*-coordinate
b) the *y*-coordinate is 5 more than the *x*-coordinate

74. In the standard form of a linear equation, $Ax + By + C = 0$, A and B cannot both be zero. Explain why.

Graphing Calculators and the Properties of Lines

1 Slope and Direction

1. Graph the following equations so that they all appear in the same standard viewing window of your graphing calculator. Sketch and label each graph in your notebook.
a) $y = 3x + 2$
b) $y = -2x - 3$
c) $y = -0.9x + 5$
d) $y = 0.5x - 4$

2. a) Which of the lines rise, or increase, from left to right?
b) Which of the lines fall, or decrease, from left to right?

3. Which number in the equation of a line determines whether the line rises or falls from left to right?

4. State whether the graphs of the following equations rise or fall from left to right. Use a graphing calculator to check your answers.
a) $y = -4x - 2$
b) $y = 5x - 8$
c) $y = -0.8x + 7$
d) $y = 3x$

2 Steepness of Slopes

1. Graph the following equations so that they all appear in the same standard viewing window of your graphing calculator. Sketch and label each graph in your notebook.
a) $y = 2x + 3$
b) $y = 6x - 7$
c) $y = 0.5x + 1$

2. Which line in question 1 has the steepest slope?

3. List the equations of the lines in question 1 in decreasing order of the steepness of their slopes.

4. Graph the following equations so that they all appear in the same standard viewing window of your graphing calculator. Sketch and label each graph in your notebook.
a) $y = -2x + 3$
b) $y = -6x - 7$
c) $y = -0.5x + 1$

5. Which line in question 4 has the steepest slope?

6. List the equations of the lines in question 4 in decreasing order of the steepness of their slopes.

7. Use your results from questions 3 and 6 to state which number in the equation of a line determines the steepness of the slope.

8. For each pair of equations, write a statement comparing the steepness and direction of the slopes.
a) $y = 2x + 3$ and $y = -2x + 3$
b) $y = 6x - 7$ and $y = -6x - 7$
c) $y = 0.5x + 1$ and $y = -0.5x + 1$

9. Graph the following equations so that they both appear in the same standard viewing window of your graphing calculator.
a) $y = 3x + 3$
b) $y = x - 1$

10. Graph an equation of a line with each of the following slopes. Explain and justify your reasoning.
a) steeper than both lines in question 9
b) not as steep as either line in question 9
c) steeper than one line but not as steep as the other line in question 9

3 Slope and y-Intercept

The y-coordinate of the point where a line crosses the y-axis is called the **y-intercept**. The x-coordinate of this point is 0.

y-coordinate is y-intercept.

1. a) Use a graphing calculator to graph the equation $y = 2x - 1$.
b) To determine the y-intercept, that is, the value of y when $x = 0$, use the table feature to display a table of values for the equation or use the Value operation.
c) Use the table of values or the Value operation to find the coordinates of another point on the line.
d) Use the coordinates from parts b) and c) to calculate the slope of the line.
e) Where do the values of the slope and the y-intercept appear in the equation $y = 2x - 1$?

2. State the slope and the y-intercept of each of the following lines. Use a graphing calculator to check your answers.
a) $y = 2x + 1$ **b)** $y = 0.5x + 2$ **c)** $y = -x - 1$

4 A Family of Lines

Lines that share a common characteristic are said to belong to a **family of lines**. For example, all five lines in the family shown in the graph pass through the point (1, 2).

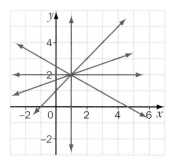

1. Graph the following equations so that they all appear in the same standard viewing window of your graphing calculator. Sketch and label each graph in your notebook.
a) $y = 0.5x + 1$ **b)** $y = 0.5x$ **c)** $y = 0.5x - 2$

2. What is the y-intercept of each line?

3. What is the slope of each line?

4. Describe this family of lines in words by noting how the lines are the same and how they are different.

5. Write the equation of another line that belongs to this family. Use your graphing calculator to check your answer. Explain how you used mathematical modelling to solve the problem.

5 A Different Family of Lines

1. Graph the following equations so that they all appear in the same standard viewing window of your graphing calculator. Sketch and label each graph in your notebook.

a) $y = 3x + 1$ **b)** $y = x + 1$ **c)** $y = -0.5x + 1$

2. What is the y-intercept of each line?

3. What is the slope of each line?

4. Describe this family of lines in words by noting how the lines are the same and how they are different.

5. Write the equation of another line that belongs to this family. Use your graphing calculator to check your answer.

6 Related Lines

1. Graph the following equations so that they appear in the same standard viewing window of your graphing calculator. Sketch and label each graph in your notebook.

a) $y = \dfrac{3}{2}x + 3$ **b)** $y = \dfrac{3}{2}x + 1$

c) $y = \dfrac{3}{2}x$ **d)** $y = \dfrac{3}{2}x - 2$

2. What is the y-intercept of each line?

3. What is the slope of each line?

4. Do the four lines belong to a family? Explain.

5. a) Use the zoom square or equivalent feature on your calculator to adjust the viewing window so that one unit on the x-axis is equal in length to one unit on the y-axis. Then, graph the equation $y = -\dfrac{2}{3}x - 1$ in this viewing window with the four graphs from question 1.
b) At what angle does the fifth line appear to intersect the other four?
c) What is the slope of the fifth line?
d) What is the product of the slope of the fifth line and the slope of each of the other four lines?

6. a) Graph the equations $y = 2x + 2$ and $y = -\dfrac{1}{2}x - 1$ in one viewing window, adjusted so that the units of length on the x- and y-axcs are equal.
b) How do the lines appear to be related?
c) What is the slope of each line?
d) What is the product of the slopes?

8.4 Linear Equations: Slope and y-Intercept Form

As the altitude of an aircraft increases, the outside air temperature decreases. An equation that shows the relationship between temperature and altitude, for a ground-level temperature of 20°C, is $150t + a = 3000$, where t is the temperature, in degrees Celsius, and a is the altitude, in metres.

Explore: Use the Graphs

The **y-intercept** of a relation is the y-coordinate of the point where the relation intersects the y-axis. In general, the coordinates of the y-intercept are $(0, b)$. The y-intercept is b. The x-coordinate has a value of zero at this point.

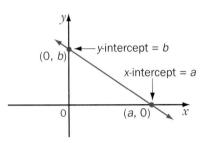

The **x-intercept** of a relation is the x-coordinate of the point where the relation intersects the x-axis. In general, the coordinates of the x-intercept are $(a, 0)$. The x-intercept is a. The y-coordinate has a value of zero at this point.

Copy and complete the following table using these steps.
- Solve each equation for y, if necessary.
- Graph each equation on a grid or a graphing calculator.
- Find the coordinates of two points on each line.
- Find the slope of each line using the coordinates of the two points.
- Find the y-intercept of each line.

	Equation	y = ▭ Form	Points	Slope	y-Intercept
a)	$y = 2x + 3$	$y = 2x + 3$			
b)	$x + y = 2$				
c)	$y - x = 0$				
d)	$3x + y + 1 = 0$				

Inquire

1. When an equation is solved for y, what is the relationship between
a) the numerical coefficient of x and the slope?
b) the constant term and the y-intercept?

2. Solve each of the following equations for y. Then, state the slope and y-intercept of each line.
a) $3y = 6x + 1$ **b)** $2x + y + 4 = 0$ **c)** $x - y = 2$ **d)** $x + 2y - 1 = 0$

3. The equation $y = mx + b$ is called the **slope and y-intercept form** of a line. Explain why.

4. a) Write the equation for the relationship between the temperature outside an aircraft and the altitude in the slope and y-intercept form, $t = \blacksquare$.
b) What is the value of t where the line crosses the t-axis? What does this value of t represent?
c) What is the slope of the line? What rate of change does the slope represent?

Example 1   Slope and y-Intercept Form

Write an equation of the line through $(0, -3)$ with slope -2.

Solution

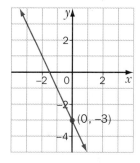

Use the point-slope form:
Substitute known values:
Simplify:
Write in slope and y-intercept form:

$$y - y_1 = m(x - x_1)$$
$$y - (-3) = -2(x - 0)$$
$$y + 3 = -2x$$
$$y = -2x - 3$$

An equation of the line through $(0, -3)$ with slope -2 is $y = -2x - 3$.

Example 2 Horizontal and Vertical Lines

Write an equation for
a) a horizontal line that passes through the point $D(0, 3)$
b) a vertical line that passes through the point $E(2, 0)$

Solution

a) A horizontal line has slope 0. Use the point-slope form.

$$y - y_1 = m(x - x_1)$$
$$y - 3 = 0(x - 0)$$
$$y - 3 = 0$$
$$y = 3$$

b) The slope of a vertical line is not defined, so the point-slope form cannot be used to find an equation. However, for the vertical line that passes through $E(2, 0)$, the x-coordinate of every point on the line is 2.
So, an equation for the line is $x = 2$.

In general, an equation for a horizontal line that passes through $(0, b)$ is $y = b$.
In general, an equation for a vertical line that passes through $(a, 0)$ is $x = a$.

In general, an equation for a line through $(0, b)$ with slope m can be found as follows.

$$y - y_1 = m(x - x_1)$$
$$y - b = m(x - 0)$$
$$y - b = mx$$
$$y = mx + b$$

The graph of the equation of a line expressed in the form $y = mx + b$, where x and y are real numbers, has a slope m and a y-intercept b.

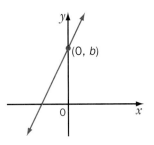

Example 3   Using the Slope and y-Intercept Form

A line has a slope of 3 and a y-intercept of 4. Write an equation of the line in standard form.

Solution

Use the slope and y-intercept form: $y = mx + b$
Substitute known values: $y = 3x + 4$
Write in standard form: $-3x + y - 4 = 0$
                                  or $3x - y + 4 = 0$

An equation of the line with slope 3 and y-intercept 4 is $3x - y + 4 = 0$.

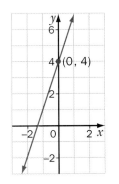

Example 4   Finding the Slope and y-Intercept

Find the slope and y-intercept of the line through the points $A(1, -2)$ and $B(4, 7)$.

Solution 1   Using Paper and Pencil

To write an equation in the form $y = mx + b$, first find the slope using the given points.

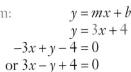

$$m_{AB} = \frac{y_2 - y_1}{x_2 - x_1}$$
$$= \frac{7 - (-2)}{4 - 1}$$
$$= \frac{9}{3}$$
$$= 3$$

Use the point-slope form and either given point for (x_1, y_1).

$$y - y_1 = m(x - x_1)$$
$$y - 7 = 3(x - 4)$$
$$y - 7 = 3x - 12$$
$$y = 3x - 5$$

For $y = mx + b$, m is the slope and b is the y-intercept. So, for $y = 3x - 5$, the slope is 3 and the y-intercept is -5.

The line through the points $A(1, -2)$ and $B(4, 7)$ has slope 3 and y-intercept -5.

Solution 2　Using a Graphing Calculator

Input the coordinates of the two given points.　Use the linear regression instruction.

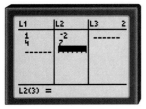

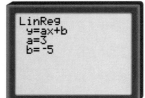

The graphing calculator uses $y = ax + b$, instead of $y = mx + b$.

The line through the points A(1, –2) and B(4, 7) has slope 3 and y-intercept –5.

To compare the slope and y-intercept form of a linear equation with the standard form, solve $Ax + By + C = 0$ for y.

$$Ax + By + C = 0$$

Subtract Ax and C from both sides:　$Ax + By + C - Ax - C = 0 - Ax - C$

Simplify:　$By = -Ax - C$

Divide both sides by B:　$y = -\dfrac{A}{B}x - \dfrac{C}{B}$

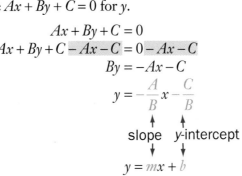

So, the slope and y-intercept of an equation written in standard form can be found using the following formulas.

$$m = -\frac{A}{B} \text{ and } b = -\frac{C}{B}$$

Example 5　Finding the Slope and y-Intercept

Find the slope and y-intercept of $3x + 4y - 8 = 0$.

Solution 1　Solving for y

Write the equation in the form $y = mx + b$.

$$3x + 4y - 8 = 0$$
$$4y = -3x + 8$$
$$\frac{4y}{4} = \frac{-3x}{4} + \frac{8}{4}$$
$$y = -\frac{3}{4}x + 2$$

So, the slope is $-\dfrac{3}{4}$ and the y-intercept is 2.

Solution 2　Using the Formulas

The equation $3x + 4y - 8 = 0$ is in the standard form $Ax + By + C = 0$.
$A = 3$, $B = 4$, and $C = -8$.

The slope, $m = -\dfrac{A}{B}$

$$= -\frac{3}{4}$$

The y-intercept, $b = -\dfrac{C}{B}$

$$= -\frac{(-8)}{4}$$
$$= 2$$

So, the slope is $-\dfrac{3}{4}$ and the y-intercept is 2.

Practice

A

Find the slope and y-intercept of each line.

1. $y = 3x + 1$

2. $y = \frac{1}{2}x - 2$

3. $y = -4x + 3$

4. $x + y = 5$

5. $x + y - 7 = 0$

6. $y + 4 = 5x$

7. $y - 2x = 0$

8. $y = 3$

Find the slope and y-intercept of each line.

9. $4x + 2y = 3$

10. $x - y = 4$

11. $3x + 2y + 6 = 0$

12. $2y + 6 = 0$

13. $x - 3y - 9 = 0$

14. $5x + 2y = 10$

15. $22x + 0.5y - 1 = 0$

16. $0 = x - 2y - 4$

17. $6.4x = 0.8y$

18. $1.2x - 0.3y = 0.12$

Find the slope and y-intercept of the line through the given points.

19. $(1, 3)$ and $(3, 5)$

20. $(2, 3)$ and $(-1, 6)$

21. $(-7, -2)$ and $(-1, -8)$

22. $(-1, -2)$ and $(-5, -10)$

23. $(2, 1)$ and $(6, 4)$

24. $(-1, 2)$ and $(3, 4)$

25. $(6, 9)$ and $(-2, -5)$

26. $(4, -5)$ and $(-2, 3)$

Given the slope and y-intercept, write an equation of the line in the slope and y-intercept form. Then, write the equation in standard form.

27. $m = 2; b = 3$

28. $m = 3; b = -2$

29. $m = -4; b = 6$

30. $m = -5; b = -7$

31. $m = \frac{1}{2}; b = 1$

32. $m = \frac{2}{3}; b = -2$

33. $m = -0.5; b = 0$

34. $m = -\frac{2}{5}; b = -\frac{1}{3}$

Write an equation for each of the following lines.

35. horizontal line through A(0, 4)

36. vertical line through B(3, 0)

37. vertical line through C(-1, 2)

38. horizontal line through D(1, -3)

Graph each line.

39. $y = 2x + 5$

40. $y = 3x - 1$

41. $y = -x + 4$

42. $y = \frac{2}{3}x - 2$

43. $y = -\frac{3}{4}x + 3$

44. $y = -0.5x$

Draw the graph of each line.

45. $y = 2$ **46.** $x = 1$ **47.** $x = -2$ **48.** $y = -2$

Find the slope and y-intercept of each line. Then, write an equation of the line.

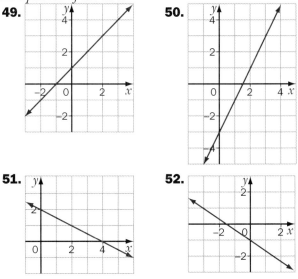

49.

50.

51.

52.

Applications and Problem Solving

B

53. Algebra An equation of a line is $y = 2x + b$. Find the value of b if the line passes through the point

a) $(4, 2)$ **b)** $(-3, 5)$ **c)** $(2, -6)$ **d)** $(-1, -3)$

54. Algebra An equation of a line is $y = mx + 3$. Find the value of m if the line passes through the point

a) $(2, 1)$ **b)** $(-4, 5)$ **c)** $(4, -5)$ **d)** $(-1, -6)$

55. Explain why these lines belong to a family.

$$y = \frac{3}{2}x - 1 \qquad 2x + y + 1 = 0$$
$$5x - 2y - 2 = 0 \qquad y + 1 = 0$$

56. Box of crackers The equation $m = 6n + 55$ relates the mass, m grams, of a box of crackers to the number of crackers, n, in the box.

a) Graph the line.

b) What is the mass of the empty box?

c) What is the mass of each cracker?

d) If the total mass of a box full of crackers is 355 g, how many crackers does the box hold?

e) Describe a different situation that could be modelled by the same equation, $m = 6n + 55$.

57. School trip A group of students is travelling by bus to visit a planetarium. The equation $13n - 2c + 500 = 0$ relates the total cost of the trip, c dollars, to the number of students, n. The total cost includes the bus rental charge and admission to the planetarium.
a) Graph the total cost versus the number of students.
b) What is the cost of renting the bus?
c) What is the admission cost per student to the planetarium?

58. Driving distances Virden, Manitoba, is 80 km west of Brandon along the Trans-Canada Highway. Marika drove west from Virden to Swift Current, Saskatchewan. Her average speed was 75 km/h.
a) Plot a graph of her distance, d kilometres, from Virden versus her driving time, t hours. Write an equation of the line in the form $d = \blacksquare$.
b) Repeat part a), but use the distance from Brandon instead of the distance from Virden.
c) If Marika drove for a total of 7 h, what is the driving distance to Swift Current from Virden? from Brandon?

59. Treasure hunting Finding treasure on sunken ships can be a very profitable business. One important consideration for treasure-hunting divers is the pressure they experience. The pressure depends on the depth. At a depth of 4 m, the pressure is 140 kPa (kilopascals). At a depth of 9 m, the pressure is 190 kPa.
a) Plot the points on a grid in the form (d, p), where d is the depth, in metres, and p is the pressure, in kilopascals. Join the points with a line.
b) Find the equation of the line and write it in the form $p = md + b$.
c) What rate of change does the slope represent?
d) What is the value of the p-intercept, and what does it represent?
e) At what depth is the pressure double the pressure on the surface?

f) The pirate Blackbeard's ship sank off the coast of North Carolina around 1718. It was discovered in 1997, at a depth of 6 m. What was the pressure on the divers at this depth?

C

60. Describe each of the following lines in terms of its slope, intercepts, domain, and range.
a) $y = 7$ **b)** $x = -2$ **c)** $y = 0$
d) $x = 5$ **e)** $x = 0$ **f)** $y = -4$

61. Algebra Describe each of the following lines in terms of its slope, intercepts, and range. The domain is R.
a) $x = a$ **b)** $y = b$
c) $y = x$ **d)** $y = mx + b$

62. Algebra The equation of a line is $x + py - q = 0$. The slope is $-\dfrac{1}{2}$, and the y-intercept is 3. What are the values of p and q?

63. Is it possible to write the equation of the line $x = -2$ in the slope and y-intercept form? Explain.

64. Do lines with equations of the form $y = mx$ all belong to a family? Explain.

65. Measurement The sum, s degrees, of the interior angles of an n-sided polygon is given by the equation $s = 180(n - 2)$.
a) Write the equation in the slope and y-intercept form.
b) What is the value of the s-intercept?
c) Does the s-intercept have any meaning for a real polygon? Explain.
d) What is the smallest value n can have?

NUMBER POWER

Find four consecutive whole numbers so that the sum of the cubes of the three smallest numbers equals the cube of the largest number.

8.5 Methods for Graphing Linear Equations

Imagine that the Great Lakes were drained of water. Then, imagine pouring all the world's oil reserves, known and estimated, into the lakebeds. The world's oil reserves would fill less than 5% of Lake Superior. The other lakes would be empty.

Explore: Draw a Graph

Oil geologists use an equation of a line to estimate the world's remaining oil reserves, starting at the year 2000. The equation is $20n + b = 1300$, where n represents the number of years after the year 2000, starting with the year 2000 equal to 0, and b represents the world's oil reserves, in billions of barrels.

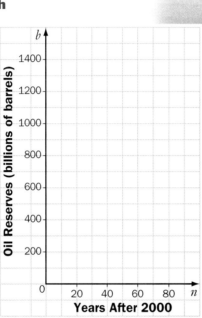

a) If $n = 0$, what is the value of b?

b) If $b = 0$, what is the value of n?

c) Use the solutions to a) and b) to write two ordered pairs in the form (n, b).

d) Draw axes like the ones shown and plot the ordered pairs. Join the ordered pairs with a straight line.

Inquire

1. What does the b-intercept represent?

2. What does the n-intercept represent?

3. Use the graph to find the reserves in the year 2030; 2045.

4. Find the slope of the line.

5. What rate of change does the slope represent?

6. What world conditions might change the slope?

It is often convenient to use the x- and y-intercepts to draw the graph of a line.

Example 1   Graphing Using the Intercepts

a) Use the intercepts to graph $3x - 4y = 12$. The domain is R.

b) Find the slope.

Solution

a) To find the x-intercept, let $y = 0$.

$$3x - 4y = 12$$
$$3x - 4(0) = 12$$
$$3x = 12$$
$$x = 4$$

One point on the line is $(4, 0)$.

To find the y-intercept, let $x = 0$.

$$3x - 4y = 12$$
$$3(0) - 4y = 12$$
$$-4y = 12$$
$$y = -3$$

Another point on the line is $(0, -3)$.
Plot the points on a grid.
Because the domain is R, draw a line through the points.

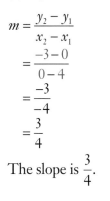

b) Use the points $(4, 0)$ and $(0, -3)$ to find the slope.

$$m = \frac{y_2 - y_1}{x_2 - x_1}$$
$$= \frac{-3 - 0}{0 - 4}$$
$$= \frac{-3}{-4}$$
$$= \frac{3}{4}$$

The slope is $\frac{3}{4}$.

Example 2   Graphing Using Different Methods

Graph the equation $y = \frac{1}{2}x + 1$, where x is a real number.

Solution 1
Use a table of values.

$$y = \frac{1}{2}x + 1$$

x	$\frac{1}{2}x + 1$	y
0	$\frac{1}{2}(0) + 1$	1
2	$\frac{1}{2}(2) + 1$	2
4	$\frac{1}{2}(4) + 1$	3

Plot $(0, 1)$, $(2, 2)$, and $(4, 3)$.
Draw the graph.

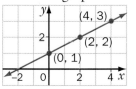

Solution 2
Use the intercepts.

$$y = \frac{1}{2}x + 1$$

When $x = 0$, $y = 1$.
When $y = 0$, $x = -2$.
Plot $(0, 1)$ and $(-2, 0)$.
Draw the graph.

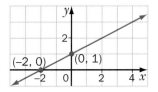

Solution 3
Use the slope and the y-intercept.

$$y = \frac{1}{2}x + 1$$

The y-intercept is 1. The slope is $\frac{1}{2}$.

Plot the point $(0, 1)$. Use the slope to locate another point on the line. Draw the graph.

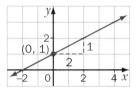

Solution 4
Use a graphing calculator.

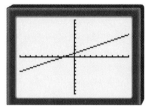

Practice

A

Use the x- and y-intercepts to graph each line.

1. $3x + 2y = 6$ **2.** $4x + 3y = 12$

3. $x + 2y = 8$ **4.** $2x + y - 4 = 0$

5. $2x - 5y = 10$ **6.** $5x - 4y + 20 = 0$

7. $x - y - 3 = 0$ **8.** $x - 3y + 6 = 0$

Graph each equation using the slope and y-intercept.

9. $y = 3x - 2$ **10.** $y = 0.5x + 4$

11. $y = -4x - 1$ **12.** $y + 3 = \frac{1}{3}x$

13. $2x + y = 0$ **14.** $x + 2y - 6 = 0$

Graph using a method of your choice. Find the intercepts and slope for each line. The domain is R.

15. $y = 3x - 9$ **16.** $5x + y + 5 = 0$

17. $y = 2(x - 3)$ **18.** $y + 4 = \frac{1}{2}x$

19. $y = -\frac{1}{3}x + 2$ **20.** $y + 2 = -(x + 1)$

21. $\frac{x}{3} + \frac{y}{2} = 2$ **22.** $3x - 4y = -24$

Find an equation for each of the following lines.

23.

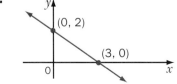

24.

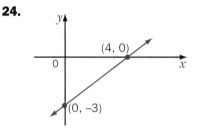

25.

26.

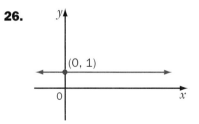

27.

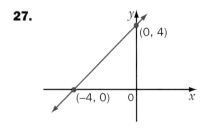

28.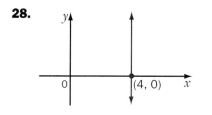

Applications and Problem Solving

29. Write an equation of a line whose graph does not have an x-intercept.

30. Write an equation of a line whose graph does not have a y-intercept.

31. Write an equation of a line whose x- and y-intercepts are the same, but not 0.

32. Write an equation of a line whose x- and y-intercepts are both 0.

B

33. If the x- and y-intercepts of a line are equal and not zero, what is the slope of the line? Explain.

34. Air travel A plane is flying from Montréal to Rome. An equation that relates the distance from Rome, d kilometres, to the flying time, t hours, is $d = 6600 - 825t$.
a) What is the d-intercept and what does it represent?
b) What is the t-intercept and what does it represent?
c) What is the slope and what does it represent?
d) What is the distance from Rome when the plane has been flying for 5.2 h?
e) For how many hours has the plane been flying when it is 3465 km from Rome?

35. Telephone lines The number of telephone lines in service in Canada was about 13 million in 1976, 15.5 million in 1986, and 18 million in 1996. Let t represent the year, with 1976 as year 0, and n represent the number of telephone lines, in millions.
a) Express the data as ordered pairs in the form (t, n).

b) Graph the points and join them with a straight line.
c) Find the slope of the line. What does this slope represent?
d) Find an equation for the line.
e) Predict the number of telephone lines that will be in service in Canada in the year 2020.
f) Do you think that your prediction is valid? Explain.

36. Algebra Find the general equation of the line with x-intercept a and y-intercept b.

C

37. Reaction time The stopping distance of a car has two components — the distance the car travels during the time you take to move your foot from the gas pedal to the brake pedal, and the distance the car travels after the brakes are applied. At a speed of 40 km/h, a car travels 8 m during the time your foot moves from the gas pedal to the brake. At 70 km/h, the car travels 14 m before your foot hits the brake.
a) Graph the points in the form (speed, distance). Join them with a straight line.
b) Find the slope of the line. What does the slope represent?
c) Find an equation for the line.
d) Find the distance a car travels while your foot is moving between the gas pedal and the brake, if the car has a speed of 50 km/h; 100 km/h.
e) What are the x- and y-intercepts? What meaning do they have? What do they suggest about the domain and range of the relation? Explain.

38. The standard form of an equation is $Ax + By + C = 0$. Describe the graph of the line when
a) $A = 0, B \neq 0, C \neq 0$
b) $B = 0, A \neq 0, C \neq 0$
c) $C = 0, A \neq 0, B \neq 0$
d) $A = 0, C = 0, B \neq 0$
e) $B = 0, C = 0, A \neq 0$

8.6 Parallel and Perpendicular Lines

A laser produces a narrow beam of very bright light. One application of a laser is to create holograms, which are three-dimensional images. Part of the process of forming a hologram involves splitting a laser beam into two perpendicular beams. Some aircraft use a hologram for projecting data onto a see-through screen above the instrument console.

◆ Explore: Use the Graphs

Part 1: Parallel Lines

a) Place a ruler on a grid so that each edge passes through at least two points whose coordinates are integers.

b) Draw a line along each edge of the ruler. Label the parallel lines AB and CD, so that the points A, B, C, and D have integer coordinates.

c) Use the labelled points to calculate the slope of each line. Compare the slopes.

d) Repeat the steps for a different pair of parallel lines.

e) Compare your results with a classmate's.

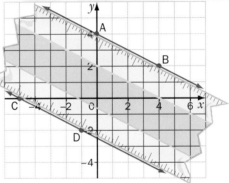

Part 2: Perpendicular Lines

a) Place the right-angled corner of a piece of paper, a plastic triangle, or a set square on a grid at a point with integer coordinates. Label the point P.

b) Rotate the paper or triangle about P until each arm of the right angle passes through at least one point with integer coordinates. The arms should not be horizontal or vertical. Label the two points A and B. Draw the perpendicular rays PA and PB.

c) Calculate the slope of each ray. Compare the slopes.

d) Repeat the steps for a different pair of perpendicular rays.

e) Compare your results with a classmate's.

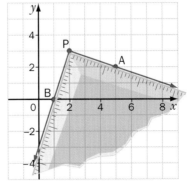

Inquire

1. How are the slopes of parallel lines related?

2. How are the slopes of perpendicular lines related?

3. What is the product of the slopes of two perpendicular lines?

4. Find the slope of each of the following lines.
a) $2x - y = 2$ **b)** $x + y = -2$ **c)** $x - y = 1$ **d)** $y - 2x = -3$

5. Which lines in question 4 are parallel? Explain.

6. Which lines in question 4 are perpendicular? Explain.

7. Suppose that a laser beam has been split into two beams to create a hologram.
a) If a grid were superimposed on the two beams, how would their slopes be related? Explain.
b) Could the beams point in directions in the coordinate plane that would make the answer to part a) untrue? Explain.

Parallel Lines
• Two non-vertical lines are parallel if they have the same slope.
• All vertical lines, which have undefined slopes, are parallel.

$m_1 = m_2$

Perpendicular Lines
• Two lines that are not vertical or horizontal are perpendicular if the product of their slopes is –1. If the product is –1, we say that the slopes are negative reciprocals.
• A vertical line is perpendicular to a horizontal line.

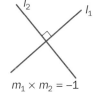

$m_1 \times m_2 = -1$

Example 1   Parallel Lines
Write an equation of the line parallel to $3x + y - 4 = 0$ and through the point A(2, –5).

Solution
An equation of the line can be found from the slope of the line and a point on the line. The slope of the new line will equal the slope of $3x + y - 4 = 0$, because the lines are parallel. To find the slope of $3x + y - 4 = 0$, write the equation in the form $y = mx + b$.

$$3x + y - 4 = 0$$
Solve for y: $\qquad y = -3x + 4$

The slope of $3x + y - 4 = 0$ is –3.

The slope of a line parallel to $3x + y - 4 = 0$ is also –3.

A point on the line is A(2, –5).

Use the point-slope form to find the equation.
$$y - y_1 = m(x - x_1)$$

Substitute known values: $y - (-5) = -3(x - 2)$
$$y + 5 = -3(x - 2)$$

Expand: $y + 5 = -3x + 6$

Write in standard form: $3x + y - 1 = 0$

An equation of the line is $3x + y - 1 = 0$.

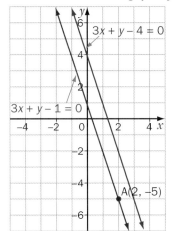

We can visualize the solution graphically.

Example 2   Perpendicular Lines

Determine an equation of the line perpendicular to the line $4x + 2y - 7 = 0$ and having the same x-intercept as the line $2x + 3y - 12 = 0$.

Solution

Find the slope of the line $4x + 2y - 7 = 0$.
The equation is in the standard form $Ax + By + C = 0$.
$A = 4$, $B = 2$, and $C = -7$.

The slope is $-\dfrac{A}{B}$, which is $-\dfrac{4}{2}$ or -2.

The slope, m, of the line perpendicular to $4x + 2y - 7 = 0$ is given by
$$m \times (-2) = -1$$
$$m = \frac{1}{2}$$ The negative reciprocal of -2 is $\frac{1}{2}$.

Find the x-intercept of $2x + 3y - 12 = 0$.
To find the x-intercept, let $y = 0$.
$$2x + 3y - 12 = 0$$
$$2x + 3(0) - 12 = 0$$
$$2x - 12 = 0$$
$$2x = 12$$
$$x = 6$$

The required line and the line $2x + 3y - 12 = 0$ have the same x-intercept, 6. So, a point on the required line is $(6, 0)$.

Use the point-slope form to find the equation.
$$y - y_1 = m(x - x_1)$$
$$y - 0 = \frac{1}{2}(x - 6)$$
$$y = \frac{1}{2}x - 3$$
$$2y = x - 6$$
$$0 = x - 2y - 6$$

An equation of the line is $x - 2y - 6 = 0$.

We can visualize the solution graphically.

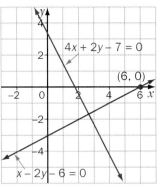

Practice

Given the slopes of two lines, determine whether the lines are parallel, perpendicular, or neither.

1. $m_1 = \dfrac{2}{3}, m_2 = \dfrac{3}{2}$

2. $m_1 = \dfrac{1}{2}, m_2 = \dfrac{4}{8}$

3. $m_1 = -3, m_2 = \dfrac{1}{3}$

4. $m_1 = \dfrac{2}{5}, m_2 = -\dfrac{2}{5}$

5. $m_1 = 1, m_2 = -1$

6. $m_1 = 2, m_2 = -2$

7. $m_1 = \dfrac{20}{25}, m_2 = \dfrac{4}{5}$

8. $m_1 = \dfrac{1}{4}, m_2 = -\dfrac{3}{12}$

9. $m_1 = -0.5, m_2 = 2$
10. $m_1 = -0.1, m_2 = 1$

Find the slope of a line perpendicular to a line with the given slope.

11. 3 **12.** $\dfrac{3}{4}$ **13.** $-\dfrac{1}{8}$

14. $-\dfrac{5}{2}$ **15.** -6 **16.** undefined

State the slope of a line
a) *parallel to each line*
b) *perpendicular to each line*

17. $y = 2x - 4$ **18.** $y = -x - 2$

19. $y = \dfrac{1}{3}x + 5$ **20.** $y = -\dfrac{2}{7}x$

21. $y + 4x = 4$ **22.** $3x + y = -2$
23. $2x - y = 8$ **24.** $5x + 3 = 2y$
25. $2x + 3y - 1 = 0$ **26.** $3x - 5y + 2 = 0$

Identify whether each pair of lines is parallel, perpendicular, or neither.
27. $x - y + 1 = 0$ and $4x + 4y + 1 = 0$
28. $3x - 2y + 12 = 0$ and $-2x - 3y - 12 = 0$
29. $2x + 5y - 13 = 0$ and $2x - 5y + 23 = 0$
30. $x + 9y + 1 = 0$ and $9x + y + 1 = 0$

31. Given the coordinates of the following 8 points, determine whether each pair of lines is parallel, perpendicular, or neither.
A(3, 2), B(6, 4), C(–8, –2), D(–2, 2), E(8, 1), F(2, 0), G(11, 3), H(6, –3)
a) AB and CD   **b)** DF and CH
c) CD and BE   **d)** AH and GH
e) DF and AF   **f)** BG and AE
g) FC and DG   **h)** BE and AB

Determine an equation for each of the following lines.
32. the line parallel to $2x - 3y + 1 = 0$ and passing through the point (1, 2)
33. the line perpendicular to $x - 5y + 2 = 0$ and passing through the point (–2, 5)
34. the line parallel to $x + 3 = 0$ and passing through (–6, –7)
35. the line perpendicular to $y - 4 = 0$ and passing through (–1, 6)
36. the line parallel to $x + 9y - 2 = 0$ and having the same x-intercept as the line $2x - 9y + 27 = 0$
37. the line perpendicular to $3x - 12y + 16 = 0$ and having the same y-intercept as $14x - 13y - 52 = 0$

38. Two perpendicular lines have the same x-intercept. An equation of one line is $y = 3x + 1$. Find an equation of the other line.

39. Plot the points R(5, 3), S(–1, 0), and T(3, –1) on a grid. Determine an equation of
a) the line through R and parallel to ST
b) the line through S and perpendicular to RT

Applications and Problem Solving

The following are slopes of parallel lines. Find the value of the variable.

40. $2, -\dfrac{6}{m}$ **41.** $-3, \dfrac{w}{4}$

42. $-\dfrac{2}{3}, -\dfrac{n}{9}$ **43.** $\dfrac{z}{3}, \dfrac{1}{2}$

44. $-\dfrac{x}{3}, -\dfrac{2}{5}$ **45.** $\dfrac{2}{k}, -\dfrac{4}{5}$

The following are slopes of perpendicular lines. Find the value of the variable.

46. $3, \dfrac{m}{6}$

47. $2, \dfrac{2}{q}$

48. $-\dfrac{1}{2}, \dfrac{4}{w}$

49. $\dfrac{2}{3}, \dfrac{x}{4}$

50. $\dfrac{z}{9}, -\dfrac{3}{5}$

51. $\dfrac{4}{t}, \dfrac{9}{2}$

52. Explain why these lines belong to a family.

$y = -\dfrac{1}{2}x + 3$ $x + 2y + 1 = 0$

$3x + 6y - 7 = 0$ $y - 2 = -\dfrac{1}{2}(x - 3)$

Plot and join the points in order on a grid. Classify each figure as a square, rectangle, parallelogram, or trapezoid. Give reasons for each answer.

53. P(–2, 5), Q(–4, 3), R(4, –5), and S(5, –2)
54. E(–1, 0), F(3, 1), G(2, 5), and H(–2, 4)
55. A(1, 3), B(–2, –3), C(2, –5), and D(5, 1)
56. U(–1, 2), V(–4, –1), W(–1, –4), and Z(2, –1)
57. J(3, –1), K(2, 2), L(–4, 4), and M(–3, 1)

58. Write an equation of the line that is perpendicular to the y-axis and has a y-intercept of –2.

59. Comparing journeys Hugo drove 255 km from Stratford to Windsor at 85 km/h. He left Stratford at 09:00. Kayla drove along the same route at the same speed, but she left Stratford at 11:00.
a) Graph the distance driven versus the time of day for both journeys on the same set of axes.
b) How are the lines related? Why are they related in this way?

60. Appliance repairs Kate and Marius repair appliances. Kate charges a fee of $50 for a service call, whereas Marius charges $40. In addition, they each charge $35.00/h for completing the repairs.
a) On the same set of axes, graph the total cost of a service call versus the time taken to complete the repairs for Kate and for Marius.

b) For jobs that take the same length of time, which person always charges more — Kate or Marius? Explain and justify your reasoning.

C

61. Algebra Find the value of k if the lines $3x - 2y - 5 = 0$ and $kx - 6y + 1 = 0$ are
a) parallel   **b)** perpendicular

62. Algebra a) Find the values of k for which the lines $kx - 2y - 1 = 0$ and $8x - ky + 3 = 0$ are parallel.
b) Are there any values of k that would make the two lines perpendicular? Explain.

63. Given the equations $2y = 3x + 4$ and $8y = 12x + 16$,
a) what are the slopes?
b) are the lines parallel? Explain.

64. State whether the slopes of the two lines on each grid are negative reciprocals. Explain.

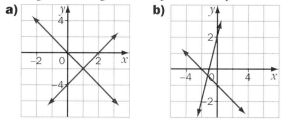

a)   **b)**

65. Write the equations of lines that form the sides of a square, so that no sides are vertical or horizontal. Have a classmate check your equations by graphing the square.

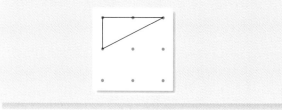

LOGIC POWER

The diagram shows one triangle on a 9-point grid. How many other sizes of triangles can you draw on a 9-point grid?

8.7 Intersecting Lines

Manitoba is a province of weather extremes. The intersection of Portage Avenue and Main Street in Winnipeg is one of the coldest intersections in Canada.

The intersection of Portage and Main is an example of two intersecting streets. In mathematics, we often use intersecting lines.

Explore: Draw the Graphs

Two video production companies charge different rates for videotaping special events, such as graduations and weddings. For such events, the New Ideas Company charges $200.00, plus $20/h. The Creative Video Company charges $60/h.
Copy and complete the table of values to show how the cost of using each company is related to the time the job takes. Graph both lines on the same set of axes.

New Ideas Company							
Time (h)	1	2	3	4	5	6	7
Cost ($)							

Creative Video Company							
Time (h)	1	2	3	4	5	6	7
Cost ($)							

Inquire

1. Which company is cheaper for a job that takes 3 h? 7 h?
 2. What does the point where the two graphs cross mean?
3. **a)** How many hours of videotaping give the same cost for each company?
b) What is the cost?

The point where lines meet is called the **point of intersection**. This point is common to the lines.

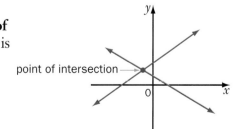

Example   Finding the Point of Intersection

Graph the lines $y = 2x - 2$ and $y = x + 1$ on the same set of axes and find the coordinates of the point of intersection.

Solution 1   Graphing Manually

Use the intercepts.

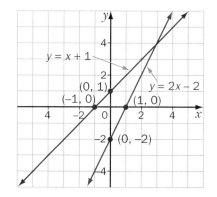

$y = 2x - 2$
When $x = 0$, $y = -2$.
When $y = 0$, $x = 1$.
Plot the points $(0, -2)$ and $(1, 0)$. Draw a line through the points.

$y = x + 1$
When $x = 0$, $y = 1$.
When $y = 0$, $x = -1$.
Plot the points $(0, 1)$ and $(-1, 0)$. Draw a line through the points.

The coordinates of the point of intersection are $(3, 4)$.

Solution 2   Using a Graphing Calculator

Graph both equations in the same standard viewing window.

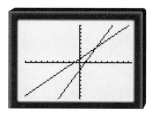

Use the Intersect operation to find the coordinates of the point of intersection.

If your calculator does not have the Intersect operation, use the TRACE instruction to find approximate values of the coordinates. Zoom in and trace again to find more accurate values.

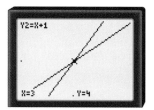

The coordinates of the point of intersection are $(3, 4)$.

Practice

A

Find the coordinates of the point of intersection for each pair of lines.

1. **2.**

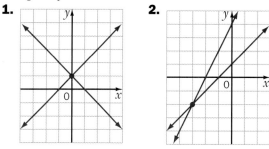

What is the point of intersection for each of the following pairs of lines?

3.

x	y
–2	–2
–1	–1
0	0
1	1
2	2

x	y
–2	2
–1	1
0	0
1	–1
2	–2

4.

x	y
2	1
1	0
0	–1
–1	–2
–2	–3

x	y
2	4
1	2
0	0
–1	–2
–2	–4

5. Write an equation for the line represented by each table of values in questions 3 and 4.

Find the coordinates of the point of intersection of each pair of lines.

6. $y = 2x$ and $y = x + 3$
7. $y = x - 1$ and $y = 3 - x$
8. $y = x + 3$ and $y = 3 - 2x$
9. $y = x + 4$ and $y = 3x$
10. $y = x + 8$ and $y = -3x$
11. $y = x + 2$ and $y = 2x - 3$
12. $y = 2x - 2$ and $y = -2x$
13. $x = 3$ and $y = 2$
14. $x = -4$ and $y = 5$
15. $x + y = 4$ and $x - y = 2$
16. $x + 2y - 1 = 0$ and $2x + y + 1 = 0$

Applications and Problem Solving

17. a) Graph the lines $y = 2x - 4$ and $y = x - 4$ on the same set of axes.
b) What figure is formed by these lines and the *x*-axis?

B

18. Truck rentals Two companies rent trucks. Company A charges $80.00 for the truck, plus $0.20/km. Company B charges $0.60/km.
a) Write an equation for each company's rental cost in terms of the distance driven.
b) Graph both equations on the same set of axes. If you graph manually, use the following numbers of kilometres in your tables of values: 50, 100, 150, 200, 250, 300.
c) Find the coordinates of the point of intersection.
d) Explain the meaning of the point of intersection.
e) Which company is cheaper if you drive 150 km? 250 km?

19. Highway driving At 12:30, Kenji left town driving at 80 km/h. At 13:00, Yvette left town along the same highway driving at 100 km/h.
a) Construct a table of distance and time values for each driver.
b) Plot both graphs on the same grid.
c) At what time did Yvette catch up with Kenji?
d) How far had they travelled?

20. a) Graph all 3 lines on the same grid or in the same viewing window of a graphing calculator.

$$y = -2x \qquad y = 2x - 4 \qquad y = -x - 1$$

b) These 3 lines are called **concurrent**. Explain what concurrent means.

C

21. Can you find the coordinates of the point of intersection of $y = -3x + 5$ and $6x + 2y - 3 = 0$? Explain.

22. Write a problem that creates 4 concurrent lines. Have a classmate solve your problem.

8.8 How Can We Model Slopes on the Earth?

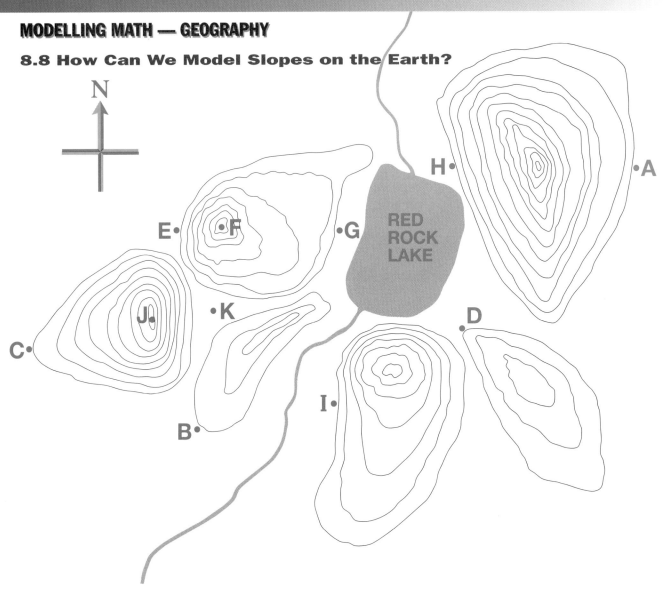

The map is called a topographical map. Like other maps, topographical maps show a top view of an area.

Topographical maps include contour lines, which are rings that represent changes in elevation. The change in elevation from one contour line to the next is given by the *contour interval* printed on the map. The contour interval on the above map is 10 m, so there is a change in elevation of 10 m from one contour line to the next.

Contour lines do not show whether a change in elevation is a rise or a drop. An easy way to decide is to look for lakes and streams. On the map, you can assume that the lake and the streams are at the lowest points. Therefore, in a group of contour lines, the innermost one shows the highest elevation relative to the surrounding area.

The scale for the map is 1:10 000. In other words, one unit of distance on the map represents 10 000 units on the Earth. Topographical maps are drawn with true north at the top of the map.

1 Modelling Distances

1. How many centimetres on the Earth does 1 cm on the map represent?

2. How many metres on the Earth does 1 cm on the map represent?

3. What is the maximum straight-line distance across the lake, in metres?

4. How many metres above the lake is the top of the hill to the northeast of the lake?

5. What are the heights of the three hills to the west of the lake and the streams?

6. The easiest hiking trail between two points follows the shortest route over level ground.
a) Describe the easiest hiking trail from A to K. About how long is the trail?
b) Describe the easiest hiking trail from C to D. About how long is the trail?

7. a) What is the shortest horizontal distance from E to G if you go over the hill?
b) What is the distance from E to G if you go around the south side of the hill?
c) A rule of thumb for hiking is that the time taken to climb 10 m equals the time taken to hike 100 m on flat ground. The time taken to hike a certain distance downhill equals the time taken to hike the same distance on flat ground. What is the fastest way to get from E to G? How long would it take at 80 m/min?
d) What is the fastest way to get from A to H? How long would it take at 70 m/min?

2 Modelling Slopes

1. Find the average slope for the climb from
a) E to F   **b)** G to F   **c)** C to J

2. If you walk the shortest distance from H to A, which is steeper — the climb or the descent?

3. Can you tell which way the stream to the south of Red Rock Lake is flowing? Explain.

4. If you hike from C to D along a trail that crosses no contour lines, do all parts of the trail have a slope of 0? Explain.

5. Suppose that one side of a hill is a vertical drop, but the other sides are sloping.
a) What is the slope of the vertical drop?
b) Sketch how the hill might be represented on a topographical map.

3 Extending the Model

1. Sketch a graph of altitude versus distance if you took the most direct route from C to G.

2. Sketch a graph of altitude versus distance if you took the most direct route from A to I to E.

3. The view from the western shore of the lake facing southeast is as shown.

Sketch the view from
a) the eastern shore of the lake facing west
b) the northern shore of the lake facing south
c) the top of the hill south of the lake facing north

Review

8.1 *Find the slope of the line passing through the points.*
1. E(3, 5) and F(5, 9)
2. W(−2, 7) and X(5, 8)
3. S(−3, 7) and T(6, −2)
4. P(0, −9) and Q(1, −6)
5. K(1.3, −5.4) and L(0.3, −0.6)
6. A(3, −1) and B(−2, −1)
7. U(1, 2) and V(1, −6)

Graph the line through the given point and with the given slope.

8. (3, 5); $m = 3$
9. (0, 4); $m = \dfrac{2}{3}$

10. (2, −6); $m = -1$
11. (4, 2); $m = -\dfrac{3}{2}$

12. (5, 0); m not defined

8.2 13. Flying speed A small plane was flying due west from Toronto. At 14:00, the plane was 100 km west of Toronto. At 16:30, the plane was 700 km west of Toronto. Express the rate of change in kilometres per hour.

14. Population statistics Statistics Canada projects that the percent of the Canadian population who will be at least 65 years old will be 14% in the year 2011 and 17.5% in the year 2021.
a) Find the rate of change as a percent per year.
b) Predict the year in which all Canadians will be at least 65 years old.
c) Is your prediction from part b) valid? Explain.

8.3 *Write an equation in standard form for the line that passes through the given point and has the given slope.*
15. (4, 5); $m = 2$
16. (−1, 3); $m = -3$
17. (2, −6); $m = -1$
18. (−4, −3); $m = \dfrac{1}{2}$
19. (−3, 0); $m = -0.2$
20. (3, −1); $m = 0$
21. (5, 1); m not defined

Write an equation in standard form for the line that passes through the given points.
22. (2, 5) and (4, 9)
23. (−2, 7) and (−1, 4)
24. (−4, 7) and (−2, 6)
25. (3, −1) and (3, 4)

26. (1, −6) and (−3, −9)
27. (−4, 2) and (−1, 2)
28. (0, −3) and (4, −2)
29. (−1, −1) and (−3, −6)

Write an equation in standard form for the line that passes through the given points. Use the equation to find two other points on the line. Check your solutions.
30. (2, 5) and (4, 13)
31. (1, −5) and (2, −6)

32. a) Plot the points (−3, −4), (−1, −1), (1, 2), (3, 4), (5, 4), and (7, 7). Draw the line of best fit.
b) Write an equation for the line of best fit in standard form.

8.4 *Find the slope and y-intercept of the following lines.*
33. $y = 4x + 6$
34. $4x + 5y − 20 = 0$
35. $x − 2y = -4$
36. $2x − 12 = 3y$

Given the slope and y-intercept, write an equation of the line in standard form.
37. $m = 5$ and $b = 2$
38. $m = -4$ and $b = -3$
39. $m = \dfrac{4}{3}$ and $b = 0$
40. $m = -\dfrac{1}{2}$ and $b = 3$

Find the slope and y-intercept of the line through the given points.
41. (2, −1) and (4, 7)
42. (−2, 2) and (1, −4)

43. Clothing sales Rolf earns a salary plus commission for selling clothes in a store. The equation $e = 480 + 0.05s$ relates his weekly earnings, e dollars, to his weekly sales, s dollars.
a) Graph the line.
b) What is Rolf's weekly salary, excluding commission?
c) What is the rate of commission, expressed as a percent?
d) If Rolf earned $600 one week, what were his sales that week?

8.5 *Find an equation for each of the following lines.*
44.

45.

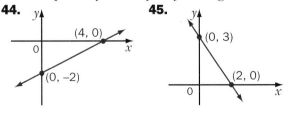

Use the x- and y-intercepts to graph each line.
46. $x + 5y = 10$ **47.** $7x - 2y - 14 = 0$
48. $y = -6x + 12$ **49.** $y = 3x - 9$

Graph each equation. If the domain is R, state the range, slope, and intercepts.
50. $y - 3 = 2(x + 1)$ **51.** $4x + 2y - 5 = 0$

8.6 State the slope of a line
a) parallel to each line
b) perpendicular to each line

52. $y = 5x + 4$ **53.** $y = \frac{1}{4}x - 4$

54. $y = -\frac{3}{5}x - 7$ **55.** $8x + 4y = 11$

56. $x - 3y - 1 = 0$ **57.** $2x + 3y + 4 = 0$

Write an equation for each of the following lines.
58. the line parallel to $3x + 2y - 4 = 0$ and passing through the point $(2, 3)$
59. the line perpendicular to $x - 2y + 3 = 0$ and passing through the point $(4, -1)$

8.7 **60.** What is the point of intersection for each of the following pairs of relations?

a)

x	y		x	y
-2	-2		2	-2
-1	-1		1	-1
0	0		0	0
1	1		-1	1

b)

x	y		x	y
-3	-5		-2	0
-2	-4		-1	-1
-1	-3		0	-2
0	-2		1	-3

Find the coordinates of the point of intersection of each pair of lines.
61. $y = x + 7$ and $y = 5 - x$
62. $y = -2x$ and $y = 3x - 5$

63. Provinces The numbers of provinces in Cameroon, x, and Finland, y, are related by the equations $y = 22 - x$ and $y = x + 2$.
a) Find the coordinates of the point of intersection of the lines.
b) Explain the meaning of the coordinates of the point of intersection.

Exploring Math

Patterns in a Table

Assume that the pattern continues.

Row	Column				
	A	B	C	D	E
1	1	2	3	4	5
2	6	7	8	9	10
3	11	12	13	14	15

1. What numbers are in row 10? row 50?

2. Write an equation in the form $N = \blacksquare$ to express a number, N, in terms of the row number, r, for the numbers in
a) column A   **b)** column B   **c)** column C
d) column D   **e)** column E

3. a) If you plotted the points for each equation from question 2, how would the five sets of points be related? Explain.
b) Would you be justified in drawing a line through each set of points in part a)? Explain.

4. Use the equations from question 2 to find the numbers in row 211; row 507.

5. What is the number in
a) row 256, column C?   **b)** row 333, column B?

6. Which row will include
a) the number 2354?   **b)** the number 3926?

7. Which column will include
a) the number 822?   **b)** the number 4443?

8. Show that the sum of *any* number in column A and *any* number in column B will be found in column C.

9. In which row and which column will you find the sum of the numbers from row 22 in column A and row 37 in column B?

10. Show that the sum of *any* number in column A and *any* number in Column D will be found in column E.

11. In which row and which column will you find the sum of the numbers from row 17 in column A and row 33 in column D?

Chapter Check

Find the slope of the line that passes through each pair of points.
1. (3, 1) and (3, –5)
2. (0, 5) and (4, 7)
3. (–1, 2) and (2, –3)
4. (–1, –2) and (–5, –2)

Write the equation in standard form for the line that passes through the given point and has the given slope.
5. $(2, -1); m = 3$
6. $(-1, -1); m = -\dfrac{2}{5}$

Write an equation in standard form for the line that passes through the given points.
7. (2, 5) and (7, 10)
8. (3, 1) and (9, –2)
9. (5, –3) and (7, –3)
10. (–1, –1) and (–1, 5)

Find the slope and y-intercept of each line.
11. $y = 2x - 3$
12. $x + 2y + 8 = 0$

13. How are the two lines in questions 11 and 12 related? Explain.

Use the slope and y-intercept to write an equation of each line in standard form.
14. $m = 2$ and $b = -1$
15. $m = -\dfrac{1}{4}$ and $b = 2$

16. Write an equation of a line parallel to $2x + y - 2 = 0$ and passing through the point (4, 5).

Use a method of your choice to graph each line. State the slope and the intercepts.
17. $y = 4x + 3$
18. $2x - 5y + 10 = 0$

19. Find the coordinates of the point of intersection of the lines $y = x + 1$ and $y = 2x - 1$.

20. **Prairie cities** Saskatoon is about 700 km from Winnipeg. The elevation of Saskatoon is 484 m. The elevation of Winnipeg is 232 m.
a) Write two ordered pairs of the form (*d*, *e*) to represent the data, where *d* is the distance from Winnipeg, in kilometres, and *e* is the elevation, in metres.
b) Graph the ordered pairs and connect them with a line segment.
c) Find the slope and state the units in which it is expressed.
d) What rate of change does the slope represent?
e) Write an equation of the line in slope and y-intercept form.
f) Use the equation to predict the elevation of a point between Winnipeg and Saskatoon, and 250 km from Winnipeg.
g) Do you think that your prediction in part f) is valid? Explain.

21. **Observatories** Stargazers can make use of a number of observatories in Canada. The number in Ontario, *x*, and the number in other provinces, *y*, are related by the equations $y = x + 6$ and $y = 3x - 2$.
a) Find the coordinates of the point of intersection of the lines.
b) Explain the meaning of the coordinates of the point of intersection.

SPEED BUMP   Dave Coverly

TONY HERE IS ALSO A PARALLEL LINE, SO I'M NOT SURPRISED YOU TWO HAVEN'T MET BEFORE...

Using the Strategies

1. Measurement A square piece of paper is folded in half as shown. The perimeter of each new rectangle formed is 24 cm. What is the perimeter of the original square?

2. Measurement This problem was part of the Canada/U.S. qualifying test for the First World Puzzle Team Championship, held in 1992.

How many triangles with side length 1 unit, with side length 2 units, with side length 3 units, with side length 4 units, and with side length 5 units are in this figure?

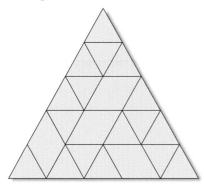

3. Melting ice You fill a glass half full of water from the tap. Then, you add enough ice cubes to the water to fill the glass. Sketch a graph of temperature versus time from the moment you add the ice to the water until the moment when the ice has all melted.

4. Guessing game Is it possible to guess any number from 1 to 1024 in 10 guesses or fewer if you are told on each guess that it is correct, too large, or too small? Explain.

5. Designs The square has been divided into 8 triangles. One way to shade 4 of the 8 triangles is shown. How many other different ways to shade 4 triangles are there?

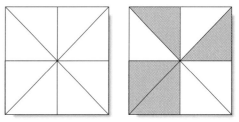

6. Cutting cheese A block of cheese, covered with wax, measures 12 cm by 12 cm by 10 cm. The block is cut into 2-cm cubes.
a) How many cubes are there?
b) How many cubes have wax on 3 faces?
c) How many cubes have wax on 2 faces?
d) How many cubes have no wax on them?

7. Book pages If you open a book and the product of the page numbers on the 2 facing pages is 45 156, what are the page numbers?

8. Line-up You are standing in line at the cafeteria. You are seventh from the front and eighth from the end. How many people are in the line?

9. Water use Assuming that each member of Canada's present population has one shower per day, about how many years would it take to use the volume of water in Lake Erie?

10. Suspension bridge About how many minutes would it take to walk across the main span of the Canadian suspension bridge with the longest main span?

11. Stair climb Each year, a stair climb is held at the CN Tower to raise money for charity.
a) Estimate how long it would take to walk up the stairs used for the charity climb.
b) Use your research skills to find out how long the fastest runners take to climb the stairs. About how many steps do they climb per second?

CUMULATIVE REVIEW, CHAPTERS 5–8

Chapter 5

Use each of the following relations.
a) *Describe the relation in words.*
b) *Complete a table of values for the domain* $\{-2, -1, 0, 1, 2\}$.
c) *Write the relation as a set of ordered pairs.*
d) *State the range.*
1. $x + y = 6$ **2.** $y = 3x + 2$

3. a) Plot the points A(2, 5), B(−4, 5) and C(−4, −2) on a grid.
b) Write the coordinates of the fourth point needed to form a rectangle.
c) Find the perimeter and area of the rectangle.

4. Ostrich An ostrich can run at a speed of 15 m/s, over short distances.
a) Copy and complete the table of values for a running ostrich.

Time (s)	Distance (m)
0	
1	
2	
3	
4	

b) Plot a graph of distance versus time.
c) Use the graph to estimate the distance an ostrich can cover in 1.4 s; in 3.6 s.

5. Graph the equation $y = -2x + 3$ for each of the following domains.
a) $\{-2, -1, 0, 1, 2\}$ **b)** the real numbers, R

a) *Graph each of the following relations.*
b) *State whether each relation is a partial variation or a direct variation.*
6. $y = -x - 3$ **7.** $y = 3x$

8. a) Graph the data
b) Draw the line of best fit
c) Determine an equation for the line of best fit.

x	y
−10	8
−5	3
0	−2
5	−8
10	−12
15	−17

9. Sketch a graph of the number of people in your school on a school day versus the time of day.

448 *Chapter 8*

Chapter 6

Simplify.
1. $2x - 4y + 3x - 7y + 2$
2. $-9 + 3a - 2b - c - 4a + 5c - 3b$
3. $x^2 + 3x - 7 - 2x^2 - 5x + 8$

Classify each polynomial and state its degree.
4. $y^2 - 3y - 4$ **5.** $4x^4 + 2x^3$ **6.** $5xy^2$

Arrange the terms in each polynomial in descending powers of x.
7. $2 + 3x^5 - 4x - 6x^3 + x^2$
8. $3x^2y + 5x^4 - xy^2 - 6x^3y^2$

Simplify.
9. $(x^2 - 4x - 7) + (2x^2 + 5x - 5)$
10. $(4y^2 - 3y - 9) - (2y^2 + y + 6)$
11. $(-4m^2 + 5m + 4) + (2m^2 - 3m + 1)$
12. $(6t^2 - t - 1) - (7t^2 + 3t - 2)$

Expand and simplify.
13. $4(2x - 3y + 5)$
14. $2(x - 4) - (3x - 7)$
15. $-3(4x + 5) + 5(x + 8)$
16. $3(2x - 5) - 3(3x - 1)$
17. $3(x^2 - 4x - 7) - 2(x^2 + x + 7)$
18. $-2(y^2 - y - 3) + 4(2y^2 - 3y + 1)$

Multiply.
19. $(11x)(2y)$ **20.** $(2xy)(5xy^2)$
21. $(-4xy)(-3x^2y^2)$ **22.** $-5m^2(-2mn)$

Simplify.
23. $(x^4)^2$ **24.** $(3x^2y)^4$
25. $(-2x^3y^4)^3$ **26.** $(-r^2s^3t^4)^4$

Expand and simplify.
27. $2x(3x - 4) + 3x(x - 2)$
28. $-3(y - 4) - 4y(2y + 1)$

Expand.
29. $3x(x^2 - 4x - 3)$ **30.** $-x(2x^2 - 7x + 1)$
31. $-2x(3x^2 + x - 7)$

Divide.
32. $\dfrac{30x^2y^5}{10xy^3}$ **33.** $\dfrac{-28x^5y^6}{7x^5y^5}$

Factor.
34. $5y^2 - 15y$ **35.** $21a^2b^2 - 3ab + 6ab^2$

Chapter 7

Solve.

1. $x + 9 = 13$ **2.** $x - 7 = 8$ **3.** $8 - x = -2$

4. $8x = 36$ **5.** $3x = -21$ **6.** $\dfrac{x}{3} = -4$

Solve and check.

7. $4x - 11 = 9$ **8.** $20 = 3x + 32$

9. $7x - 3x + x = 11 - 15 - 1$

10. $4x - 3x - 5x = 13 - 17 - 4$

Solve and check.

11. $3x + 10 = 5x - 12$ **12.** $x - 11 = 2x - 4x - 5$

13. $4x + 9 + 2x = 7x - 2 - 12x$

Solve and check.

14. $3(x - 5) = 5(x + 1) + 4$

15. $4(2x - 3) - (x + 5) = 11$

16. $2(x + 3) - (2x - 5) = 2(x + 1) + 1$

Solve and check.

17. $0.2x - 0.7 = 0.8x + 1.7$

18. $1.2x + 2.3 = 3.6 - 2.4x - 8.5$

Solve and check.

19. $\dfrac{x}{3} + \dfrac{1}{3} = -\dfrac{2}{3}$ **20.** $\dfrac{5x}{4} - \dfrac{x}{2} = -\dfrac{3}{4}$

21. $\dfrac{x-1}{2} = \dfrac{x+3}{3}$ **22.** $\dfrac{3x+1}{2} - \dfrac{x}{3} = 4$

23. Measurement The side lengths of a triangle are consecutive whole numbers of metres. The perimeter of the triangle is 132 m. Find the side lengths.

26. Measurement a) Copy and complete the table for the areas of 4 triangles, each with a fixed height of 10 cm.

Base (cm)	4	6	8	10
Area (cm²)				

b) Write a formula for the area of a triangle with a height of 10 cm.

c) Use the formula to find the area of a triangle with a height of 10 cm and a base of 35 cm.

27. Car rally Heidi and Kelly drove in an antique car rally. Kelly left a checkpoint at 09:00 travelling at 45 km/h. One hour later, Heidi left the same checkpoint travelling at 50 km/h. At what time did Heidi overtake Kelly?

Chapter 8

Find the slope of the line passing through the points.

1. A(1, 4) and B(3, 8)

2. C(−3, 8) and D(−8, 3)

3. E(0, −6) and F(1, −2)

4. G(−4, 0) and H(6, 0)

5. Commission Bianca is paid a base salary plus commission for selling clothes. One week, her sales totalled $10 000 and she earned $900. The next week her sales totalled $14 000 and she earned $1100.

a) What rate of commission is Bianca paid?

b) What is her weekly base salary?

Write an equation in standard form for the line that passes through the given point and has the given slope.

6. A(7, 4); $m = 5$ **7.** B(−3, −2); $m = -\dfrac{1}{2}$

Write an equation in standard form for the line that passes through the given points.

8. A(3, −2) and B(4, 5)

9. C(1, 7) and D(−3, 5)

10. Write an equation in standard form for the line that passes through (−4, 2) and (2, 0). Use the equation to find two other points on the line.

Find the slope and y-intercept of each line.

11. $y = 3x + 7$ **12.** $2x + y - 6 = 0$

13. $x - 2y = 8$ **14.** $3x - 4y - 12 = 0$

Graph each equation using a method of your choice.

15. $y = 4x - 5$ **16.** $3x - 2y - 6 = 0$

17. Write an equation of the line parallel to $3x + y - 5 = 0$ and passing through the point (1, −1).

18. Write an equation of the line perpendicular to $y = -2x - 4$ and passing through the point (−6, 4).

19. Write an equation of the line parallel to the line $2x - 3y - 3 = 0$ and having the same y-intercept as the line $4x - 7y - 14 = 0$.

20. Find the coordinates of the point of intersection of the lines $y = 2x - 3$ and $y = 3x - 4$.

CHAPTER 9

Measurement

How Can We Model the Earth in Two Dimensions?

The position of a place on the Earth can be described using its latitude and longitude.

1. Parallels of latitude are imaginary circles around the Earth parallel to the equator, which has been assigned a latitude of 0°.
a) What is located at a latitude of 90°N? 90°S?
b) Which parallel of latitude has a radius equal to the radius of the Earth?
c) What is the radius of the 90°N or the 90°S parallel of latitude? Explain.

2. Meridians of longitude are imaginary half-circles that connect both poles. In 1884, the meridian through Greenwich, near London, England, was selected as the prime meridian and assigned a longitude of 0°.
a) How does the length of a meridian of longitude compare with the length of the equator? Explain.
b) Longitudes are described as being east (E) or west (W) of Greenwich. How are the meridians at 180°E and 180°W related? Explain.
c) Use an atlas or other source to find the longitude of where you live, to the nearest degree. If the prime meridian were through where you live, what would the longitude of Greenwich be? Explain.

In Modelling Math — Cartography on pages 501 to 503, you will learn more about how we can model the Earth in two dimensions.

GETTING STARTED

Perimeter and Area

1 Polyominoes

A polyomino is a polygon formed by joining identical squares along whole sides.

These are polyominoes:

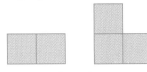

These are not polyominoes:

1. A pentomino is made up of 5 identical squares joined at their sides. A number of different pentominoes can be formed by rearranging the squares.

Two pentominoes are shown:

a) Draw as many different pentominoes as possible on grid paper.
b) Which shape has the smallest perimeter?

2. A tetromino is made up of 4 identical squares joined at their sides.
a) Draw as many different tetrominoes as possible on grid paper.
b) Which shape has the smallest perimeter?

3. A hexomino is made up of 6 identical squares joined at their sides.
a) Predict which shape of hexomino has the smallest perimeter.
b) Explain your reasoning.

2 Areas of Irregular Figures

The figure has been drawn on a grid, with each square equal to 1 square unit.

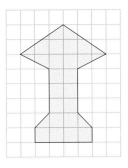

The area of the figure can be estimated by counting the number of whole and part squares that it covers.

The number of whole squares is 16. The number of part squares is 14.

Total Area = (Number of whole squares)
$$+ \frac{1}{2}(\text{Number of part squares})$$
$$= 16 + 0.5(14)$$
$$= 16 + 7$$
$$= 23$$

The total area of the figure is about 23 square units.

1. Why do you think you calculate one half of the part squares?

2. Trace your hand on a sheet of 1-cm grid paper. Estimate the area of your hand, in square centimetres, by counting whole squares and part squares.

3. Measure your arm length, in centimetres.

4. Collect a class set of arm lengths and hand areas. Graph hand area versus arm length.

5. Can you make a general conclusion about arm length and hand area from the data? If you can, what is it? Explain and justify your reasoning.

3 The Pythagorean Theorem

In a right triangle, the longest side is opposite the right angle and is called the **hypotenuse**. The other two sides are called **legs**. The Pythagorean Theorem states that, in any right triangle, if c is the length of the hypotenuse, and a and b are the lengths of the legs, then $a^2 + b^2 = c^2$.

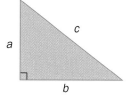

Find the unknown side length in each right triangle. If necessary, round answers to the nearest tenth of a unit.

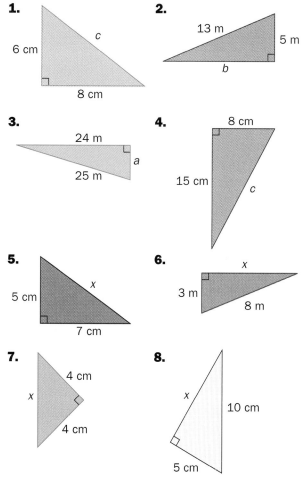

1.

6 cm

8 cm

c

2.

13 m

5 m

b

3.

24 m

25 m

a

4.

8 cm

15 cm

c

5.

5 cm

7 cm

x

6.

3 m

8 m

x

7.

4 cm

4 cm

x

8.

10 cm

5 cm

x

Mental Math

Operations With Decimals

Calculate.

1. 3.14×1000 **2.** $3.14 \div 100$

3. 2.5×6 **4.** $15.5 \div 5$

5. $0.5(3.9 + 8.1)$ **6.** $0.5(6.2 + 4.8)$

Estimate.

7. $(3.14)(2.2)^2$ **8.** $(3.14)(4.9)^2$

9. $(3.14)(9.8)^2$ **10.** $(3.14)(2.1)(3.2)$

11. $(3.14)(5.2)(2.4)$ **12.** $(3.14)(7.2)(10.4)$

Subtracting Using Compatible Numbers

Suppose that you are subtracting one number from another and that the number you are subtracting is close to a multiple of 10. The mental subtraction is easier if you adjust both numbers so that you subtract a multiple of 10.

For $83 - 49$, think

$(83 + 1) - (49 + 1) = 84 - 50$

$= 34$

So, $83 - 49 = 34$

For $91 - 42$, think

$(91 - 2) - (42 - 2) = 89 - 40$

$= 49$

So, $91 - 42 = 49$

Calculate.

1. $55 - 19$ **2.** $73 - 28$ **3.** $80 - 39$

4. $81 - 22$ **5.** $70 - 31$ **6.** $61 - 23$

Adapt the method to calculate the following. Describe how you adapted the method.

7. $6.4 - 2.9$ **8.** $10 - 3.8$ **9.** $7.2 - 4.3$

10. $650 - 280$ **11.** $1800 - 990$ **12.** $710 - 320$

13. a) Complete the following, where x, y, n, m, b, and c represent whole numbers.

$(10x + y) - (10n + m)$

$(10x + y + b) - (10n + m + b)$

$(10x + y - c) - (10n + m - c)$

b) Explain how the subtractions in part a) are related to the method shown above.

c) For the method to work as shown, what is the value of $m + b$? the value of $m - c$?

INVESTIGATING MATH

Reviewing Formulas

Recall the formulas for the perimeter, *P*, and the area, *A*, of the following plane figures.

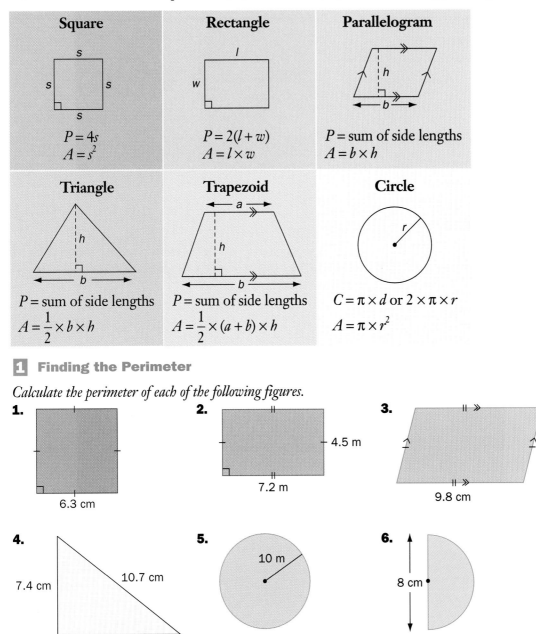

Square

$P = 4s$
$A = s^2$

Rectangle

$P = 2(l + w)$
$A = l \times w$

Parallelogram

$P = $ sum of side lengths
$A = b \times h$

Triangle

$P = $ sum of side lengths
$A = \dfrac{1}{2} \times b \times h$

Trapezoid

$P = $ sum of side lengths
$A = \dfrac{1}{2} \times (a + b) \times h$

Circle

$C = \pi \times d$ or $2 \times \pi \times r$
$A = \pi \times r^2$

1 Finding the Perimeter

Calculate the perimeter of each of the following figures.

1.

6.3 cm

2.

4.5 m

7.2 m

3.

5.6 cm

9.8 cm

4.

7.4 cm

10.7 cm

9.6 cm

5.

10 m

6.

8 cm

2 Finding the Area

Calculate the area of each of the following figures. If necessary, round answers to the nearest tenth of a square unit.

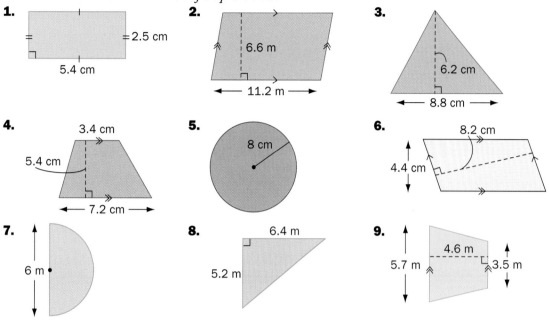

1. 2.5 cm, 5.4 cm

2. 6.6 m, 11.2 m

3. 6.2 cm, 8.8 cm

4. 3.4 cm, 5.4 cm, 7.2 cm

5. 8 cm

6. 8.2 cm, 4.4 cm

7. 6 m

8. 6.4 m, 5.2 m

9. 4.6 m, 5.7 m, 3.5 m

3 Finding the Perimeter and the Area

Calculate the perimeter and the area of each figure.

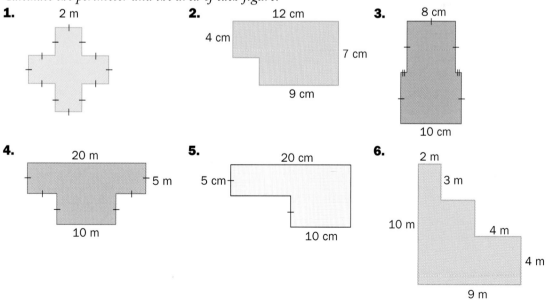

1. 2 m

2. 12 cm, 4 cm, 7 cm, 9 cm

3. 8 cm, 10 cm

4. 20 m, 5 m, 10 m

5. 20 cm, 5 cm, 10 cm

6. 2 m, 3 m, 10 m, 4 m, 4 m, 9 m

9.1 Areas of Composite Figures

A **composite figure** is a figure made up of two or more distinct figures, such as a rectangle and a semicircle. To find the area of a composite figure, add the areas of the individual parts.

Explore: Use a Diagram

The first recorded Olympic games were held in 776 B.C., near the small city of Olympia, in Greece. Other Greek cities and towns based the plans for their Olympic sites on the plan used at Olympia.

The games were held in a *stadion*, from which we get the modern word stadium. The name *stadion* came about because the first race was 1 *stade*, or about 192 m, in length. A stadion was usually set into a valley to provide seating for the spectators, who, in some cases, numbered about 50 000.

A stadion was a rectangle with a semicircle at one end. The dimensions of a typical Greek stadion are shown in the diagram.

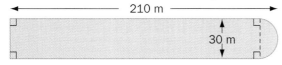

210 m

30 m

a) What is the diameter of the semicircle?
b) What is the radius of the semicircle?
c) What is the length of the rectangle?

Inquire

1. What is the area of the rectangular part of the stadion?

2. What is the area of the semicircle, to the nearest square metre?

3. What is the total area of the stadion, to the nearest square metre?

4. a) Which modern-day Olympic race is most like the first race in the ancient Olympics?
b) Name the Canadians who have won the gold medal in this modern-day race and state the years in which they won.

Example   Landscaping

The diagram shows a house on a lot that is in the shape of a trapezoid. The parallel sides of the trapezoid measure 18 m and 24 m. The height of the trapezoid is 26 m. The dimensions of the house, the path to the front door, and the driveway are shown in the diagram. The remaining area of the lot is to be covered with sod. What is the area that needs to be covered with sod?

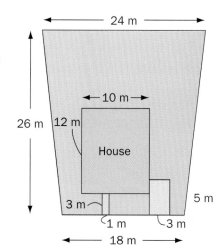

Solution

Calculate the total area of the house, path, and driveway. Then, subtract this area from the area of the lot.

Area of the house: $A_h = 12 \times 10$
$\qquad = 120$

Area of the path: $A_p = 3 \times 1$
$\qquad = 3$

Area of the driveway: $A_d = 5 \times 3$
$\qquad = 15$

Total Area: $120 + 3 + 15 = 138$

Area of the lot:
$$A_l = \frac{1}{2} \times (a+b) \times h$$
$$= \frac{1}{2} \times (18 + 24) \times 26$$
$$= \frac{1}{2} \times 42 \times 26$$
$$= 21 \times 26$$
$$= 546$$

Estimate

$20 \times 30 = 600$

Estimate

$550 - 150 = 400$

Area to be covered with sod: $546 - 138 = 408$

The area of the lot that needs to be covered is 408 m².

Practice

A

Calculate the area of each figure. Round answers to the nearest tenth of a square unit, if necessary.

1.

6 cm
6 cm
4.4 cm
8.3 cm

2.

2 m
5 m
9.8 m

3.

9 m
3 m
8.2 m
12.4 m

4.

8 m
3 m
14 m
5 m
4 m
20 m

5.

7 m
3 m
8 m
5 m
20 m

6.

5.4 m
7.6 m

7.

10 cm
4.6 cm
2.6 cm
3 cm   5 cm

8.

10.5 cm
6.2 cm

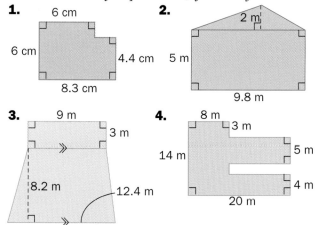
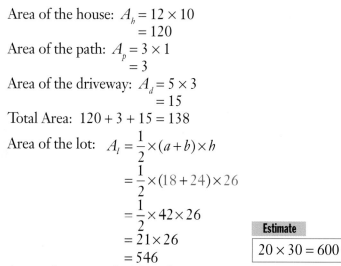
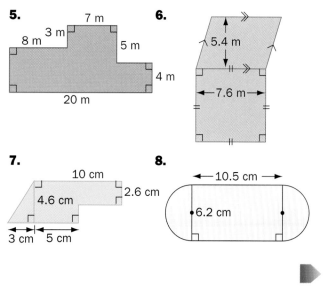
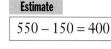

9.

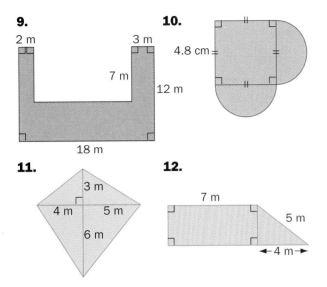

2 m   3 m

7 m

18 m

10.

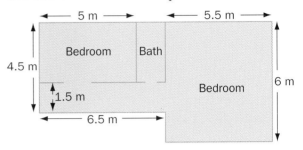

4.8 cm

12 m

11.

3 m

4 m   5 m

6 m

12.

7 m

5 m

← 4 m →

Applications and Problem Solving

Calculate the area of each shaded region. Round answers to the nearest tenth of a square unit, if necessary.

13.

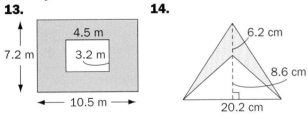

4.5 m

7.2 m   3.2 m

← 10.5 m →

14.

6.2 cm

8.6 cm

20.2 cm

15.

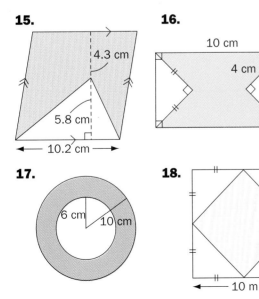

4.3 cm

5.8 cm

← 10.2 cm →

16.

10 cm

4 cm

5.6 cm

17.

6 cm   10 cm

18.

← 10 m →

B

19. Carpeting The diagram shows the plan of the second floor of a new house. The hall and the two bedrooms are to be carpeted.

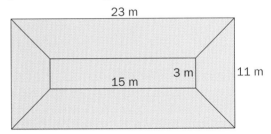

5 m   5.5 m

Bedroom   Bath

4.5 m

Bedroom   6 m

1.5 m

6.5 m

Calculate the area of carpet needed, in square metres.

20. Roofing Sandrine needs to replace the roofing material on her home. The roof has a rectangle on top and sloping trapezoids on each side. The dimensions of the roof are shown. Each trapezoid has a height of 4.5 m.

23 m

3 m   11 m

15 m

a) Calculate the area of the roof.
b) The trapezoids are to be covered with shingles. If a package of shingles covers 10 m^2, how many packages will be needed?

21. Carpentry Lamar works as a carpenter. He is framing a window that measures 100 cm by 80 cm. The frame is made up of four trapezoids. The frame is 10 cm wide. Find the total area of the four trapezoids.

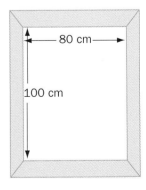

80 cm

100 cm

22. Each "step" of the polygon has a width of 3 cm and a height of 3 cm. Calculate the area of the polygon.

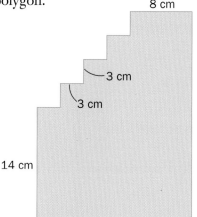

23. Picture framing The picture measures 30 cm by 15 cm. The mat around the picture is 10 cm wide. Calculate the area of the mat.

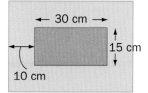

24. Archery One of the targets used in archery competitions has a diameter of 80 cm. The circle in the centre is gold and has a radius of 8 cm. The gold circle is surrounded by 4 rings, which are coloured red, blue, black, and white. Each of these 4 rings is 8 cm wide.

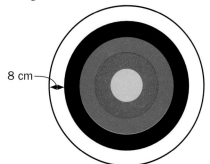

a) Calculate the area of the blue ring, to the nearest square centimetre.
b) What percent of the target is blue?

C

25. House roof A diagram of the roof of a house is shown. The top of the roof is a rectangle. The four trapezoids have the same height. Calculate the area of the roof.

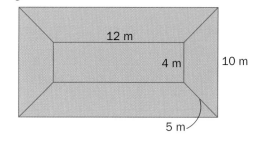

26. The two circles are identical, and figure ABCD is a rectangle.

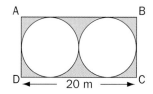

a) Determine the total area of the shaded regions. Write your answer in terms of π.
b) Calculate the total area of the shaded regions, to the nearest square metre.

27. The four circles are identical, and figure ABCD is a square.

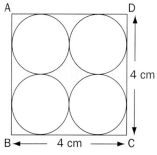

a) Determine the area of the shaded region. Write your answer in terms of π.
b) Calculate the area of the shaded region, to the nearest tenth of a square centimetre. Explain how you can judge whether your answer is reasonable.

INVESTIGATING MATH

Optimizing Perimeter and Area

1 Fencing on Four Sides

1. Fencing a garden a) A landscaper has 24 sections of fence, each 1 m long, to enclose a rectangular garden. The diagram models one of the possible rectangular shapes with a perimeter of 24 m. Sketch all the other rectangles that have whole-number dimensions and a perimeter of 24 m.
b) Copy and complete the table, or use a spreadsheet like the one shown.

Rectangle	Width (m)	Length (m)	Perimeter (m)	Area (m²)
1			24	
2			24	
3			24	
⋮				

	A	B	C	D	E
1	Rectangle	Width (m)	Length (m)	Perimeter (m)	Area (m²)
2	1	1	=12–B2	24	=B2*C2
3	2	=B2+1	=12–B3	24	=B3*C3

c) What dimensions give the maximum area?
d) What is the maximum area?

2. Repeat question 1 for 32 sections of fence and a garden with a perimeter of 32 m.

3. Without restricting the dimensions to whole numbers of metres, use a table or spreadsheet to determine the maximum area of a garden with a perimeter of 30 m.

4. What shape of rectangle gives the maximum area for a given perimeter?

5. a) Describe a method for calculating the maximum area of a rectangular garden from its perimeter.
b) Use your method to calculate the maximum area of a rectangular garden with a perimeter of 34 m; 27.6 m; 36.8 m.

6. Fencing a pen a) A farmer wants to fence a rectangular animal pen with the minimum amount of fencing, so that the pen has an area of 36 m². The rectangle shown has an area of 36 m². Sketch the other rectangles that have whole-number dimensions and an area of 36 m².

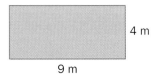

4 m

9 m

b) Copy and complete the table, or use a spreadsheet like the one shown.

Rectangle	Width (m)	Length (m)	Area (m²)	Perimeter (m)
1			36	
2			36	
3			36	
⋮				

	A	B	C	D	E
1	Rectangle	Width (m)	Length (m)	Area (m²)	Perimeter (m)
2	1	1	=36/B2	36	=2*B2+2*C2
3	2	2	=36/B3	36	=2*B3+2*C3

c) What dimensions use the minimum amount of fencing?
d) What is the minimum perimeter?

7. Repeat question 6 for a pen with an area of 16 m².

8. Without restricting the dimensions to whole numbers of metres, use a table or spreadsheet to determine the minimum perimeter of a pen with an area of 30.25 m².

9. What shape of rectangle gives the minimum perimeter for a given area?

10. a) Describe a method for calculating the minimum perimeter of a rectangular pen from its area.
b) Use your method to calculate the minimum perimeter of a rectangular pen with an area of 20.25 m²; 27 m²; 35 m². Round your answers to the nearest tenth of a metre, if necessary.

2 Fencing on Three Sides

1. Fencing a corral a) A rancher is adding a rectangular corral to the side of a barn. The barn will form one side of the rectangle, as shown in the diagram. The rancher has 16 m of fence. The rectangle shown uses 16 m of fence. Sketch all the other rectangular corrals that have whole-number dimensions and use 16 m of fence.

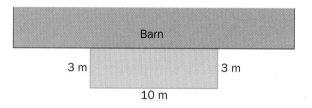

b) Copy and complete the table, or use a spreadsheet like the one shown on the following page.

Rectangle	Width (m)	Length (m)	Fence Used (m)	Area (m²)
1			16	
2			16	
3			16	
⋮				

	A	B	C	D	E
1	Rectangle	Width (m)	Length (m)	Fence Used (m)	Area (m^2)
2	1	1	=16–2*B2	16	=B2*C2
3	2	=B2+1	=16–2*B3	16	=B3*C3

c) What dimensions give the maximum area?
d) What is the maximum area?

2. Repeat question 1 for a corral that uses 28 m of fence.

3. Without restricting the dimensions to whole numbers of metres, use a table or spreadsheet to determine the maximum area of a corral that uses 26 m of fence.

4. Describe the shape of a corral that gives the maximum area for a given length of fence.

5. a) Describe a method for calculating the maximum area of a rectangular corral from the length of fence used.
b) Use your method to calculate the maximum area of a rectangular corral, if the length of fence used is 30 m; 21.8 m; 26.4 m. Round your answers to the nearest tenth of a metre, if necessary.

6. Fencing a playground a) An architect is adding a rectangular kindergarten playground to the side of a school. The school will form one side of the rectangle, as shown in the diagram. The area of the playground is to be 72 m^2. The rectangle shown has an area of 72 m^2. Sketch all the other rectangles that have whole-number dimensions and an area of 72 m^2.
b) Copy and complete the table, or use a spreadsheet like the one shown.

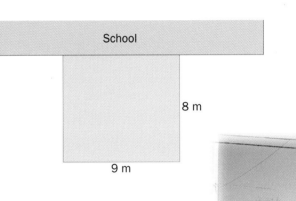

School

8 m

9 m

Rectangle	Width (m)	Length (m)	Area (m^2)	Fence Used (m)
1			72	
2			72	
3			72	
⋮				

	A	B	C	D	E
1	Rectangle	Width (m)	Length (m)	Area (m^2)	Fence Used (m)
2	1	1	=72/B2	72	=C2+2*B2
3	2	2	=72/B3	72	=C3+2*B3

c) What dimensions use the minimum length of fence?
d) What is the minimum length of fence?

7. Repeat question 6 for a playground with an area of 128 m^2.

8. Without restricting the dimensions to whole numbers of metres, use a table or spreadsheet to determine the minimum length of fence for a playground with an area of 60.5 m^2.

9. How are the side lengths related in a rectangular playground that uses the minimum length of fence for a given area?

10. a) Describe a method for calculating the minimum length of fence needed for a playground from its area.
b) Use your method to calculate the minimum length of fence for a playground with an area of 50 m^2; 112.5 m^2; 70 m^2. Round your answers to the nearest tenth of a metre, if necessary.

3 Applications and Problem Solving

1. Corkboards a) If you were designing a rectangular corkboard with an area of 1 m^2 and with a wooden frame, what shape would you make it so that the manufacturing cost was as small as possible? Explain.
b) If you were designing a corkboard with an area of 9 m^2 for use in a classroom, why might you not make the corkboard the same shape as in part a)?

2. Animal pen If an animal pen does not have to be rectangular, predict the shape that would require the minimum length of fence for a given area. Test your prediction and share your results with your classmates.

3. Garden Pose a problem involving the relationship between the perimeter and the area of a garden of a shape that you choose. Check that you can find the solution, and then have a classmate solve your problem.

4. Describe other applications in which it is important to know
a) the minimum perimeter of a rectangle for a given area
b) the maximum area of a rectangle for a given perimeter

INVESTIGATING MATH

Surface Areas and Volumes of Right Prisms

A **polyhedron** is a 3-dimensional object in which the faces are polygons. A **prism** is a polyhedron with two parallel congruent bases that are in the shape of a polygon. The lateral faces are parallelograms.

In a **right prism**, the lateral edges are perpendicular to the bases. So, in a right prism, the lateral faces are rectangles. The height of a right prism is the length of a lateral edge. Assume that all the prisms referred to in this book are right prisms.

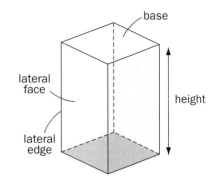

Prisms are named according to the shape of the bases. For example, a prism with square bases is a square-based prism. A prism with triangular bases is a triangular prism.

1 Modelling the Surface Area

The surface area of a prism is found by adding the areas of all the faces.

1. A rectangular prism and its net are shown. Calculate the surface area of the prism.

2. A triangular prism and its net are shown. Calculate the surface area of the prism.

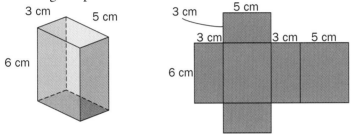

3. Calculate the surface area of each prism.

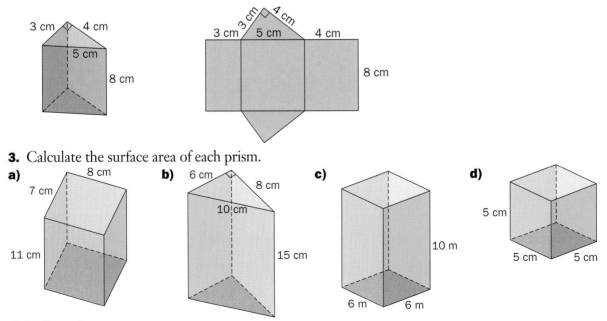

2 Modelling the Volume

Volume is the amount of space that a figure occupies. Volume is measured in cubic units, such as cubic centimetres (cm^3) and cubic metres (m^3).

1. The rectangular prism is made up of 1-cm cubes.
a) How many cubes make up the prism?
b) What is the volume of the prism?
c) What is the area of the base of the prism?
d) What is the height of the prism?
e) How does the product of the area of the base and the height compare with the volume of the prism?
f) Write an equation that expresses the volume of a prism, V, in terms of the area of the base, B, and the height, h.

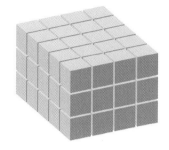

2. Given the area of the base and the height of each prism, calculate the volume.

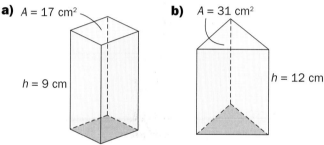
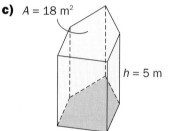

a) A = 17 cm² h = 9 cm
b) A = 31 cm² h = 12 cm
c) A = 18 m² h = 5 m

3. Calculate the volume of each prism.

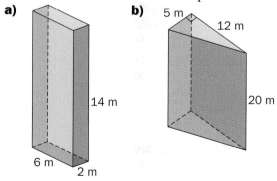
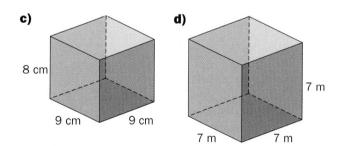

a) 14 m, 6 m, 2 m
b) 5 m, 12 m, 20 m
c) 8 cm, 9 cm, 9 cm
d) 7 m, 7 m, 7 m

9.2 Surface Area and Volume of a Prism

The right rectangular prism has two **bases**, which are parallel, congruent polygons. The **height** of the prism, h, is the perpendicular distance between the two bases.

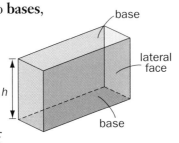

The **lateral faces**, the faces that are not bases, are rectangles. The **lateral area** of a prism is the sum of the areas of the lateral faces. The **surface area** is the sum of the areas of the lateral faces and the two bases.

Explore: Develop a Formula

Easter Island, also known as Rapa Nui, belongs to Chile. The island is located in the Pacific Ocean, about 3700 km west of Chile. Easter Island is important to archaeologists because of the gigantic statues found there. The statues consist of large heads with elongated noses and ears.

The construction of the statues started about 1800 years ago. They were carved from prisms made of volcanic rock. Many of the statues were carved from rectangular prisms with bases measuring 1 m by 2 m and with a height of 6 m. For one of the rectangular prisms, calculate the area of
a) each base   **b)** each lateral face

Inquire

1. What is the total area of the bases?

2. What is the lateral area?

3. What is the surface area of the prism?

4. What is the perimeter of a base?

5. Multiply the perimeter of a base by the height.

6. How do the answers to questions 2 and 5 compare? Explain why they compare in this way.

7. Write a formula for the lateral area, $L.A.$, in terms of the perimeter of a base, P, and the height, h.

8. Write a formula for the surface area, $S.A.$, in terms of
a) $L.A.$ and the area of each base, B
b) P, h, and B

You can find the surface area of a prism by adding the areas of all the faces. However, a formula can be developed to make the process much faster. To find the formula for the surface area of a prism, first find a formula for the lateral area.

In the prism shown, a, b, c, and d are the measures of the sides of the base, and h is the height. The perimeter of the base, P, is the sum of its side lengths, $a + b + c + d$.

Use the net to write the formula for the lateral area, $L.A.$
Add the areas of the lateral faces: $L.A. = ah + bh + ch + dh$
Remove the common factor: $L.A. = h(a + b + c + d)$
Substitute P for $a + b + c + d$: $L.A. = hP$ or Ph

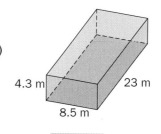

The bases of a prism are congruent polygons, so they have the same area, B.
The surface area, $S.A.$, of a prism is found by adding the lateral area and the total area of the two bases, $2B$.
So, $S.A. = Ph + 2B$

The formula $S.A. = Ph + 2B$ can be used to find the surface area of any right prism.

Example 1   Anik E-2 Satellite
Canada's *Anik E-2* is a communications satellite that provides services to television networks and telephone systems. The satellite approximates a rectangular prism with a length of 23 m, a width of 8.5 m, and a height of 4.3 m. Calculate the surface area of the satellite.

Solution
Draw a diagram.
Calculate the perimeter of a base, P: $P = 2(l + w)$
$\qquad\qquad\qquad\qquad\qquad\qquad = 2(23 + 8.5)$
$\qquad\qquad\qquad\qquad\qquad\qquad = 2(31.5)$
$\qquad\qquad\qquad\qquad\qquad\qquad = 63$

Calculate the area of a base, B: $B = (23)(8.5)$
$\qquad\qquad\qquad\qquad\qquad\qquad\quad = 195.5$

Estimate

$20 \times 10 = 200$

Calculate the surface area, $S.A.$: $S.A. = Ph + 2B$
$\qquad\qquad\qquad\qquad\qquad\qquad\quad = (63)(4.3) + 2(195.5)$
$\qquad\qquad\qquad\qquad\qquad\qquad\quad = 661.9$

The surface area of the satellite is 661.9 m^2.

Estimate

$60 \times 4 + 2 \times 200$
$= 240 + 400$
$= 640$

```
2(23+8.5)
                    63
23*8.5
                 195.5
63*4.3+2*195.5
                 661.9
```

Example 2   Volumes of Packages
Calculate each volume.

a)

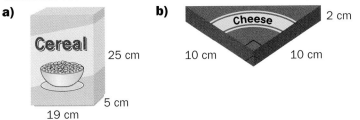

25 cm

5 cm

19 cm

b)

2 cm

10 cm   10 cm

Solution
The volume of a prism is the area of its base times its height.

a) The cereal box is a rectangular prism.

$V = B \times h$

$\quad = [(19)(5)](25)$

$\quad = 2375$

> **Estimate**
>
> $(20)(5)(25) = 2500$

The volume of the box is 2375 cm^3.

b) The cheese box is a triangular prism. The base and height of the triangle are 10 cm each.

$V = B \times h$

$\quad = [\frac{1}{2}(10)(10)](2)$

$\quad = (50)(2)$

$\quad = 100$

The volume of the box is 100 cm^3.

Example 3   Triangular Prism
The triangular prism has a height of 13 cm and a right triangular base, with one leg measuring 9 cm and a hypotenuse of 15 cm. Calculate the volume and surface area of the prism.

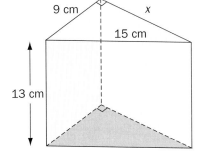

9 cm   x

15 cm

13 cm

Solution
Use the Pythagorean Theorem to find the length, x, of the third side of the triangular base.

$$x^2 + 9^2 = 15^2$$
$$x^2 + 81 = 225$$
$$x^2 = 225 - 81$$
$$x^2 = 144$$
$$x = \sqrt{144}$$
$$x = 12$$

Find the area of a base.

$B = \frac{1}{2} \times b \times h$

$\quad = \frac{1}{2}(12)(9)$

$\quad = 54$

Now, find the volume.

$V = B \times h$

$\quad = 54 \times 13$

$\quad = 702$

> **Estimate**
>
> $50 \times 13 = 650$

$S.A. = Ph + 2B$
The perimeter of the base is $9 + 12 + 15$ or 36.

So, $S.A. = (36)(13) + 2(54)$
$= 576$

Estimate

$40 \times 10 + 100 = 500$

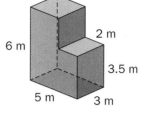

```
36*13+2*54
                    576
```

The volume of the prism is 702 cm^3, and the surface area is 576 cm^2.

A composite solid is made up of 2 or more prisms joined together.

Example 4   Composite Solid
Find the volume of the composite solid.

6 m

2 m

3.5 m

5 m

3 m

Solution
The solid is composed of a smaller prism, where $l = 3$ m, $w = 2$ m, and $h = 3.5$ m, and a larger prism, where $l = 3$ m, $w = 3$ m, and $h = 6$ m.

Volume of smaller prism $= (3)(2)(3.5)$
$= 21$

Volume of larger prism $= (3)(3)(6)$
$= 54$

Total volume $= 21 + 54$
$= 75$

The volume of the composite solid is 75 m^3.

Practice
A

Name each prism.

1.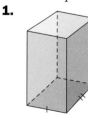

2.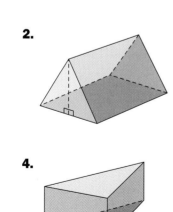

3.

4.

Which prisms in questions 1–4 can be formed from each of the following nets?

5.

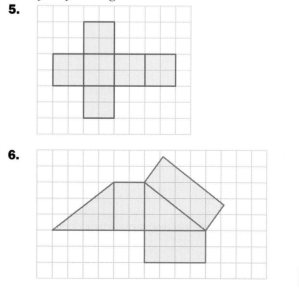

6.

*Estimate the surface area of each prism. Then,
calculate it, to the nearest square centimetre or
square metre.*

7.

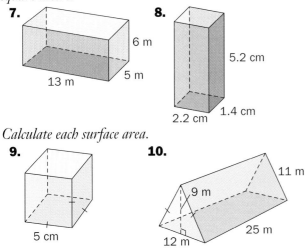

6 m

13 m

5 m

8.

5.2 cm

2.2 cm

1.4 cm

Calculate each surface area.

9.

5 cm

10.

11 m

9 m

25 m

12 m

*Estimate, then calculate the volume of each
rectangular prism.*

11.

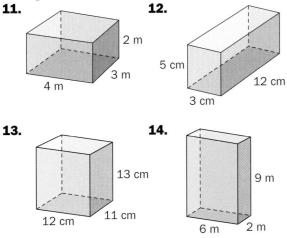

2 m

4 m

3 m

12.

5 cm

3 cm

12 cm

13.

13 cm

12 cm

11 cm

14.

9 m

6 m

2 m

*Calculate the surface area and volume of each prism,
to the nearest square or cubic unit.*

15.

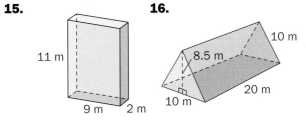

11 m

9 m

2 m

16.

10 m

8.5 m

20 m

10 m

17.

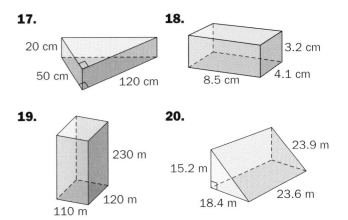

20 cm

50 cm

120 cm

18.

3.2 cm

8.5 cm

4.1 cm

19.

230 m

120 m

110 m

20.

23.9 m

15.2 m

18.4 m

23.6 m

Calculate the surface area and volume of each prism.

21.

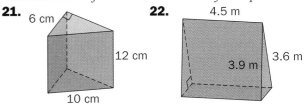

6 cm

12 cm

10 cm

22.

4.5 m

3.9 m

3.6 m

*Calculate the surface area and volume of each
composite solid.*

23.

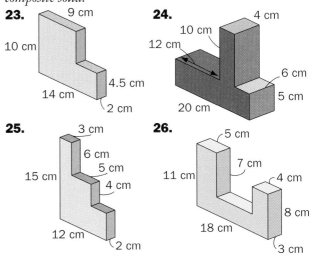

9 cm

10 cm

14 cm

4.5 cm

2 cm

24.

4 cm

10 cm

12 cm

6 cm

5 cm

20 cm

25.

3 cm

6 cm

5 cm

15 cm

4 cm

12 cm

2 cm

26.

5 cm

7 cm

11 cm

4 cm

18 cm

8 cm

3 cm

Applications and Problem Solving

27. Garbage bin A
covered garbage bin is to be
built so that it measures
1.5 m by 1.2 m by 1.0 m.
How much plywood will it
take to build the garbage
bin?

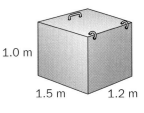

1.0 m

1.5 m

1.2 m

28. Painting a) Calculate the surface area of this room.

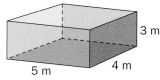

3 m
5 m
4 m

b) One 4-L can of paint will cover 36 m². If you want to give the ceiling and walls of the room two coats of paint, how many 4-L cans will you need? What assumptions have you made? Explain how you can judge whether your answer is reasonable.

29. Composter a) The dimensions of the square base of a composter are 1 m by 1 m. Its height is 0.65 m. It is a prism with a top, a bottom, and 4 sides. Calculate its surface area.
b) The cost of material to build this composter is $9.98/m². What is the total cost of the material?
c) If a town has set aside $1 250 000 for the materials to build these composters, how many composters can be built?

30. a) A prism has a height of 10 cm. Find its surface area if the dimensions of the base are 8 cm by 2 cm.
b) Draw and label a diagram of the prism on dot paper or centimetre grid paper.
c) What is the name of the prism?

31. Tent How many cubic metres of air does the tent contain?

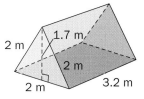

2 m
1.7 m
2 m
2 m
3.2 m

32. Office tower The Toronto-Dominion Bank Tower is one of Canada's tallest buildings. It approximates a rectangular prism with a height of 168 m and a base of 60 m by 36 m. Calculate the total area of the outside walls and the roof.

33. The surface area of a cube is 216 cm². What are the dimensions of this cube?

34. Swimming pool The diagram shows the side view of a pool.

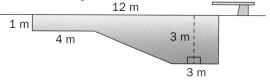

12 m
1 m
4 m
3 m
3 m

a) The pool is 5 m wide. Calculate its volume.
b) A pump can drain water from the pool at 0.3 m³/min. How long does it take to drain the pool?

35. Greenhouse The top and sides of a greenhouse are made of plastic. Calculate the amount of plastic needed to construct the greenhouse.

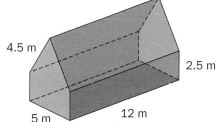

4.5 m
2.5 m
5 m
12 m

36. Garden shed A garden storage shed is to be built in the shape of a rectangular prism before the roof is added. The volume of the shed before the roof is put on is 24 m³. What are the most appropriate dimensions for the rectangular prism? Explain and justify your reasoning.

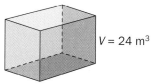

V = 24 m³

37. Calculate the surface area and volume of the interior of your classroom.

38. Write a problem that requires the calculation of the surface area and volume of a prism. Have a classmate solve your problem.

INVESTIGATING MATH

Surface Area and Volume of a Cylinder

A **cylinder** is a three-dimensional object with two bases, which are congruent circles, and a curved surface connecting the two bases. The **height** of a cylinder, h, is the perpendicular distance between the two bases.

The surface area of a cylinder is found by adding the areas of the bases and the area of the curved surface.

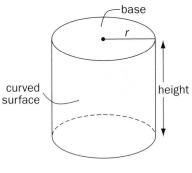

1 Modelling the Surface Area

A cylinder and its net are shown. The area of a base is $\pi \times r^2$.
In terms of π, the area of a base is $\pi \times 3^2$, or 9π cm^2.

1. What is the sum of the areas of the two bases, in terms of π?

2. In the net, the curved surface of the cylinder becomes a rectangle.
a) How is the height of the rectangle related to the height of the cylinder?
b) What is the height of the rectangle?

3. a) How is the length of the rectangle related to the circumference of the circular base of the cylinder?
b) What is the circumference of the circular base, in terms of π?
c) What is the length of the rectangle, in terms of π?

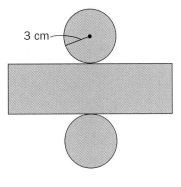

4. a) How is the area of the rectangle related to the area of the curved surface of the cylinder? Explain.
b) What is the area of the rectangle, in terms of π?
c) What is the area of the curved surface of the cylinder, in terms of π?

5. What is the surface area of the cylinder
a) in terms of π?   **b)** to the nearest square centimetre?

Draw the nets and determine the surface area of each cylinder.
Express your answers in terms of π.

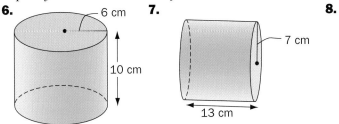

6. 6 cm, 10 cm   **7.** 7 cm, 13 cm   **8.** r, h

9. Use your formula from question 8 to find the surface area of the given cylinder, to the nearest square metre.

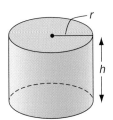

4 m, 8 m

2 Modelling the Volume

For this investigation, you will need an empty cylindrical tin can. Make sure that there are no sharp edges. You will also need a graduated cylinder.

1. Use a graduated cylinder to fill the can with water. Record the volume of water in the can.

2. What is the volume of the can, in cubic centimetres? Explain.

3. a) Measure the inside diameter of the can, in centimetres.
b) What is the inside radius of the can?

4. Calculate the area of the inside base of the can, in square centimetres.

5. Measure the inside height of the can, in centimetres.

6. Find the product of the area of the inside base of the can and the height of the can.

7. How do your answers to questions 2 and 6 compare? Share your findings with your classmates.

8. Use your results to write a formula for the volume of a cylinder, V, in terms of the area of the base, B, and the height, h.

9. Write a formula for the volume of a cylinder, V, in terms of the radius of a base, r, and the height of the cylinder, h.

Use your formula from question 9 to determine the volume of each of the following cylinders
a) *in terms of* π
b) *to the nearest cubic centimetre*

10.
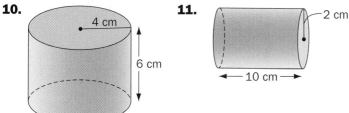
4 cm

6 cm

11.
2 cm

← 10 cm →

INVESTIGATING MATH

Surface Area and Volume of a Cone

A **cone** is a three-dimensional object with a circular base and a curved lateral surface, which extends from the base to a point called the **vertex**. The **height**, or **altitude**, of a cone is the perpendicular distance from the vertex to the base. The **slant height**, s, of a cone is the distance from the vertex to a point on the edge of the base.

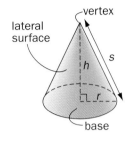

The surface area of a cone can be found by adding the area of the base and the area of the lateral surface.

1 Modelling the Surface Area

A cone and its net are shown. The cone has a base of radius 2 cm and a slant height of 8 cm.

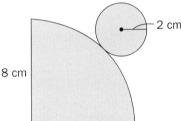

In the net, the lateral surface of the cone is called a **sector**. It is a part of the large circle whose radius is the slant height of the cone, which is 8 cm.
In terms of π, the circumference of the large circle is $2 \times \pi \times r$, which is $2 \times \pi \times 8$, or 16π cm.

1. What is the circumference of the base of the cone, in terms of π?

2. What fraction of the circumference of the large circle is the circumference of the base?

3. What is the area of the large circle, in terms of π?

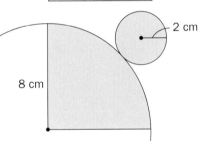

4. a) The area of the sector is the same fraction of the area of the large circle as you found in question 2. Explain why.
b) What is the area of the sector, in terms of π?

5. What is the area of the base of the cone, in terms of π?

6. What is the surface area of the cone,
a) in terms of π?
b) to the nearest square centimetre?

7. Use questions 1 to 6a) as a guide to complete the following statements for a general cone with a slant height, s, and a base of radius r. The circumference of the large circle is $2 \times \pi \times s$ or $2\pi s$.

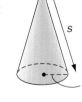

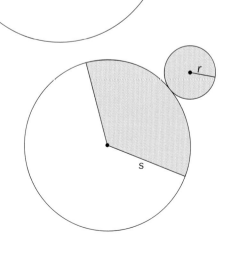

a) The circumference of the base of the cone is ▨▨▨.

b) The circumference of the base is $\dfrac{▨▨}{▨▨}$ of the circumference of the large circle.

c) The area of the large circle is ▨▨▨.

d) The area of the sector is ▭ / ▭ × ▭ or ▭.

e) The area of the lateral surface of the cone is ▭.

f) The area of the base of the cone is ▭.

g) The surface area of the cone is ▭.

2 Modelling the Volume

For this investigation, you will need an empty cylindrical tin can. Make sure that there are no sharp edges. You will also need construction paper, scissors, tape, and sand, rice, or some other suitable material.

Use a piece of construction paper to form a cone whose tip just touches the bottom of the tin can. The curved surface of the cone should just touch the inside surface of the top of the can. Tape the cone and cut it so that its height is the same as the height of the cylinder.

1. Estimate the ratio of the volume of the cylinder to the volume of the cone.

2. Fill the cone with sand, rice, or another suitable material, so that the material is level with the open end of the cone. Then, empty the material from the cone into the cylinder. Repeat until the cylinder is full.

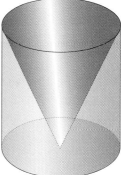

a) How many cones full of material does it take to fill the cylinder?

b) How close was your estimate in question 1?

3. From your results, what fraction of the volume of the cylinder is the volume of the cone?

4. In the preceding section, you wrote a formula for the volume of a cylinder in terms of the radius of the base, r, and the height, h. Use this formula and your result from question 3 to write a formula for the volume, V, of a cone in terms of the radius of the base, r, and the height, h.

9.3 Surface Area and Volume of a Cylinder and a Cone

Nearly perfect cylindrical shapes can be found in nature. An example is this part of the trunk of one of Canada's biggest trees. It is a Douglas fir that grows near Port Renfrew on Vancouver Island.

Recall that a cylinder is a three-dimensional figure, with two congruent circular bases connected by a curved lateral surface. The height of a cylinder, h, is the perpendicular distance between the two bases.

In a right cylinder, the segment joining the centres of the bases is perpendicular to the bases. Assume that all the cylinders referred to in this book are right cylinders.

Explore: Develop a Formula

In the diagram of the cylinder, each base has radius r, and the height is h. The net of the cylinder is also shown.

a) How does the surface area of the net compare with the surface area of the cylinder? Explain.

b) What shape in the net has the same area as the curved lateral surface of the cylinder?

Inquire

1. a) What name is given to the distance around the top of the cylinder?
b) Write a formula for this distance in terms of r.

2. a) How does the length of the rectangle compare with the distance around the top of the cylinder?
b) What is the length of the rectangle in terms of r?

3. Write a formula for the area of the rectangle in terms of r and h.

4. Write a formula for the combined area of the two bases.

5. Use the results of questions 3 and 4 to write a formula for the surface area of the cylinder.

Example 1 Surface Area of a Juice Can

The cylindrical juice can has a diameter of 6 cm and a height of 13 cm. Find the surface area, to the nearest square centimetre.

Solution

The formula for the lateral area, $L.A.$, of a cylinder is $L.A. = 2\pi rh$.
The formula for the surface area, $S.A.$, of a cylinder is $S.A. = 2\pi r^2 + 2\pi rh$.

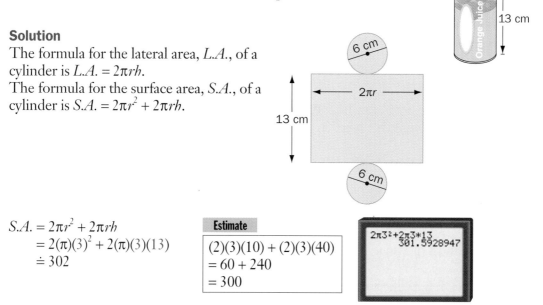

$$S.A. = 2\pi r^2 + 2\pi rh$$
$$= 2(\pi)(3)^2 + 2(\pi)(3)(13)$$
$$\doteq 302$$

Estimate

$(2)(3)(10) + (2)(3)(40)$
$= 60 + 240$
$= 300$

```
2π3²+2π3*13
        301.5928947
```

The surface area of the juice can is 302 cm², to the nearest square centimetre.

2 ⊠ π ⊠ 3 x² ⊕ 2 ⊠ π ⊠ 3 ⊠ 13 ⊜
301.5928947

As with a prism, the volume of a cylinder can be found by multiplying the area of the base and the height.

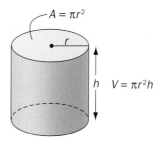

$A = \pi r^2$

$h \quad V = \pi r^2 h$

Example 2 Volume of a Tennis-Ball Can

Find the volume of the tennis-ball can, to the nearest cubic centimetre.

Solution

$$V = \pi r^2 h$$
$$= (\pi)(3.8)^2(20.3)$$
$$\doteq 921$$

Estimate

$(3)(4)^2(20) = 960$

```
π3.8²*20.3
        920.9013377
```

π ⊠ 3 ⊡ 8 x² ⊠ 20 ⊡ 3 ⊜ 920.9013377

The volume of the tennis-ball can is 921 cm³, to the nearest cubic centimetre.

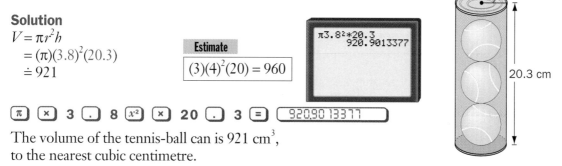

Recall that a **cone** is a three-dimensional figure, with a circular base connected by a curved lateral surface to a point called the vertex.

In a **right cone**, the segment joining the centre of the base to the vertex is perpendicular to the base. Assume that all the cones referred to in this book are right cones.

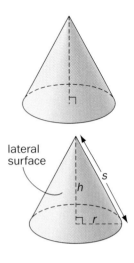

lateral surface

The height, h, of a cone is the perpendicular distance from the vertex to the base. The slant height, s, is the distance from the vertex to a point on the edge of the base.

The surface area, $S.A.$, of a cone is the sum of the lateral area, $L.A.$, and the area of the circular base.

The formula for the lateral area of a cone is $L.A. = \pi r s$.
The formula for the surface area of a cone is $S.A. = \pi r^2 + \pi r s$.

Example 3 Surface Area of a Cone
Calculate the surface area of the cone, to the nearest square centimetre.

Solution

$$S.A. = \pi r^2 + \pi r s$$
$$= (\pi)(6)^2 + (\pi)(6)(10)$$
$$\doteq 302$$

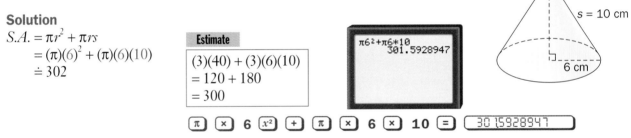

Estimate

$(3)(40) + (3)(6)(10)$
$= 120 + 180$
$= 300$

π62+π6*10
301.5928947

π × 6 x² + π × 6 × 10 = 301.5928947

The surface area of the cone is 302 cm², to the nearest square centimetre.

The volume of a cone is one third of the volume of a cylinder with the same base and height.

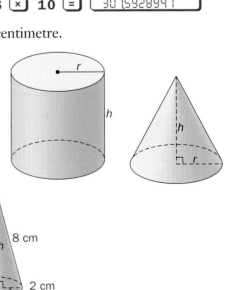

Example 4 Volume of a Cone
Find the volume of the cone, to the nearest cubic centimetre.

8 cm

2 cm

Solution

Use the Pythagorean Theorem to find the height, h.

$$h^2 + r^2 = s^2$$
$$h^2 + 2^2 = 8^2$$
$$h^2 + 4 = 64$$
$$h^2 = 60$$
$$h = \sqrt{60}$$

We could evaluate $\sqrt{60}$ as about 7.7, but $\sqrt{60}$ is the exact value.

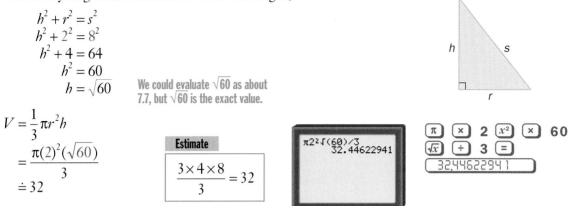

$$V = \frac{1}{3}\pi r^2 h$$
$$= \frac{\pi(2)^2(\sqrt{60})}{3}$$
$$\doteq 32$$

Estimate
$$\frac{3 \times 4 \times 8}{3} = 32$$

```
π2²√(60)/3
        32.44622941
```

```
π  ×  2  x²  ×  60
√x̄  ÷  3  =
    32.44622941
```

The volume of the cone is 32 cm^3, to the nearest cubic centimetre.

Practice

 A

Calculate each surface area, to the nearest square centimetre.

1.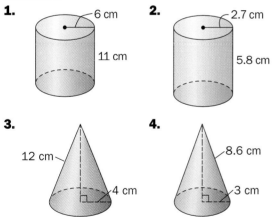
6 cm
11 cm

2.
2.7 cm
5.8 cm

3.
12 cm
4 cm

4.
8.6 cm
3 cm

Estimate, and then calculate each volume, to the nearest cubic unit.

5.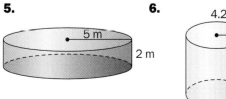
5 m
2 m

6.
4.2 cm
12.4 cm

7.
14 cm
10 cm

8.
4 m
3 m

Calculate the lateral area, to the nearest square centimetre.

9.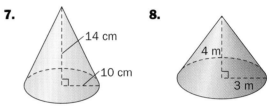
7 cm
18 cm

10.
14 cm
6 cm

Calculate the surface area, to the nearest square unit.

11.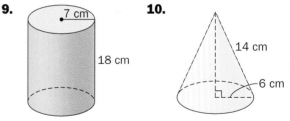
8 m
9 m

12.
5 cm
8.4 cm

13.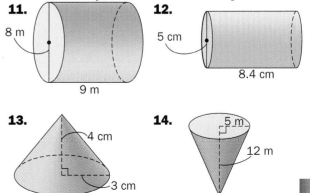
4 cm
3 cm

14.
5 m
12 m

Calculate the surface area and volume of the following, to the nearest square or cubic unit.

15.

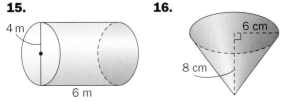

4 m

6 m

16.

6 cm

8 cm

Applications and Problem Solving

17. Paper cup A paper cup at a water dispenser has a conical shape. The radius of the cup is 3 cm, and its height is 6 cm.
a) Find the slant height of the cup, to the nearest tenth of a centimetre.
b) Calculate how much paper, to the nearest square centimetre, is required to make the cup.

B

18. Canadarm Canada's contribution to the International Space Station is a Space Station Remote Manipulator System. It is a larger version of the Canadarm that is used on the space shuttle. The arm is a cylinder that is 17 m long with a diameter of 40 cm. What is the lateral area, to the nearest square centimetre?

19. Asphalt compactor An asphalt compactor, used for paving highways, has two large cylindrical drums, one at the front and one at the rear. Each drum has a radius of 1 m and a width of 2.2 m. Calculate the area of asphalt that a single revolution of a drum compacts, to the nearest tenth of a square metre.

20. Water tank A hobby club runs remote-controlled boats in a tank that is shaped as shown.

2.2 m   4.2 m

What volume of water can this tank hold, to the nearest cubic metre?

21. Container A cone-shaped container has a diameter of 20 cm and a height of 20 cm. How many litres of water will the cone hold, to the nearest litre?

C

22. Storm sewers The dimensions for a section of concrete pipe used to make storm sewers is shown in the diagram.

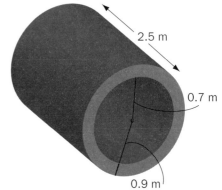

2.5 m

0.7 m

0.9 m

Calculate the volume of concrete that is needed to make this section of pipe, to the nearest tenth of a cubic metre.

23. Frustum of a cone The frustum of a cone is the part that remains after the top portion has been cut off by a plane parallel to the base. A frustum of a cone is shown. Calculate the volume, to the nearest cubic metre.

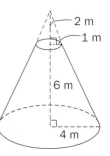

2 m
1 m
6 m
4 m

24. Shipping carton Paper towels are sold in packages of 2 rolls. Each roll is a cylinder with a height of 30 cm and an outer diameter of 12 cm.
a) Design a shipping carton that will contain 12 packages of paper towels.
b) The inner diameter of each roll is 4 cm. How much wasted space is there in the carton?

25. Write a problem that requires the calculation of the surface area and volume of a cylinder or a cone. Have a classmate solve your problem.

Varying the Dimensions of Prisms and Cylinders

1 Volumes and Surface Areas of Prisms

1. Sketch the three rectangular prisms with the dimensions shown, or build models using linking cubes. Then, copy and complete the table, or complete the calculations using a spreadsheet.

Prism	Width (cm)	Length (cm)	Height (cm)	Volume (cm³)	Surface Area (cm²)
1	1	2	3		
2	2	4	6		
3	3	6	9		

2. How many times as great are
a) the dimensions of prism 2 as the dimensions of prism 1?
b) the volume of prism 2 as the volume of prism 1?
c) the surface area of prism 2 as the surface area of prism 1?

3. How many times as great are
a) the dimensions of prism 3 as the dimensions of prism 1?
b) the volume of prism 3 as the volume of prism 1?
c) the surface area of prism 3 as the surface area of prism 1?

4. How does the volume of a prism change when all dimensions are increased by a factor of
a) 2?　　　　**b)** 3?

5. How does the surface area of a prism change when all dimensions are increased by a factor of
a) 2?　　　　**b)** 3?

6. Predict how the volume of a prism would change if all dimensions were increased by a factor of
a) 4　　　　**b)** 10

7. Predict how the surface area of a prism would change if all dimensions were increased by a factor of
a) 4　　　　**b)** 10

8. a) Calculate the surface area and volume of the prism shown.
b) If the dimensions were halved, what would the volume be?
c) What fraction would the smaller volume be of the larger volume?
d) If the dimensions were halved, what would the surface area be?
e) What fraction would the smaller surface area be of the larger surface area?

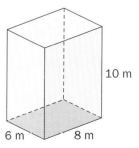

10 m

6 m　　8 m

9. Write a statement about the change in the volume of a prism when all dimensions are changed by a factor of k.

10. Write a statement about the change in the surface area of a prism when all dimensions are changed by a factor of k.

2 Volumes and Surface Areas of Cylinders

1. Copy and complete the table for the three cylinders, or use a spreadsheet. Express each volume and surface area in terms of π. For example, the volume of the first cylinder is $\pi \times 1^2 \times 3$, or 3π cm^2.

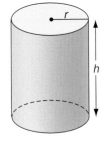

Cylinder	Radius (cm)	Height (cm)	Volume (cm³)	Surface Area (cm²)
1	1	3		
2	2	6		
3	3	9		

2. How many times as great are
a) the dimensions of cylinder 2 as the dimensions of cylinder 1?
b) the volume of cylinder 2 as the volume of cylinder 1?
c) the surface area of cylinder 2 as the surface area of cylinder 1?

3. How many times as great are
a) the dimensions of cylinder 3 as the dimensions of cylinder 1?
b) the volume of cylinder 3 as the volume of cylinder 1?
c) the surface area of cylinder 3 as the surface area of cylinder 1?

4. How does the volume of a cylinder change when all dimensions are increased by a factor of
a) 2?   **b)** 3?

5. How does the surface area of a cylinder change when all dimensions are increased by a factor of
a) 2?   **b)** 3?

6. Predict how the volume of a cylinder would change if all dimensions were increased by a factor of
a) 4   **b)** 10

7. Predict how the surface area of a cylinder would change if all dimensions were increased by a factor of
a) 4   **b)** 10

8. a) Calculate, in terms of π, the volume and surface area of a cylinder with a radius of 4 cm and a height of 6 cm.
b) If the dimensions were halved, what would the volume be, in terms of π?
c) What fraction would the smaller volume be of the larger volume?
d) If the dimensions were halved, what would the surface area be, in terms of π?
e) What fraction would the smaller surface area be of the larger surface area?

9. Write a statement about the change in the volume of a cylinder when all dimensions are changed by a factor of k.

10. Write a statement about the change in the surface area of a cylinder when all dimensions are changed by a factor of k.

11. a) Calculate the volumes of cylinders 1 and 2 to the nearest tenth of a cubic centimetre, instead of expressing them in terms of π.
b) Divide the larger volume from part a) by the smaller volume from part a). Is the result a whole number?
📝 **c)** Explain why the volumes and surface areas compared in questions 2, 3, and 8 were expressed in terms of π.

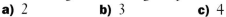

3 Changing Selected Dimensions of Prisms

1. The prism has a length of 3 m, a width of 2 m, and a height of 4 m. Calculate
a) the volume
b) the surface area

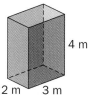

2. Calculate the new volume when the width and height are not changed but the length of the original prism is increased by a factor of
a) 2   **b)** 3   **c)** 4

📝 **3. a)** What happens to the volume when only the length of the prism is multiplied by 2? by 3? by 4?
🧩 **b)** If only the length of the prism were changed, would a graph of volume versus length be linear? If so, would the variation be direct or partial? Explain.

4. Calculate the new surface area when the width and height are not changed but the length of the original prism is increased by a factor of
a) 2   **b)** 3   **c)** 4

📝 **5. a)** What happens to the surface area when only the length of the prism is multiplied by 2? by 3? by 4?
🧩 **b)** If only the length of the prism were changed, would a graph of surface area versus length be linear? If so, would the variation be direct or partial? Explain.

6. Calculate the new volume when the height is not changed but both the length and the width of the original prism are increased by a factor of
a) 2   **b)** 3   **c)** 4

📝 **7.** What happens to the volume when both the length and the width of the prism are multiplied by 2? by 3? by 4?

8. Calculate the new surface area when the height is not changed but both the length and the width of the original prism are increased by a factor of
a) 2   **b)** 3   **c)** 4

📝 **9.** What happens to the surface area when both the length and the width of the prism are multiplied by 2? by 3? by 4?

INVESTIGATING MATH

Surface Area and Volume of a Regular Pyramid

A **pyramid** is a polyhedron with one base in the shape of a polygon and the same number of lateral triangular faces as there are sides in the base. The lateral triangular faces meet at a point called the **vertex** of the pyramid.

A **regular pyramid** has a regular polygon as its base. All the sides of the base are the same length, and all the lateral faces are congruent triangles. Assume that all the pyramids referred to in this book are regular pyramids.

The **height**, h, of a pyramid is the perpendicular distance from the vertex to the base. The **slant height**, s, is the height of each triangular face.

Regular Pyramid

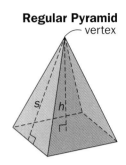

1 Modelling the Surface Area

The surface area of a pyramid can be found by adding the areas of the lateral triangular faces and the area of the base.

1. A square-based pyramid and its net are shown. Calculate the surface area of the pyramid.

2. A regular triangular pyramid and its net are shown. Calculate the surface area of the pyramid.

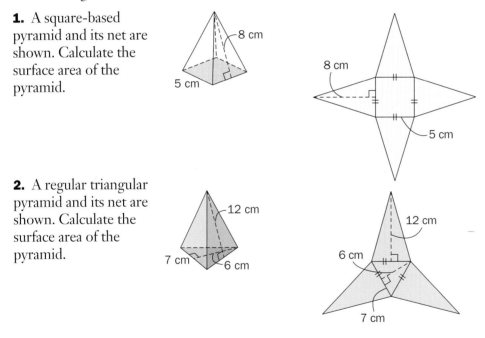

3. Calculate the surface area of each regular pyramid.

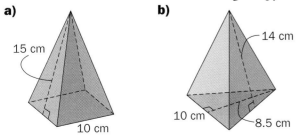

a)

15 cm

10 cm

b)

14 cm

10 cm

8.5 cm

2 Modelling the Volume

For this investigation, you will need an empty 250-mL milk carton, construction paper or cardboard, scissors, tape, and sand, rice, or another suitable material. The investigation involves finding the formula for the volume of a pyramid by comparing it to a prism with the same base and height as the pyramid.

Cut the top from an empty 250-mL milk carton to form a prism. On construction paper or cardboard, draw the net of a pyramid that has the same base dimensions and the same height as the prism. Cut out the net, tape it, and place the pyramid inside the prism.

1. Estimate the ratio of the volume of the prism to the volume of the pyramid.

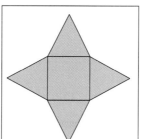

2. Cut along three sides of the base of the pyramid. Fill the pyramid with sand, rice, or another suitable material, so that the material is level with the open end of the pyramid. Then, empty the material from the pyramid into the prism. Repeat until the prism is full.

a) How many pyramids full of material does it take to fill the prism?

b) How close was your estimate in question 1?

3. From your results, what fraction of the volume of the prism is the volume of the pyramid?

4. The formula for the volume of a prism, V, with base area B and height h is $V = B \times h$. What is the formula for the volume of a pyramid, V, with the same base area, B, and the same height, h?

INVESTIGATING MATH

Surface Area and Volume of a Sphere

1 Modelling the Surface Area

For this investigation you will need a ball, such as a baseball or tennis ball, which approximates a sphere. You will also need a tape measure, scissors, compasses, paper, and tape.

1. Use a tape measure to find the circumference of the ball, which is the greatest distance around its surface.

2. Substitute the circumference, C, into the formula $C = 2\pi r$, where r is the radius of the ball. Find r, to the nearest tenth of a centimetre.

3. Draw a circle whose radius is equal to the radius of the ball. Cut out the circle.

4. Fold the circle into eighths. Then, unfold it and cut the pieces apart.

5. Rearrange the pieces into the pattern shown, and tape the pattern together.

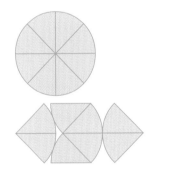

6. Tape the pattern to the ball.

7. Estimate the fraction of the surface of the ball that the pattern appears to cover.

8. How many patterns would be needed to cover the sphere?

9. What is the area of the pattern in terms of r, the radius of the sphere?

10. Write a formula for the surface area of a sphere, in terms of r.

11. For each sphere with the given radius, use the formula from question 10 to calculate the surface area, to the nearest square centimetre.
a) 8 cm   **b)** 10 cm   **c)** 20 cm

2 Modelling the Volume

1. A sphere of radius r fits inside the cylinder, so that the sphere just touches the top, bottom, and sides of the cylinder.

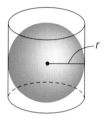

a) State the radius of the cylinder, in terms of r.

b) State the height of the cylinder, in terms of r.

2. Write a formula for the volume of the cylinder, in terms of r.

3. The volume of the sphere is two thirds of the volume of the cylinder. Write a formula for the volume of the sphere, in terms of r.

4. For each sphere with the given radius, use the formula from question 3 to calculate the volume, to the nearest cubic metre.
a) 4 m   **b)** 5 m   **c)** 7 m

5. Suppose you have a sphere and a cylinder, with sizes that compare as described in question 1. You also have a measuring cylinder and a supply of water.

a) Design an experiment you could perform to show how the volume of the cylinder and the volume of the sphere are related.

b) If possible, carry out the experiment. Do your results verify that the volume of the sphere is two thirds of the volume of the cylinder?

9.4 Surface Area and Volume of a Pyramid and a Sphere

A **regular pyramid** is a polyhedron with a base that is a regular polygon and lateral faces that are congruent triangles. The **slant height**, *s*, is the length of the altitude of a triangular face. The **height**, *h*, of the pyramid is the perpendicular distance from the vertex to the base.

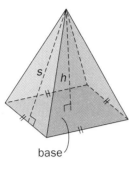

base

The **lateral area** of a pyramid is the sum of the areas of the lateral triangular faces. The **surface area** is the sum of the areas of all the faces, or the sum of the lateral area and the area of the base.

The Great Pyramid of Khufu is an example of a regular pyramid. It is the largest of the three pyramids built at Giza by an ancient Egyptian civilization around 2500 B.C. Each side of the square base of the pyramid measures about 230 m. The slant height of a lateral face is 187 m. It is believed that 4000 workers took 30 years to build the pyramid.

Explore: Use the Information

The diagram shows a square-based pyramid. The side length of the base is 12 m, and the height is 8 m.

In the red triangle, use the Pythagorean Theorem to calculate the slant height.

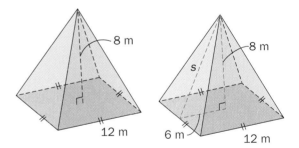

Inquire

1. What is the area of each triangular face?

2. What is the lateral area of the pyramid?

3. What is the area of the base?

4. What is the surface area of the pyramid?

5. a) What is the lateral area of the Great Pyramid of Khufu?
b) How many football fields would it take to cover this area?

The surface area of a pyramid can be found by adding the areas of all the faces. However, a formula can be developed to find the surface area.

For the regular pyramid shown, b is the side length of the base, and s is the slant height of each triangular face.
The perimeter of the base, P, is the sum of the side lengths, $b + b + b + b$ or $4b$.
Use the net to write the formula for the lateral area, $L.A.$

Add the areas of the lateral faces: $\quad L.A. = \dfrac{1}{2}bs + \dfrac{1}{2}bs + \dfrac{1}{2}bs + \dfrac{1}{2}bs$

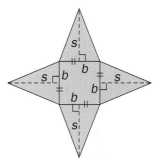

Use the distributive property: $\quad L.A. = \dfrac{1}{2}s(b + b + b + b)$

$$= \dfrac{1}{2}s(4b)$$

Substitute P for $4b$: $\quad L.A. = \dfrac{1}{2}sP$ or $\dfrac{1}{2}Ps$

The surface area, $S.A.$, is found by adding the lateral area and the area of the base, B.

So, $S.A. = \dfrac{1}{2}Ps + B$

The formula $S.A. = \dfrac{1}{2}Ps + B$ can be used to find the surface area of any regular pyramid.

Example 1   Surface Area of a Square-Based Pyramid
Calculate the surface area of the pyramid.
The side length of the base is 8 m and the slant height is 10 m.

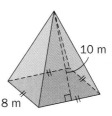

Solution
Calculate the perimeter of the base, P: $\quad P = 4 \times 8$
$$= 32$$
Calculate the area of the base, B: $\quad B = 8 \times 8$
$$= 64$$
Calculate the surface area, $S.A.$: $\quad S.A. = \dfrac{1}{2}Ps + B$
$$= \dfrac{1}{2} \times 32 \times 10 + 64$$
$$= 160 + 64$$
$$= 224$$

The surface area is 224 m^2.

The volume of a pyramid is one third of the volume of a prism with the same base and height.

Prism   Pyramid

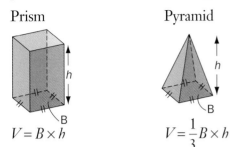

$V = B \times h$ $V = \dfrac{1}{3} B \times h$

B is the area of the base and h is the height.

Example 2   Volume of a Pyramid

Find the volume of the pyramid, to the nearest cubic metre.

9 m

4 m

Solution

The slant height, s, is 9 m and the side length of the base is 4 m.
Use the Pythagorean Theorem to find the height, h.

$$h^2 + 2^2 = 9^2$$
$$h^2 + 4 = 81$$
$$h^2 = 77$$ We could evaluate $\sqrt{77} \doteq 8.8$, but there is no need to
$$h = \sqrt{77}$$ approximate at this stage when using a calculator.

9 m h

2 m   4 m

Calculate the area of the base: $B = 4 \times 4$
$$= 16$$

Calculate the volume: $V = \dfrac{1}{3} \times B \times h$

$$= \dfrac{1}{3} \times 16 \times \sqrt{77}$$

$$\doteq 47$$

16 $\boxed{\times}$ 77 $\boxed{\sqrt{x}}$ $\boxed{\div}$ 3 $\boxed{=}$

$\boxed{46.7998\,1007}$

Estimate

$$\dfrac{1}{3} \times 16 \times 9 = 48$$

The volume of the pyramid is 47 m^3, to the nearest cubic metre.

The formula for the surface area of a sphere with radius r is $S.A. = 4\pi r^2$.

r

$S.A. = 4\pi r^2$

Example 3   Surface Area of a Volleyball

The radius of a volleyball is 10.2 cm. Calculate the surface area of the volleyball, to the nearest square centimetre.

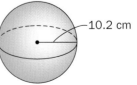

10.2 cm

Solution

The radius, r, is 10.2 cm.

$S.A. = 4\pi r^2$

$\quad = 4 \times \pi \times 10.2^2$

$\quad \doteq 1307$

The surface area of the volleyball is
1307 cm^2, to the nearest square centimetre.

Estimate

$4 \times 3 \times 100 = 1200$

To find the formula for the volume of a sphere, imagine a
sphere being filled with a large number, n, of small identical
pyramids, each with a base area B.

The vertex of each pyramid is the centre of the sphere.
The height of each pyramid, h, is the radius of the sphere, r.
The sum of the areas of the bases of all n pyramids, nB,
approximates the surface area of the sphere, $4\pi r^2$.

The volume of each pyramid is $\dfrac{1}{3}Bh$ or $\dfrac{1}{3}Br$.

Express the total volume, V, of all n pyramids: $\quad V = n \times \dfrac{1}{3}Br$

Rearrange the right side: $\qquad\qquad\qquad V = \dfrac{1}{3} \times nB \times r$

Substitute $4\pi r^2$ for nB: $\qquad\qquad\qquad V = \dfrac{1}{3} \times 4\pi r^2 \times r$

Simplify: $\qquad\qquad\qquad\qquad\qquad V = \dfrac{4}{3}\pi r^3$

So, the formula for the volume of a sphere is $V = \dfrac{4}{3}\pi r^3$.

Example 4   Volume of a Baseball

The diameter of a baseball is 7.4 cm. Calculate the volume of
the baseball, to the nearest cubic centimetre.

Solution

The diameter is 7.4 cm. The radius is 3.7 cm.

$V = \dfrac{4}{3}\pi r^3$

$\quad = \dfrac{4}{3}(\pi)(3.7)^3$

$\quad \doteq 212$

Estimate

$1 \times 3 \times 64 = 192$

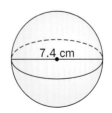

The volume of the baseball is 212 cm^3, to the
nearest cubic centimetre.

Practice

Calculate the surface area. Round to the nearest square unit, if necessary.

1.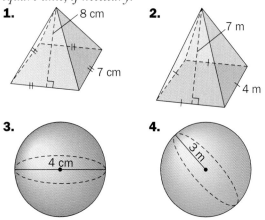
8 cm
7 cm

2.
7 m
4 m

3.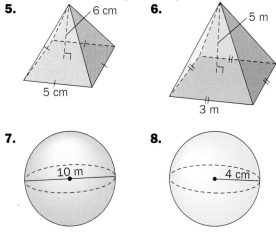
4 cm

4.
3 m

Estimate, and then calculate each volume. Round to the nearest cubic unit, if necessary.

5.
6 cm
5 cm

6.
5 m
3 m

7.
10 m

8.
4 cm

Calculate the surface area and the volume. Round to the nearest square or cubic metre, if necessary.

9.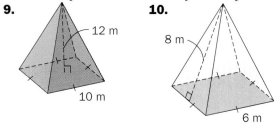
12 m
10 m

10.
8 m
6 m

11. Calculate the surface area of the regular triangular pyramid.

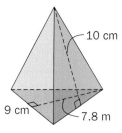
10 cm
9 cm
7.8 m

Applications and Problem Solving

12. Golf ball A golf ball is in the shape of a sphere with radius 20 mm. What is its surface area, to the nearest square millimetre?

13. Calculate the surface area and volume of the hemisphere, to the nearest square or cubic metre.

6 m

Find the surface area and volume of each composite figure. Round to the nearest square or cubic unit, if necessary.

14.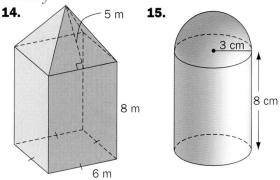
5 m
8 m
6 m

15.
3 cm
8 cm

16. A sphere has a surface area of 250 cm^2. What is its radius, to the nearest tenth of a centimetre?

17. Frustum of a pyramid The frustum of a pyramid is the part that remains after the top portion has been cut off by a plane parallel to the base. A frustum of a regular pyramid is shown. Find the surface area.

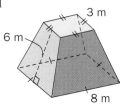
3 m
6 m
8 m

18. What is the volume, in terms of π, of a sphere with a surface area of 16π m^2? Explain how you used mathematical modelling to solve the problem.

19. Two spheres have diameters of 10 cm and 20 cm.
a) Calculate the surface area of each sphere, to the nearest square centimetre.
b) Divide the larger surface area by the smaller surface area from part a).
c) Can you be sure of the exact answer to part b)? Explain.
d) Express the surface area of each sphere in terms of π.
e) Divide the larger surface area by the smaller surface area from part d).
f) Can you be sure of the exact answer to part e)? Explain.
g) What is the advantage of expressing surface areas in terms of π before comparing them?

20. Use your findings in question 19 to help answer each of the following.
a) What happens to the surface area of a sphere when its diameter is doubled? tripled? halved?
b) What happens to the volume of a sphere when its diameter is doubled? tripled? halved?

21. Planets The radius of Neptune is 10 times the radius of Mercury. State the ratio of
a) the surface area of Neptune to the surface area of Mercury
b) the volume of Neptune to the volume of Mercury

22. Canada's area The diameter of the Earth is 12 756 km.
a) Calculate the area of the Northern Hemisphere, to the nearest square kilometre.
b) What assumptions have you made?
c) The area of Canada is 9 970 610 km^2. Estimate the fraction of the Northern Hemisphere that Canada covers.

23. What happens to the volume of a square pyramid under each of the following conditions?
a) The base is unchanged, but the height is doubled.
b) The base is unchanged, but the height is tripled.
c) The height is unchanged, but the area of the base is doubled.

C

24. Earth's mantle The Earth's core has a radius of about 3470 km. The core is surrounded by the mantle, which is about 2900 km thick. What is the volume of the mantle, to the nearest billion cubic kilometres?

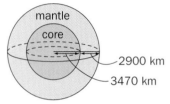

25. A pyramid sits inside a cube, so that the base of the pyramid is a face of the cube. What is the maximum possible volume of the pyramid, if the edge length of the cube is 24 cm?

26. A pyramid and a prism have congruent square bases and equal volumes. How do their heights compare? Explain and justify your reasoning.

27. Oranges If an orange of diameter 6 cm costs 25¢, and an orange of diameter 9 cm costs 50¢, which is the better value? Explain your answer, and state any assumptions that you made.

PATTERN POWER

Copy and complete the following.

$1^3 = 1$
$1^3 + 2^3 = 9$
$1^3 + 2^3 + 3^3 =$ ▆▆▆
$1^3 + 2^3 + 3^3 + 4^3 =$ ▆▆▆
$1^3 + 2^3 + 3^3 + 4^3 + 5^3 =$ ▆▆▆

Describe the pattern.

TECHNOLOGY

Design Problems in Three Dimensions

1 Designing Boxes

Many cardboard boxes are made in the shape of a rectangular prism. Suppose you are an industrial designer who must decide what dimensions to use for a box to hold 12 objects, each the size of a one-centimetre cube. The surface area of the box must be a minimum, so that the least amount of material is used to make the box.

1. Make a hypothesis in which you predict the dimensions of the box, if it must be
a) a square-based prism
b) a rectangular prism

Note that rectangular prisms include square-based prisms.

2. Using 12 one-centimetre cubes in each case, make the following prisms. Alternatively, sketch the prisms. Record their dimensions.
a) 2 different square-based prisms
b) 4 different rectangular prisms

3. Set up a computer spreadsheet to determine the surface area of
a) each square-based prism
b) each rectangular prism

	A	B	C	D	E	F
1	Prism	Width (cm)	Length (cm)	Height (cm)	Volume (cm^3)	Surface Area (cm^2)
2	1				12	
3	2				12	
4	3				12	
5	4				12	

4. The most cost-effective, or cheapest, container of a given volume is the one that uses the least material. What dimensions of the prism make the most cost-effective box if it is
a) square based?
b) rectangular?

5. Compare the dimensions from question 4 with each hypothesis from question 1.

6. a) Add a final column to each spreadsheet to calculate the rate $\dfrac{\text{volume}}{\text{surface area}}$, to 2 decimal places, for each prism.
b) What happens to this rate as a box becomes more cost-effective?

7. Many boxes do not have whole-number dimensions. Suppose you had to design a box to hold 8 m^3 of product. Possible dimensions of the box would include 8 m × 1 m × 1 m, 2 m × 2 m × 2 m, 1.6 m × 2 m × 2.5 m, and 1 m × 1.25 m × 6.4 m. For dimensions that you choose, complete a spreadsheet to find the surface area of
a) each square-based prism
b) each rectangular prism

8. What are the dimensions and the shape of the 8-m^3 box that is most cost-effective, if it is
a) square based?   **b)** rectangular?

9. Are the following boxes made in the shape that is most cost-effective? If not, give possible reasons.
a) square-based cracker boxes
b) rectangular cereal boxes

2 Designing Cans

Industrial designers must also decide the height and radius to use for a cylindrical container. If the surface area is a minimum, the least amount of material is used to make the container.

1. The spreadsheet shows the radii and heights of four cylindrical cans.

	A	B	C	D	E
1	Can	Radius (cm)	Height (cm)	Volume (cm³)	Surface Area (cm²)
2	1	1	36		
3	2	2	9		
4	3	3	4		
5	4	6	1		

Make a hypothesis in which you predict which of the 4 cans is the most cost-effective. You may want to build models of the cans.

2. Use the spreadsheet to calculate each volume and surface area. Round each volume and surface area to the nearest whole number.

3. a) Which of the 4 cans is the most cost-effective?
b) Compare your answer from part a) with your hypothesis in question 1.

4. a) Sketch the front view of the most cost-effective can as it would appear to a customer in a grocery store.
b) Why do you think cylindrical cans are not all made in this shape?

5. Think about food products that come in cylindrical cans. Give possible reasons why each shape of cylinder is used for each can.

3 Heat Loss

1. Hot box You have been asked to design a rectangular container, called a hot box, for catering companies to use to transport hot food. The container must have a volume of 125 000 cm³. Once the hot food is placed in the container, the container loses heat through its sides, top, and bottom. In order to keep the heat loss to a minimum, the total area of the faces must be a minimum.
a) What shape for the container has the minimum surface area?
b) What is the minimum surface area?

2. a) If you were not restricted to a rectangular shape, what shape would have the minimum surface area?
b) What are the disadvantages of using this shape for a hot box?

3. Use your answer to question 2a) to explain why cats curl up in a ball when they sleep.

CAREER CONNECTION

Architecture

Architecture is the science and art of planning, designing, and constructing buildings. A skilled architect designs buildings that are long-lasting, useful, comfortable, and pleasing to the eye.

Moshe Safdie is one of Canada's most famous architects. His best-known buildings in Canada are Habitat, in Montréal, and the National Gallery, in Ottawa.

Habitat consists of about 150 private homes. Each is a prefabricated concrete unit. The units are arranged irregularly, so that there is as much privacy as possible.

Habitat, designed by Canadian architect Moshe Safdie.

There are two common types of drawings that architects use to display an object.

An **isometric view** is an attempt to represent a three-dimensional object in a two-dimensional drawing. An isometric view can also be called a corner view of the object. When drawing an isometric view, it is helpful to use isometric dot paper.

An **orthographic view** represents two dimensions of an object, as it appears from the top, front, and right side. When drawing orthographic views, it is helpful to use grid paper or square dot paper.

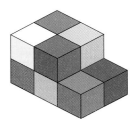

In an orthographic view, any hidden edges of an object are shown as dashed lines. In an isometric view, any hidden edges are not shown.

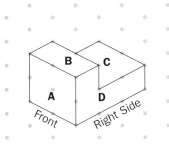

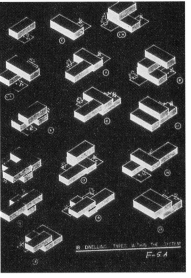

Moshe Safdie's isometric views of the homes in Habitat.

496 *Chapter 9*

1 Isometric and Orthographic Views

1. Use the isometric view of each object to draw its orthographic views.

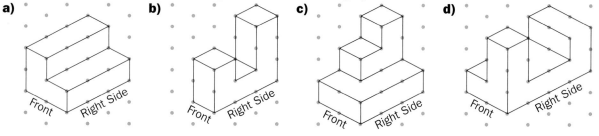

a)   b)   c)   d)

2. Use the orthographic views of each object to draw its isometric view.

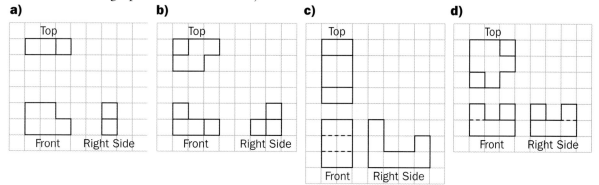

a)   b)   c)   d)

3. In the isometric views in question 1, assume that the shortest distance between two grid points represents 1 unit of length. For each object in question 1, determine the volume, the surface area, and the rate $\dfrac{\text{volume}}{\text{surface area}}$.

4. Why would an architect want to know the rate $\dfrac{\text{volume}}{\text{surface area}}$ for a building?

2 Base Designs

For an object built from linking cubes, the **base design** shows the top view of the object and the number of cubes in each column.

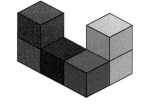

Base Design

Use the following base designs to draw the orthographic and isometric views of each object.

1.
4.

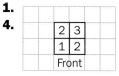

2	3
1	2

Front

2.

1	2	2
1	1	2

Front

3.

3	2	1
1		1

Front

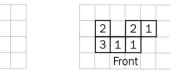

2		2	1
3	1	1	

Front

TECHNOLOGY

Graphing Calculator Programs for Surface Area and Volume

1 Using a Program

The graphing calculator program shown can be used to calculate the surface area of a cone.

This is the program.   This example used the program.

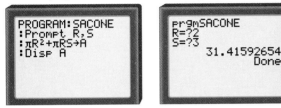

1. Describe what each line of the program does.

2. Explain why the symbol π is used in the program, rather than the value 3.14.

3. Input the program and use it to calculate the surface area of a cone with a base of radius 3.5 cm and a slant height of 4.3 cm. Round your answer to the nearest tenth of a square centimetre.

2 Writing Programs

1. Write a program that can be used to calculate the surface area of each of the following. In each case, describe what each line of the program does.
a) cylinder   **b)** sphere   **c)** square-based pyramid

2. Write a program that can be used to calculate the volume of each of the following. In each case, describe what each line of the program does.
a) cylinder   **b)** sphere   **c)** cone   **d)** square-based pyramid

To check that the programs work, use them to calculate each of the following. Round each answer to the nearest tenth of a square or cubic unit.
3. surface area and volume of a cylinder with a base of radius 4.5 cm and a height of 5.9 cm

4. surface area and volume of a sphere of radius 3.9 m

5. volume of a cone with a base of radius 2.1 m and a height of 3.8 m

6. surface area and volume of a square-based pyramid with base dimensions 2.4 cm by 2.4 cm, a height of 1.6 cm, and a slant height of 2 cm

9.5 Volume, Capacity, and Mass

The world's sixth largest reservoir is the Daniel Johnson Reservoir at Manicouagan, Québec. The volume of water in this reservoir when it is full is 141 852 000 000 m³.

The greatest volume a container, such as a reservoir, can hold is known as the container's **capacity**. The capacity of a container is expressed in litres and millilitres. Large capacities may be expressed in kilolitres.

$$1000 \text{ mL} = 1 \text{ L}$$
$$1000 \text{ L} = 1 \text{ kL}$$

The **mass** of an object is a measure of the quantity of matter in the object. Mass is measured in milligrams, grams, kilograms, and tonnes.

$$1000 \text{ mg} = 1 \text{ g}$$
$$1000 \text{ g} = 1 \text{ kg}$$
$$1000 \text{ kg} = 1 \text{ t}$$

Explore: Interpret the Diagrams

The diagrams of three different containers filled with water illustrate a special relationship between the volume and mass of water. Note that the diagrams are not drawn to scale.

	Container 1	Container 2	Container 3
Capacity of Container	1 mL	1000 mL or 1 L	1000 L or 1 kL
Volume of Water	1 cm³	1000 cm³ or 1 dm³	1000 dm³ or 1 m³
Mass of Water	1 g	1000 g or 1 kg	1000 kg or 1 t

Inquire

1. a) Which container has a capacity of 1 kL?
b) What is the volume of water in this container?
c) What is the mass of water in this container?

2. a) Which container has a capacity of 1 L?
b) What is the volume of water in this container?
c) What is the mass of water in this container?

3. State the capacity of the Daniel Johnson Reservoir, in kilolitres.

4. State the mass of water in the Daniel Johnson Reservoir, in tonnes.

5. What mass of water could a 100-mL container hold?

6. State the capacity of a container that holds 5 kg of water.

Practice

A

Express each volume in cubic centimetres.
1. 5 dm^3 **2.** 0.032 m^3
3. 0.4 dm^3 **4.** 10 m^3

Express each volume in cubic metres.
5. 5000 dm^3 **6.** $45\,000 \text{ cm}^3$
7. 1 cm^3 **8.** $25\,200 \text{ dm}^3$

Express each capacity in litres.
9. 275 mL **10.** 15 mL
11. 1.5 kL **12.** 0.1 kL

Express each capacity in millilitres.
13. 7 L **14.** 0.25 L
15. 1 kL **16.** 0.045 L

Express each mass in grams.
17. 15 kg **18.** 4500 mg
19. 325 mg **20.** 0.35 kg

Express each mass in kilograms.
21. 28 000 g **22.** 15 t
23. 540 g **24.** 100 mg

State the volume, in cubic centimetres, of each mass of water.
25. 10 g **26.** 6.1 kg
27. 3.3 mg **28.** 0.1 g

Applications and Problem Solving

29. Food products Food products are sold in different units of measurement.
a) List 3 food products sold in units of mass.
b) List 3 food products sold in units of capacity.

30. Container State the capacity, in kilolitres, of the smallest container needed to hold 50 t of water.

31. Juice servings About how many 150-mL servings of grape juice can you pour from a 1-L container?

B

32. Orange juice A can of frozen orange juice holds 355 mL of concentrate. If you add 3 times this volume of water, how many litres of orange juice do you have? Explain how you can judge whether your answer is reasonable.

33. Trench A trench on a building site is 75% full of water. The trench measures 3 m long by 1 m wide by 2 m deep.
a) What is the volume of water in the trench?
b) What is the capacity of the trench?
c) How long does it take a pump that draws water at 0.6 m^3/min to empty the trench?

C

34. Comparing containers Two containers have the same outside dimensions but different capacities. Explain how this situation is possible.

35. Gasoline can A can with a capacity of 4 L holds 4 dm^3 of gasoline. Can you state the mass of the gasoline? Explain.

36. Milk carton a) What is the volume of milk in a 1-L carton?
b) Is the capacity of the carton exactly 1 L?
c) Would it be better to label the carton as 1 L of milk or 1 dm^3 of milk? Explain.

37. In your own words, distinguish the meanings of the terms "capacity" and "volume." Compare your answer with a classmate's.

9.6 How Can We Model the Earth in Two Dimensions?

Cartography, or the making of maps and charts, is a very old profession. For thousands of years, cartographers have tried to model the three-dimensional Earth using two-dimensional maps. The earliest surviving maps, dating from about 2300 B.C., are on clay tablets found in Iraq. Aboriginal people drew maps of parts of Canada long before Europeans arrived.

In the 2nd century A.D., an Egyptian named Ptolemy wrote a geography book that included maps of the known world. Vast parts of the world, including the Americas, were omitted. When Columbus sailed from Europe to the Americas in 1492, he thought that he had sailed to Asia! It was not until the 16th century that Gerardus Mercator's maps revolutionized navigation.

Cartography has changed dramatically. Maps, which were drawn by hand for centuries, are now created on computers. Information, often obtained from aerial photography or satellite imaging, is converted into digital form. Cartographers work with the digital information to decide colour, lines, lettering, and scales. A laser plotter draws maps directly onto photographic film for printing.

1 Modelling With Map Projections

A map projection models the three-dimensional Earth on a two-dimensional surface. It is impossible to do this without distortion. The projection a cartographer uses depends upon the purpose of the map, its scale, and the region of the Earth being mapped. Equal-area projections keep areas correct. Equidistant projections keep distances correct. Conformal projections keep shapes correct.

1. Using several different atlases, find
a) how many different projections are used
b) which projections are used most

2. To represent certain parts of the world, are some projections used more than others? If so, give possible reasons.

2 Modelling Antipodal Points

The city of Nanking, China, has a latitude of about 35°N and a longitude of about 120°E. If you travelled from Nanking through the centre of the Earth and out the other side, you would arrive close to the city of Buenos Aires, Argentina. Buenos Aires has a latitude of about 35°S and a longitude of about 60°W.

A location's antipodal point is the place on Earth directly opposite it. Nanking is the antipodal point to Buenos Aires. Two other cities related in this way are Lima, Peru, and Phnom Penh, Cambodia. Lima is located at about 10°S, 75°W. Phnom Penh is located at about 10°N, 105°E.

1. For each pair of cities, what is the relationship between the latitudes?

2. For each pair of cities, what is the relationship between the longitudes?

3. Without using latitudes and longitudes, use a map projection to estimate the location of the antipodal point to where you live.

4. Use a map to estimate the latitude and the longitude of the place where you live, to the nearest degree.

5. a) Find the latitude and the longitude of the antipodal point to where you live.
b) Does anyone live there?
c) About how far is this point from the location you estimated in question 3?

6. If two places are at antipodal points on the Earth, what is the straight-line distance between them?

3 Modelling the Area of the Earth

1. Assume that both the equatorial and polar radii of the Earth are 6400 km. Calculate the following, to the nearest whole number.

a) the surface area of the Earth

b) the equatorial circumference

c) the semi-circumference from pole to pole

d) the area that seems to be represented by the following Mercator projection, using dimensions from parts b) and c)

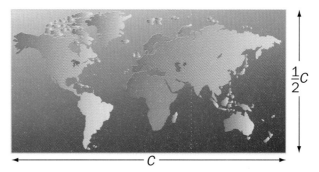

$\frac{1}{2}C$

C

2. About how many times as great as the surface area of the Earth is the area that seems to be represented by this Mercator projection?

3. Which parts of the Earth are most distorted by a Mercator projection? Explain.

4 Extending the Model

Use your research skills to find more information about each of the following.

1. the Mercator projection, and why it revolutionized navigation

2. other projections and what they distort

3. Canada's role in mapping the Earth using satellite imaging

4. the angles whose measures are a location's latitude and longitude

Review

9.1 Calculate the area of each composite figure. Round to the nearest square unit, if necessary.

1.
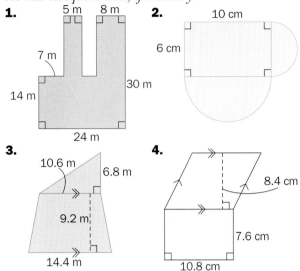
5 m   8 m
7 m
30 m
14 m
24 m

2.
10 cm
6 cm

3.
10.6 m
6.8 m
9.2 m
14.4 m

4.
8.4 cm
7.6 cm
10.8 cm

Calculate the area of each shaded region.

5.
8 cm
24 cm
13 cm
20 cm

6.
14.2 m
10.5 m
20.2 m

9.2 *Name each prism.*

7.
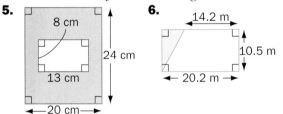

8.

Calculate the surface area.

9.
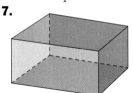
17 m
17 m
17 m

10.
14.2 cm
6.1 cm
3.5 cm

Calculate the volume.

11.
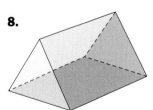
6 cm
12 cm
9 cm

12.
53 cm
41 cm
27 cm

13. Calculate the surface area and volume of the composite figure.
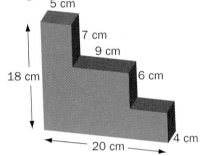
5 cm
7 cm
9 cm
18 cm
6 cm
20 cm
4 cm

9.3 *Calculate the surface area, to the nearest square unit.*

14.
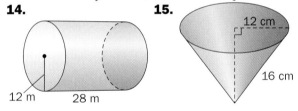
12 m
28 m

15.
12 cm
16 cm

Calculate the volume, to the nearest cubic metre.

16.
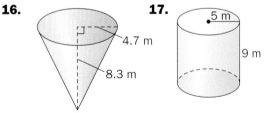
4.7 m
8.3 m

17.
5 m
9 m

18. Concrete pipe Calculate the volume of concrete that is needed to make this section of pipe, to the nearest tenth of a cubic metre.
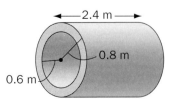
2.4 m
0.8 m
0.6 m

9.4 *Calculate the surface area. Round to the nearest square unit, if necessary.*

19.   **20.**

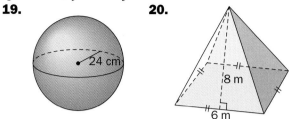

Calculate the volume. Round to the nearest cubic unit, if necessary.

21.   **22.**

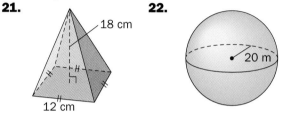

23. Calculate the surface area and volume of the hemisphere, to the nearest square or cubic centimetre.

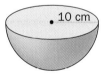

24. How would the volume and surface area of a prism change if all the dimensions were tripled? Explain and justify your reasoning.

9.5 **25.** **Container** A container has the shape of a rectangular prism. Its inside dimensions are 12 cm by 10 cm by 15 cm.
a) Find the volume of water the container holds, in cubic centimetres; in cubic decimetres.
b) Find the mass of water, in kilograms, the container holds.
c) Find the capacity, in litres, of the container.

26. **Tomato juice** If you empty three 540-mL cans of tomato juice into a pitcher, how many litres of juice are in the pitcher?

Exploring Math

Designing a Theatre

You have been asked to submit a design for the seating in a theatre that will be located in an old movie house. The floor already slopes to the stage and orchestra pit, so all you need to do is to place the seats and the aisles.

The seating area measures 40 m wide by 50 m deep. The stage and orchestra pit are centred at the front of the theatre and measure 30 m across. There are two entrance/exit doors evenly spaced at the back of the theatre, and an extra exit door in the middle of each side. There is no balcony.

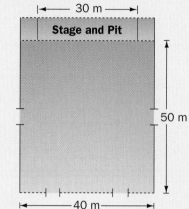

Each seat measures 50 cm by 50 cm, including arm rests. There is to be a 50-cm space in front of each seat for leg room and access. There should be no more than 20 seats in a row. Aisles must be at least 2 m wide.

The owners of the theatre want you to design a pleasant, comfortable seating arrangement. However, when you decide how many seats to include, keep in mind that the owners are in the business of selling tickets. If you include too few seats, your design may not be accepted.

1. Design the placement of the seats and aisles so that people have easy access to their seats.

2. Label each aisle and each seat for the purpose of ticket sales.

Chapter Check

Calculate the area. Round to the nearest square metre, if necessary.

1.

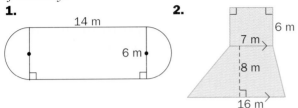

14 m

6 m

2.

6 m

7 m

8 m

16 m

Calculate the surface area. Round to the nearest square unit, if necessary.

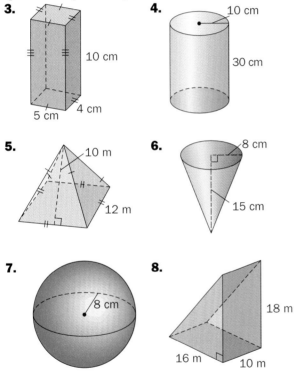

3.

10 cm

5 cm   4 cm

4.

10 cm

30 cm

5.

10 m

H

12 m

6.

8 cm

15 cm

7.

8 cm

8.

18 m

16 m   10 m

Calculate the volume. Round to the nearest cubic unit, if necessary.

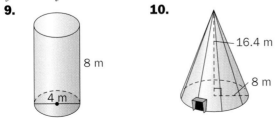

9.

8 m

4 m

10.

16.4 m

8 m

11.

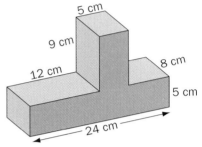

10 cm

12.

150 cm

280 cm   310 cm

13. Calculate the surface area and volume of the composite solid.

5 cm

9 cm

12 cm

8 cm

5 cm

24 cm

14. How would the volume and surface area of a prism change if all the dimensions were doubled?

15. Tuna can A tuna can is a cylinder with a diameter of 8 cm and a height of 3.5 cm. Calculate the volume and surface area, to the nearest cubic or square centimetre.

16. Juice box A juice box measures $10 \text{ cm} \times 6 \text{ cm} \times 3 \text{ cm}$.
a) What is its surface area?
b) How many millilitres of juice can the juice box hold?

17. Wooden block A wooden block is a rectangular prism of volume 600 cm^3. What is the height of the block if its length is 20 cm and its width is 10 cm?

Using the Strategies

1. Whole numbers Jason chose a whole number less than 10. He multiplied the number by 6 and added 1. The result was a perfect square. What numbers could he have chosen?

2. Comparing models The map shows the locations of 4 houses, the train station, and the airport.

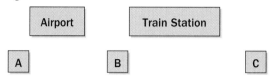

Match each house with the correct number on the distance graph. Give reasons for your answer.

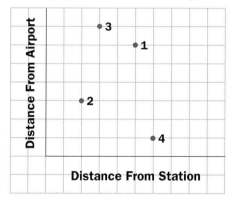

3. TV watching Sketch a graph to show the length of time you spend watching TV versus the day of the week.

4. Square design The area of the large square is 64 cm^2.

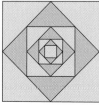

Each smaller square is formed by joining the midpoints of the sides of the next larger square. What is the area of the smallest square?

5. Copy the diagram. Fill in the boxes with the digits 2, 3, 4, and 5 to make the greatest possible sum

6. Consecutive integers Find 3 consecutive integers whose product is 1716.

7. Junk mail Estimate the number of pieces of junk mail delivered in Ontario in a year.

8. Perfect squares The number 2601 is a 4-digit number that is a perfect square, because $51^2 = 2601$. What is the smallest 4-digit number that is a perfect square and that has all even digits?

9. Compact discs Tania has a collection of compact discs. When she puts them in piles of 2, she has 1 left over. She also has 1 left over when she puts them in piles of 3 and piles of 4. She has none left over when she puts them in piles of 7. What is the smallest number of compact discs she can have?

10. Floor tiles A rectangular floor is tiled with 36 square tiles. The tiles around the outside edge of the rectangle are red, and the tiles on the inside are white. How many red tiles are there? Is there more than one possible answer?

11. Making a cube What is the edge length of a cube that can be made with 294 cm^2 of cardboard? What assumptions have you made?

12. Purchase price The amount of a purchase is $12.43. How can the exact amount be paid without using a $10.00 bill, but using the smallest number of bills and coins?

13. Populations What is the mean of the populations of all the countries in the world?

CHAPTER 10

Geometry

How Can We Model Your Field of Vision?

Your field of vision, or your peripheral vision, includes everything you can see when you look straight ahead *with your eyes fixed*. Your side-to-side, or horizontal, peripheral vision is the horizontal angle through which you can see. Your up-and-down, or vertical, peripheral vision refers to the two angles, one upward and the other downward, through which you can see.

The field of vision varies from one creature to another. For example, a dog has an angle of horizontal peripheral vision of about 240°, or about 120° on each side of the centre line.

For a horse, the angle of horizontal peripheral vision is about 340°, or 170° on each side. When a horse looks straight ahead, it cannot see an area within an angle of 10° directly in front of it or 10° directly behind it.

1. How does the placement of the eyes give dogs and horses different angles of horizontal peripheral vision?

2. Why is it not a good idea to approach a horse silently from directly in front or directly behind?

3. Among mammals, the angles of horizontal peripheral vision are smaller for dogs and other predators than for horses and other prey. What are the advantages to each type of mammal?

4. Use your research skills to find out
a) the field of vision for another type of creature, such as insects, fish, or birds
b) whether racehorses are running blind when they wear blinkers

5. Estimate your horizontal, upward, and downward angles of peripheral vision when you look straight ahead with your eyes fixed.

In Modelling Math — Biology on pages 555 to 557, you will experiment with the mathematical model to determine your own field of vision.

GETTING STARTED

Seeing Shapes

1 Length

1. Horizontal and vertical lines can create an illusion involving length. In the diagram, does the horizontal or the vertical line seem longer?

2. a) Measure the lines and compare their lengths.
b) Explain your results.

2 Perspective

1. Do the sides of the triangle appear to be straight or bent?

2. Describe the effect the circles have on the sides of the triangle.

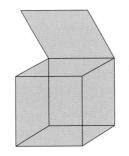

3 Reversing Figures

1. Focus on this box until you see it change position.

2. Describe the second position as you perceive it.

4 Impossible Figures

1. Focus on the figure and describe what you see.

2. Is the figure in question 1 possible in the real world? Explain.

5 More Illusions

1. Which line segment do you think is longer? Check and explain.

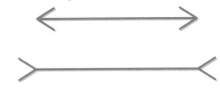

2. Do you think that the horizontal lines are straight or bent? Check and explain.

3. Describe the different ways you see each figure.
a) 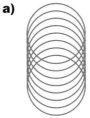   **b)**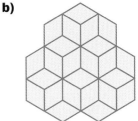

4. What is wrong with each figure?
a)   **b)**

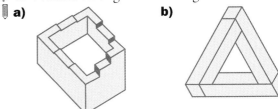

5. Are these 3 girls all the same height? Check and explain.

Warm Up

1. List 5 points and 5 lines in the diagram.

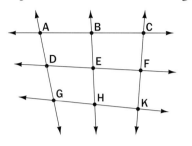

2. Name 5 line segments in this diagram.

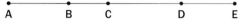

3. Name 8 angles in this diagram.

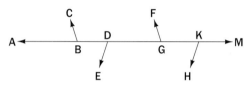

4. Name the following from the figure shown below.

a) 3 points **b)** 3 lines
c) 6 angles **d)** 3 rays
e) 3 line segments

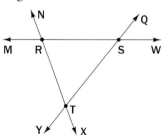

5. In how many different ways can 3 lines intersect? Draw diagrams to illustrate your answer.

6. How many line segments are in this diagram? Name them.

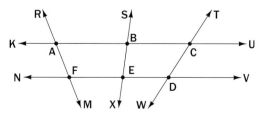

Mental Math

Performing Operations and Solving Equations

Calculate.

1. $90 - 14$ **2.** $90 - 39$
3. $90 - 61$ **4.** $180 - 44$
5. $180 - 98$ **6.** $180 - 137$
7. $180 - 35 - 10$ **8.** $180 - 88 - 33$
9. $180 - (43 + 47)$ **10.** $180 - (29 + 77)$
11. $180 - 2(35)$ **12.** $180 - 2(67)$

Solve for x.

13. $x + 48 = 79$ **14.** $x + 91 = 156$
15. $x + x + x = 180$ **16.** $x + x + 2x = 180$
17. $x + 2x + 3x = 180$ **18.** $x + x + x + x = 360$

Multiplying by Multiples of 12

To multiply a number by 12, first multiply the number by 10, and then add twice the number. For 12×34,

multiply by 10:	$10 \times 34 = 340$
add 2×34, or 68:	$340 + 68 = 408$

So, $12 \times 34 = 408$

Calculate.

1. 12×18 **2.** 12×21 **3.** 12×33
4. 12×48 **5.** 12×130 **6.** 12×450
7. 12×1.5 **8.** 12×2.6 **9.** 12×4.1

To multiply by 1.2, 120, and so on, first multiply by 12, and then place the decimal point.
Thus, $1.2 \times 34 = 40.8$, and $120 \times 34 = 4080$.

Calculate.

10. 120×16 **11.** 120×31 **12.** 1200×22
13. 1.2×25 **14.** 1.2×32 **15.** 1.2×44

16. Explain why the rule for multiplying by 12 works.

17. Modify the rule for multiplying by 12 to write a rule for multiplying by 22.

Calculate using your rule from question 17.

18. 22×14 **19.** 22×22 **20.** 22×43

INVESTIGATING MATH

Angles, Intersecting Lines, and Triangles

1 Angles

Recall that angles are classified according to their sizes in degrees.

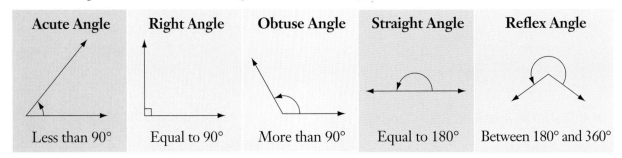

Acute Angle	Right Angle	Obtuse Angle	Straight Angle	Reflex Angle
Less than 90°	Equal to 90°	More than 90°	Equal to 180°	Between 180° and 360°

Some pairs of angles have special names.

Supplementary angles add to 180°.

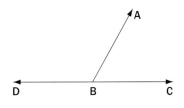

∠ABC and ∠ABD are supplementary because ∠ABC + ∠ABD = 180°.

Complementary angles add to 90°.

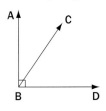

∠ABC and ∠CBD are complementary because ∠ABC + ∠CBD = 90°.

1. Determine the size of each of the following angles drawn on the protractor. Then, classify each angle as acute, right, obtuse, or straight.

a) ∠BAC   b) ∠BAD   c) ∠BAE
d) ∠BAF   e) ∠HAJ   f) ∠GAJ
g) ∠IAJ   h) ∠FAJ   i) ∠DAJ
j) ∠BAH   k) ∠BAI   l) ∠BAJ

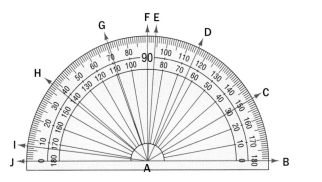

2. Estimate the size of each angle, and then classify each angle.

a)   b)   c)   d)

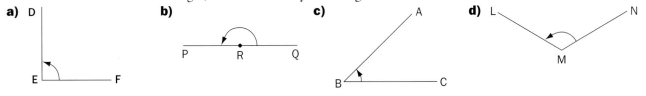

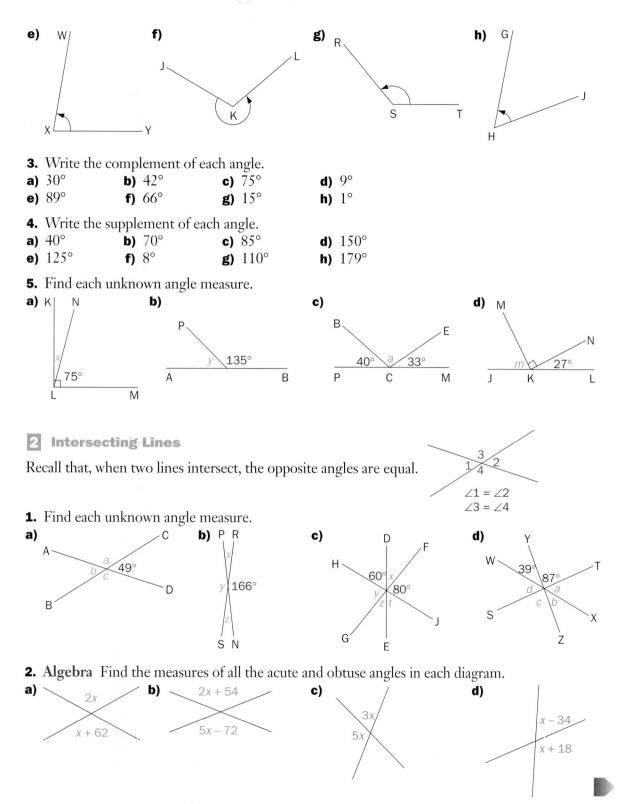

e)

f)

g)

h)

3. Write the complement of each angle.
a) 30°   **b)** 42°   **c)** 75°   **d)** 9°
e) 89°   **f)** 66°   **g)** 15°   **h)** 1°

4. Write the supplement of each angle.
a) 40°   **b)** 70°   **c)** 85°   **d)** 150°
e) 125°   **f)** 8°   **g)** 110°   **h)** 179°

5. Find each unknown angle measure.
a)   **b)**   **c)**   **d)**

2 Intersecting Lines

Recall that, when two lines intersect, the opposite angles are equal.

$\angle 1 = \angle 2$
$\angle 3 = \angle 4$

1. Find each unknown angle measure.
a)   **b)**   **c)**   **d)**

2. Algebra Find the measures of all the acute and obtuse angles in each diagram.
a)   **b)**   **c)**   **d)**

3 Triangles

Triangles can be classified according to the lengths of their sides and the measures of their angles.

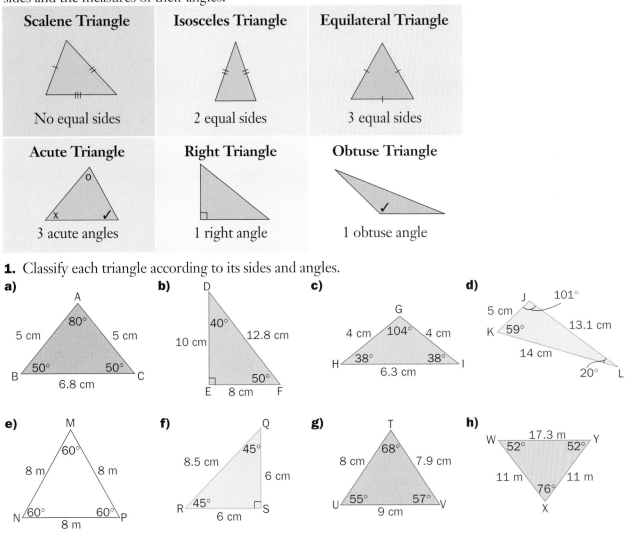

Scalene Triangle	Isosceles Triangle	Equilateral Triangle
No equal sides	2 equal sides	3 equal sides

Acute Triangle	Right Triangle	Obtuse Triangle
3 acute angles	1 right angle	1 obtuse angle

1. Classify each triangle according to its sides and angles.

a) Triangle A B C: A at top, 80°, 5 cm on each side (AB and AC), 50° at B, 50° at C, 6.8 cm base BC.

b) Triangle D E F: D at top, 40°, 10 cm (DE), 12.8 cm (DF), right angle at E, 8 cm (EF), 50° at F.

c) Triangle G H I: G at top, 104°, 4 cm on each side, 38° at H, 38° at I, 6.3 cm base HI.

d) Triangle J K L: 5 cm, 101° at J, 13.1 cm, 59° at K, 14 cm, 20° at L.

e) Triangle M N P: M at top, 60°, 8 m each side, 60° at N, 60° at P, 8 m base.

f) Triangle Q R S: 45° at Q, 8.5 cm, 6 cm, 45° at R, right angle at S, 6 cm base RS.

g) Triangle T U V: T at top, 68°, 8 cm, 7.9 cm, 55° at U, 57° at V, 9 cm base UV.

h) Triangle W X Y: 17.3 m (WY), 52° at W, 52° at Y, 11 m each, 76° at X.

2. Flags Triangles are found in the flag designs of many countries. Classify each triangle in each of the following flags in two ways.

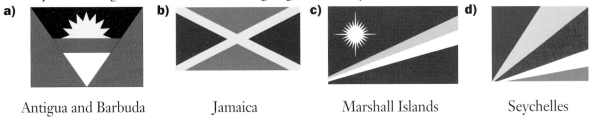

a) Antigua and Barbuda   b) Jamaica   c) Marshall Islands   d) Seychelles

Exploring Interior and Exterior Angles Using Geometry Software

Complete the following explorations using geometry software or a graphing calculator with geometry capabilities. If suitable technology is not available, complete the equivalent paper-and-pencil explorations on pages 518–519.

1 Interior Angles of a Triangle

The three angles inside a triangle are known as **interior angles**. In △ABC, ∠A , ∠B, and ∠C are interior angles. ∠A is opposite side BC, ∠B is opposite side AC, and ∠C is opposite side AB.

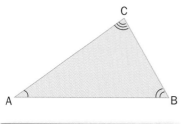

1. a) Construct a scalene triangle.
b) Measure the lengths of the sides.
c) Measure the interior angles.
d) Calculate the sum of the interior angles.
e) List the sides from longest to shortest length and the angles from greatest to least measure.

2. a) Drag a vertex to change the size and the shape of the triangle.
b) Calculate the sum of the interior angles.
c) List the sides from longest to shortest length and the angles from greatest to least measure.
d) Repeat parts a) to c) at least twice, or until you see a pattern in the sum of the interior angles.

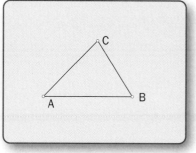

3. Write a statement to describe the relationship between the measures of the three interior angles of a triangle.

4. a) In a scalene triangle, how is the position of the greatest angle related to the position of the longest side?
b) In a scalene triangle, how is the position of the smallest angle related to the position of the shortest side?
c) Write a statement to describe the relationship between the measures of the angles and the lengths of the sides in a scalene triangle.

5. a) Construct an isosceles triangle.
b) Measure the angles opposite the equal sides.
c) Drag the vertex of the equal sides to change the size and the shape of the triangle.
d) Compare the angle measures.
e) Repeat parts c) and d) at least twice, or until you see a pattern.

6. Write a statement to describe the relationship between the measures of the angles opposite the equal sides in an isosceles triangle.

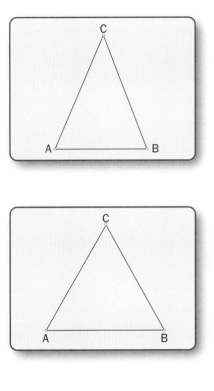

7. a) Construct an equilateral triangle.
b) Measure the interior angles.
c) Drag a vertex to change the size of the triangle.
d) Compare the angle measures.
e) Repeat parts c) and d) at least twice, or until you see a pattern.

8. Write a statement to describe the relationship between the measures of the angles in an equilateral triangle.

2 Exterior Angles of a Triangle

When each side of a triangle is extended in one direction, three angles are created outside the triangle. ∠BAE, ∠CBF, and ∠ACD are **exterior angles** of △ABC.

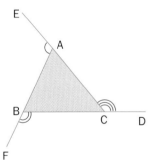

There are two interior angles opposite each exterior angle. ∠BAC and ∠ABC are opposite ∠ACD. ∠ABC and ∠BCA are opposite ∠BAE. ∠BCA and ∠BAC are opposite ∠CBF.

1. a) Construct a triangle.
b) Extend one side to create an exterior angle.
c) Measure the exterior angle.
d) Measure the two interior angles opposite the exterior angle.
e) Calculate the sum of the two interior and opposite angles, and compare the sum to the measure of the exterior angle.

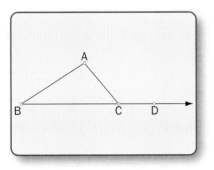

2. a) Drag a vertex of the triangle.
b) Calculate the sum of the two interior and opposite angles, and compare the sum to the measure of the exterior angle.
c) Repeat parts a) and b) at least twice, or until you see a pattern.

3. Write a statement to describe the relationship between the measure of an exterior angle and the measures of the two interior and opposite angles.

3 Interior Angles of a Quadrilateral

1. a) Construct a quadrilateral.
b) Measure the interior angles.
c) Calculate the sum of the interior angles.

2. a) Drag a vertex of the quadrilateral.
b) Calculate the sum of the interior angles.
c) Repeat parts a) and b) at least twice, or until you see a pattern.

3. Write a statement to describe the relationship between the measures of the four interior angles of a quadrilateral.

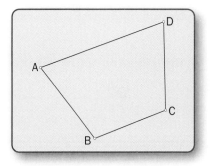

4 Exterior Angles of a Quadrilateral

1. a) Construct a quadrilateral.
b) Extend each side in one direction, as shown, creating four exterior angles.
c) Measure the exterior angles.
d) Calculate the sum of the exterior angles.

2. a) Drag a vertex of the quadrilateral.
b) Calculate the sum of the exterior angles.
c) Repeat parts a) and b) at least twice or until you see a pattern.

3. Write a statement to describe the relationship between the measures of the exterior angles of a quadrilateral.

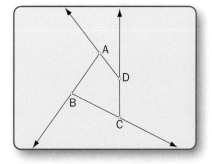

INVESTIGATING MATH

Exploring Interior and Exterior Angles

The three angles inside a triangle are known as **interior angles**. In the diagram, ∠A, ∠B, and ∠C are the interior angles.

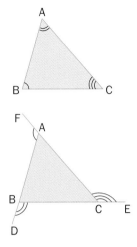

When the sides of the triangle are extended as shown, three more angles are created, ∠BAF, ∠CBD, and ∠ACE. These angles outside the triangle are called **exterior angles**.

1 Interior Angles of a Triangle

Draw a triangle of each of the following types in your notebook. Name the vertices.

a) isosceles   **b)** equilateral   **c)** scalene

1. Measure the three sides and the three angles in each triangle.

2. Calculate the sum of the interior angles in each triangle. Compare your findings with your classmates.

3. Write a statement to describe the relationship between the three interior angles of a triangle.

4. What is the measure of each angle in an equilateral triangle?

5. In △XYZ, ∠X is opposite side YZ, ∠Y is opposite side XZ, and ∠Z is opposite side XY.
a) For the scalene triangle you drew, list the side lengths from greatest to least and the angle measures from greatest to least.
b) Write a statement to describe the relationship between the measures of the angles and the lengths of the sides.

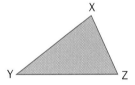

6. For the isosceles triangle you drew, how are the measures of the angles opposite the equal sides related?

2 Exterior Angles of a Triangle

In the diagram, ∠ACD is an exterior angle of △ABC. In your notebook, draw a diagram like the one shown.

1. Measure ∠ACD.

2. Measure ∠A and ∠B, which are the angles that are interior and opposite to ∠ACD.

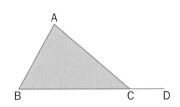

3. Find the sum of these two interior angles. How does the sum compare with the measure of ∠ACD? Compare your findings with a classmate's.

4. Repeat questions 1–3 for other exterior angles drawn at points A and B. In each case, compare the measure of the exterior angle with the sum of the measures of the interior and opposite angles.

5. Write a statement to describe the relationship between the measure of an exterior angle of a triangle and the measures of the two interior and opposite angles.

3 Interior Angles of a Quadrilateral

1. In your notebook, draw two quadrilaterals like the ones shown. Then, measure the four interior angles in each quadrilateral.

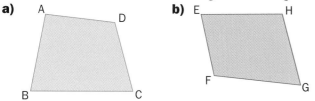

a)   **b)**

2. What is the sum of the measures of the interior angles in each quadrilateral? Compare your findings with a classmate's.

3. Write a statement to describe the relationship between the interior angles of a quadrilateral.

4 Exterior Angles of a Quadrilateral

1. In your notebook, draw two quadrilaterals like the ones shown. Then, measure the four exterior angles shown for each quadrilateral.

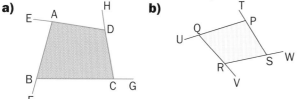

a)   **b)**

2. What is the sum of the measures of the exterior angles for each quadrilateral? Compare your findings with a classmate's.

3. Write a statement to describe the relationship between the exterior angles of a quadrilateral.

10.1 Interior and Exterior Angles of Triangles and Quadrilaterals

Triangles and quadrilaterals are seen in many types of construction. How many different types of triangles and quadrilaterals do you see in this photograph of the Canadian Mint in Winnipeg?

Explore: Perform an Experiment

a) Draw an acute triangle, △ABC, on a piece of paper. Label the vertices inside the triangle, as shown.

b) Extend BC to D to make an exterior angle, ∠ACD.

c) Cut out the triangle and the exterior angle, as shown.

d) Tear off ∠A and ∠B, which are the interior and opposite angles to ∠ACD. Place them in the exterior angle, as shown.

e) Repeat steps a) to d) for a △ABC where ∠B = 90°; where ∠B is obtuse.

Inquire

1. Write a statement about the sum of the interior angles of a triangle.

2. Is it possible for a triangle to have two 90° angles? Explain.

3. Is it possible for a triangle to have more than one obtuse angle? Explain.

4. Write a statement about the relationship between an exterior angle of a triangle and the sum of the two interior and opposite angles. Compare your statement with a classmate's.

Explore: Use a Diagram

In quadrilateral ABCD, the diagonal AC creates two triangles, △ABC and △ADC. What is the sum of the measures of the interior angles of

a) each triangle?   **b)** the two triangles?

c) the quadrilateral?

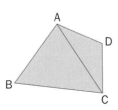

Inquire

1. Write a statement about the sum of the measures of the interior angles of a quadrilateral. Compare your statement with a classmate's.

2. In the diagram, the sides of quadrilateral ABCD have been extended to form 4 exterior angles. At each vertex, there is one interior angle and one exterior angle. Each pair of interior and exterior angles forms a straight angle.
a) What is the measure of a straight angle?
b) What is the sum of the measures of the 4 straight angles?
c) What is the sum of the measures of the 4 interior angles?
d) What is the sum of the measures of the 4 exterior angles?

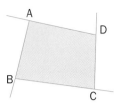

3. Write a statement about the angle sum of the exterior angles of a quadrilateral.

Example 1   Interior Angles of Triangles
Classify each triangle and find the missing angle measures.

a)

b)

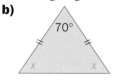

c)

Solution

a) The triangle has 3 equal sides and 3 equal angles. It is an equilateral triangle.
$$3x = 180°$$
$$x = 60°$$

b) The triangle has 2 equal sides and 2 equal angles. It is an isosceles triangle.
$$2x + 70° = 180°$$
$$2x = 180° - 70°$$
$$2x = 110°$$
$$x = 55°$$

c) The triangle has no equal parts. It is a scalene triangle.
$$x + 73° + 56° = 180°$$
$$x + 129° = 180°$$
$$x = 180° - 129°$$
$$x = 51°$$

Example 2   Angles and Triangles
Find the missing angle measures.

a)

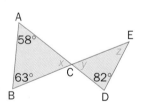

b)

Solution

a) $\angle KMN$ is an exterior angle of $\triangle KLM$. $\angle K$ and $\angle L$ are the interior and opposite angles.
$$124° = 43° + x$$
$$124° - 43° = x$$
$$81° = x$$

b) In $\triangle ABC$, $x + 58° + 63° = 180°$
$$x + 121° = 180°$$
$$x = 180° - 121°$$
$$x = 59°$$
Since x and y are opposite angles,
$$y = x$$
$$y = 59°$$
In $\triangle CDE$, $59° + 82° + z = 180°$
$$141° + z = 180°$$
$$z = 180° - 141°$$
$$z = 39°$$

Example 3 Angles and Quadrilaterals
Find the missing angle measures.

a)
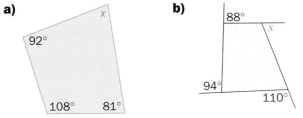

b)

Solution

a) The sum of the interior angles is 360°.

$$x + 92° + 108° + 81° = 360°$$
$$x + 281° = 360°$$
$$x = 360° - 281°$$
$$x = 79°$$

b) The sum of the exterior angles is 360°.

$$x + 88° + 94° + 110° = 360°$$
$$x + 292° = 360°$$
$$x = 360° - 292°$$
$$x = 68°$$

Practice

A

Find the missing angle measures.

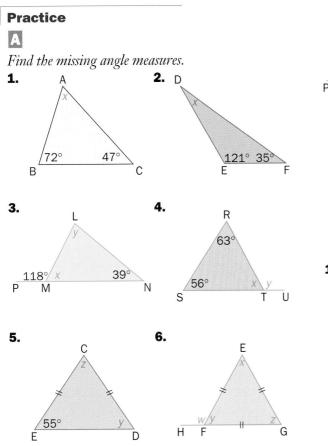

1.

2.

3.

4.

5.

6.

7.
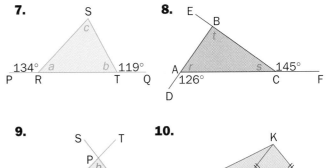

8.

9.

10.
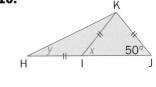

11.
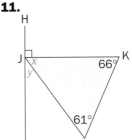

12.
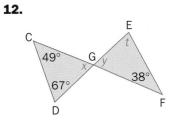

Find the missing angle measures.

13.

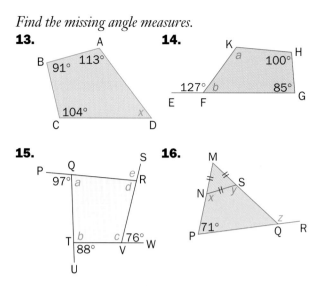

14.

15.

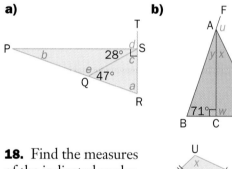

16.

Applications and Problem Solving

B

17. Find the measures of the indicated angles.

a)

b)

18. Find the measures of the indicated angles.

19. Algebra Find the value of x. Then, find the measures of all the angles.

a)

b)

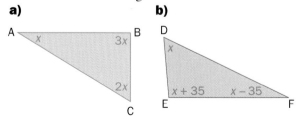

c)

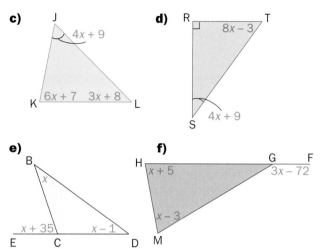

d)

e)

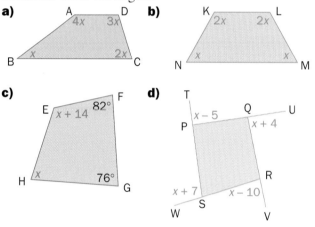

f)

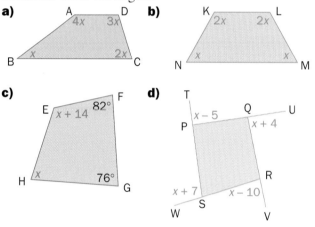

20. Algebra Find the value of x. Then, find the measures of all the angles.

a)

b)

c)

d)

21. The midpoints of the legs of the isosceles right triangle have been joined to form a quadrilateral and a smaller triangle.

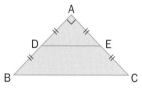

Find the measures of the interior angles of the quadrilateral and of the triangle.

22. If you know the measure of ∠A, how can you find the measures of ∠B and ∠C?

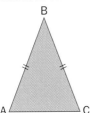

23. If you know the measure of ∠D, how can you find the measure of ∠A?

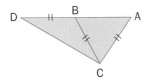

24. A kite has 1 line of symmetry. A line of symmetry is an imaginary line that divides a figure into two identical pieces. How many lines of symmetry do the following types of triangles have?
a) equilateral **b)** isosceles
c) scalene

C

25. Can a right triangle have a line of symmetry? Explain.

26. One angle of an isosceles triangle has a measure of 40°. What are the possible measures of the other angles?

27. One angle of an isosceles triangle has a measure of 140°. What are the possible measures of the other angles?

28. Copy and complete each statement with the word always, sometimes, or never. Explain and justify your reasoning.
a) A scalene triangle is ▓▓▓ isosceles.
b) An obtuse triangle is ▓▓▓ isosceles.
c) An equilateral triangle is ▓▓▓ acute.
d) An acute triangle is ▓▓▓ isosceles.

29. Tree height The distance from the ground to Nassir's eye level is 1.7 m. To measure the height of a tree, Nassir stood where the angle to the top of the tree was 45°. At that point, he was 10.2 m from the tree. How tall is the tree?

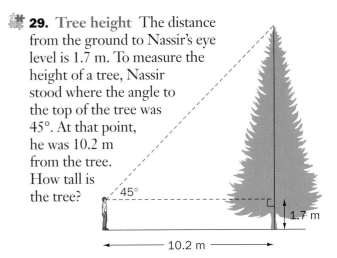

30. To show that the sum of the measures of the interior angles of any quadrilateral is 360°, join the four vertices to a point inside the quadrilateral.

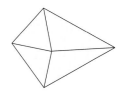

How can you use the sum of the measures of the interior angles of the four triangles to show that the sum of the interior angles of the quadrilateral is 360°?

31. Can a quadrilateral have each of the following sets of interior angles? If so, show an example in a diagram. Compare your diagrams with a classmate's.
a) four obtuse angles
b) one obtuse angle and three acute angles
c) one acute angle and three obtuse angles
d) two right angles and two acute angles

32. a) Some types of triangles named in the table exist, while others do not. Work with a classmate to draw the types of triangles that exist.

	Scalene	Isosceles	Equilateral
Acute	A	B	C
Right	D	E	F
Obtuse	G	H	I

b) If a triangle does not exist, explain why not. You may wish to use a diagram.

Exploring Angle Bisectors, Medians, and Altitudes Using Geometry Software

Complete the following explorations using geometry software or a graphing calculator with geometry capabilities. If suitable technology is not available, complete the pencil-and-paper explorations on pages 527–528 and page 529.

1 Angle Bisectors of a Triangle

1. a) Construct an acute triangle.
b) Bisect each interior angle.
c) Describe how the bisectors meet.
d) The point at which the bisectors of the interior angles of a triangle intersect is called the **incentre**. Construct this point.

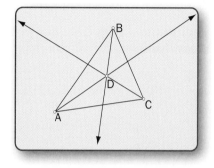

2. a) Construct a perpendicular line through the incentre and one side.
b) Construct the point at the intersection of the perpendicular line and the side.
c) Construct a circle with the incentre as the centre and the point at the intersection of the perpendicular line and the side as the point on the circle.
d) This circle, called the **incircle**, touches each side of the triangle exactly once. Construct the point at the intersection of the circle and each of the other two sides to confirm this.

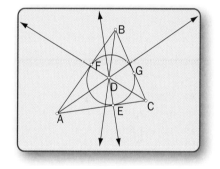

3. a) Drag one of the vertices to change the triangle to a variety of sizes and shapes.
b) Do other acute triangles have incircles?
c) Do right triangles have incircles?
d) Do obtuse triangles have incircles?

2 Medians of a Triangle

A **median** of a triangle is a line segment that joins a vertex to the midpoint of the opposite side.

1. a) Construct an acute triangle.
b) Construct the midpoints of the sides.
c) Construct a segment between each midpoint and the opposite vertex.
d) Describe how the segments meet.
e) The point at which the medians of a triangle intersect is called the **centroid**. Construct this point.

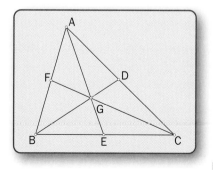

2. If you were to print and cut out your triangle, tape it to a piece of cardboard, and turn it upside down with one of your fingers at the centroid, the triangle should be perfectly balanced. Use this information to explain why the centroid of a triangle is sometimes referred to as its *centre of gravity*.

3. a) Drag one of the vertices to change the triangle to a variety of sizes and shapes.
b) Do other acute triangles have centroids?
c) Do right triangles have centroids?
d) Do obtuse triangles have centroids?

3 Altitudes of a Triangle

An **altitude** of a triangle is the perpendicular from a vertex to the opposite side.

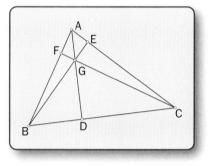

1. a) Construct an acute triangle.
b) Construct a perpendicular line through each vertex to the opposite side.
c) Construct the point at the intersection of the perpendicular line and the side.
d) Construct a segment between each vertex and the point at the intersection of the perpendicular line and the side.
e) Hide the perpendicular lines.
f) Describe how the altitudes intersect.
g) The point at which the altitudes of a triangle intersect is called the **orthocentre**. Construct this point.

2. a) Drag one of the vertices to change the triangle to a variety of sizes and shapes. Describe what happens.
b) Do other acute triangles have orthocentres?
c) What happens to the orthocentre when the triangle becomes a right triangle?
d) What happens to the orthocentre when the triangle becomes an obtuse triangle?
e) Construct an obtuse triangle, extend the sides meeting at the obtuse angle, and construct the orthocentre. Where is it?

4 Making and Testing a Conjecture

1. Using the results from the first three explorations, make a conjecture about the three perpendicular bisectors of the sides of a triangle.

2. Test your conjecture. Construct a triangle and the perpendicular bisectors of the sides. Drag one of the vertices to change the triangle to a variety of different sizes and shapes. Describe what happens.

3. Use your research skills to define the terms **circumcentre** and **circumcircle**.

4. Construct the circumcircle of a triangle.

5. Communicate your findings to your classmates.

Geometric Constructions

1 Angle Bisectors

The **bisector** of an angle divides the angle into two equal parts.

1. Steps 1 to 4 show how to bisect an angle using ruler and compasses. Repeat the construction in your notebook. Work with a partner to write a description of the steps.

2. Describe how to bisect an angle using paper folding.

3. Describe how an angle can be bisected using a Mira.

4. Draw a 60°-angle, a 120°-angle, a right angle, and a straight angle. Then, bisect each of the angles. What is the measure of each new angle?

2 Right Bisectors

The right bisector of a line segment divides the line segment at right angles into two equal parts.

1. Steps 1 to 3 show how to construct the right bisector of a line segment using ruler and compasses. Repeat the construction in your notebook. Work with a partner to write a description of the steps.

2. Describe how to construct the right bisector of a segment by paper folding.

3. Describe how to construct the right bisector of a line segment using a Mira.

4. Draw a line segment at least 8 cm long. Construct its right bisector.

5. Draw a line segment at least 8 cm long. Divide the line segment into 4 equal parts by constructing 3 right bisectors.

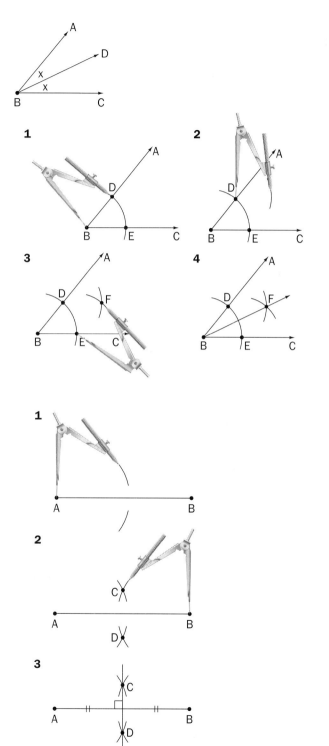

3 Perpendicular Lines

Perpendicular lines meet at 90°. There are several ways to construct a perpendicular to a line from a point not on the line.

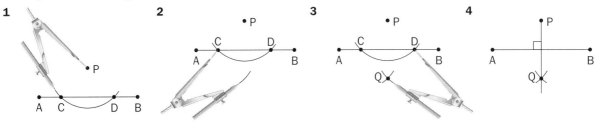

1. The following steps 1 to 4 show how to construct a perpendicular to a line from a point not on the line. Repeat the construction in your notebook. Work with a partner to write a description of the steps.

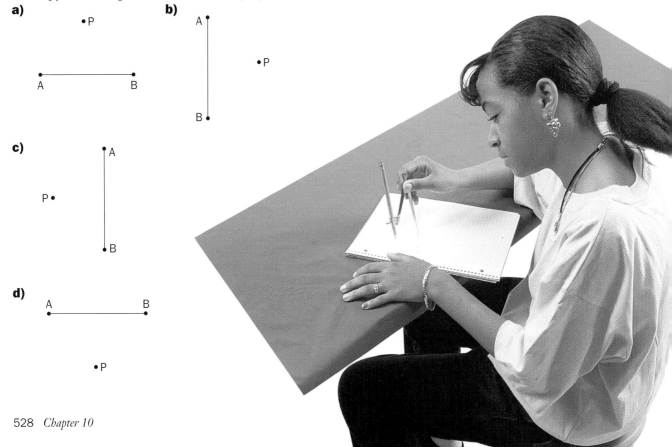

2. Describe how to draw a perpendicular to a line from a point not on the line using paper folding.

3. Describe how to draw a perpendicular to a line from a point not on the line using a Mira.

4. Copy these diagrams and construct perpendiculars from P to AB.

a)

b)

c)

d)

Exploring Angle Bisectors, Medians, and Altitudes

1 Angle Bisectors of a Triangle

1. Draw an acute △ABC. Construct the bisector of each angle. The three bisectors should intersect at a common point, called the **incentre**. Let D be the incentre.

2. Using D as the centre, draw a circle that touches all three sides of the triangle. This circle is the **incircle**.

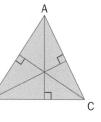

3. a) Repeat steps 1 and 2 for a right triangle and for an obtuse triangle.
b) Does a right triangle have an incircle?
c) Does an obtuse triangle have an incircle?

2 Medians of a Triangle

A **median** of a triangle is a line segment that joins a vertex of a triangle to the midpoint of the opposite side.

1. Draw an acute △ABC. Construct the right bisector of BC. Let D be the midpoint of BC. Join AD, which is a median of △ABC. Also construct the medians from B to AC and from C to AB. The three medians should meet at a common point, called the **centroid**.

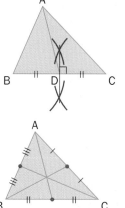

2. If you were to cut out the triangle, tape it to a piece of cardboard, and turn it upside down with one of your fingers at the centroid, the triangle should be perfectly balanced. Use this information to explain why the centroid of a triangle is sometimes known as its *centre of gravity*.

3. a) Repeat step 1 for a right triangle and for an obtuse triangle.
b) Does a right triangle have a centroid?
c) Does an obtuse triangle have a centroid?

3 Altitudes of a Triangle

An **altitude** of a triangle is the perpendicular from a vertex to the opposite side.

1. Draw an acute △ABC. Construct the three altitudes of the triangle. The three altitudes should intersect at a common point, called the **orthocentre**.

2. Repeat step 1 for a right triangle. Where is the orthocentre of a right triangle?

3. Repeat step 1 for an obtuse triangle. Extend the sides, if necessary. Where is the orthocentre of an obtuse triangle?

4 Making and Testing a Conjecture

1. Using the results from the first three explorations, make a conjecture about the three perpendicular bisectors of the sides of a triangle.

2. Test your conjecture for various types of triangles.

3. Use your research skills to define the terms **circumcentre** and **circumcircle**.

4. Construct the circumcircle of a triangle.

5. Communicate your findings to your classmates.

TECHNOLOGY

Exploring Angles and Parallel Lines Using Geometry Software

Complete the following explorations using geometry software or a graphing calculator with geometry capabilities. If suitable technology is not available, complete the Explore and Inquire parts of Section 10.2 on page 533 using pencil and paper.

A line that intersects two or more lines is called a **transversal**. When the transversal, t, intersects lines m and n, eight angles are formed.

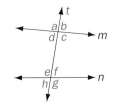

Pairs of these angles are given special names.

In the diagrams shown, $\angle d$ and $\angle f$ are a pair of **alternate angles**. Another pair of alternate angles is $\angle c$ and $\angle e$.

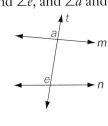

In the following, $\angle b$ and $\angle f$ are a pair of **corresponding angles**. Other pairs of corresponding angles are $\angle c$ and $\angle g$, $\angle a$ and $\angle e$, and $\angle d$ and $\angle h$.

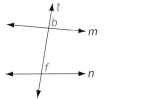 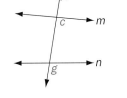 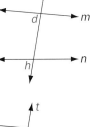 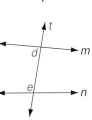

In the diagrams shown, $\angle c$ and $\angle f$ are a pair of **co-interior angles** on the same side of the transversal. Another pair of co-interior angles on the same side of the transversal is $\angle d$ and $\angle e$.

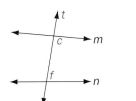

1 Constructing Parallel Lines and a Transversal

Parallel lines are lines in the same plane that do not intersect.
1. Construct a line segment.
2. Construct a point on one side of the line segment.
3. Construct a line parallel to the line segment through the point.
4. Construct a point on the line segment. Then, construct a line through the point on the line segment and the point on the parallel line.

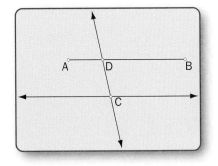

2 Alternate Angles

Use the figure from the previous exploration.
1. On the parallel line and the transversal, construct other points needed to define angles using three points.

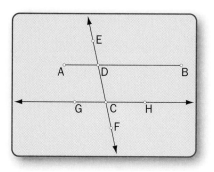

2. Measure one pair of alternate angles. How do their measures compare?
3. Measure the other pair of alternate angles. How do their measures compare?
4. Drag the point at which the transversal intersects the line segment to change the position of the transversal. How do the measures of alternate angles compare?
5. Drag the point at which the transversal intersects the parallel line to change the distance between the line segment and the line, and the position of the transversal. How do the measures of alternate angles compare?
6. Write a statement to describe the relationship between pairs of alternate angles formed when a transversal intersects two parallel lines.

3 Corresponding Angles

Use the figure from the previous exploration.
1. Measure one pair of corresponding angles. How do their measures compare?
2. Measure each of the three other pairs of corresponding angles. How do their measures compare?
3. Drag the point at which the transversal intersects the line segment to change the position of the transversal. How do the measures of corresponding angles compare?
4. Drag the point at which the transversal intersects the parallel line to change the distance between the line segment and the line, and the position of the transversal. How do the measures of corresponding angles compare?
5. Write a statement to describe the relationship between pairs of corresponding angles formed when a transversal intersects two parallel lines.

4 Co-Interior Angles

Use the figure from the previous exploration.
1. Measure one pair of co-interior angles. What is the sum of their measures?
2. Measure the other pair of co-interior angles. What is the sum of their measures?
3. Drag the point at which the transversal intersects the line segment to change the position of the transversal. What is the sum of the measures of co-interior angles?
4. Drag the point at which the transversal intersects the parallel line to change the distance between the line segment and the line, and the position of the transversal. What is the sum of the measures of co-interior angles?
5. Write a statement to describe the relationship between pairs of co-interior angles formed when a transversal intersects two parallel lines.

10.2 Angles and Parallel Lines

A **transversal** is a line that crosses or intersects two or more lines, each at a different point. Some pairs of angles formed by a transversal have special names.

In Diagram 1, ∠4 and ∠6 are **alternate interior angles**, or simply **alternate angles**. Another pair of alternate angles is ∠3 and ∠5. Alternate angles form a **Z** pattern or a **S** pattern.

Diagram 1

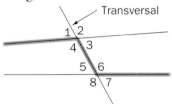

In Diagram 2, ∠3 and ∠7 are a pair of **corresponding angles**. Other pairs of corresponding angles are ∠2 and ∠6, ∠4 and ∠8, and ∠1 and ∠5. Corresponding angles form an **F** pattern, or an **⅂**, **Ⱡ**, or **⅃** pattern.

Diagram 2

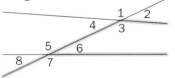

In Diagram 3, ∠4 and ∠5 are a pair of **co-interior angles**. Co-interior angles are on the same side of the transversal. Another pair of co-interior angles is ∠3 and ∠6. Co-interior angles form a **Ⲥ** pattern or a **Ⴑ** pattern.

Diagram 3

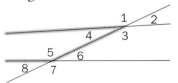

Canada's Donovan Bailey set a new world record of 9.84 s when he won the 100-m race at the Summer Olympics in Atlanta. In a 100-m race, runners compete in lanes separated by parallel markings. In geometry, we often use **parallel lines**, which are lines in the same plane that do not intersect.

Explore: Discover the Relationship

a) Use a ruler to draw 2 parallel lines and a transversal. Label the angles as shown.

b) Measure the 8 angles formed.

Inquire

1. How are the pairs of alternate angles related?

2. How are the pairs of corresponding angles related?

3. How are the pairs of co-interior angles related?

4. Repeat the activity for two more parallel lines and another transversal.

5. Write a statement to describe the relationship between each of the following pairs of angles formed when a transversal intersects two parallel lines.
a) alternate angles
b) corresponding angles
c) co-interior angles

Example 1   Using Alternate and Co-Interior Angles

Find the measures of the indicated angles.

a)

b)

Solution

a) Since AB||CD, alternate angles are equal. || means "is parallel to"
∠DGF = ∠AFG (alternate angles)
$y = 71°$
Since AB||CD, co-interior angles are supplementary.
∠AFG + ∠CGF = 180° (co-interior angles)
$71° + x = 180°$
$x = 109°$
The measures are $x = 109°$ and $y = 71°$.

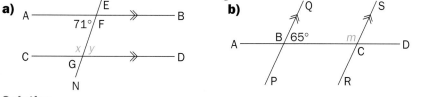

b) Since PQ||RS, co-interior angles are supplementary.
∠BCS + ∠CBQ = 180° (co-interior angles)
$m + 65 = 180°$
$m = 115°$
The measure is $m = 115°$.

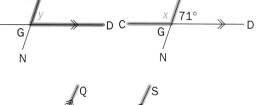

Example 2   Using Corresponding and Opposite Angles

Find the measures of the indicated angles.

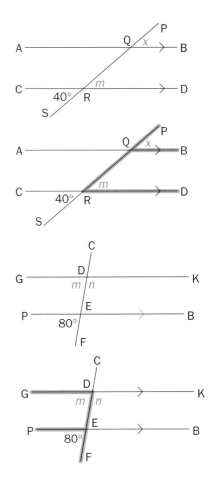

Solution

∠DRQ = ∠CRS (opposite angles)

$m = 40°$

Since AB||CD, corresponding angles are equal.

∠BQP = ∠DRQ (corresponding angles)

$x = 40°$

The measures are $m = 40°$ and $x = 40°$.

Example 3   Using Corresponding and Straight Angles

What are the measures of m and n in this diagram?

Solution

Since GK||PB, corresponding angles are equal.

∠EDG = ∠FEP (corresponding angles)

$m = 80°$

∠EDK + ∠EDG = 180° (straight angle)

$n + 80° = 180°$

$n = 100°$

The measures are $m = 80°$ and $n = 100°$.

Example 4   Angles in Triangles and Quadrilaterals

Find the measures of the indicated angles.

a)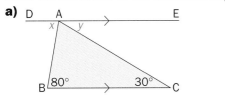

b)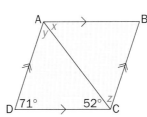

Solution

a) Since DE||BC, alternate angles are equal.

∠BAD = ∠ABC (alternate angles)

$x = 80°$

∠CAE = ∠ACB (alternate angles)

$y = 30°$

The measures are $x = 80°$ and $y = 30°$.

b) Since AB||DC, alternate angles are equal.

∠BAC = ∠ACD (alternate angles)

$x = 52°$

In △ADC, the sum of the angles is 180°.

$y + 71° + 52° = 180°$

$y + 123° = 180°$

$y = 57°$

Since AD||BC, alternate angles are equal.

∠ACB = ∠CAD (alternate angles)

$z = 57°$

The measures are $x = 52°$, $y = 57°$, and $z = 57°$.

Practice

A

Find the indicated angle measures. Give reasons for your answers.

1.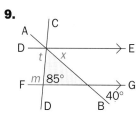

2.

3.

4.

5.

6.

Find the measure of each indicated angle.

7.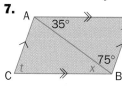

8.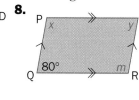

9.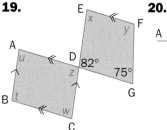

10.

11.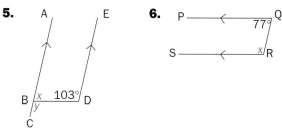

12.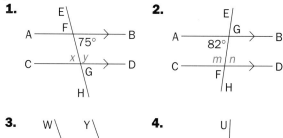

13.

14.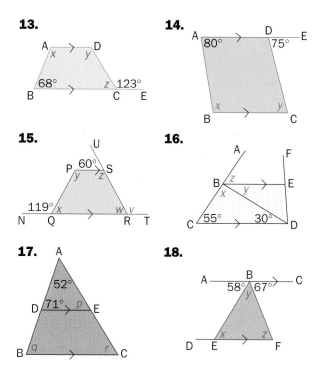

15.

16.

17.

18.

Applications and Problem Solving

B

Find the measure of each indicated angle.

19.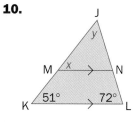

20.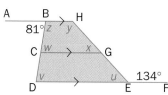

21.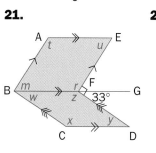

22.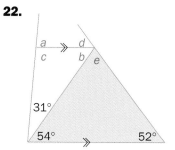

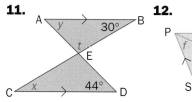

23. Algebra Find the value of *x*. Then, find the measures of the indicated angles.

a)

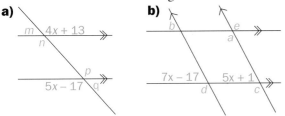

m 4x + 13
n

p
5x – 17 q

b)

b
e
a

7x – 17 5x + 1
d c

24. Algebra Find the values of *x* and *y*. Then, find the measures of the indicated angles.

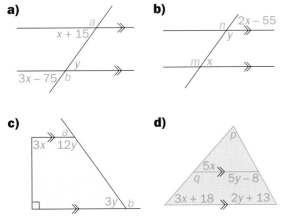

a)

a
x + 15

y
3x – 75 b

b)

n 2x – 55
y

m x

c)

a
3x 12y

3y b

d)

p

5x
q 5y – 8

3x + 18 2y + 13

25. List all the angles in this diagram. Then, calculate each angle's measure.

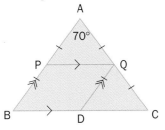

A

70°

P Q

B D C

26. Periscope A periscope is an instrument used on submarines to see above the surface of the water. The diagram shows how two parallel mirrors are used in a periscope.

mirror
4
3

2
1 mirror

eye

Show that ∠1 = ∠4. Explain and justify your reasoning

27. One way to show the sum of the interior angles of a triangle is to draw a line through one vertex of the triangle parallel to the opposite side. How does this show the following?

∠BAC + ∠B + ∠C = 180°

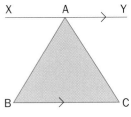

X A Y

B C

28. Geography Places on Earth are located using parallels of latitude and meridians of longitude. Are parallels of latitude really parallel lines? Explain why or why not.

29. Lines that do not lie in the same plane are called **skew lines**. Lines *m* and *n* in this diagram are skew lines. How are skew lines and parallel lines different? How are they the same?

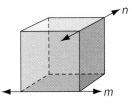

n

m

30. Sports Parallel dividers create lanes for 100-m races. Work with a partner to list other examples of the use of parallel lines in sports.

31. Write a problem that involves angles and parallel lines. Have a classmate solve your problem.

LOGIC POWER

Draw a chessboard in your notebook. Put a marker on each of 8 different squares so that no 2 markers are in the same row, column, or diagonal.

Polygons

A **polygon** is a closed figure formed by joining three or more line segments at their endpoints.

Polygons of many different types appear in nature. On this black rat snake, a reptile native to Ontario, the most prominent type of polygon has 6 sides and is called a hexagon.

Polygons are classified according to their number of sides.

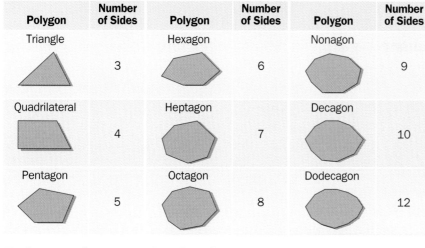

Polygon	Number of Sides	Polygon	Number of Sides	Polygon	Number of Sides
Triangle	3	Hexagon	6	Nonagon	9
Quadrilateral	4	Heptagon	7	Decagon	10
Pentagon	5	Octagon	8	Dodecagon	12

Each point where two sides of a polygon meet is called a **vertex** of the polygon. A **diagonal** is the line segment that joins any two non-consecutive vertices of a polygon.

vertex

diagonal

A **convex** polygon is one in which any line segment joining two points on the polygon has no part outside the polygon.

Convex Polygon

A polygon is **concave** if a line segment joining two points on the polygon can be drawn so that a part of the segment lies outside the polygon.

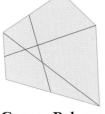

Concave Polygon

In this book, the term *polygon* means a convex polygon, unless otherwise stated.

Polygons can be *equilateral* (all sides equal) or *equiangular* (all angles equal).
When a polygon is both equilateral and equiangular, it is called a **regular polygon**.

This hexagon is neither equilateral nor equiangular.

This is an equilateral hexagon.

This is an equiangular hexagon.

This is a regular hexagon.

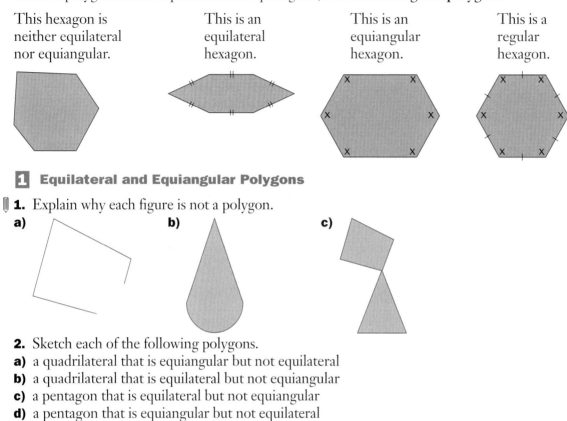

1 Equilateral and Equiangular Polygons

1. Explain why each figure is not a polygon.

a)

b)

c)

2. Sketch each of the following polygons.
a) a quadrilateral that is equiangular but not equilateral
b) a quadrilateral that is equilateral but not equiangular
c) a pentagon that is equilateral but not equiangular
d) a pentagon that is equiangular but not equilateral
e) a regular pentagon

3. Name a type of quadrilateral that is equilateral but not equiangular.

4. Name a type of quadrilateral that is equiangular but not equilateral.

2 Diagonal Pattern

1. A quadrilateral has 2 diagonals, as shown.
Copy and complete the table.

Polygon	Number of Diagonals
Quadrilateral	2
Pentagon	
Hexagon	
Heptagon	

2. Describe the pattern in the number of diagonals.

3. Use the pattern to predict the number of diagonals
in each of the following polygons.
a) octagon   **b)** nonagon   **c)** decagon

3 Angles and Regular Polygons

1. ABCDE is a regular pentagon. The point P is the centre of the pentagon. When a line segment is drawn from P to each vertex, five identical triangles are formed.

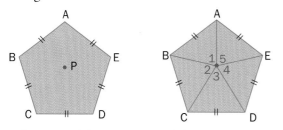

a) What is the sum of the measures of the central angles, $\angle 1$, $\angle 2$, $\angle 3$, $\angle 4$, and $\angle 5$?
b) What is the measure of each central angle?
c) What type of triangle is formed?
d) What are the measures of the other two angles in each triangle?
e) What is the sum of the measures of the five interior angles of a regular pentagon?
f) What is the measure of each interior angle of a regular pentagon?

2. ABCDEF is a regular hexagon. The point P is the centre of the hexagon. When a line segment is drawn from P to each vertex, six identical triangles are formed.

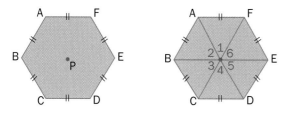

a) What is the measure of each central angle?
b) What type of triangle is formed?
c) What are the measures of the other two angles in each triangle?
d) What is the sum of the measures of the six interior angles of a regular hexagon?
e) What is the measure of each interior angle of a regular hexagon?

3. a) What is the measure of each central angle of a regular octagon?
b) What is the sum of the measures of the eight interior angles of a regular octagon?
c) What is the measure of each interior angle of a regular octagon?

TECHNOLOGY

Exploring the Sides and Diagonals of Polygons Using Geometry Software

Complete the following explorations using geometry software or a graphing calculator with geometry capabilities. If suitable technology is not available, complete the pencil-and-paper explorations on pages 544–547.

The explorations involve some special types of quadrilaterals, as follows.

• A **parallelogram** is a quadrilateral with both pairs of opposite sides parallel and equal in length.

• A **rectangle** is a quadrilateral with both pairs of opposite sides parallel and equal in length, and all angles 90°.

• A **rhombus** is a quadrilateral with both pairs of opposite sides parallel and all sides the same length.

• A **square** is a quadrilateral with both pairs of opposite sides parallel, all sides the same length, and all angles 90°.

• A **kite** is a quadrilateral with two pairs of adjacent sides equal.

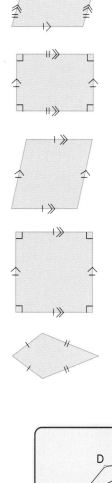

1 Sides

1. a) Write a conjecture about the type of quadrilateral formed when the midpoints of the sides of a quadrilateral are joined.
b) Construct a quadrilateral.
c) Construct the midpoint of each side.
d) Join the midpoints to form a quadrilateral within the quadrilateral.

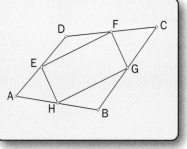

e) Measure the sides of the inner quadrilateral. How do the lengths compare?

f) Measure the interior angles in the inner quadrilateral. How do the angle measures compare?

g) Drag one of the vertices to change the quadrilateral to a variety of sizes and shapes. How do the side lengths compare and the angle measures compare for the inner quadrilateral in each case?

h) Is your conjecture from part a) valid? Explain.

2. a) Write a conjecture about the type of quadrilateral formed when the midpoints of the sides of a parallelogram are joined.

b) Construct a parallelogram.

c) Construct the midpoint of each side.

d) Join the midpoints to form a quadrilateral within the parallelogram.

e) Measure the sides of the inner quadrilateral. How do the lengths compare?

f) Measure the interior angles in the inner quadrilateral. How do the angle measures compare?

g) Drag one of the vertices to make a variety of parallelograms. How do the side lengths compare and the angle measures compare for the inner quadrilateral in each case?

h) Is your conjecture from part a) valid? Explain.

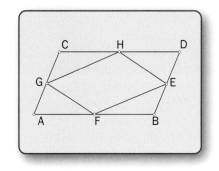

Repeat question 2 starting with each specific quadrilateral.

3. a rectangle

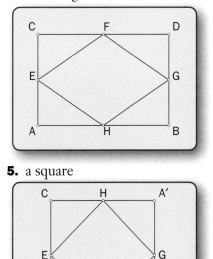

4. a rhombus

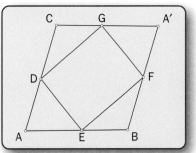

5. a square

6. a kite

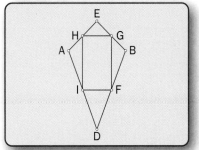

2 Diagonals

1. a) Construct a parallelogram.
b) Construct the diagonals.
c) Measure the lengths of the diagonals. How do the lengths compare?
d) Construct the point at the intersection of the diagonals.
e) Measure the distance from the point of intersection to each vertex. How do the distances compare?
f) Measure the four angles formed at the point of intersection of the diagonals. How do the angle measures compare?
g) Drag one of the vertices to make a variety of parallelograms. In each case, how do the distances from the point of intersection of the diagonals to the vertices compare? How do the measures of the angles formed at the point of intersection compare?
h) Write a statement describing the relationship between the lengths of the diagonals of a parallelogram, whether they bisect each other, and whether they intersect at 90°.

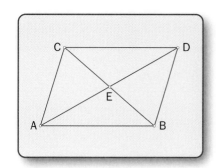

Repeat question 1 starting with each specific quadrilateral.

2. a rectangle

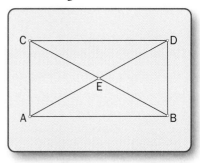

3. a rhombus

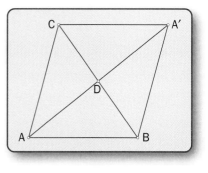

4. a square

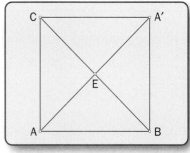

5. a kite

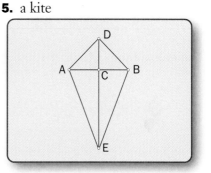

6. For which of the 5 quadrilaterals, do the diagonals
a) have the same length?
b) bisect each other?
c) intersect at 90°?
d) bisect each other at 90°?

7. a) Write a conjecture about the type of pentagon formed when the intersection points of the diagonals of a regular pentagon are joined.
b) Construct a regular pentagon.
c) Construct all the diagonals.
d) Construct all the points at the intersections of the diagonals.
e) Measure the distance between each pair of adjacent points of intersection to find the side lengths of the inner pentagon. How do the side lengths compare?
f) Measure the interior angles of the inner pentagon. How do the angle measures compare?
g) Drag one of the vertices to change the larger pentagon to a variety of sizes. For the inner pentagon in each case, how do the side lengths compare and how do the angle measures compare?
h) Is your conjecture from part a) valid? Explain.

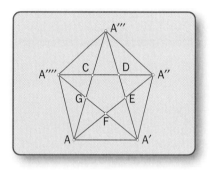

8. Golden ratio a) Construct a regular pentagon and one diagonal.
b) Measure the length of one side of the pentagon and the length of the diagonal.
c) Calculate the ratio of the length of the diagonal to the length of the side.
d) The number you found in part c) is an approximation of the **golden ratio**, a number found in nature, art, and architecture. Use your research skills to find examples of the golden ratio.

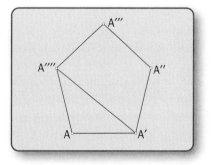

INVESTIGATING MATH

Exploring Sides and Diagonals of Polygons

Complete the following explorations using grid paper and a ruler.
Use a protractor when necessary.

The explorations involve some special types of quadrilaterals, as follows.
• A **parallelogram** is a quadrilateral with both pairs of opposite sides parallel and equal in length.
• A **rectangle** is a quadrilateral with both pairs of opposite sides parallel and equal in length, and all angles 90°.
• A **rhombus** is a quadrilateral with both pairs of opposite sides parallel and all sides the same length.
• A **square** is a quadrilateral with both pairs of opposite sides parallel, all sides the same length, and all angles 90°.
• A **kite** is a quadrilateral with two pairs of adjacent sides equal.

1 Sides

1. a) Make a conjecture about the type of quadrilateral that is formed when the midpoints of the sides of a square are joined.
b) Construct a square ABCD. Mark the midpoints of the four sides and label them E, F, G, and H, as shown. Join the midpoints to make quadrilateral EFGH.
c) Find the lengths of EF, FG, GH, and HE. How do the lengths compare?
d) Find the measures of ∠HEF, ∠EFG, ∠FGH, and ∠GHE. How do the angle measures compare?
e) Is your conjecture from part a) valid? Explain.

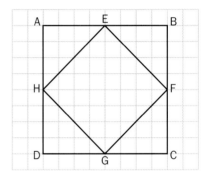

2. a) Make a conjecture about the type of quadrilateral that is formed when the midpoints of the sides of a rectangle are joined.
b) Construct a rectangle DEFG. Mark the midpoints of the four sides and label them K, L, M, and N, as shown. Join the midpoints to make quadrilateral KLMN.
c) Find the lengths of KL, LM, MN, and NK. How do the lengths compare?
d) Find the measures of ∠KLM, ∠LMN, ∠MNK, and ∠NKL. How do the angle measures compare?
e) Is your conjecture from part a) valid? Explain.

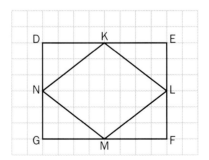

3. a) Make a conjecture about the type of quadrilateral that is formed when the midpoints of the sides of a quadrilateral are joined.
b) Construct any quadrilateral WXYZ. Find the midpoints of the four sides and label them P, Q, R, and S, as shown. Join the midpoints to make quadrilateral PQRS.
c) Find the lengths of SP and RQ. How do the lengths compare?
d) Find the lengths of PQ and SR. How do the lengths compare?
e) Find the measures of ∠SPQ, ∠PQR, ∠QRS, and ∠RSP. How do the angle measures compare?
f) Is your conjecture from part a) valid? Explain.

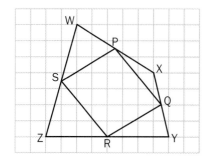

4. a) Make a conjecture about the type of quadrilateral that is formed when the midpoints of the sides of a kite are joined.
b) Construct a kite ABCD. Mark the midpoints of the four sides and label them E, F, G, and H, as shown. Join the midpoints to make quadrilateral EFGH.
c) Test your conjecture by measuring the sides and angles of quadrilateral EFGH.
d) Is your conjecture from part a) valid? Explain.

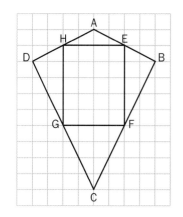

5. a) Make a conjecture about the type of quadrilateral that is formed when the midpoints of the sides of a rhombus are joined.
b) Construct a rhombus GHIJ. Mark the midpoints of the four sides and label them X, Y, Z, and W, as shown. Join the midpoints to make quadrilateral XYZW.
c) Test your conjecture by measuring the sides and angles of quadrilateral XYZW.
d) Is your conjecture from part a) valid? Explain.

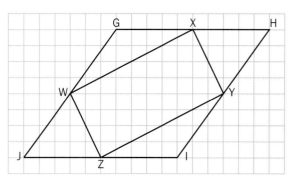

▯ 2 Diagonals

1. a) Construct a rectangle ABCD. Draw the diagonals AC and BD. Label the point of intersection E.
b) Find the lengths of AC and BD. How do the lengths compare?
c) Find the lengths of AE and CE. How do the lengths compare?
d) Find the lengths of BE and DE. How do the lengths compare?

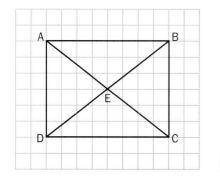

e) Find the measures of ∠AED, ∠DEC, ∠CEB, and ∠BEA. How do the angle measures compare?

f) Write a statement describing the relationship between the lengths of the diagonals of a rectangle, whether they bisect each other, and whether they intersect at 90°.

2. a) Construct a parallelogram DEFG. Draw the diagonals DF and EG. Label the point of intersection H.

b) Find the lengths of DF and EG. How do the lengths compare?

c) Find the lengths of DH and FH. How do the lengths compare?

d) Find the lengths of EH and GH. How do the lengths compare?

e) Find the measures of ∠DHG, ∠GHF, ∠FHE, and ∠EHD. How do the angle measures compare?

f) Write a statement describing the relationship between the lengths of the diagonals of a parallelogram, whether they bisect each other, and whether they intersect at 90°.

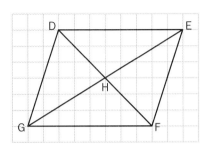

3. a) Construct a kite JKLM. Draw the diagonals JL and KM. Label the point of intersection N.

b) Find the lengths of JL and MK. How do the lengths compare?

c) Find the lengths of JN and LN. How do the lengths compare?

d) Find the lengths of KN and MN. How do the lengths compare?

e) Find the measures of ∠JNM, ∠MNL, ∠LNK, and ∠KNJ. How do the angle measures compare?

f) Write a statement describing the relationship between the lengths of the diagonals of a kite, whether they bisect each other, and whether they intersect at 90°.

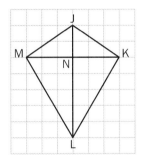

4. a) Construct a rhombus RSTQ. Draw the diagonals RT and SQ. Label the point of intersection W.

b) Find the lengths of RT and QS. How do the lengths compare?

c) Find the lengths of RW and TW. How do the lengths compare?

d) Find the lengths of SW and QW. How do the lengths compare?

e) Find the measures of ∠RWQ, ∠QWT, ∠TWS, and ∠SWR. How do the angle measures compare?

f) Write a statement describing the relationship between the lengths of the diagonals of a rhombus, whether they bisect each other, and whether they intersect at 90°.

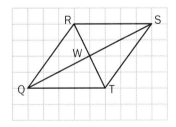

5. a) Construct a square WXYZ. Draw the diagonals WY and XZ. Label the point of intersection T.
b) Find the lengths of WY and XZ. How do the lengths compare?
c) Find the lengths of WT and YT. How do the lengths compare?
d) Find the lengths of ZT and XT. How do the lengths compare?
e) Find the measures of ∠WTZ, ∠ZTY, ∠YTX, and ∠XTW. How do the angle measures compare?
f) Write a statement describing the relationship between the lengths of the diagonals of a square, whether they bisect each other, and whether they intersect at 90°.

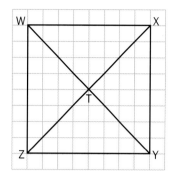

6. For which of the five quadrilaterals you have investigated in questions 1–5, do the diagonals
a) have the same length?
b) bisect each other?
c) intersect at 90°?
d) bisect each other at 90°?

7. a) Construct a regular pentagon ABCDE. Draw all the diagonals. Label the points of intersection of the diagonals P, Q, R, S, and T.
b) Find the lengths of PQ, QR, RS, ST, and TP. How do the lengths compare?
c) Find the measures of ∠PQR, ∠QRS, ∠RST, ∠STP, and ∠TPQ. How do the angle measures compare?
d) Is the pentagon PQRST a regular pentagon?

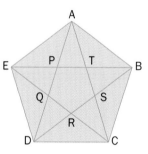

8. Golden ratio a) Construct a regular pentagon and draw one diagonal.
b) Find the length of one side of the pentagon and the length of the diagonal.
c) Find the ratio of the length of the diagonal to the length of the side. Round your answer to the nearest tenth.
d) The number you found in part c) is an approximation of the **golden ratio**, a number found in nature, art, and architecture. Use your research skills to find a more accurate value of the golden ratio and examples of where it is found.

CAREER CONNECTION

Design

In 1997, Canada Post issued a 45¢ stamp to acknowledge Canadian achievements in industrial design. The stamp was launched at Toronto's Design Exchange, where some of the items shown on the stamp are on display.

Stamp reproduced courtesy of Canada Post Corporation.

Designers work in many fields, including fashion, interior design, urban design, landscape architecture, and Website design. We constantly see the work of designers, which ranges from logos, packaging, and stage sets to the magazines we read, the cars we drive, and the streets we drive along.

1 Designing With Triangles and Quadrilaterals

1. Design 1 was created by connecting the midpoints of the sides of the equilateral triangles.
a) What is the measure of each angle in the largest triangle?
b) How many triangles in the design have these angle measures?

2. The triangles in Design 2 are congruent isosceles triangles.
a) What are the angle measures in each triangle in the design?
b) What are the angle measures in each quadrilateral in the design?

Design 1

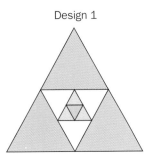

Design 2

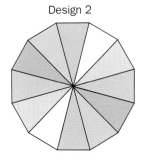

3. Design 3 was created by connecting the midpoints of the sides of the squares.
a) What are the angle measures in a triangle in the design?
b) How many triangles in the design have these angle measures?

Design 3

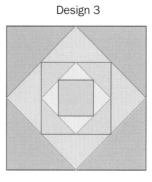

4. Design 4 consists of eight congruent rhombuses.
a) What are the angle measures in each rhombus?
b) How many right angles are formed by sides of rhombuses?

Design 4

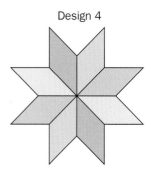

5. a) Create your own design from triangles and/or quadrilaterals.
b) Write a problem about angle measures in your design. Have a classmate solve your problem.

2 Locating Information

1. Choose a design field that interests you. Use your research skills to find out how people train for this field and who employs them.

2. Describe a Canadian achievement in the field that you chose.

INVESTIGATING MATH

Posing Questions and Testing Conjectures

In the following explorations, you will
a) pose a question about a geometric relationship
b) make a conjecture, which is a possible answer to the question
c) test your conjecture
d) communicate your findings

1 Posing Questions Related to Triangles

1. Pose a question about how the sum of the lengths of any two sides of a triangle compares with the length of the third side. Make a conjecture, test it, and communicate your findings.

2. △ABC is any triangle. Line segment DE joins the midpoints of AB and AC. Pose a question about the relationship between the line segments DE and BC. Make a conjecture, test it, and communicate your findings.

3. △ABC is any triangle. DE, DF, and EF join the midpoints of the sides of △ABC. Pose a question about the relationship between the lengths of the sides of △ABC and the lengths of the sides of △DEF, or a question about the measures of the angles of △ABC and the measures of the angles of △DEF. Make a conjecture, test it, and communicate your findings.

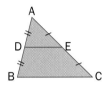

4. a) You have 3 straws that are 6 cm long, 3 straws that are 7 cm long, and 3 straws that are 8 cm long. Pose a question about the number of different triangles that can be made using 3 straws as the sides. Make a conjecture, test it, and communicate your findings.
b) Repeat part a) but use 3 straws that are 4 cm long, 3 straws that are 8 cm long, and 3 straws that are 9 cm long.
c) Write a similar question using straws of lengths that you choose. Make a conjecture, test it, and communicate your findings.

2 Posing Questions Related to Parallel Lines

1. In the diagram, ∠1 and ∠2 are exterior angles on the same side of the transversal intersecting two parallel lines. Pose a question about the relationship between ∠1 and ∠2. Make a conjecture, test it, and communicate your findings.

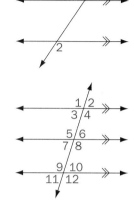

2. a) Pose a question about the relationship between ∠12 and ∠1 in the diagram. Make a conjecture, test it, and communicate your findings.
b) Pose a question about the relationship between ∠11 and ∠4 in the diagram. Make a conjecture, test it, and communicate your findings.

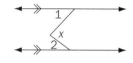

3. Pose a question about the relationship between ∠1 and ∠2 in the diagram. Make a conjecture, test it, and communicate your findings.

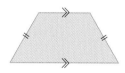

3 Posing Questions Related to Quadrilaterals

1. Quadrilateral ABCD is a concave quadrilateral. Pose a question about the sum of the interior angles of a concave quadrilateral. Make a conjecture, test it, and communicate your findings.

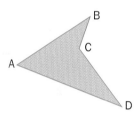

2. An **isosceles trapezoid** is a trapezoid whose two non-parallel sides are equal in length. Pose a question about the relationship between the interior angles of an isosceles trapezoid. Make a conjecture, test it, and communicate your findings.

3. ABCD is any rectangle. Pose a question about the relationship between the lengths of AC and BD. Make a conjecture, show how to test it without measuring, and communicate your findings.

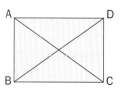

10.3 Analyzing Conjectures Using Examples and Counterexamples

It is important to be cautious when making conjectures. They may or may not be true. To demonstrate that a conjecture is false, you need describe only one **counterexample**, which is an example for which the conjecture is false.

Many years ago, people thought the Earth was flat. Whenever a ship left on a voyage of exploration and never returned, it was believed that the ship had fallen off the edge of the Earth. The flat-Earth conjecture was believed by many until Ferdinand Magellan's ship arrived back in Portugal on September 6, 1522, after taking three years to sail around the world. This trip was seen as a counterexample to the conjecture that the Earth was flat.

Explore: Look for a Pattern

When 2 points are placed on the circumference of a circle and joined, 2 regions are formed.

When 3 points are placed on the circle, and each point is joined to every other point, 4 regions are formed.

When 4 points are used, 8 regions are formed.

🖉 Make a conjecture by describing the pattern in the number of regions formed.

Inquire

1. a) Use the pattern to predict the number of regions formed when 5 points are used.
b) Use a diagram to check your prediction. Is the pattern valid for 5 points?

2. a) Use the pattern to predict the number of regions formed when 6 points are used.

b) Use a diagram to check your answer. Is the pattern valid for 6 points?

3. What conclusion can you make about your conjecture for describing the pattern in the number of regions formed?

4. Give a counterexample to show that each of the following conjectures is false.

a) If you live in a country bordering the United States, then you live in Canada.

b) If a quadrilateral has four right angles, then it is a square.

c) A heavier-than-air mechanically driven vehicle that flies is an airplane.

Example   Isosceles Triangles

Consider the conjecture:

In any isosceles triangle, all three angles are acute.

a) Draw two examples of triangles for which the conjecture holds.

b) Draw one counterexample that shows the conjecture is not true.

Solution

a)

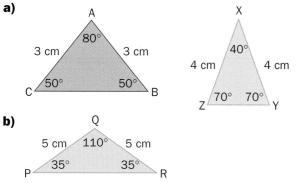

b)

Since ∠Q is obtuse, this counterexample shows the conjecture is not true.

Practice

A

Give one example that supports each conjecture, and then give one counterexample that shows the conjecture is false.

1. Provinces in Canada share a land border with the United States.

2. If the name of a province in Canada contains the letter *s*, then the province has a coastline.

3. Canadian provincial capitals are south of the 53°N parallel of latitude.

4. The square root of a number is smaller than the number.

5. If the *x*-coordinate of a point in the Cartesian plane is positive, then the point is in the first quadrant.

6. The square of a number is greater than the number.

7. All multiples of 4 are divisible by 8.

8. The square root of a number is a rational number.

Draw a diagram to illustrate each of the following conjectures. Then, draw a counterexample diagram showing the conjecture is not true.

9. If a quadrilateral has two equal diagonals, then it is a rectangle.

10. If two opposite angles in a quadrilateral are equal, then the other two opposite angles are supplementary.

11. If a quadrilateral has four equal sides, then it is a square.

12. If a triangle has exactly two obtuse exterior angles, then it is a right triangle.

13. An altitude of a triangle lies within the triangle.

14. If the measures of two sides of a right triangle are 3 cm and 4 cm, then the third side measures 5 cm.

Applications and Problem Solving

B

Use examples or counterexamples to confirm or deny each conjecture in questions 15–24.

15. If a scalene triangle has a 60° angle, then this angle is opposite the shortest side of the triangle.

16. From a point not on a line, it is possible to draw two perpendiculars to the line.

17. If a transversal is perpendicular to one of two parallel lines, then it is perpendicular to the other line.

18. If a quadrilateral has perpendicular diagonals, then it is a square.

19. A quadrilateral cannot have exactly three interior angles that are right angles.

20. If two interior angles of a quadrilateral are right angles, then the quadrilateral is a rectangle.

21. If a quadrilateral has four equal sides and four equal angles, then it is a square.

22. If two opposite angles of a quadrilateral both measure 90°, then the quadrilateral is a rectangle.

23. If an exterior angle of a triangle is acute, then the triangle is obtuse.

24. A pentagon with five equal sides is a regular pentagon.

25. Danielle conjectured that, if point P is the vertex of two angles, ∠APB and ∠BPC, then ∠APC is obtuse. Draw a diagram for which the conjecture is true and one counterexample diagram to show that the conjecture is false.

26. Pascal conjectured that, if line segments AB and BC have the same length, then B is the midpoint of line segment AC. Draw a diagram for which his conjecture is true and one counterexample diagram to show that his conjecture is false.

C

27. Sarita conjectured that, if the diagonals of a quadrilateral are perpendicular, then the quadrilateral cannot have all sides with different lengths. Draw diagrams to show whether her conjecture is true or false.

28. Ray conjectured that, if one diagonal of a quadrilateral bisects two interior angles, then the quadrilateral is a parallelogram. Draw diagrams to show whether his conjecture is true or false.

LOGIC POWER

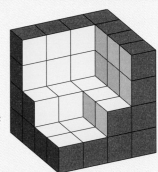

Assume that no small cubes are missing from the back of the stack.

1. How many small cubes are needed to complete the large cube?

2. The faces on the outside of the large cube must all be red. The faces hidden inside the large cube must all be yellow. Some of the small cubes you found in question 1 need to have 2 red faces and 4 yellow faces.

a) What other combinations of red and yellow faces are needed?

b) Find how many small cubes are needed with each combination of red and yellow faces.

10.4 How Can We Model Your Field of Vision?

Angles of peripheral vision were introduced on page 509 at the beginning of this chapter. Complete the following experiment to determine your angles of peripheral vision. You will need to work in a group of at least three.

1 Modelling Horizontal Peripheral Vision

To determine your angle of horizontal peripheral vision, you will need a chalkboard protractor. If one is not available, make one from cardboard and mark the scale in 5° intervals.

1. Decide who is to be tested (the subject), who is to do the testing (the tester), and who is to perform the angle measurements (the recorder). Then, use the following steps.
• The subject and the tester sit in chairs and face each other with their knees almost touching.
• To test the left eye, the subject covers the right eye and stares at the tester's nose.
• The tester holds a pen vertically just behind and about 25 cm from the subject's left ear.
• The subject keeps staring at the tester's nose while the tester slowly moves the pen in a horizontal arc toward the centre of the subject's field of vision.
• The subject says "stop" when the pen first comes into view.
• The recorder places the protractor under the subject's chin and measures the angle formed by two lines — one that connects the subject's nose and the tester's nose, and the other that connects the subject's nose and the pen.

2. To test the subject's right eye, repeat the above steps but with the subject's left eye covered and the pen behind the subject's right ear.

3. Add the two angle measures found above to find the subject's angle of horizontal peripheral vision.

4. Change roles until all students in the class have been tested. Record all the results.

5. How does your own angle of horizontal peripheral vision compare with your estimate from page 509?

6. Calculate the mean angle of horizontal peripheral vision for the students in your class.

2 Modelling Vertical Peripheral Vision

Recall from page 509 that there are two angles of vertical peripheral vision. They are upward and downward from the horizontal. The procedure for finding these angles is similar to the procedure for finding the angle of horizontal peripheral vision.

1. Find the upward angle of peripheral vision as follows.
• With the subject and the tester positioned as before, the subject stares at the tester's nose with both eyes.
• The tester holds a pen horizontally about 25 cm above the subject's head.
• The subject keeps staring at the tester's nose while the tester moves the pen in a vertical arc down toward the centre of the subject's field of vision.
• The subject says "stop" when the pen first comes into view.
• The recorder measures the angle formed by two lines — one that connects the subject's nose and the tester's nose, and the other that connects the subject's nose and the pen.

2. Find the subject's downward angle of peripheral vision in a similar way, except that the tester holds the pen horizontally below the subject's chin and moves it up toward the centre of the subject's field of vision.

3. Change roles until all students in the class have been tested. Record all the results.

4. How do your own upward and downward angles of peripheral vision compare with your estimates from page 509?

5. Calculate the mean upward and downward angles of peripheral vision for the students in your class.

6. Which is greater — the upward or the downward angle of peripheral vision? Explain why it is greater.

3 Analyzing and Displaying Data

1. As well as calculating the mean of each set of values, how could you analyze the data?

2. Prepare a report using the class results. Organize and analyze the data in ways that you choose.

1. Helmets One standard for bicycle helmets recommends an angle of vertical peripheral vision of 40° upward and an angle of horizontal peripheral vision of 240°, or 120° from the centre line on each side. For go-kart racing helmets, the recommended angles of vertical peripheral vision are 5° upward and 20° downward, and the angle of horizontal peripheral vision is 180°, or 90° from the centre line on each side.

a) Why are the angles of horizontal peripheral vision different for the two helmets?

b) Why is there a recommended angle of downward peripheral vision for a go-kart helmet, but not for a bicycle helmet?

c) For what other types of headgear do designers need to consider the horizontal and vertical angles of peripheral vision?

2. Tunnel vision An eye condition called glaucoma can result in "tunnel vision." What is tunnel vision and why is it given this name?

3. Eye tests Describe other methods that ophthalmologists use to determine angles of peripheral vision.

Review

10.1 *Find the missing angle measures.*

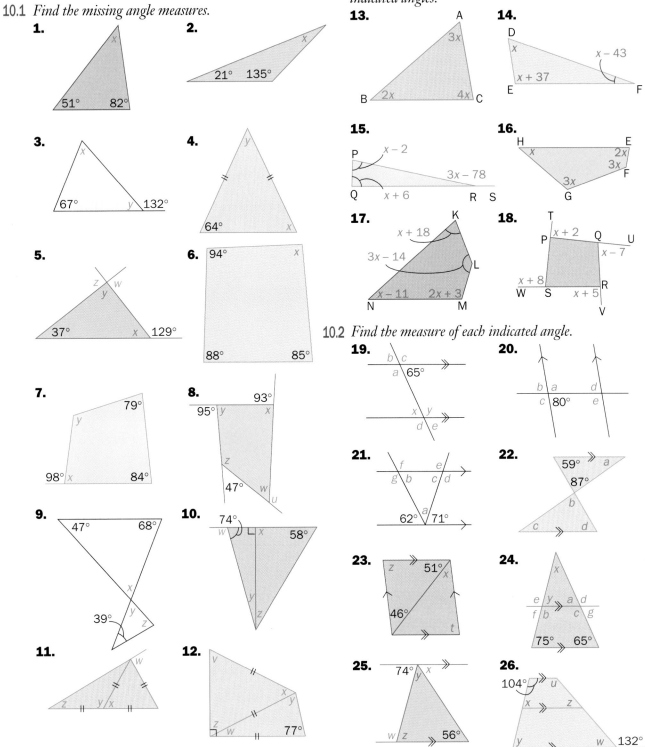

1.

x

$51°$ $82°$

2.

x

$21°$ $135°$

3.

x

$67°$ y $132°$

4.

y

$64°$ x

5.

z w
y

$37°$ x $129°$

6.

$94°$ x

$88°$ $85°$

7.

$79°$
y

$98°$ x $84°$

8.

$93°$
$95°$ y x

z

$47°$ w
u

9.

$47°$ $68°$

x

$39°$ y
z

10.

$74°$
w x $58°$

y

z

11.

w

z y x

12.

v

x
y

z
w $77°$

Find the value of x. Then, find the measures of all the indicated angles.

13.

A
$3x$

B $2x$ $4x$ C

14.

D
x $x - 43$

E $x + 37$ F

15.

P $x - 2$
$3x - 78$
Q $x + 6$ R S

16.

H E
x $2x$
$3x$ F
$3x$
G

17.

K
$x + 18$
$3x - 14$
L
$x - 11$ $2x + 3$
N M

18.

T
P $x + 2$ Q U
$x - 7$
$x + 8$ R
W S $x + 5$
V

10.2 *Find the measure of each indicated angle.*

19.

b c
a $65°$

x y
d e

20.

b a d
c $80°$ e

21.

f e
g b c d

$62°$ a $71°$

22.

$59°$ a
$87°$

b

c d

23.

z $51°$
x
$46°$
t

24.

x
e y a d
f b c g

$75°$ $65°$

25.

$74°$ x
y

w z $56°$

26.

$104°$ u
x z
y w $132°$

558   *Chapter 10*

Find the value of x. Then, find the measures of the indicated angles.

27. **28.**

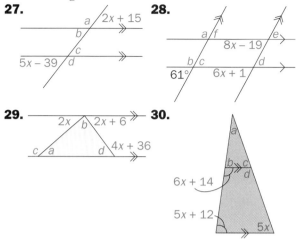

29. **30.**

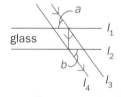

31. Refraction of light In the diagram, light enters the pane of glass along l_3 and leaves along l_4. If $l_3 \parallel l_4$, $l_1 \parallel l_2$, and $\angle a = 55°$, find the measure of $\angle b$. Give reasons for your answer.

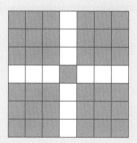

10.3 *Draw a diagram to illustrate each of the following conjectures. Then, draw a counterexample diagram showing the conjecture is not true.*

32. The three altitudes of a triangle intersect at a point inside the triangle.

33. If a quadrilateral has two equal diagonals, then it is a square.

Confirm or deny each statement using examples or counterexamples.

34. If a quadrilateral has four equal angles, then it is a square.

35. If a quadrilateral contains no right angles and has two pairs of equal angles, then it is a parallelogram.

36. It is not possible for the sum of the lengths of two sides of a triangle to equal the length of the third side.

37. If one interior angle of a quadrilateral is a reflex angle, then the quadrilateral is concave.

Exploring Math

Tetrominoes

Polyominoes are shapes formed by joining identical squares along their edges. The domino, which is made up of two squares, can have only one shape.

A triomino, which is made up of three squares, can have two shapes.

Tetrominoes are made up of four squares and can have the following five shapes.

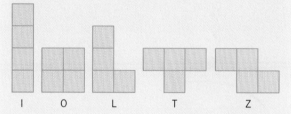

I   O   L   T   Z

On the 7-by-7 grid shown, squares have been shaded so that no group of shaded squares forms the I shape, either vertically or horizontally. The maximum number of squares that can be shaded without shading the I shape is 37, as shown.

Determine the maximum number of squares that can be shaded on a 7-by-7 grid without shading the following shapes. Allow for all possible orientations; for example, an upside down T shape is still considered a T shape.

1. the O shape

2. the L shape

3. the I, O, and Z shapes

4. the I, O, T, Z, and L shapes

Chapter Check

Find the missing angle measures.

1.

55°
67° x

2.

25°
127° x y

3.

x
131° y 49°

4.

x
118°
93° 91°

5.

77° x
95° y 109°

6.

114° u w 82°
z
x
120° y

7.

34° 72°
x
y z
38°

8.

72°
y
24° x
z

Find the measure of each indicated angle.

13.

a b
c 123°
d e
g f

14.

a d
b c
38° 47°

15.

a b
81° c

16.

42° d
51°
a b c

17.

82° e
a
b 77°
c d

18.

c
34° a b
e d

Find the value of x. Then, find the measures of the indicated angles.

19.

a 2x + 15
b c
d 3x − 5

20.

n 3x + 7
3x m 4x + 12

Find the value of x. Then, find the measures of all the indicated angles.

9.

A
x + 16
B x + 21 x + 35 C

10.

H
x − 4
3x − 64 x + 8
E F G

11.

Y
x + 17
3x − 11 X
Z 2x − 2 2x − 12 W

12.

H
E A x − 12 D
x + 13
x + 11
C G
B x + 16
F

Draw a diagram to illustrate each of the following conjectures. Then, draw a counterexample diagram that shows the conjecture is not true.

21. If the measure of one angle in a triangle is 85°, the triangle is not scalene.

22. A quadrilateral with four equal sides is regular.

23. A trapezoid has two pairs of equal angles.

24. Two co-interior angles on the same side of a transversal that intersects two parallel lines are equal.

Confirm or deny each statement using examples or counterexamples.

25. A quadrilateral cannot have three interior angles that are obtuse angles.

26. A kite has two pairs of equal angles.

27. The exterior angles of an acute triangle are obtuse.

Using the Strategies

1. Latin Squares The diagram shows a Latin Square. The numbers 1, 2, and 3 have been placed so that each number appears only once in each row and column.

1	2	3
2	3	1
3	1	2

There are 11 other different Latin Squares that use the numbers 1, 2, and 3. Draw them.

2. Smallest sum Use each of the digits 1, 3, 4, 6, 7, and 8 only once. Make the smallest possible sum by arranging the numbers as indicated in the diagram. What is the sum?

3. Counterfeit coin What is the minimum number of mass comparisons an inspector needs to make to find 1 counterfeit coin in a collection of 40 coins? Assume that the counterfeit coin is lighter than the others.

4. Phone calls About how many hours do all the high school students in Ontario spend on the telephone in a year?

5. Shopping You spend $2.75 in a store and receive $7.25 change from $10.00. Notice that the arrangement of the digits in the amount you spent is a rearrangement of the digits in your change. Find 4 other pairs of amounts spent and change from $10.00 that share this property.

6. The numbers in the large squares are found by adding the numbers in the small squares. What are the numbers in the small squares?

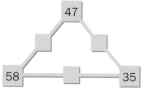

7. GCF The greatest common factor of two numbers, m and n, is 14. If $m = 2 \times 5 \times 7^2$, name three numbers that could be n.

8. Design Each rectangular design is made with red border squares and white interior squares. Each square has a side length of 1 unit.

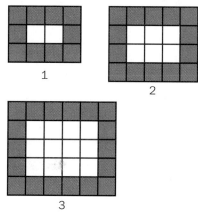

a) How many red squares are in the fourth diagram? the fifth diagram?
b) Write an expression for the number of red squares in terms of the length of the design, l.
c) How many red squares are there in the design with a length of 14? 40?

9. Running Lauryn and Yolanda had a 100-m race. Lauryn beat Yolanda by 10 m. For the second race, Yolanda suggested that Lauryn start 10 m behind the starting line. Yolanda thought this way of starting would give her a fair chance.
a) Who won the race and by how much?
b) What assumptions did you make?

10. Rivers What percent of Canada's 20 longest rivers flow into Hudson Bay?

Chapter 9

Calculate the area. Round to the nearest square unit, if necessary.

1.
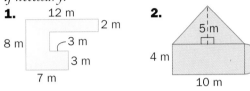

2.

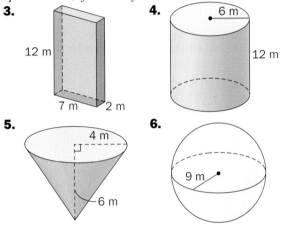

Calculate the surface area. Round to the nearest square metre, if necessary.

3.

4. 6 m

12 m

12 m

7 m   2 m

5. 4 m

6 m

6.

9 m

Calculate the volume. Round to the nearest cubic centimetre, if necessary.

7.

10 cm

8 cm

8.

7 cm

5 cm   13 cm

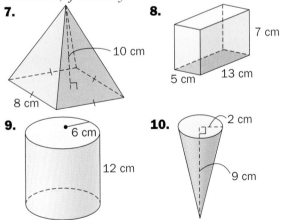

9. 6 cm

12 cm

10. 2 cm

9 cm

11. Soup can A soup can is a cylinder with a diameter of 6.5 cm and a height of 9.5 cm.
a) Calculate the volume, to the nearest cubic centimetre.
b) How many millilitres of soup will the soup can hold?

Chapter 10

Find the missing angle measures.

1.

57°

72°   *x*

2.

y

133° *x*   62°

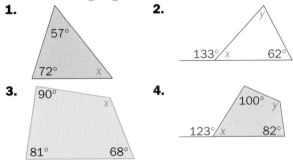

3.

90°

x

81°   68°

4.

100° *y*

123° *x*   82°

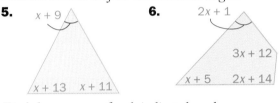

Find the measures of all the indicated angles.

5. *x* + 9

x + 13   *x* + 11

6. 2*x* + 1

3*x* + 12

x + 5   2*x* + 14

Find the measure of each indicated angle.

7.

a/*b*
67°

f/*c*
e/*d*

8. *a*   36° *d*

42°

b   *c*

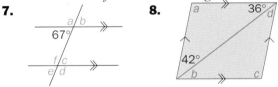

Find the value of x. Then, find the measures of all the indicated angles.

9.

a/*b*
c/3*x* + 11

d/2*x* + 4
e/*f*

10. 2*x* + 39   *a*

b   *c*
4*x* – 7

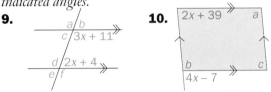

Draw a diagram to illustrate each of the following conjectures. Then, draw a counterexample diagram showing the conjecture is not true.

11. If the diagonals of a quadrilateral bisect each other at 90°, then it is a square.
12. If two opposite angles in a quadrilateral are equal, then the other two opposite angles are equal.

Confirm or deny each statement using examples or counterexamples.

13. If a triangle has one exterior angle that is acute, then the triangle is scalene.
14. If two exterior angles of a quadrilateral measure 90°, then it is a rectangle.

Estimate, and then calculate.

1. $34.6 + 121.9 + 55.2$ **2.** $11.2 - 5.9 + 0.8$

3. 5.2×115 **4.** $45.36 \div 7.2$

5. Evaluate $4x - 7$ when x equals

a) 9.4 **b)** 7.3 **c)** 10.6

6. Evaluate for $x = 2$ and $y = 3$.

a) $x^4 - y^2$ **b)** $(y - x)^3$ **c)** $7x^2 - y^2$

Simplify. Express each answer in exponential form.

7. $2^5 \times 2^3$ **8.** $5^6 \div 5^4$ **9.** $(7^3)^4$

10. $x^7 \times x^4$ **11.** $x^8 \div x^3$ **12.** $(x^5)^2$

Evaluate.

13. $3 - (-5) - 4 - 2$ **14.** $5 - 8 - 9 - 2$

15. -7×8 **16.** $-30 \div (-5)$

17. $(-4)^2$ **18.** -5^3

Evaluate.

19. $14 \div (-7) - 2^3$ **20.** $(3 - 6)^2 - 5 \times 2$

21. $3 \times (-1)^3 + 4 \times (-3)$ **22.** $-5 \times 3 - 8$

23. Evaluate for $x = -4$ and $y = -3$.

a) $5x - 6y$ **b)** $3xy - 2$

c) $2x^2 - xy$ **d)** $x^2 - y^3$

Write each ratio in simplest form.

24. 15 to 20 **25.** 8:10 **26.** $\dfrac{18}{27}$

Solve for x.

27. $\dfrac{x}{1.5} = \dfrac{10}{3}$ **28.** $\dfrac{3}{2} = \dfrac{7}{x}$

29. Running speed A jackrabbit can run at a speed of 72 km/h. How far can it run in 1 s?

30. Comparison shopping Decide which is the better value.
$4.60 for 4 L of milk or $2.45 for 2 L of milk

Write as percents.

31. 0.55 **32.** 0.09 **33.** 1.34

Write each percent as a decimal.

34. 24% **35.** 0.8% **36.** 143%

37. Markup The cost price for a sweater for a retailer was $110. The retailer marked it up by 30%. What was the selling price before taxes?

Write in scientific notation.

38. 12 300 000 **39.** 0.000 042

Write in standard form.

40. 3.2×10^8 **41.** 5.8×10^{-6}

Simplify.

42. $4^{-3} \times 4^4$ **43.** $3^{-3} \div 3^{-4}$ **44.** $(5^{-2})^{-5}$

Evaluate.

45. $3^0 \times 3^2$ **46.** $4^3 \div 4^5$ **47.** $(3^{-2})^{-2}$

Calculate.

48. $-3.4 \times (-6.5)$ **49.** -5.2^2

50. $10.8 \div (-0.2)$ **51.** $-3.9 - 6.8$

52. $-\dfrac{7}{2} \div \dfrac{7}{6}$ **53.** $-4 - 5\dfrac{5}{8}$

54. $-\dfrac{5}{4} \times \dfrac{8}{7}$ **55.** $11\dfrac{3}{5} - 17$

Evaluate.

56. $2(4.6 - 5.1) \div (-0.5)$

57. $(-3.2)^2 + 4$

58. $8 - \dfrac{3}{4} \times \dfrac{8}{5}$

59. $(8 - 12)^2 \div \dfrac{1}{4}$

Estimate. Then, calculate to the nearest tenth.

60. $\sqrt{531}$ **61.** $\sqrt{4562}$ **62.** $\sqrt{0.85}$

63. Measurement A square has an area of 60 m². Calculate the perimeter, to the nearest tenth of a metre.

64. Music lessons Identify the population and suggest a sampling procedure that could be used to answer the following question.

What percent of secondary school students in your city or town take music lessons?

65. Test scores a) Draw a box-and-whisker plot to represent the following geography test scores.
71, 78, 79, 68, 70, 72, 72, 81, 84, 61, 63, 63, 86, 86, 79, 77, 74, 87, 83
b) About what percent of the values lie in the box? in each whisker?

66. Education spending The table gives the amount, in billions of dollars, spent on elementary and secondary education in Canada in several years.

Year	1971	1976	1981	1986	1991	1996
Spending ($Billions)	5	10	17	23	33	36

a) Display the data on a scatter plot.
b) Draw the line of best fit.
c) Use the graph to estimate the amount that will be spent on elementary and secondary education in 2012.

67. Measurement a) Plot the points A(2, 2), B(5, 2) and C(2, 6) on a grid. Join them to form a triangle.
b) Find the perimeter and area of the triangle.

68. Giant tortoise A giant tortoise moves at a speed of 4 m/min.
a) Copy and complete the table of values for a moving giant tortoise.

Time (min)	Distance (m)
0	
1	
2	
3	
4	

b) Draw a graph of distance versus time.
c) Use the graph to estimate the distance a giant tortoise can cover in 1.7 min; in 3.3 min.

a) *Graph the following relations using paper and pencil or a graphing calculator.*
b) *State whether each relation is a direct variation or a partial variation.*
69. $y = -2x + 2$ **70.** $y = -0.5x$

71. Modelling motion Sketch a graph of the distance you are from your locker versus time on a typical school day, from when you enter the school until you leave.

Simplify.
72. $(x^2 - 3x + 8) + (3x^2 + 7x - 9)$
73. $(2y^2 + y - 11) - (5y^2 - y + 4)$

Expand and simplify.
74. $5(y - 3) + 7(y + 2)$
75. $3(3x - 5) - (4x - 9) + 7$

76. $-2(x^2 - 6x - 1) - 3(2x^2 - x + 4)$
77. $3x(x - 4) + 2x(3x + 1)$

Simplify.
78. $(-4x^2)(-3xy)$ **79.** $(2de)(-3d^2e^3)$
80. $(-3x^2y^3)^2$ **81.** $(-2wx^3y^3)^3$
82. $\dfrac{40x^4y^5}{-8x^2y^2}$ **83.** $\dfrac{-42r^2s^3t^4}{-6r^2s^3t}$

Factor.
84. $15x^2 - 10x$ **85.** $9x^2y^2 - 3x^2y + 6xy^2$

Solve and check.
86. $3x - 13 = 11$ **87.** $15 = 2y + 21$
88. $5x + 12 = x - 12$ **89.** $6y - 11 = 5 + 8y$
90. $8(m + 1) = 3(m - 4)$
91. $2(x + 4) = 5(x - 1) - 2$
92. $0.3x + 0.4 = 0.8x - 0.1$
93. $\dfrac{x}{6} - \dfrac{2}{3} = \dfrac{x}{2}$ **94.** $\dfrac{x+1}{2} = \dfrac{x+2}{3}$

95. National parks The total area of Point Pelee National Park and Georgian Bay Islands National Park is 40 km^2. The area of Point Pelee National Park is 10 km^2 less than the area of Georgian Bay Islands National Park. Find the area of each park. Explain how you used a mathematical model to solve the problem.

Find the slope of the line passing through each pair of points, if possible.
96. A(2, 5) and B(4, 11)
97. C(-3, 4) and D(-2, 2)
98. E(-1, 7) and F(5, 7)
99. G(3, -4) and H(3, 6)

Write an equation in standard form for the line passing through the given point and having the given slope.
100. A(3, 5); $m = 4$ **101.** B(-1, 2); $m = -\dfrac{3}{4}$

Write an equation in standard form for the line passing through the given points.
102. A(3, 8) and B(1, -6)
103. C(2, -3) and D(-4, -5)

Find the slope and y-intercept of each of the following lines.
104. $3x + y - 4 = 0$ **105.** $5x - 2y + 10 = 0$

Graph each equation using a method of your choice.
106. $2x + y - 5 = 0$ **107.** $5x - 3y + 15 = 0$

108. Write an equation of a line perpendicular to $3x + y - 4 = 0$ and passing through the point $(-2, 5)$.

109. Use paper and pencil or a graphing calculator to find the coordinates of the point of intersection of the lines $y = 4x + 1$ and $y = 2x + 3$.

110. a) Graph the ordered pairs and draw the line of best fit.
$(5, 6), (3, 4), (3, 2), (0, 0), (0, -2), (-2, -4), (-2, -6)$
b) Find an equation of the line of best fit.

Calculate the area of each shaded region. Round answers to the nearest tenth of a square unit, if necessary.

111.   **112.**

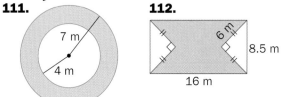

Calculate the surface area and volume. Round answers to the nearest whole number of square or cubic units, if necessary.

113.   **114.**

115.   **116.**

117.   **118.**

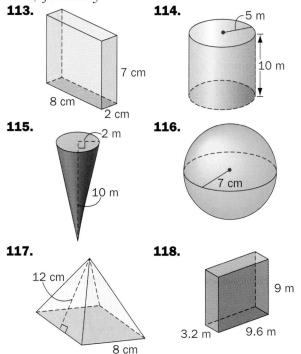

119. Tomato paste can A tomato paste can has the shape of a cylinder with a radius of 2.5 cm and a height of 8 cm.
a) Calculate the volume of the can, to the nearest cubic centimetre.
b) How many millilitres of paste will it hold?

Find the missing angle measures.

120.   **121.**

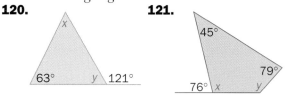

122.   **123.**

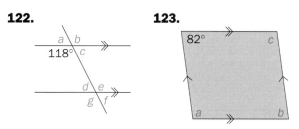

Find the value of x. Then, find the measures of all the indicated angles.

124.   **125.**

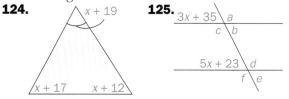

126. Draw a diagram to illustrate the following conjecture. Then, draw a counterexample diagram showing the conjecture is not true.

If the exterior angles of a triangle are obtuse, then the triangle is equilateral.

127. Confirm or deny the statement using examples or a counterexample.

If a quadrilateral has exactly two exterior angles that measure 90°, then it is a kite.

ANSWERS

Math Standards

Number and Operation p. xxii
1 Numbers of Possibilities **1.** 12 **2.** 8 **3.** 12 **4.** 128
2 Working With Numbers **1. a)** 20 100 **b)** 500 500
c) 500 000 500 000 **d)** 400
3 Sequences **1.** 18, 22, 26 **2.** 63, 127, 255 **3.** 6, 2, $\frac{2}{3}$
4. 29, 47, 76

Patterns, Function, and Algebra p. xxiii
1 Patterns in Polygons **1. a)** 7 squares **b)** 16, 20
c) Add 4 to the previous perimeter. **d)** $P = 4n$ **e)** 80;
220 **2. a)** Add 2 to the previous perimeter; $P = 2n + 2$;
42; 112 **b)** Add 4 to the previous perimeter;
$P = 4n + 4$; 84; 224 **c)** Add 2 to the previous
perimeter; $P = 2n + 6$; 46; 116
2 Solving Equations **1.** 8 **2.** 12 **3.** 8 **4.** 6 **5.** 5 **6.** 9
7. 3 **8.** 2
3 Finding Values **1.** 10 **2.** 3 **3.** 3 **4.** 4 **5.** 0
4 Patterns in Tables **1.** y is 8 less than x; x is 8
more than y **2.** y is half of x; x is twice y **3.** The sum
of x and y is 20 **4.** y is 1 more than twice x; x is half
of 1 less than y

Geometry and Spatial Sense p. xxiv
1 Cubes **1. a)** 16 **b)** 48 **c)** 8

Measurement p. xxv
1 Flying Times **1. a)** 1.5 h **b)** 3 h **c)** 1.1 h **2.** 10 min
3. There is usually a tailwind when flying from west
to east, and a headwind when flying from east to
west.
2 Blizzard Hours **1.** Charlottetown **2.** Halifax
3. Montréal **4.** Moncton and Fredericton **5.** No.

Data Analysis, Statistics, and Probability
p. xxvi
1 Comparing Climates **1.** Edmonton; Prince
Rupert **2.** Prince Rupert; Toronto **3.** Answers may
vary. **4.** Answers may vary.
2 Selecting Marbles **1. a)** There are 3 red marbles
out of 10 in the bag. **b)** $\frac{1}{5}$; $\frac{1}{2}$ **2.** 50% **3.** 50

Problem Solving p. xxvii
1 Solving Problems **1.** 3 **2.** 40 **3.** 6
2 Describing Methods **1.** 14; Draw a diagram.
2. 8; Use formulas. **3.** 3; Draw a diagram.

Reasoning and Proof p. xxviii
1 Number Sentences **1.** $4 \times 5 + 8 \div 2$
2. $(7 - 4 \div 4) \times 4$ **3.** $(7 - 4) \times (4 + 4)$

2 Logic Problems **1.** Sari: blue math book; Terri:
green geography book; Dmitri: black science book

Connections p. xxx
1 Mathematics and Art **1.** square 1: 196 square
units; square 4: 64 square units; square 5: 1 square
unit; square 6: 49 square units; square 7: 16 square
units; square 8: 324 square units; square 9: 225 square
units **2.** squares 5 and 8 **3.** squares 8 and 3; squares 4
and 7; squares 1 and 6 **4.** squares 3, 4, 5, and 7
5. No. Its dimensions are 33 units by 32 units.

Representation p. xxxi
1 Using a Tree Diagram **a)** ABE: 18 min; ABDE:
21 min; ACDE: 23 min; ACE: 20 min **b)** ABE
c) 20 min
2 Drawing a Tree Diagram **2.** ABDEG **3.** ABFEG
4. ABFG

Chapter 1

Connecting Numbers and Variables p. 1
1. 4 500 000 000 km **2.** 780 000 000 km
3. 3750 times as great as **4.** The distances are too
small. **5. a)** The distances are much larger than 1 AU
b) light-years

Getting Started pp. 2–3
1 The Stubborn Coin Trick **2.** You always end up
on the red card in the third row, third column.
3. Step b) puts you on the upper left or in the second
column. Step c) puts you in the second row, first
column or first row, second column. Step d) puts you
in the third row, second column or second row, third
column. Step e) requires you to move right or down
to the third row, third column.
2 Repeat, Repeat, Repeat **1.** Your number
repeated 5 times. **2.** Your number repeated 5 times.
3. $47 \times 271 = 11\ 111$. If you multiply 11 111 by any
number from 2 to 9, the result is that number
repeated 5 times.
3 Lucky Number **1. d)** 7 **3.** The difference between
the number of lines left after the first cross out, and
the sum of the digits of that number is always 9.
4 The Stubborn Card Trick **2.** on B **3.** B is the
same number of steps as A from a card on the circle.
By staying on the circle, you go to B instead of A.
Warm Up **1.** +9 **2.** +1 **3.** −6 **4.** +5 **5.** −5 **6.** −1 **7.** −9
8. 0 **9.** +12 **10.** +10 **11.** +1 **12.** −9 **13.** 0 **14.** −13
15. +5 **16.** +3 **17.** −15 **18.** +10 **19.** +20 **20.** −7 **21.** −2
22. +22 **23.** +9 **24.** +14 **25.** −8 **26.** −11 **27.** −13
28. +6 **29.** +28 **30.** −24 **31.** +18 **32.** −81 **33.** +24

34. -6 **35.** -40 **36.** -18 **37.** $+12$ **38.** $+50$ **39.** 0
40. $+32$ **41.** $+3$ **42.** -5 **43.** $+2$ **44.** -5

Mental Math

Operations **1.** 687 **2.** 777 **3.** 919 **4.** 999 **5.** 422
6. 121 **7.** 601 **8.** 111 **9.** 8008 **10.** 6060 **11.** 6868
12. 3636 **13.** 202 **14.** 2020 **15.** 4321 **16.** 103

Multiplying by Multiples of 5 **1.** 130 **2.** 270 **3.** 365
4. 510 **5.** 4490 **6.** 2175 **7.** 26 **8.** 64 **9.** 182 **10.** 2800
11. 3050 **12.** 6700 **13.** $12\ 800$ **14.** 155 **15.** 510
16. You do not have to multiply by 10. Just divide by
2. **17.** 44 **18.** 28.5 **19.** 66 **20.** 225 **21.** 4.8 **22.** 7.2
23. Multiplying by 10 and then dividing by 2 is
multiplying by $\dfrac{10}{2}$, or 5.

Section 1.1 pp. 6–7

Practice **Estimates may vary.** **1.** $700; 714$ **2.** $250; 247$
3. $\$90; \$92.45$ **4.** $\$300; \$270.18$ **5.** $200; 212$ **6.** $\$60;$
$\$62$ **7.** $\$1600; \$1602$ **8.** $160; 160$ **9.** $\$200; \$203.32$
10. $\$70; \$68.70$ **11.** $\$25; \$24.74$ **12.** $2150; 2156$
13. $\$11; \$10.90$ **14.** $\$115; \$115.08$ **15.** $600; 755.55$
16. $\$400; \$453.53$ **17.** $\$10; \$10.83$ **18.** $\$33; \$32.50$
19. $\$500; \$548.04$ **20.** $\$100; \$107.95$ **21.** $60; 50.74$
22. $100; 91.16$ **23.** $300; 367.033$ **24.** $140; 128.846$
25. $280; 233.242$ **26.** $25; 21.572$

Applications and Problem Solving **Estimates may
vary.** **27.** $\$70; \$70.22$ **28.** $\$20; \$15.30$ **29.** $\$6; \$6.29$
30. $\$12; \$11.61$ **31.** $\$3; \$2.81$ **32. a)** 50 h; 62.5 h
b) Answers may vary. Assuming a walking speed of
5 km/h, it would take 200 h. **33.** $\$210; \$209$
34. Balance estimated: $\$545, \$630, \$510, \$440, \$600;$
Balance calculated: $\$543.96, \$628.96, \$505.51,$
$\$437.91, \$597.91$ **35.** yes; $\$1$ too little change
36. 360 km; 351 km **37.** 150 min; 174.4 min
38. $1\ 120\ 000$ km^2; $1\ 152\ 412$ km^2 **39. a)** 2 h; 2.40 h
b) 160 h; 167.12 h **c)** $60\ 000$ h; $63\ 913.04$ h **40.** Not
likely. The school would have to have 2380 students.
41. Answers may vary. For 1998 population: 3.040
42. Answers may vary. **a)** 6 **b)** 6 **c)** 28 **d)** 300
43. Answers may vary.

Investigating Math pp. 8–9

1 Icebergs $6t$
2 Numbers **1.** $n + 5$ **2.** $n - 1$ **3.** $n \div 9$ **4.** $n - 2$
5. $n + 3$ **6.** $5n$ **7.** $6 - n$ **8.** $2 + n$ **9.** $3n$ **10.** $n + 1$
11. $n - 5$ **12.** $6n$ **13.** $n \div 5$ **14.** $2n + 3$ **15.** $10 - n$
16. $7 \div n$ **17.** $x + 4$ **18.** $7x$ **19.** $5x$ **20.** $3 \div x$ **21.** $x + 7$
22. $\dfrac{1}{2}x$ **23.** $x - 8$ **24.** $2x$
3 Tables **1.** $26, y + 8, y + 13; 37, 48, x - 4, 3m - 8,$
$t + 3$ **2.** $12, x - 4, 5y - 4, 3w + 4; 23, m + 4, 4t + 4$

3. $78, 6x, 24m, 3n; 12,\ \dfrac{y}{6}$

4 Rectangles **1. a)** width **b)** $x + 5$ **d)** $4x + 10$
2. $4x$ **3. a)** $13, 18, x + 3, 10x + 3, 4x + 4$ **b)** 46 m,
66 m, $4x + 6$ m, $40x + 6$ m, $16x + 10$ m **4. a)** $10, 17, x,$
$y - 7, 3t, 4n - 7, 5z + 4; 17, 24, x + 7, y, 3t + 7, 4n,$
$5z + 11$ **b)** 54 m, 82 m, $4x + 14$ m, $4y - 14$ m,
$12t + 14$ m, $16n - 14$ m, $20z + 30$ m

Section 1.2 p. 11

Practice **1.** 7×11 **2.** $3x$ **3.** $5 + 8$ **4.** $9 + y$ **5.** xy
6. $m + 7$ **7.** $y - 8$ **8.** $\dfrac{y}{x}$ **9.** $4t$ **10. a)** 8 **b)** 12 **c)** 16 **d)** 4
e) 0 **f)** 36 **g)** 40 **h)** 140 **11. a)** 7 **b)** 10 **c)** 1 **d)** 31 **e)** 11.5
f) 4.3 **g)** 19.6 **h)** 27.4 **12. a)** 3 **b)** 1 **c)** 9 **d)** 19 **e)** 2 **f)** 5.2
g) 15.4 **h)** 18 **13. a)** 5 **b)** 17 **c)** 28 **d)** 18 **e)** 16 **f)** 32 **g)** 14
h) 7 **i)** 0 **14. a)** 14.6 **b)** 20.6 **c)** 58.5 **d)** 18 **15. a)** 12.9
b) 53.1 **c)** 39.7 **d)** 134 **e)** 358.36 **f)** 155.444

Applications and Problem Solving **16. a)** $13n$
b) $\$533; \$695.50$ **17. a)** $300 + 35n$ **b)** $\$9050$ **18. a)** st
b) 262.5 km **19. a)** $2x + 2$ **b)** $2x + 1$ **c)** $2x - 2$
20. $\$75.20$ **21. a)** $x = 5, 6, 7, \ldots$ **b)** $n = 4, 5, 6, \ldots$

Section 1.3 p. 13

Applications and Problem Solving **1.** 3285
2. $18\ 750$ **3.** $\$372\ 757.50$ **4. a)** 315 km **b)** 280 km
c) 90 km **5.** $\$15.50$ **6.** $\$734.80$
7. $9\ 397\ 728\ 000\ 000$ km **8.** the same time as it is now
9. $\$98.05$ **10.** $450\ 000\ 000$ pigeons

Section 1.4 pp. 15–16

Practice **1.** base: 5, exponent: 3 **2.** base: 10,
exponent: 7 **3.** base: x, exponent: 5 **4.** base: t,
exponent: 2 **5.** 3^5 **6.** 4^6 **7.** 10^3 **8.** 6^4 **9.** m^7 **10.** r^8
11. 5×5 **12.** $1 \times 1 \times 1 \times 1 \times 1 \times 1$ **13.** $2 \times 2 \times 2 \times 2 \times 2$
14. $10 \times 10 \times 10 \times 10$ **15.** $0 \times 0 \times 0$ **16.** $y \times y \times y \times y$
17. $5 \times x \times x \times x$ **18.** $2m \times 2m \times 2m$ **19.** 81 **20.** 8
21. 125 **22.** $100\ 000$ **23.** 2^2 **24.** 4^3 **25.** x^3 **26.** y^2
27. 10^2 **28.** 10^3 **29.** 10^5 **30.** 10^4 **31.** 10^8 **32.** 10^7 **33.** 32
34. 125 **35.** 256 **36.** 343 **37.** $10\ 000\ 000$ **38.** 729
39. 0.25 **40.** 1.331 **41.** 0.0001 **42.** 2^4 **43.** 2^6 **44.** 2^8
45. 5^3 **46.** 5^2 **47.** neither **48.** 2^3 **49.** 58 **50.** 48 **51.** 24
52. 8 **53.** 0.1 **54.** $0.005\ 12$ **55.** 1.6 **56.** 0.001 **57.** 76
58. 60 **59.** 32 **60.** 4 **61. a)** 64 **b)** 11 **c)** 73 **d)** 64
62. a) 13 **b)** 125 **c)** 19 **d)** 14 **e)** 36 **f)** 57

Applications and Problem Solving **63. a)** 2000
b) 8000 **c)** $64\ 000$ **64. a)** 2^7 **b)** 2^{10} **65. a)** 25 m; 45 m;
40 m **b)** 6 s **66. a)** Each term is of the form n^n, where
$n = 1, 2, 3, 4, \ldots$. **b)** $5^5, 6^6$ **67. a)** 64 **b)** 2187 **c)** $65\ 536$
d) 0.027 **68. a)** 49 **b)** 301 **c)** 1 **69.** 4 years old
70. 6 years old **71. a)** sometimes true; true if the

number is greater than 2 **b)** always true **c)** sometimes true; true if the base is 0 or 1 **72. a)** 8, 16, 32, 64 **b)** about 18 000 000 000 000 km high

Section 1.5 p. 18
Practice **1.** 5^7 **2.** 2^{10} **3.** 7^{10} **4.** 10^7 **5.** 4^{11} **6.** 3^7 **7.** y^6 **8.** x^9 **9.** a^7 **10.** 4^2 **11.** 3 **12.** 1 **13.** 10 **14.** 4^6 **15.** 1 **16.** m **17.** x^2 **18.** 2^{12} **19.** 3^{10} **20.** 4^{14} **21.** 10^{15} **22.** 5^{16} **23.** x^{20} **24.** y^9 **25.** t^{42} **26.** m^{10}
Applications and Problem Solving **27.** 4 **28.** 2 **29.** 6 **30.** 1 **31.** 3 **32.** 2 **33.** 3 **34.** 1 **35.** 4 **36.** 2 **37.** 7 **38.** 10 **39.** 1 **40.** 9 **41.** 4 **42.** 5 **43.** 2 **44.** 3 **45.** 4 **46.** 2 **47.** 3 **48.** 3 **49.** 5 **50.** 1 **51.** 10^5 times **52. a)** The student multiplied the bases and added the exponents even though the bases are different. **b)** 72 **53. a)** The student divided the bases and subtracted the exponents even though the bases are different. **b)** 54

Section 1.6 pp. 23–24
Practice **1.** Answers may vary; the integers greater than 0 **2.** Answers may vary; the integers less than 0 **3.** Answers may vary; the integers greater than −5 **4.** −3, −2, 0, 5 **5.** −4, −3, −2, −1 **6.** −15, −11, 14, 18 **7.** −2, −1, 1, 2 **12.** 4, 5, 6, … **13.** −1, −2, −3, … **14.** 4, 3, 2, … **15.** −2, −1, 0, … **16.** −5, −4, −3, … **17.** −7, −8, −9, … **18. a)** +5 **b)** −4 **c)** −7 **d)** 0 **e)** +2 **f)** +4 **19. a)** −7 **b)** 17 **c)** −2 **d)** −23 **e)** 11 **f)** 0 **20. a)** 7 **b)** −3 **c)** −9 **d)** 0 **e)** 6 **f)** −6 **21.** Estimates may vary. **a)** 40; 45 **b)** −560; −561 **c)** −300; −306 **d)** −100; −143 **e)** −700; −711 **f)** 100; 111 **22. a)** +3 **b)** +13 **c)** −8 **d)** +15 **e)** 0 **f)** −1 **23. a)** 10 **b)** −1 **c)** −5 **d)** 2 **e)** −10 **f)** 0 **g)** −5 **h)** −58 **24. a)** 14 **b)** 2 **c)** −16 **d)** 5 **e)** −6 **f)** −2 **25. a)** 4 **b)** 3 **c)** −4 **d)** −3 **e)** −2 **f)** 6 **g)** 3 **h)** −2 **26. a)** −30 **b)** +33 **c)** +24 **d)** −30 **27. a)** −35 **b)** 30 **c)** −56 **d)** 56 **e)** 0 **f)** −45 **g)** −30 **h)** 55 **28. a)** +60 **b)** −48 **c)** 30 **d)** −42 **e)** −48 **f)** −60 **g)** 0 **h)** −12 **i)** 0 **j)** 32 **29. a)** −9 **b)** +4 **c)** +2 **d)** −8 **30. a)** 3 **b)** −9 **c)** 0 **31. a)** −7 **b)** 5 **c)** −5 **d)** 7 **32. a)** +4 **b)** −4 **c)** −10 **d)** +6 **e)** −3 **f)** −10
Applications and Problem Solving **33. a)** 2, 3 **b)** −1, 0, 1, 2, 3, 4, 5 **c)** −2, −1, 0, 1, 2, 3, 4, 5, 6 **d)** −4, −3, −2, −1, 0, 1 **e)** −5, −4, −3, −2, −1, 0 **f)** −8, −7, −6, −5, −4, −3, −2, −1, 0 **34. a)** 7, 6, 5, 4, 3, 2, 1 **b)** −2, −3, −4, −5, −6, −7, −8 **c)** −4, −5, −6, −7, −8 **d)** −4, −2, 0, 2, 4 **35.** −1°C **36.** 57°C **37. a)** 8949 m **b)** Death Valley by 314 m **38. a)** −15 **b)** 12 **c)** −19 **d)** −5 **e)** −5 **f)** 0 **39. a)** 6 **b)** 18 **c)** −30 **d)** 144 **e)** −15 **f)** 21 **40. a)** −10°C **b)** −7°C **41.** −2°C **42.** −350 m/min **43. a)** −68 **b)** 64 **c)** −214 **d)** 145 **e)** −994 **f)** 1176 **g)** −6 **h)** 14 **44. a)** Answers may vary. $(-4) + (-3) + (-2) = -9$; $5 + 6 + 7 + 8 = 26$; $(-7) + (-6) + (-5) + (-4) = -22$; $3 + 4 + 5 + 6 = 18$ **b)** Answers may vary. $(-6) + (-7) + (-8) = -21$, $(-6) + (-5) + (-4) + (-3) + (-2) + (-1) = -21$,

$(-10) + (-11) = -21$; $4 + 5 = 9$, $2 + 3 + 4 = 9$, $(-3) + (-2) + (-1) + 0 + 1 + 2 + 3 + 4 + 5 = 9$; $(-10) + (-9) + (-8) = -27$, $(-14) + (-13) = -27$, $(-7) + (-6) + (-5) + (-4) + (-3) + (-2) = -27$

Technology p. 25
1 Sorting Integers **1. a)** −2 and −8 **b)** −8 and 5 **c)** −2 and 5 **d)** yes **2. a)** −12 and 14 **b)** −12 and 0 **c)** 14 and 0 **d)** yes
2 Other Sorting Methods **1.** no **2.** yes
3 Sorting With a Graphing Calculator **1.** Answers may vary. For a TI-83, use SortA(or SortD(in the EDIT menu.

Section 1.7 pp. 28–29
Practice **1.** 49 **2.** 4 **3.** −27 **4.** 8 **5.** 16 **6.** 16 **7.** −1 **8.** 1 **9.** 1 **10.** 2 **11.** −5 **12.** 1 **13.** −9 **14.** 5 **15.** 2 **16.** 0 **17.** 1 **18.** $(-4)^3$ **19.** $(-3)^5$ **20.** p^6 **21.** $(-n)^4$ **22.** $3^4 \times (-2)^3$ **23.** $(-2) \times (-2) \times (-2) \times (-2) \times (-2)$ **24.** $-2 \times 2 \times 2 \times 2 \times 2$ **25.** $(-x) \times (-x) \times (-x)$ **26.** 9 **27.** 9 **28.** 1 **29.** −1 **30.** −125 **31.** −125 **32.** −0.125 **33.** 1.4641 **34.** 6.25 **35.** 5^9 **36.** $(-8)^5$ **37.** $(-2)^7$ **38.** 2^6 **39.** $(-2.1)^8$ **40.** $(-0.2)^5$ **41.** 5 **42.** 6^6 **43.** $(-4)^2$ **44.** $(-9)^5$ **45.** 2^6 **46.** $(-3)^{28}$ **47.** $(-5)^6$ **48.** $(-6)^{15}$ **49.** $(-4)^{42}$ **50.** $(-2.3)^{12}$ **51.** x^6 **52.** y^7 **53.** z^7 **54.** $(-m)^{10}$ **55.** s^8 **56.** $(-r)^6$ **57.** −3125 **58.** 279 936 **59.** 1024 **60.** 1 **61.** 8528.910 374 41 **62.** 9 **63.** 10 000 **64.** −4 **65.** 16 **66.** 729 **67.** −243 **68.** 729 **69.** −64 **70.** 256 **71.** 256 **72.** 81 **73.** 64 **74.** 36 **75.** 64 **76.** −384 **77.** 324 **78.** 26 **79.** 781 **80.** −2592 **81.** −10.125 **82.** 6400 **83.** 27.04 **84.** −0.018 **85. a)** 45 **b)** −162 **c)** 1702 **d)** 9 **86. a)** −8 **b)** 405 **c)** 13 **d)** −648 **e)** −125 **f)** 25 **g)** 36 **h)** −432 **i)** −47 **j)** −216
Applications and Problem Solving **87. a)** 4 **b)** 9 **c)** 4 **d)** 10 **e)** 4 **f)** 1.3 **g)** 4 **h)** −0.6 **88. a)** 320 **b)** 1280
89. a) $(-2)^3$ **b)** No; $2^4 = 16$ and $(-2)^4 = 16$ **90.** 10, 8; 125, 343, 74.088 **91. a)** $\frac{1}{16}$ **b)** $-\frac{27}{8}$ **c)** $-\frac{32}{243}$ **d)** 1 **e)** $-\frac{1}{32}$
f) $-\frac{1025}{1024}$ **92.** positive; Even powers of negative numbers are positive. **93.** negative; Odd powers of negative numbers are negative. **94. a)** Yes. They are both equal to $(-4)^5$ or −1024. **b)** No. One is equal to −4 and the other is equal to $-\frac{1}{4}$.
c) Yes. They are both equal to $(-4)^6$ or 2048.
95. Answers may vary. $(-2)^4 = (-2) \times (-2) \times (-2) \times (-2)$; $-2^4 = -2 \times 2 \times 2 \times 2$

Section 1.8 p. 31

Applications and Problem Solving **1.** Each number is 3 more than the previous number; 17, 20 **2.** Each number is 2 less than the previous number; 6, 4 **3.** Add 2 to the first number to get the second number, then subtract 3 from the second number to get the third number. Continue adding 2 and subtracting 3; 9, 6 **4.** Each number is twice the previous number; 80, 160 **5.** Each number is half the previous number; 16, 8 **6. a)** 16 **b)** 19 **c)** 151 **7. a)** 9 **b)** 36 **c)** 100 **d)** The sum of the first n cubes is equal to $\dfrac{n^2(n+1)^2}{4}$. **e)** 2025 **8.** 1, 121, 12 321, 1 234 321, 123 454 321, 12 345 654 321 **9.** $1 900 000 **10.** 15 **11.** 9 zeros, 19 of every other digit **12.** 65 **13.** 45 **14.** 156

Section 1.9 pp. 34–35

Practice **1.** 13 **2.** 54 **3.** 12 **4.** 12 **5.** 38 **6.** 54 **7.** 3 **8.** 56 **9.** 5 **10.** 2 **11.** 1 **12.** 1 **13.** 3 **14.** 5 **15.** 1 **16.** 29 **17.** 6.4 **18.** 32.3 **19.** 4.4 **20.** 13.9 **21.** 13.39 **22.** 26.068 **23.** 9.84 **24.** 11.9 **25.** 9.8 **26.** 31.5 **27.** 135 **28.** 3 **29.** 10 **30.** 22 **31.** −16 **32.** 13 **33.** −57 **34.** 10 **35.** 13 **36.** 30 **37.** −14 **38.** 3 **39.** 37 **40.** 18 **41.** −30 **42.** −13 **43.** 36 **44.** 11 **45.** −30 **46.** −13 **47.** 1 **48.** 3 **49.** 7 **50.** 21 **51.** −11 **52.** −5 **53.** 5 **54.** 15 **55.** 22 **56.** 26 **57.** −6 **58.** 4 **59.** −1 **60.** −1 **61.** 4 **62.** 1

Applications and Problem Solving

63. a) $(7 + 1) \div 2 = 4$ **b)** $5 \times (8 − 6) = 10$ **c)** $15 \div (3 + 2) + 1 = 4$ **d)** $(6 + 4) \div (2 \times 2) = 2.5$ **e)** $4.8 + (1.6 − 1.2) \times 5 = 6.8$ **f)** $3 \times (1.7 + 5.7) \div 3 = 7.4$ **g)** $(15 + 2^2) \div (7 + 12) = 1$ **64.** $239.60 **65. a)** $(−1 − 3 − 8) \div 4 = −3$ **b)** $3^2 + 4 \times (2 − 5) = −3$ **c)** $(6^2 − 20) \div (2 + 6) = 2$ **66.** Answers may vary. For an age of 9 or less, or 12, 13, and 14, $(2x − 20)^2$ is larger. For $x = 10$ and 15 or greater, $\dfrac{1}{2}(x − 9)^3$ is larger. For $x = 11$, they are the same. **67. a)** −8 **b)** 86 **c)** 897 **d)** 488 **e)** −741 **68. a)** $(−3 − 5)^2$, $(−3)^2 − 5$ **b)** 64, 4 **c)** 5 less than −3 all squared; 5 less than the square of −3 **69.** Answers may vary. $2 + 2 + 2 − 2^2 = 2$; $2^2 + 2 \div 2 − 2 = 3$; $(2 + 2 + 2 + 2) \div 2 = 4$; $2 + 2 + 2 − 2 \div 2 = 5$; $2^2 \div 2 + 2 \times 2 = 6$; $2^2 + 2 \div 2 + 2 = 7$; $2^2 \times 2^2 \div 2 = 8$; $2(2 + 2) + 2 \div 2 = 9$

Section 1.10 p. 37

Practice **1. a)** 8 **b)** 4 **c)** 0 **d)** −4 **e)** 5 **f)** 8 **2. a)** −6 **b)** 2 **c)** 12 **d)** −4 **e)** 8 **f)** −3 **3. a)** −10 **b)** −24 **c)** 1 **d)** 5 **e)** 18 **f)** −1 **4. a)** 24 **b)** −15 **c)** 25 **d)** −20 **e)** 10 **f)** 2 **g)** −11 **h)** 40 **i)** −38 **5. a)** 5 **b)** −2 **c)** 32 **d)** −3 **e)** −8 **f)** 5 **g)** 81 **h)** 4 **6. a)** −14 **b)** −5 **c)** 17 **d)** −25 **e)** 31 **f)** 125 **g)** 81 **h)** 5 **i)** 27 **j)** 10

Applications and Problem Solving **7. a)** 3, 1, −1, −3, −5 **b)** 7, 4, 3, 4, 7 **c)** 3, 2, 1, 0, −1 **d)** 0, −1, −2, −3, −4 **8. a)** 225 m; 65 m **b)** 0 m; The object hits the water after 7 s. **9. a)** 15 m; 20 m; 15 m **b)** 0 m; The rock is back at the edge of the cliff. **c)** −25 m; The rock is 25 m below the edge of the cliff. **d)** 6 s **10. a)** −3°C **b)** −2°C

Section 1.11 p. 39

Applications and Problem Solving **Answers may vary.** **1. a)** 915 km **b)** 1365 km **c)** 450 km **2.** Answers may vary. **3.** 21:45 **4.** −47°C **5.** 1.4 times **6.** Nunavut **7.** 18:00 **8.** (1998 population data) PE: 24.063; NS: 16.870; ON: 10.673; NB: 10.245; PQ: 4.760; AB: 4.406; BC: 4.235; MB: 1.756; SK: 1.572; NF: 1.339 **9.** Answers may vary.

Career Connection p. 40

1 Forest Fires **1.** The missing numbers are: 804, 650, 264, 32, 483, 81, 354, 14, 0, 216, 1 **2.** Humans: 4900, 4772; Lightning: 3200, 3395; Unknown: 200; 200 **3.** Humans **4. a)** Answers may vary. The lightning may strike in more than one place, igniting a larger area. **b)** 382 000 ha; 6 100 000 ha

Computer Data Bank p. 41

1 Movie Costs **2. a)** Multiply the cost in millions of dollars by 1 000 000 and divide by the length in minutes. **3.** *True Lies, Easy Rider* **2 Winning Times** **3.** 11.08 s; The 8th and 9th times are both 11.08 s. **4.** 11.50 s; 3 times **5.** 11.28 s **3 Food Graphs** **2. a)** Divide protein (or carbohydrates or fat) in grams by mass in grams and multiply by 100. **4 Ski Trails** **1.** 111 **2.** 88, $\dfrac{88}{111}$ **5 Nations Around the World** **1.** 18.4% **2.** $23.388 billion **3.** Africa; 83%

Section 1.12 pp. 42–43

1 Modelling Diameters in the Solar System **1.** Earth's diameter is used as the standard unit to describe the diameters of the sun and the planets. **2.** The ratio of the diameter of the sun or planet to Earth's diameter is calculated. **3. a)** 550 times **b)** 545 **4.** Venus and Earth, Uranus and Neptune **5.** Sun: 1 390 840 km; Mercury: 4849 km; Venus: 12 122 km; Mars: 6763 km; Jupiter: 142 912 km; Saturn: 119 944 km; Uranus: 51 040 km; Neptune: 48 488 km; Pluto: 2552 km **2 Modelling Distances From the Sun** **1.** The planets are listed in order, beginning with the planet closest to the sun. **2.** The distance of Earth from the sun is used as the standard astronomical unit to describe distance from the sun. **3.** The distances are in millions of kilometres: Mercury: 58.5; Venus: 108; Earth: 150; Mars: 228; Jupiter; 780; Saturn: 1425; Uranus: 2880; Neptune: 4515; Pluto: 5940

3 Extending the Model 2. a) diameter 5.1 cm **b)** diameter 2.8 cm **c)** diameter 1.3 cm **4.** 0.05 cm

Review pp. 44–45
Estimates may vary for 1.–21. 1. $155; $155.46 **2.** $35; $33.11 **3.** $37; $37.02 **4.** $120; $122.60 **5.** $60; $59.79 **6.** $360; $360.50 **7.** $400; $396.68 **8.** 750; 748 **9.** $21; $21 **10.** 280; 277 **11.** 1600; 1633 **12.** 0.7; 0.69 **13.** 0.2; 0.248 **14.** 17 500; 18 630 **15.** 740 000; 614 283 **16.** 2.8; 3.0456 **17.** 11.4; 10.773 **18.** 19; 23 **19.** 300; 254 **20.** 5; 5.2 **21.** 6; 5.6 **22. a)** 49 **b)** 138 **c)** 3 **d)** 26 **23. a)** 32.4 **b)** 26.8 **c)** 37.6 **24. a)** $675 + 35n$ **b)** 5925 **c)** $39.50 **25.** 3^3 **26.** 3^5 **27.** 134 **28.** 80 **29.** 60 **30.** 3 **31. a)** 13 **b)** 125 **c)** 28 **d)** 78 **32. a)** 10 m; 10 m **b)** Assume the twirler catches the baton at the same height from which it was released; 3 s **33.** 2^8 **34.** 5^4 **35.** 2^8 **36.** 7^{12} **37.** 3^9 **38.** 6^4 **39.** n^7 **40.** g^4 **41.** r^6 **42.** 2 **43.** 3 **44.** 4 **45.** 3 **46.** −3 **47.** −17 **48.** 7 **49.** 12 **50.** −99 **51.** −36 **52.** 42 **53.** 12 **54.** 24 **55.** 16 **56.** −16 **57.** 12 **58. a)** 1 **b)** −1 **c)** 28 **d)** 18 **e)** −10 **f)** 10 **59.** 3°C **60.** 81 **61.** −135 **62.** 72 **63.** 26 **64.** 9 **65.** 12.96 **66.** −8 **67.** 2 **68.** −125 **69.** 100 **70. a)** −27 **b)** 16 **c)** 144 **d)** 1 **71.** 29 **72.** 89 **73.** 40 **74.** 28.9 **75.** 10.21 **76.** 0 **77.** −4 **78.** 22 **79.** 4 **80.** 0 **81.** −4 **82.** 4 **83.** −7 **84.** −2 **85. a)** −12 **b)** 36 **c)** 1 **d)** 174 **e)** −3 **f)** −17 **g)** −1 **h)** 11 **86. a)** 120 m **b)** 105 m **c)** 45 m **d)** 0 m

Exploring Math
1. 3, 5, 8, 13, 21 **2.** The number of designs is the sum of the number for one panel fewer and the number for two panels fewer. **3. a)** 89 **b)** 987

Chapter Check p. 46
Estimates may vary for 1.–8. 1. 900; 883 **2.** 23; 23.04 **3.** 100; 116 **4.** 35; 35.28 **5.** 2500; 2520 **6.** 36; 32.766 **7.** 80; 81 **8.** 0.06; 0.065 **9. a)** 40 **b)** 85 **10. a)** 7.5 **b)** 5 **11. a)** 34 **b)** 16 **c)** 19 **d)** 145 **12.** 2^3 **13.** 2^5 **14.** 2^7 **15.** 3^9 **16.** 2^4 **17.** 5^8 **18.** x^6 **19.** y^3 **20.** a^{10} **21.** −11 **22.** 3 **23.** − 12 **24.** 15 **25.** 12 **26.** 3 **27.** −3 **28.** −8 **29.** 2 **30.** 11 **31.** −10 **32.** 3 **33. a)** −8 **b)** 48 **c)** 256 **d)** 8 **34.** 2 **35.** 12 **36.** 21 **37.** 11 **38.** 30.8 **39.** 72.36 **40.** 26 **41.** −4 **42.** − 9 **43.** −26 **44. a)** $40 + 25n$ **b)** $640 **45. a)** 15 m **b)** 20 m **c)** 15 m

Using the Strategies p. 47
1. The first number in each pair represents a number from the first set, the second a number from the second set. (1, 8), (2, 2), (3, 13), (4, 12), (5, 11), (6, 10), (7, 9), (8, 1), (9, 7), (10, 6), (11, 5), (12, 4), (13, 3) **2.** 8 **3.** 15, 21, 28 **4.** 542.5 km **5.** 1, 3, 4, 7, 8, 9 **6.** 4 **7.** 10 201, 40 804, 91 809; $404 \times 404 =$ 163 216, $505 \times 505 = 255\ 025$ **8.** Answers may vary. **a)** $6 + 7 + 8 + 9 + 10 + 11 + 12$ **b)** $33 + 34 + 35 + 36$ **9.** January 1, December 31 **10.** 19 **11.** three 15-year-olds and two 14-year-olds **12.** 16 **13.** 1296 m **14.** approximately 86 km² **15.** 23 h

Chapter 2

Ratio, Rate, and Percent p. 49
1. $\frac{1}{80}$ **2.** $\frac{79}{80}$ **3.** $\frac{13}{100}$ **4.** Answers will vary.

Getting Started pp. 50–51
2 Patterns in Letters 1. UVW **2.** PIT **3.** L **4.** ERA **5.** I **6.** T
3 Patterns in Numbers 1. add 3; 13, 16, 19 **2.** subtract 4; 9, 5, 1 **3.** multiply by 2; 16, 32, 64 **4.** add 1, add 2, add 3, …; 22, 29, 37 **5.** add 4, subtract 1; 14, 13, 17 **6.** subtract 3, add 1; 14, 11, 12 **7.** sum of previous two terms: 13, 21, 34

Warm Up 1. b) $\frac{27}{50}, \frac{54}{100}$ **c)** $\frac{3}{5}, \frac{60}{100}$ **d)** 0.1, $\frac{10}{100}$ **e)** 0.75, $\frac{75}{100}$ **f)** 0.28, $\frac{28}{100}$ **g)** $\frac{1}{2}, \frac{50}{100}$ **h)** $\frac{1}{4}, \frac{25}{100}$ **i)** $\frac{19}{25}, \frac{76}{100}$ **j)** 0.35, $\frac{35}{100}$ **2. a)** $\frac{3}{10}$, 0.3 **b)** $\frac{1}{2}$, 0.5 **c)** $\frac{1}{5}$, 0.2 **d)** $\frac{7}{10}$, 0.7 **e)** $\frac{4}{5}$, 0.8 **f)** $\frac{1}{2}$, 0.5 **g)** $\frac{2}{5}$, 0.4 **h)** $\frac{3}{5}$, 0.6

Mental Math
Equivalent Fractions   Answers may vary for 1.–8.
1. $\frac{2}{4}, \frac{-3}{6}$ **2.** $\frac{2}{10}, \frac{3}{15}$ **3.** $\frac{2}{6}, \frac{3}{9}$ **4.** $\frac{2}{8}, \frac{3}{12}$ **5.** $\frac{6}{8}, \frac{9}{12}$ **6.** $\frac{6}{4}, \frac{9}{6}$ **7.** $\frac{8}{14}, \frac{12}{21}$ **8.** $\frac{2}{1}, \frac{4}{2}$ **9.** $\frac{1}{2}$ **10.** $\frac{3}{7}$ **11.** $\frac{3}{7}$ **12.** $\frac{5}{8}$ **13.** $\frac{5}{2}$ **14.** $\frac{8}{3}$ **15.** $\frac{9}{2}$ **16.** $\frac{7}{2}$

Dividing by Multiples of 5 1. 17 **2.** 21 **3.** 27 **4.** 2.8 **5.** 7.8 **6.** 8.4 **7.** 12.2 **8.** 24.6 **9.** 20.2 **10.** 3.2 **11.** 4.2 **12.** 7.4 **13.** 19.6 **14.** 2.7 **15.** 5.7 **16.** 23 **17.** 0.9 **18.** 1.3 **19.** You just need to multiply by 2. **20.** 52 **21.** 106 **22.** 236 **23.** 1300 **24.** 19 **25.** 6.4 **26.** Dividing by 5 is the same as multiplying by $\frac{2}{10}$.

Section 2.1 pp. 54–55

Practice **1. a)** 5 to 6, $\frac{5}{6}$, 5:6, **b)** 5 to 4, $\frac{5}{4}$, 5:4

c) 2 to 3, $\frac{2}{3}$, 2:3 **d)** 1 to 3, $\frac{1}{3}$, 1:3 **e)** 5 to 2, $\frac{5}{2}$,

5:2, **f)** 2 to 5, $\frac{2}{5}$, 2:5, **g)** 4 to 5, $\frac{4}{5}$, 4:5 **3. a)** $\frac{3}{5}$, 3:5,

3 to 5 **b)** $\frac{3}{1}$, 3:1, 3 to 1 **c)** $\frac{50}{1}$, 50:1, 50 to 1 **d)** $\frac{25}{4}$, 25:4,

25 to 4 **e)** $\frac{2}{3}$, 2:3, 2 to 3 **4. a)** $\frac{2}{5}$ **b)** 1:3 **c)** 1:2 **d)** 1 to 6

e) 3:5 **f)** 2:1 **g)** 6 to 1 **h)** 4:9 **i)** $\frac{12}{5}$ **j)** 9:2 **k)** 2:5 **l)** 2:1

5. a) 4:3 **b)** 8:1 **c)** 1:5 **d)** 2:1 **e)** 1:3 **f)** 4:7

Applications and Problem Solving **6.** 8:5 **7. a)** 1:1
b) 4:5 **c)** 2:1 **d)** 5:2 **e)** 4:3 **f)** 3:4 **g)** 7:4 **h)** 1:1 **i)** 1:1 **j)** 3:2
8. 3:4 **9.** 7:6 **10. a)** 5:3 **b)** 2:3 **c)** 4:15 **d)** 3:2 **11. a)** 5:7
b) 12:5 **c)** 7:12 **9. a)** 4:3 **b)** 1:2 **c)** 3:2 **12. a)** 5:3 **b)** 9:20
c) 4:3 **13.** The other term is a multiple of the prime
number.

Section 2.2 p. 57

Applications and Problem Solving **1.** Count the
number in one page, then multiply by the number of
pages. **2.** Measure the thickness of all the pages, then
divide by the number of pages. **3.** Have someone
time you reading 1 page, then multiply by 250.
4. 100 **5.** 10 100 **6.** 40 **8.** 324 **9.** 90 **11.** 4096 **12.** 301
13. 401 **14.** 756

Investigating Math pp. 58–59

1 Famous Canadians **1.** A = 4, B = 16, C = 5, D =
27, E = 24, F = 12, G = 25, H = 7, I = 45, J = 3, L = 6,
M = 26, N = 20, O = 84, R = 8, S = 21, T = 1, U = 11,
W = 40, X = 14, Y = 15 **2. a)** SHANIA TWAIN;
musician **b)** MICHAEL J. FOX; actor **c)** LUCY
MAUD MONTGOMERY; author **d)** LINCOLN
ALEXANDER; former lieutenant governor of
Ontario **e)** LAURA SECORD; heroine of the War of
1812 **f)** ROBERT BATEMAN; nature artist **3.** This
house is the setting for *Anne of Green Gables*. Lucy
Maud Montgomery wrote *Anne of Green Gables*.
2 Sets of Equations **1.** 3; 2, 6 or 6, 2; 4, 5 or 5, 4;
7, 1 **2.** 3; 4, 5 or 7, 8; 1, 9; 7, 8 or 4, 5 **3.** 4; 3, 5 or 5,
3; 1, 7; 6, 8 **4.** 6; 5, 4; 8, 9; 3, 0, 1 or 3, 1, 0

Section 2.3 pp. 63–64

Practice **Answers may vary for 1.–9.** **1.** 12:10, 18:15

2. 6:2, :3 **3.** 2:10, 3:15 **4.** 5:8, 10:16 **5.** $\frac{1}{4}, \frac{3}{12}$ **6.** $\frac{9}{5}, \frac{27}{15}$

7. 3:2, 6:4 **8.** $\frac{8}{1}, \frac{24}{3}$ **9.** $\frac{8}{14}, \frac{12}{21}$ **10.** yes **11.** yes **12.** no
13. no **14.** no **15.** yes **16.** yes **17.** yes **18.** 9 **19.** 15
20. 4 **21.** 6 **22.** 4 **23.** 15 **24.** 4 **25.** 27 **26.** 8.75 **27.** 4
28. 1.2 **29.** 2.5

Applications and Problem Solving **30. a)** 12 **b)** 10
31. $70 **32.** 250 mL; 750 mL **33.** 150 mL
34. 10.8 cm **35. a)** 9:4 **b)** 54 cm^2 **36. a)** 7:5 **b)** 12.5 m
37. a) copper: 92 g, tin: 8 g **b)** 1150 g **c)** 8.7 g **38.** not
possible

Section 2.4 pp. 67–69

Practice **1.** 3 hot dogs/person **2.** 50 words/min
3. 80 km/h **4.** $10.60/h **5.** $3.16/can **6.** $31/day
7. 72 heartbeats/min **8.** 0.15 km/min or 9 km/h
9. 5.5 h/day **10.** $7/barrel **11.** $6/m **12.** 2 km/min
13. 25 m/min **14.** 34 students/bus
15. 2 hamburgers/person **16.** 55 km/h
17. 125 mL/person **18.** 3.5 km/h **19.** $10.75/h
20. 225 g/cake **21.** $5.10/pizza **22.** $0.42/marker
23. $0.329/pen **24.** $3.20/hat **25.** $4.75/sandwich
26. $1.75/100 g **27.** $40/h
Applications and Problem Solving **28.** 2200 beats/s
29. $19.50; $94; $87; $20.85 **30.** $12.50/h
31. a) 35 km/min **b)** 2100 km/h **32. a)** Elk Island:
25.9 ha; Wind Cave: 35.2 ha; Wood Buffalo:
1327.5 ha; Yellowstone: 315.2 ha **b)** Wood Buffalo,
Yellowstone, Wind Cave, Elk Island **33.** 7 L
34. a) 0.05 h/$ **b)** reciprocals **c)** 1 **35.** 150° **36.** 441 kJ
37. Nicole by $0.15/h **38.** Kingston **39.** fingernails
40. speed skaters **41. a)** uranium: 19.05 g/cm^3; gold:
18.88 g/cm^3 **b)** uranium **42. a)** $340 for 35 people
b) $4.30 for 4 L **c)** 28 g for $0.98 **d)** $72.00 for 5 h
e) 2.5 L for $3.50 **f)** 2000 sheets for $36.00 **g)** 8 L for
$4.72 **43. a)** 450 g for $3.00 **b)** 700 g for $5.60
c) 0.6 L for $21.00 **d)** 110 straws for $1.49
44. a) $6.98 **b)** $11.45 **45.** 36 000 years, assuming the
clock only loses time or only gains time. **46.** Answers
may vary. **47. a)** 5.3, 5.8, 5.5, 7.4, 6.6 **b)** D, E, B, C, A
c) 18.9, 17.3, 18.2, 13.5, 15.2

Section 2.5 p. 71

Applications and Problem Solving **1.** Assume
Frank makes the same amount each month; $2589
2. Assume each member sells 43 cases; 860 **3.** Assume
the 40 students are a representative sample of the
whole school; 200 **4.** Assume the boat travels at a
constant speed of 15 km/h; 75 km **5.** He assumed he
could reduce his time by 0.5 s every 5 weeks. If he
keeps going at this rate, he will run 100 m in 0 s in
115 weeks, which is impossible. **6.** She assumed that
bike buyers formed a representative sample for the

whole town. **7.** Assume measurements are made from the centre of each tent; 26 m **8. a)** Assume Paulina drives the speed limit and does not stop; 7 h **b)** 23:45 **9. a)** Assume the rope is not folded; 2 cuts **b)** Assume the rope is not folded; 3 cuts **10.** Assume there are 28 days in February; 2 419 200 s **11.** Assume the patterns continue in the same way. **a)** 12.5, 6.25, 3.125 **b)** 32, 39, 47 **c)** 63, 127, 255 **12.** Assume the distance is 2735 km and the average speed is 80 km/h; 13:11 on Sunday

Section 2.6 p. 73
Practice 1. 36% **2.** 68% **3.** 52% **4.** 46% **5.** 40% **6.** 75% **7.** 30% **8.** 25% **9.** 45% **10.** 60% **17.** 17% **18.** 61% **19.** 90% **20.** 30% **21.** 5% **22.** 8% **23.** 29% **24.** 65% **25.** 58% **26.** 60% **27.** 5% **28.** 2% **29.** 50% **30.** 70% **31.** 80% **32.** 85% **33.** 52% **34.** 58%
Applications and Problem Solving 35. 40% **36.** 98% **37.** 90% **38.** 40% **39.** On 70% of the days with similar weather conditions, it rained. **40.** 52% **41. a)** Answers may vary, but you can think of the % symbol as being made up of a 1 and two 0s. **b)** It comes from *per centum* in Latin, which means by the hundred.

Section 2.7 pp. 77–78
Practice 1. 65% **2.** 83% **3.** 98% **4.** 2% **5.** 8% **6.** 60% **7.** 70% **8.** 75.2% **9.** 86.3% **10.** 0.5% **11.** 15% **12.** 49% **13.** 10% **14.** 60% **15.** 37.5% **16.** 50% **17.** 90% **18.** 35% **19.** 81.25% **20.** 44% **21.** 80% **22.** 33.3% **23.** 45.5% **24.** 77.8% **25.** 29.2% **26.** 50% **27.** 80% **28.** 45% **29.** 12.5% **30.** 56.25% **31.** 8% **32.** 0.19 **33.** 0.35 **34.** 0.9 **35.** 0.01 **36.** 0.666 **37.** 0.375 **38.** 0.045 **39.** 0.008 **40.** 0.0055 **41.** $\frac{3}{10}$ **42.** $\frac{6}{25}$ **43.** $\frac{13}{25}$ **44.** $\frac{3}{4}$ **45.** $\frac{22}{25}$ **46.** $\frac{1}{20}$ **47.** $\frac{1}{50}$ **48.** $\frac{16}{25}$ **49.** $\frac{19}{50}$ **50.** 3 **51.** 4 **52.** 3.5 **53.** 5 **54.** 1.1 **55.** 1.15 **56.** 1.25 **57.** 1.01 **58.** 2.5 **59.** 120% **60.** 175% **61.** 250% **62.** 300% **63.** 150% **64.** 260% **65.** 20% **66.** 45% **67.** 25% **68.** 90% **69.** 160% **70.** 150%
Applications and Problem Solving 71. 40% **72. a)** 84.2% **b)** 80.8% **c)** 60.9% **73. a)** 7% **b)** 93% **74. a)** $1.00 **b)** 20% **c)** 120% **75. a)** 35% **b)** 135% **76.** 3000% **77.** 2000% **78.** Answers may vary. **79.** Answers may vary. **80. a)** 25% **b)** 62.5% **c)** Canada is not included in the sum. **81. a)** Answers may vary. It should be "The price increased by 100%...." **b)** It should be "A dollar is worth 300% more...." **82. a)** $\frac{36}{71}$ **b)** $\frac{43}{67}$ **c)** $\frac{02}{98}$ **d)** $\frac{01}{24}$

Section 2.8 pp. 82–84
Practice 1. 32 **2.** 30 **3.** 136 **4.** 9.9 **5.** $6.00 **6.** 30 **7.** 300 **8.** 525 **9.** $0.48 **10.** $8.00 **11.** 50% **12.** 27% **13.** 10% **14.** 20% **15.** 40% **16.** 300% **17.** 40 **18.** 20 **19.** 150 **20.** 700 **21.** 400 **22.** 30 **23.** $3.50, $31.50 **24.** $1.50, $8.50 **25.** $11.12, $44.48 **26.** $20.19, $60.57 **27.** $2.92, $2.93 **28.** $5.00, $44.99 **29.** $0.55, $6.05 **30.** $0.90, $6.90 **31.** $2.20, $11.00 **32.** $15.00, $90.00 **33.** $18.00, $78.00 **34.** $3.25, $13.00 **35.** 0.04 **36.** 0.085 **37.** 0.0625 **38.** 0.0575 **39.** 0.076 **40.** 0.069 **41.** $1200.00 **42.** $107.88 **43.** $350.00 **44.** $57.53
Applications and Problem Solving 45. 47% **46.** 792 **47.** $18.80 **48. a)** $70.00 **b)** $129.99 **49.** Assuming PST: 8%; GST: 7% **a)** $3.20 **b)** $2.80 **50.** 65% **51. a)** 0.8% **b)** 1.7% **52.** 31 300 km² **53.** 80 km/h **54.** $26.46 **55.** 15.3% **56.** Assuming PST: 8%; GST: 7%; $149.44 **57.** $369.75 **58. a)** $30 **b)** $530 **59. a)** $18.86 **b)** $1368.86 **60.** $65.50 at 15% off **61.** $67.40 **62.** $59.45 **63.** $1250 **65. a)** 4% **b)** 12.5%

Career Connection p. 85
1 Consumer Price Index 1. Divide $350 by 75, the CPI for 1985, then multiply the result by 104.2, the CPI for 1995. **2.** Answers may vary. For 1986: **a)** $279.13 **b)** $688.86 **3. a)** Find what percent 98.5 is of 93.3, and subtract 100%. **b)** 4.4% **c)** 1981; 12.4%

Section 2.9 p. 87
1. Maria–grade 11, Paula–grade 9, Shelly–grade 10 **2.** Al–golf, Bjorn–swimming, Carl–running, Dion–bowling **3.** Susan–pilot, Irina–writer, Traci–doctor, Dolores–dentist **4.** 25 m **5.** 3 quarters, 4 dimes, 4 pennies **6.** 110 km **7.** 20 **8.** 24 **9.** 23:59 **10.** 8 **11.** 9 **12.** Evans–artist, Thompson–plumber, Wong–banker, DiMaggio–teacher

Technology p. 88
1 Coin Collection 2. Answers may vary. 1 half dollar, 22 quarters, 3 dimes, 20 nickels, 2 pennies **3.** Guess and check **4.** Yes

Technology p. 89
1 Hockey Scoring-Leader Statistics 1. PTS: 87, 91, 87, 90, 102, 87, 90; +/–: 30, 6, 12, –11, 17, –2, 5; Pct: 16.8, 12.4, 13.2, 11.4, 13.4, 16.2, 15.5 **2.** Answers may vary. Players may be ranked by PTS, +/–, Pct, points per game, number of goals, etc.

Section 2.10 pp. 90–91
1 Populations 1. about 400 000 **2.** about 24 000 **3.** about 6% **4. a)** about 30%; **b)** about 25%; **c)** about 10% **5.** about 90%

2 Modelling the Distribution of Black Bears

1. Answers may vary. **a)** 5% **b)** 75% **c)** 30%
2. Washington, New Hampshire, Vermont, Maine

Review pp. 92–93

1. 2:3 **2.** 5:4 **3.** 3:4 **4.** 1:8 **5.** $\frac{3}{11}$ **6.** $\frac{12}{5}$ **7.** 4:1

8. 200:3 **9. a)** 10:3 **b)** 2:1 **c)** 1:1

Answers may vary for 10.–12. **10.** 6:8 **11.** 7:3

12. $\frac{16}{10}$ **13.** 3 **14.** 12 **15.** 40 **16.** 3 **17.** yes **18.** no

19. 3.6 L **20.** 15 m; 25 m **21.** 80 km/h
22. \$20.65/CD **23.** 10.7 m/s **24.** 350 mL for \$4.59
25. 75 min **26.** Maria **27.** 51% **28.** 4% **29.** 96%
30. 33% **31.** 70% **32.** 1% **33.** 60% **34.** 95% **35.** 44%
36. a) 25% **b)** 25% **c)** 65% **37.** 60% **38.** 80%
39. 250% **40.** 43% **41.** 25% **42.** 640% **43.** 0.8%
44. 0.43 **45.** 0.765 **46.** 0.002 **47.** 0.000 03 **48.** 1.4
49. 6 **50. a)** 60% **b)** 50% **c)** 20% **d)** 200% **51.** 10%
52. 280% **53.** 0.39 **54.** 8 **55.** 220 **56.** \$8.75 **57.** 300
58. \$13.50 **59.** \$128 **60.** \$1511.25 **61.** \$90.00
62. \$57.86 **63.** 61.6 m

Chapter Check p. 94

1. 2:3 **2.** 1:3 **3.** \$0.83/can **4.** 80 km/h **5.** 15 **6.** 6

7. 9% **8.** 261% **9.** 10% **10.** 20% **11.** 0.85, $\frac{17}{20}$

12. 1.6, $\frac{8}{5}$ **13.** 0.005, $\frac{1}{200}$ **14.** 175 **15.** 55 **16. a)** 75 g

b) 50 g **17.** 16 **18.** 90% **19.** 24 cans for \$4.99
20. \$243.75 **21.** \$23.40 **22.** \$99 **23.** \$900
24. 2.5 km/h

Using the Strategies p. 95

1. forty **2.** 1; 3; 5; 7; 19; 39; 199; $2n - 1$ **3.** \$593.75
4. a) 17, 21 **b)** The number of toothpicks is one more
than four times the diagram number. **c)** $4n + 1$
d) 201, 321 **5.** 17 **6.** Answers may vary.

$(9 + \frac{9}{9}) \times (9 + \frac{9}{9}) = 100$ **7.** 6 **8.** 3, 5; 7, 1, 8, 2; 4, 6

9. 2.5 min, assuming the animals can keep up that
speed for 1 km **10.** Answers may vary. 1165 km

Chapter 3

Real Numbers p. 97

1. 306.25 h **2.** Assume an average arm span of 1.25 m,
and a population (1998) of 30 million; Yes.
3. a) Trans-Canada Highway **b)** St. John's, NF and
Victoria, BC **4.** 4900 km

Getting Started pp. 98–99
Fractions

1 Fractions and Words 1. BALL **2.** IN **3.** ANT
4. NUMB **5.** TANGLE **6.** PEN **7.** TAR
2 Championship Fractions 1. A: 4, B: 2, C: 1, D: 3

2. $\frac{1}{2}$ **3.** $\frac{1}{4}$ **4.** $\frac{3}{4}$ **5.** $\frac{1}{3}$ **6.** $\frac{2}{3}$ **7.** $\frac{1}{4}$; $\frac{1}{8}$; $\frac{1}{16}$; $\frac{3}{16}$

3 Operations With Fractions 1. $\frac{1}{2}$ **2.** 1 **3.** $\frac{2}{3}$ **4.** $\frac{5}{8}$

5. $\frac{7}{10}$ **6.** $\frac{11}{12}$ **7.** $\frac{13}{12}$ or $1\frac{1}{12}$ **8.** $\frac{9}{10}$ **9.** $\frac{2}{5}$ **10.** $\frac{1}{4}$ **11.** $\frac{1}{4}$

12. $\frac{5}{8}$ **13.** $\frac{3}{10}$ **14.** $\frac{1}{6}$ **15.** $\frac{1}{12}$ **16.** $\frac{3}{10}$ **17.** $\frac{1}{4}$ **18.** $\frac{2}{9}$

19. $\frac{3}{8}$ **20.** $\frac{5}{9}$ **21.** $\frac{3}{10}$ **22.** $\frac{3}{16}$ **23.** $\frac{2}{5}$ **24.** $\frac{2}{3}$ **25.** 1 **26.** $\frac{1}{3}$

27. $\frac{1}{2}$ **28.** $\frac{3}{2}$ or $1\frac{1}{2}$ **29.** $\frac{3}{2}$ or $1\frac{1}{2}$ **30.** $\frac{3}{4}$ **31.** $\frac{2}{3}$ **32.** $\frac{3}{2}$ or $1\frac{1}{2}$

33. $\frac{3}{5}$ **34.** $\frac{4}{5}$

Perfect Squares

1 Odd Numbers and Perfect Squares
$1 + 3 + 5 = 9; 1 + 3 + 5 + 7 = 16; 1 + 3 + 5 + 7 + 9 = 25$
1. 64 **2.** 100 **3.** 1 000 000
2 Triangular Numbers and Perfect Squares 1. A
triangular number of objects can be arranged in the
shape of a right triangle. **2.** 15, 21, 28 **3.** a perfect
square
Mental Math
Order of Operations 1. 35 **2.** 41 **3.** 21 **4.** 19 **5.** 9
6. −7 **7.** 20 **8.** 37 **9.** 48 **10.** 6 **11.** −11 **12.** −48 **13.** 80
14. 8 **15.** 28 **16.** 2 **17.** 50 **18.** 10 **19.** 15 **20.** 15 **21.** 30
22. 4 **23.** −21 **24.** 34 **25.** 36 **26.** 36 **27.** 150 **28.** −20
Subtracting in Two Steps 1. 25 **2.** 25 **3.** 54 **4.** 28
5. 39 **6.** 36 **7.** 64 **8.** 61 **9.** 87 **10.** 86 **11.** 81 **12.** 83
13. 1.9 **14.** 1.9 **15.** 2.6 **16.** 10.8 **17.** 17.6 **18.** 16.7
19. 350 **20.** 380 **21.** 290 **22.** 470 **23.** 530 **24.** 880

Investigating Math pp. 100–101
1 Multiplying by Powers Greater Than 1 1. a) 916
b) 9160 **c)** 91 600 **d)** 916 000 **e)** 0.4 **f)** 4 **g)** 40 **h)** 400
2. If you are multiplying by 10^n, move the decimal
point n spaces to the right. **3. a)** 320 **b)** 120 **c)** 346 000
d) 20 300 **e)** 60 **f)** 50 **g)** 3280 **h)** 5666 **i)** 70
2 Multiplying by Powers Less Than 1 1. a) 6.75
b) 0.675 **c)** 0.0675 **d)** 0.02 **e)** 0.002 **f)** 0.0002 **2.** If you
are multiplying by 10^{-n}, move the decimal point n
spaces to the left. **3. a)** 8.8 **b)** 0.56 **c)** 8.9 **d)** 0.004
e) 0.067 **f)** 0.003 33 **g)** 0.008 **h)** 0.111 **i)** 6
3 Dividing by Powers Greater Than 1 1. a) 70 **b)** 7
c) 0.7 **d)** 0.07 **e)** 0.14 **f)** 0.014 **g)** 0.0014 **h)** 0.000 14
2. If you are dividing by 10^n, move the decimal point

n spaces to the left. **3. a)** 5.6 **b)** 0.062 **c)** 0.97 **d)** 0.2
e) 0.06 **f)** 0.55 **g)** 0.328 **h)** 0.066 **i)** 700
4 Dividing by Powers Less Than 1 **1. a)** 600
b) 6000 **c)** $60\ 000$ **d)** 12 **e)** 120 **f)** 1200 **2.** If you are
dividing by 10^{-n}, move the decimal point n spaces to
the right. **3. a)** 340 **b)** 920 **c)** $330\ 000$ **d)** $23\ 400$ **e)** 90
f) 4 **g)** 800 **h)** $450\ 000$ **i)** 9900
5 Mixed Questions **1. a)** 1200 **b)** 0.12 **c)** 0.7 **d)** 1200
e) 880 **f)** 0.88 **g)** 0.4 **h)** 30 **i)** 0.0034 **j)** 0.08 **k)** 8.8 **l)** 960
m) 56 **n)** 4 **o)** 9900

Section 3.1 p. 103
Practice **1.** 8.1×10^4 **2.** 3×10^5 **3.** 1.5×10^5
4. 2×10^8 **5.** 4.2×10^6 **6.** 7.13×10^7 **7.** 7.6×10^8
8. 5.02×10^9 **9.** left to right, top to bottom:
$4.5 \times 10\ 000$, 4.5×10^4; $85\ 000$, 8.5×10^4; $110\ 000$,
1.1×10^5; $978\ 000\ 000$, $9.78 \times 100\ 000\ 000$;
$20\ 300\ 000$, $2.03 \times 10\ 000\ 000$ **10.** 2 **11.** 6 **12.** 4 **13.** 7
14. 5 **15.** 8 **Estimates may vary for 16.–18.**
16. 1.5×10^{10}; 1.7×10^{10} **17.** 4×10^{15}; 4.8×10^{15}
18. 6.3×10^{14}, 5.963×10^{14} **19.** 6×10^{12} **20.** 6.3×10^{14}
21. 1.5×10^3 **22.** 1×10^2
Applications and Problem Solving **23.** 9.1×10^4 km
24. 8×10^{23} km **25.** $\$9.5 \times 10^7$ **26. a)** 6.7×10^7
b) 7.6×10^6 **c)** 9.8×10^8 **27. a)** 2.3×10^5 **b)** 6.7×10^3
c) 1.3×10^6 **28. a)** 2.2×10^{16} **b)** 2325 years
29. a) 1×10^{13} m² **b)** 3×10^7 (in 1998) **c)** $333\ 333$ m²
30. 56 is not less than 10.

Technology p. 104
1 One Digit Repeating **1. a)** $0.777\ldots$ **b)** $0.0777\ldots$
c) $0.00777\ldots$ **2. a)** $\dfrac{5}{9}$ **b)** $\dfrac{2}{3}$ **c)** $\dfrac{4}{45}$ **d)** $\dfrac{1}{450}$ **e)** $\dfrac{1}{900}$ **f)** $1\dfrac{1}{3}$
g) $2\dfrac{2}{45}$ **h)** $7\dfrac{1}{450}$ **3. a)** 1; From the pattern, $0.\overline{9} = \dfrac{9}{9}$,
or 1. **b)** 1; Yes.
2 Two Digits Repeating **1. a)** $0.\overline{47}$ **b)** $0.0\overline{47}$
c) $0.00\overline{47}$ **2. a)** $\dfrac{32}{99}$ **b)** $\dfrac{16}{33}$ **c)** $\dfrac{1}{22}$ **d)** $\dfrac{14}{2475}$ **e)** $3\dfrac{5}{11}$ **f)** $6\dfrac{23}{33}$
g) $11\dfrac{7}{198}$ **h)** $22\dfrac{13}{1650}$
3 Non-Repeating Parts **1. a)** $\dfrac{31}{90}$ **b)** $\dfrac{17}{30}$ **c)** $\dfrac{61}{495}$ **d)** $\dfrac{211}{900}$
e) $4\dfrac{23}{90}$

Investigating Math p. 105
1 Terminating Decimals to Fractions **1. a)** $\dfrac{3}{10}$
b) $\dfrac{3}{5}$ **c)** $1\dfrac{1}{2}$ **d)** $3\dfrac{3}{4}$ **e)** $2\dfrac{3}{50}$ **f)** $1\dfrac{7}{8}$

2 Non-Terminating Repeating Decimals to
Fractions **1. a)** $\dfrac{2}{9}$ **b)** $\dfrac{1}{3}$ **c)** $\dfrac{8}{9}$ **d)** $\dfrac{7}{9}$ **e)** $\dfrac{1}{3}$ **f)** $\dfrac{23}{99}$ **g)** $\dfrac{46}{99}$ **h)** $\dfrac{52}{99}$
i) $3\dfrac{1}{9}$ **j)** $5\dfrac{4}{11}$ **2. a)** $\dfrac{4}{15}$ **b)** $\dfrac{7}{45}$ **c)** $\dfrac{2}{5}$ **d)** $3\dfrac{9}{10}$

Technology pp. 106-107
1 Exploring $y = 2^x$ 0.25, $\dfrac{1}{4}$, $\dfrac{1}{2^2}$; 0.5, $\dfrac{1}{2}$, $\dfrac{1}{2^1}$

2 Exploring $y = 3^x$ $0.\overline{1}$, $\dfrac{1}{9}$, $\dfrac{1}{3^2}$; $0.\overline{3}$, $\dfrac{1}{3}$, $\dfrac{1}{3^1}$

3 Exploring $y = 4^x$ 0.0625, $\dfrac{1}{16}$, $\dfrac{1}{4^2}$; 0.25, $\dfrac{1}{4}$, $\dfrac{1}{4^1}$

4 Exponent Zero **1. a)** 1 **b)** 1 **c)** 1 **2.** The value of
any number with the exponent 0 is 1. **3. a)** 1 **b)** 1 **c)** 1
d) 1
5 Negatives Exponents **1.** $\dfrac{1}{2^3}$; $\dfrac{1}{2^2}$; $\dfrac{1}{3^2}$; $\dfrac{1}{3^1}$;

$\dfrac{1}{4^2}$; $\dfrac{1}{4^1}$; **2.** A number with a negative exponent may
be written as a fraction where the numerator is 1 and
the denominator is the number with the same, but
positive, exponent. **3. a)** $\dfrac{1}{5^2}$ **b)** $\dfrac{1}{6^2}$ **c)** $\dfrac{1}{5^3}$ **d)** $\dfrac{1}{8^4}$
e) $\dfrac{1}{10^5}$

Section 3.2 pp. 111–112
Practice **1.** 1 **2.** 64 **3.** $\dfrac{1}{3}$ **4.** $\dfrac{1}{16}$ **5.** -1 **6.** $\dfrac{1}{1000}$ **7.** 1
8. $\dfrac{1}{8}$ **9.** $\dfrac{1}{81}$ **10.** $-\dfrac{1}{1000}$ **11.** 1000 **12.** 1 **13.** 3 **14.** 16
15. 6 **16.** $\dfrac{1}{2^3}$ **17.** $\dfrac{1}{4^1}$ **18.** $\dfrac{1}{10^7}$ **19.** $\dfrac{1}{9^8}$ **20.** $\dfrac{1}{1^4}$
21. 2^6 **22.** $\dfrac{1}{(-7)^6}$ **23.** $\dfrac{1}{(-2)^3}$ **24.** 2^3 **25.** 4^2 **26.** 5^4
27. 3^5 **28.** 7^9 **29.** 9^2 **30.** 8^{-8} **31.** 6^4 **32.** 5^{-5} **33.** 4^{-8}
34. 3^{12} **35.** 9^{-8} **36.** 8^5 **37.** -2^6 **38.** 2^3 **39.** 3^{-6} **40.** 5^{-2}
41. 8^1 **42.** $(-2)^{-6}$ **43.** $(-3)^0$ **44.** 81 **45.** 16 **46.** 2 **47.** 27
48. $\dfrac{1}{25}$ **49.** $\dfrac{1}{36}$ **50.** 7 **51.** 1 **52.** 2000 **53.** $\dfrac{1}{1728}$
54. $10\ 000$ **55.** 100 **56.** $\dfrac{1}{2}$ **57.** 1 **58.** 28 **59.** 15.5
60. 134 **61.** 1.25 **62.** 9 **63.** $\dfrac{1}{9}$ **64.** $\dfrac{1}{2}$ **65.** 7 **66.** 1.5

67. $-\frac{1}{9}$ 68. 3 69. $\frac{1}{25}$ 70. 1 71. 100 72. $-\frac{27}{8}$ 73. $\frac{16}{9}$

74. x^7 75. x^1 76. $\frac{1}{y^4}$ 77. t^4 78. m^8 79. b^2 80. m^8

81. $\frac{1}{y^8}$ 82. y^{10} 83. m^5 84. $\frac{1}{a^8}$ 85. $\frac{1}{t^2}$ 86. $\frac{1}{y^1}$

87. t^8 88. $\frac{1}{n^2}$

Applications and Problem Solving **89. a)** not equal:

$0.25 = 2^{-2}$ **b)** not equal: $0.027 = \left(\frac{3}{10}\right)^3$ **c)** not equal:

$2^{-3} = \frac{1}{2\times2\times2}$ **d)** not equal: $10^{-2} = \frac{1}{10\times10}$ **90. a)** 8

b) 81 **c)** 1 **d)** $\frac{1}{8}$ **e)** $\frac{1}{9}$ **f)** $\frac{1}{16}$ **g)** $\frac{1}{36}$ **h)** $\frac{1}{5}$ **i)** -1 **j)** $\frac{1}{25}$ **91. a)** 3

b) 4 **c)** 0 **d)** -2 **e)** -3 **f)** 3 **g)** ±2 **h)** 10 **92. a)** 1 **b)** $\frac{27}{8}$

c) $-\frac{8}{9}$ **d)** $\frac{7}{16}$ **e)** $\frac{25}{16}$ **f)** $\frac{9}{25}$ **93. a)** $\frac{1}{32}$ **b)** 2^{-5} **c)** $\frac{1}{2^5}$

d) 39 900 years **94. a)** sometimes true; true if the base is negative and the power is odd **b)** sometimes true; true if the exponent is positive and the fraction is less than 1 **c)** sometimes true; true if neither base is 0
95. a) Terry multiplied the bases and added the exponents. Sean multiplied the exponents instead of adding them. Michel multiplied the bases and multiplied the exponents. **b)** $\frac{1}{4}$ **96.** $(-3)^{-2}$ is equal to

$\frac{1}{(-3)\times(-3)} = \frac{1}{9}$. -3^{-2} is equal to $-\frac{1}{3\times3} = -\frac{1}{9}$.

Section 3.3 p. 115
Practice 1. 4.5×10^6 **2.** 8.9×10^{-2} **3.** 2×10^{-1}
4. 5.5×10^{-5} **5.** 1.3×10^{-3} **6.** 1.01×10^{-7} **7.** 23 000
8. 0.0047 **9.** 0.000 07 **10.** 0.000 001 **11.** 4.5×10^8
12. 3.4×10^5 **13.** 3.3×10^{-7} **14.** 1×10^{-8} **15.** 6×10^{-9}
16. 1×10^{-12} **Estimates may vary for 17.–21.**
17. 1.25×10^{-6}; 1.25×10^{-6} **18.** 8×10^{-6}; 9.6×10^{-6}
19. 1.2×10^{-4}; 1.312×10^{-4} **20.** 2.5×10^5; 2.6×10^5
21. 5×10^{-2}; 5×10^{-2}
Applications and Problem Solving **22. a)** 2×10^6 J
b) 8×10^{-4} J **c)** 1.5×10^6 J **d)** 8×10^{-11} J
23. a) 2.3×10^7 **b)** 4.5×10^{-8} **c)** 5×10^{-6} **d)** 10^{-10}
24. a) 7.8×10^8 **b)** 6.8×10^{-7} **c)** 8×10^{-11} **d)** 10^{-8}
25. a) 4.35×10^{-3}, 4.3×10^{-3}, 10^{-3}, 8.4×10^{-4}

b) 5.6×10^{-8}, $\frac{1}{10^8}$, 5.6×10^{-9}, 10^{-9}

c) 10^{-2}, 2.12×10^{-3}, 2.1×10^{-3}, $\frac{1}{1000}$ **26.** 4×10^{41}
27. 0.23 is not greater than or equal to 1.
28. a) 1×10^{-14} cm; 1×10^9 cm **29.** $c = ab$;
$(a\times10^m)\times(b\times10^n) = ab\times10^m\times10^n = ab\times10^{m+n}$

Section 3.4 p. 117
Applications and Problem Solving **1.** 6 **2.** 9 **3.** 78, 79, 80 **4.** 46, 48, 50, 52 **5.** 55 **6.** 4 **7.** 2 if order is not important **8.** 13 m by 17 m **9.** The numbers are 33 (between 59 and 74), 41 (between 74 and 67), and 26 (between 59 and 67). **10.** 16 **11.** 7 **12.** 7 cm by 6 cm by 8 cm **13.** In each triangle, begin at a corner and insert the numbers in clockwise order. A: 1, 6, 3, 2, 5, 4; B: 2, 5, 4, 1, 6, 3; C: 4, 3, 5, 1, 6, 2
14. Companion: 15, Officer: 50, Member: 100

Section 3.5 pp. 121–123
Practice 1. a) rational **b)** rational **c)** rational **d)** not rational **e)** rational **f)** rational **g)** rational **h)** not rational **i)** not rational **j)** rational **k)** rational **l)** not rational **Answers may vary for 2.–9.** **2.** $\frac{2}{-5}$ **3.** $\frac{-7}{-1}$

4. $\frac{-1}{2}$ **5.** $\frac{-8}{3}$ **6.** $\frac{-6}{8}$ **7.** $\frac{15}{-3}$ **8.** $\frac{-4}{6}$ **9.** $\frac{2}{5}$ **10.** $\frac{1}{2}$

11. $\frac{-1}{2}$ **12.** $\frac{-1}{4}$ **13.** -7 **14.** $\frac{-6}{7}$ **15.** $-\frac{4}{5}$ **16.** $-\frac{1}{3}$

17. $\frac{4}{5}$ **18.** $\frac{11}{4}$ **19.** $\frac{16}{3}$ **20.** $-\frac{7}{2}$ **21.** $-\frac{2}{3}$ **22.** $\frac{3}{4}$ **23.** $\frac{8}{3}$

24. $-\frac{3}{4}$ **25.** $\frac{-4}{-5}$ **26.** $\frac{1}{2}$ **27.** $-\frac{2}{5}$ **28.** $\frac{7}{5}$ **29.** $\frac{4}{5}$ **30.** $-\frac{11}{4}$

31. $\frac{5}{4}$ **32.** $-\frac{9}{25}$ **33.** $\frac{13}{4}$ **34.** $\frac{81}{50}$ **35.** $-\frac{37}{5}$ **36.** $-\frac{58}{25}$

37. $\frac{31}{10}$ **38.** $0.3\overline{1}$ **39.** $0.\overline{6}$ **40.** $0.9\overline{5}$ **41.** $5.\overline{61}$

42. $32.\overline{4287}$ **43.** $-18.\overline{52}$ **44.** $0.\overline{6}$ **45.** -0.875 **46.** 4.5
47. $-0.41\overline{6}$ **48.** -2.2 **49.** $0.\overline{36}$ **50.** $0.\overline{428571}$ **51.** $-0.\overline{7}$
52. -0.35 **53.** 2, 1 **54.** 63, 2 **55.** 6, 1 **56.** 3, 1 **57.** 3, 1
58. 3, 1 **59.** < **60.** < **61.** = **62.** > **63.** > **64.** < **65.** <
66. < **67.** = **68.** > **69.** > **70.** = **71.** > **72.** < **73.** > **74.** =

75. $\frac{1}{3}, \frac{1}{2}, 0.59, \frac{3}{5}$ **76.** $0.71, \frac{711}{1000}, 0.7\overline{1}, 0.\overline{7}$

77. $-9.\overline{1}, -9.01, -8.\overline{9}, -8.93$

78. $0.\overline{1}, 0.113, 0.11\overline{3}, 0.1\overline{13}$

79. $-\frac{4}{7}, \frac{3}{8}, 0.3\overline{75}, 0.3\overline{7}$

Applications and Problem Solving **80.** Answers may vary. **a)** $\frac{1}{7}$ **b)** $-\frac{4}{5}$ **c)** $\frac{1}{-16}$ **81.** $\frac{2}{1}$ **82. a)** $\frac{5}{3}$ **b)** $\frac{4}{3}$ **c)** $\frac{3}{4}$ **d)** $\frac{5}{4}$ **e)** $\frac{1}{1}$ **f)** $\frac{3}{2}$ **g)** $\frac{7}{4}$ **h)** $\frac{2}{1}$ **83. a)** $\frac{2}{1}, \frac{7}{4}, \frac{5}{3}, \frac{3}{2}, \frac{4}{3}, \frac{5}{4}, \frac{1}{1}, \frac{3}{4}$

b) Gander **84. a)** gold: $\frac{1}{3}$, silver: $\frac{5}{18}$, bronze: $\frac{7}{18}$

b) $0.\overline{3}, 0.2\overline{7}, 0.3\overline{8}$ **85.** elephants: $-\frac{2}{9}$, monkeys: $\frac{1}{1}$, giraffes: $\frac{5}{14}$, rhinoceroses: $-\frac{2}{3}$, hyenas: $\frac{0}{8}$ **86.** 1.2 times; each storey is the same height **87. a)** $0.\overline{09}, 0.\overline{18}, 0.\overline{27}$

b) The period is 9 times the numerator. **c)** $0.\overline{63}; 0.\overline{90}$
88. There are no temperatures lower than 0 on the Kelvin scale. **89.** No, because $\frac{-3}{4} + \frac{(-4)}{3} \neq 0$.
90. $\frac{8}{0} = x$ means $x \times 0 = 8$, which is impossible, because $x \times 0 = 0$ for all values of x. **91. a)** sometimes true; true if both numerator and denominator are greater than 0 **b)** sometimes true; true if the numerator is greater than 0 **c)** always true **d)** always true **e)** sometimes true; $\sqrt{2}$ is real but not rational

Investigating Math pp. 124–125
1 Completing the Table **1.** $A = \frac{11}{12}$ **2.** $B = \frac{5}{12}$
3. $C = \frac{3}{8}$ **4.** $D = \frac{3}{4}$ **5.** $E = \frac{1}{10}$ **6.** $F = \frac{7}{12}$ **7.** $G = \frac{13}{12}$ or $1\frac{1}{12}$ **8.** $H = \frac{20}{3}$ or $6\frac{2}{3}$ **9.** $I = \frac{21}{4}$ or $5\frac{1}{4}$ **10.** $K = \frac{32}{5}$ or $6\frac{2}{5}$ **11.** $L = \frac{4}{3}$ or $1\frac{1}{3}$ **12.** $M = \frac{11}{5}$ or $2\frac{1}{5}$
13. $N = \frac{25}{6}$ or $4\frac{1}{6}$ **14.** $O = \frac{55}{6}$ or $9\frac{1}{6}$ **15.** $P = \frac{15}{4}$ or $3\frac{3}{4}$ **16.** $R = \frac{5}{8}$ **17.** $S = \frac{19}{10}$ or $1\frac{9}{10}$ **18.** $T = \frac{13}{10}$ or $1\frac{3}{10}$ **19.** $U = \frac{27}{8}$ or $3\frac{3}{8}$ **20.** $V = \frac{25}{9}$ or $2\frac{7}{9}$ **21.** $Z = \frac{27}{40}$
2 Finding Place Names **1.** DRUM **2.** ELVIS
3. NASHVILLE **4.** DANCE **5.** BLUEGRASS
6. DISCO **7.** MOZART **8.** GUITAR **9.** POLKA
3 Locating Information
1. Drum Creek, Alberta
2. Lac Elvis, Québec
3. Nashville, Ontario

4. Dance, Ontario
5. Bluegrass Brook, Newfoundland
6. Lac du Disco, Québec
7. Mozart, Saskatchewan
8. Guitar Creek, British Columbia
9. Polka Lake, Ontario

Section 3.6 pp. 128–129
Practice **Estimates may vary for 1.–6.** **1.** 9 **2.** −21
3. −9 **4.** −10 **5.** 48 **6.** −30 **7.** $-\frac{3}{20}$ **8.** 1 **9.** $-\frac{3}{10}$ **10.** $\frac{5}{12}$
11. −0.075 **12.** −0.375 **13.** 0.23 **14.** 0.495 **15.** $\frac{39}{8}$
16. 0 **17.** $-\frac{15}{8}$ **18.** $\frac{5}{2}$ **19.** 4.375 **20.** −5.4 **21.** −10.5
22. 3.15 **23.** $\frac{27}{64}$ **24.** $\frac{4}{25}$ **25.** $-\frac{1}{16}$ **26.** −3.375
27. 0.4096 **28.** −14.44

Applications and Problem Solving **29. a)** $\frac{3}{10}$ **b)** $-\frac{9}{20}$
c) $-\frac{9}{40}$ **d)** $-\frac{27}{64}$ **30.** −$360 **31.** 28.75 km **32.** −6.5°C
33. 546 h **34.** 15 000 **35. a)** 500 000 **b)** Answers may vary; pollution, habitat destruction **36.** 13.824 cm³
37. a) never true; squares are always positive or 0
b) always true; the product is positive **c)** sometimes true; not true if one or both numbers are 0 **38. a)** any positive or negative even n **b)** any positive or negative odd n **c)** all values of n

Section 3.7 p. 132
Practice **1.** negative **2.** positive **3.** negative
4. positive **5.** negative **6.** negative **7.** positive
8. positive **9.** 4 **10.** −2 **11.** $\frac{3}{-5}$ **12.** $\frac{2}{7}$ **13.** $\frac{1}{3}$ **14.** $\frac{4}{7}$
15. not defined **16.** $-\frac{5}{11}$ **Estimates may vary for 17.–24.**
17. 2 **18.** −2 **19.** $-\frac{1}{6}$ **20.** 3 **21.** 0.625 **22.** −0.2 **23.** −8
24. 3 **25.** 7 **26.** $\frac{7}{2}$ **27.** −42 **28.** −125 **29.** not defined
30. 1 **31.** $-\frac{14}{3}$ **32.** $-\frac{7}{16}$ **33.** 2.25 **34.** 3.5 **35.** −2.8
36. 0.6
Applications and Problem Solving **37.** 11
38. 92 km/h **39. a)** $2.57 **b)** $641.68 **40.** $\frac{1}{16}$ **41.** 8 L
42. 420 **43.** For 1998 population: 144 000 m³ **44.** −1

45. Answers may vary. **a)** $\dfrac{5}{3} \div \dfrac{4}{3}$ **b)** $-\dfrac{1}{5} \div \dfrac{2}{5}$ **c)** $-\dfrac{4}{7} \div \dfrac{2}{7}$

Career Connection p. 133
1 Calculating Distances **1. a)** 1.5×10^6 km
b) 9×10^6 km **c)** 9×10^7 km **2. a)** 9.5×10^{12} km
b) 6.6×10^{20} km **c)** 7×10^7 years
2 Comparing Sizes **1.** 400 **2. a)** 175 **b)** 70 000

Section 3.8 p. 135
Applications and Problem Solving **1.** 4 **2.** 3 **3.** 17
4. 16 **5.** 9; They are swimming at a constant speed
and do not stop. **6.** 6 **7.** 6 **8.** 16 **9.** The farmer takes
the wolf across, and goes back to get the goat. The
farmer takes the goat across, and brings the wolf
back. The farmer takes the cabbage across, and brings
the goat back. The farmer takes the wolf across, then
returns to get the goat. **10.** 4 people

Section 3.9 pp. 137–138
Practice **1.** 10 **2.** 8 **3.** 12 **Estimates may vary for**
4.–13. **4.** 4 **5.** 2 **6.** −1.5 **7.** −3 **8.** −0.5 **9.** 7 **10.** 10
11. −2.5 **12.** 7 **13.** −6.5 **14.** true **15.** false **16.** false
17. true **18.** false **19.** true **Estimates may vary for**

20.–37. **20.** $-2; -\dfrac{25}{12}$ **21.** 4; 3.75 **22.** 1; $\dfrac{10}{9}$ **23.** $\dfrac{1}{2}; \dfrac{3}{5}$

24. −1; −0.92 **25.** $\dfrac{1}{2}; \dfrac{7}{20}$ **26.** $-2; -\dfrac{19}{10}$ **27.** $\dfrac{3}{2}; \dfrac{25}{16}$

28. $-\dfrac{15}{2}; -\dfrac{68}{9}$ **29.** $0; -\dfrac{1}{25}$ **30.** 10; 9.88 **31.** $\dfrac{1}{3}; \dfrac{23}{100}$

32. 1; $\dfrac{99}{100}$ **33.** −14.5; −14.56 **34.** −6.5; −6.45

35. −0.5; −0.66 **36.** 4; $\dfrac{15}{4}$ **37.** $-2; -\dfrac{11}{6}$

Applications and Problem Solving **38.** −1.45
39. −1.9°C **40.** $\dfrac{3}{4}$ **41. a)** $\dfrac{39}{40}$ **b)** $46 **42.** 1 min 27.66 s

43. $\dfrac{1}{5}$ **44. a)** They are opposites. **b)** They are both 0.

45. a) sometimes true; true if the second number is
greater than the first **b)** sometimes true; true if both
numbers are positive **c)** sometimes true; for example
$\dfrac{3}{2} - \dfrac{1}{2} = 1$, or $5 - 2 = 3$ **46.** Answers may vary.

a) $3.2 + (-4.8) = -0.6$

b) $-\dfrac{1}{4} + \left(-\dfrac{3}{4}\right) + \left(-1\dfrac{1}{4}\right) = -2\dfrac{1}{4}$

c) $1\dfrac{1}{4} - \dfrac{5}{8} = \dfrac{7}{8}$

Technology p. 139
Answers may vary.

Section 3.10 pp. 141–142
Practice **1.** 20 **2.** 21 **3.** −34 **4.** 0 **5.** 7.8 **6.** 49

7. −116 **8.** $-\dfrac{3}{10}$ **9.** $-\dfrac{11}{4}$ **10.** −4 **11.** 5 **12.** $-\dfrac{5}{8}$

13. $\dfrac{35}{36}$ **14.** 16 **15.** −0.15 **16.** $-\dfrac{2}{27}$

17. $\dfrac{2}{3} + 4 \times \left(\dfrac{1}{2} + \dfrac{1}{4}\right) \div 3 = \dfrac{5}{3}$

18. $(0.5^2 - 0.1) \times 8 \div 2 = 0.6$
19. $-2 \times (18.5 - 6.3) \div 4 = -6.1$

Applications and Problem Solving **20. a)** $\dfrac{33}{2}$ **b)** $\dfrac{33}{2}$

c) 39 **d)** −9 **e)** −36 **f)** 0 **g)** −1 **h)** $-\dfrac{1}{4}$ **i)** −144 **j)** −18

21. a) 2.7 **b)** 2.7 **c)** −2 **d)** −6.48 **e)** 2.05 **f)** 52.09
g) −51.59 **h)** 12.6 **i)** 81 **j)** −14.4 **22.** The clue answers
are: across: 19, 25, 12, 50, 84, 81, 95; down: 113, 92,
254, 50, 81, 85 **23. b)** 2.5 **c)** 11 **d)** −2 **25.** Answers may

vary. **a)** $\dfrac{1}{2} - \dfrac{1}{2} + \dfrac{1}{2} + \dfrac{1}{2} = 1$; $\dfrac{\dfrac{1}{2} \times \dfrac{1}{2}}{\dfrac{1}{2} \times \dfrac{1}{2}} = 1$; $\dfrac{\dfrac{1}{2} \div \dfrac{1}{2}}{\dfrac{1}{2} \div \dfrac{1}{2}} = 1$

b) $\left(-\dfrac{1}{2}\right) - \left(-\dfrac{1}{2}\right) - \left(-\dfrac{1}{2}\right) - \left(-\dfrac{1}{2}\right) = 1$; $\dfrac{-\dfrac{1}{2} + \left(-\dfrac{1}{2}\right)}{-\dfrac{1}{2} + \left(-\dfrac{1}{2}\right)} = 1$;

$\dfrac{-\dfrac{1}{2} \times \left(-\dfrac{1}{2}\right)}{-\dfrac{1}{2} \times \left(-\dfrac{1}{2}\right)} = 1$ **c)** $\dfrac{\dfrac{1}{2} + \dfrac{1}{2} + \dfrac{1}{2}}{\dfrac{1}{2}} = 3$ **d)** $\dfrac{-\dfrac{1}{2} - \dfrac{1}{2} - \dfrac{1}{2}}{-\dfrac{1}{2}} = 3$

Computer Data Bank p. 143
1 Favourite Type of Movie **3.** action, 45, 3, 6.7%;
comedy, 67, 8, 11.9%; drama, 90, 28, 31.1%; family,
25, 2, 8.0%; horror, 3, 1, 33.3%; musical, 31, 10,
32.3%; science fiction, 11, 5, 45.5%; western, 8, 3,
37.5% **4.** science fiction, action
2 Academy Awards **1.** *Ben-Hur*, 11
3 Comparing Profits **1.** 63 **2. a)** Subtract the cost
in millions of dollars from the income in millions of
dollars. **3.** *Star Wars, Jurassic Park, Return of the Jedi,
The Empire Strikes Back, Jaws* **4.** Yes. Five of the

sorted records have negative profits. **6.** *Gone With the Wind, Star Wars, Fantasia, Pinocchio, Jaws; Star Wars* and *Jaws* are in both lists.

Section 3.11 p. 145
Answers may vary.

Section 3.12 pp. 149–151
Practice 1. ±7 **2.** ±9 **3.** ±11 **4.** ±25 **5.** ±0.8 **6.** ±0.1
7. ±1.4 **8.** ±0.5 **9.** 5 **10.** 10 **11.** 15 **12.** 16 **13.** −13
14. 0.6 **15.** 0.2 **16.** 1.1 **17.** −0.9 **Estimates may vary for**
18.–58. 18. 5 **19.** 8 **20.** −10 **21.** 30 **22.** 30 **23.** 60
24. 90 **25.** 200 **26.** −900 **27.** 0.9 **28.** 0.9 **29.** −0.2
30. 0.3 **31.** 0.2 **32.** 0.05 **33.** −0.01 **34.** 0.02 **35.** 0.01
36. 0.02 **37.** 6; 5.6 **38.** 7; 6.6 **39.** 8; 7.9 **40.** −9; −8.9
41. 10; 10.0 **42.** 15; 14.4 **43.** 30; 33.5 **44.** 150; 142.1
45. 300; 293.3 **46.** 400; 449.6 **47.** 5; 4.4 **48.** 1; 0.9
49. 9; 9.9 **50.** −30; −28.8 **51.** 2; 2.4 **52.** −2; −1.1
53. 2; 1.7 **54.** $\frac{1}{6}$; 0.2 **55.** 69; 65.2 **56.** $\frac{14}{3}$; 4.5

57. 11.25; 10.8 **58.** 1.375; 1.4
Applications and Problem Solving 59. a) 5 cm;
20 cm **b)** 15 m; 60 m **c)** 7.4 m; 29.7 m **d)** 9.5 cm;
37.9 cm **e)** 14.1 m; 56.6 m **f)** 28.3 cm; 113.1 cm
60. a) 4 **b)** 5 **c)** 6 **d)** 7 **e)** −10 **f)** 8 **g)** 20 **h)** −9 **i)** 51.1 **j)** 20
61. a) 20.8 cm **b)** 14.1 m **62. a)** 16.2 cm² **b)** 113.9 cm²
c) 24 m² **d)** 13.8 m² **63. a)** 100 m by 100 m **b)** 20 m by
20 m **64. a)** 6.0 cm **b)** 10.1 m **c)** 28.3 mm **d)** 45.0 cm
65. a) 7.3 km/h; 10.1 km/h **b)** 18.5 km/h; 15.6 km/h
66. 3.3 s **67. a)** 2.83 **b)** 2.83 **c)** They are equal.

$$\sqrt{8} = \sqrt{2^2 \times 2} = \sqrt{2^2} \times \sqrt{2} = 2\sqrt{2}$$ **68. a)** 340 m/s

b) 330 m/s **c)** 324 m/s **69.** 6.5 cm; The diameter
would be equal to the side length of the square, or 13
cm. Thus, the radius is equal to 13 cm ÷ 2, or 6.5 cm.
70. opposites **71.** error; There is no real square root
of a negative number. **72.** Nyla gave the exact value.
Jill rounded the answer to the nearest hundredth. **73.**
a) 4 $\sqrt{5}$ b) By the Pythagorean theorem, the
hypotenuse is the square root of the sum of 1² + 2² or
$\sqrt{5}$. Construct a square on the hypotenuse of the
given triangle. **74. a)** 17; 24; 28; 33 **b)** The sum of the
first *n* odd numbers is *n*². **75.** 11 040 km/h

Section 3.13 p. 153
Applications and Problem Solving 1. $380 **2.** $5.90
3. a) 25 m **b)** 44.8 m **c)** 60 m **d)** 76.8 m **4.** *v* = 15.5*h*
5. a) *C* = 45 + 0.15*d* **b)** $71.25 **6.** 4.4 s
7. a) 11.9 years **b)** 0.2 years **c)** 84.1 years

Section 3.14 p. 155
1 Modelling Directions 1. Answers may vary.
From Barry's Bay, go north on the local road to
Bonnechere, then northeast on 58 to Pembroke.
From Pembroke drive south on 41 to Eganville, then
southwest on 512 to Foymount, and on 515 to
Latchford Bridge. **2.** From Whitney go east on 60 to
Barry's Bay, then south on 62 to Combermere.
From Combermere go southeast on 515 to Latchford
Bridge, then south on 514 to Hardwood Lake, and
southwest on 28 to McArthur Mills. From McArthur
Mills return to Hardwood Lake via 28. Continue
southeast on 28 to Denbigh and northeast on 41 to
Dacre. **2 Modelling Distances and Times 1. a)**
130 km **b)** 151 km **c)** 174 km **2. a)** The route in part
a) takes 128 min. **b)** Yes, the route from Cobden
southwest on 8, then west on 60 to Barry's Bay, and
south and west on 62 to Maynooth takes 119 min.
c) The route in part b) takes 156 min. **3. a)** 162 km
b) 185 km **4. a)** The route in part a) takes 1 h 7 min
b) The route in part b) takes 3 h 2 min.

Review pp. 156–157
1. 2.73×10^7 **2.** 7.01×10^8 **3.** 253 000 000
4. 5 200 000 **5.** 7.75×10^8 **6.** 3.44×10^5 **7.** $-\frac{2}{3}$ **8.** $\frac{3}{8}$
9. 2^{-2} **10.** n^2 **11.** 3^{-8} **12.** $-x^5$ **13.** 0.4^{-8} **14.** 4^{-2}
15. 15 625 **16.** 8 **17.** 27 **18.** 4096 **19.** $\frac{1}{2}$ **20.** 16
21. $\frac{1}{64}$ **22.** $\frac{1}{9}$ **23. a)** 36 **b)** −32 **c)** 36 **d)** 125 **e)** 172
f) 36 **24.** 7×10^{-6} **25.** 1.9×10^{-8} **26.** 0.000 34
27. 0.000 052 **28.** 2.294×10^{-1} **29.** 6×10^{-6}
30. 1.6×10^{-3} km² **31.** $\frac{1}{2}$ **32.** $-\frac{1}{2}$ **33.** $-\frac{1}{4}$ **34.** −7 **35.** $-\frac{6}{7}$
36. $-\frac{4}{5}$ **37.** $-\frac{1}{3}$ **38.** $\frac{4}{5}$ **39.** 2, $\frac{7}{5}, \frac{4}{5}, \frac{-7}{-10}, \frac{1}{2}, 0, \frac{-1}{2}$
40. $\frac{11}{8}, \frac{-11}{-9}, \frac{4}{-3}, \frac{-5}{3}$ **41.** −0.6 **42.** $-3.\overline{6}$
43. $0.\overline{142857}$ **44.** $-\frac{6}{25}$ **45.** $-\frac{3}{50}$ **46.** $\frac{5}{8}$ **47.** −4.5
48. −3.5 **49.** $\frac{65}{8}$ **50.** $-\frac{4}{3}$ **51.** $\frac{9}{16}$ **52.** −3 **53.** 7.2
54. −9.261 **55.** $\frac{3}{16}$ **56.** 9 **57.** $\frac{3}{100}$ **58.** −24 **59.** −2
60. 1.3 **61.** 5.4 cm **62.** $\frac{11}{2}$ **63.** $-\frac{13}{2}$ **64.** 1.8 **65.** 5.4
66. 62.85 **67.** $\frac{15}{8}$ **68.** $\frac{13}{6}$ **69.** 6.58 **70.** 77.5 **71.** 111
72. −128 **73.** $\frac{1}{15}$ **74.** −14.4 **75.** 1 **76.** $\frac{1}{3}$ **Estimates may**

vary for 77.–79. 77. 20; 19.3 **78.** −200; −202.7 **79.** 0.1; 0.1 **80.** −0.4 **81.** 1.9 **82. a)** 341 m/s **b)** 348 m/s **c)** 327 m/s **83.** $9.95 **84.** $54.95

Exploring Math

1. a) 4, 7 **b)** 7 **c)** 8, 9, and 10 are all possible (5 + 3, 3 + 3 + 3, 5 + 5). Add field goals to these for all higher scores. **2. a)** 1, 2, 4, 5, 8, 11 **b)** 11 **c)** 12, 13, and 14 are all possible. Add field goals to these for all higher scores. **3. a)** 1, 2, 3, 5, 6, 9, 10, 13, 17 **b)** 17 **c)** 18, 19, 20, and 21 are all possible. Add field goals to these for all higher scores. **4. a)** 1, 2, 3, 5, 7, 9, 11, 13, 15, 17, … **b)** No; odd totals are impossible. **5. a)** 1, 2, 4, 5, 7, 8, 10, 11, 13, 14 **b)** No; only totals that are multiples of 3 are possible. **6. a)** If the two numbers have a common divisor greater than 1, no highest impossible score exists.

Chapter Check p. 158

1. 6.1×10^5 **2.** 5.01×10^7 **3.** 4×10^{-4} **4.** 2.31×10^{-12} **Estimates may vary for 5.–7. 5.** 1.6×10^{14}; 1.584×10^{14} **6.** 5×10^{-7}; 4.845×10^{-7} **7.** 3×10^3; 3.5×10^3 **8.** $-\dfrac{1}{3}$ **9.** s^{-3} **10.** 2^3 **11.** 3^{-2} **12. a)** 48 **b)** −27 **13.** $\dfrac{4}{5}, \dfrac{7}{10}, \dfrac{1}{2}$ **14.** $-1\dfrac{1}{4}, -1\dfrac{1}{2}, -2$ **15.** $\dfrac{8}{7}$, 1.12, 1.1 **16.** 1.7, $\dfrac{3}{2}, \dfrac{4}{3}$ **17.** $-\dfrac{7}{20}$ **18.** $\dfrac{7}{5}$ **19.** $-\dfrac{13}{10}$ **20.** $\dfrac{3}{5}$ **21.** $0.\overline{285714}$ **22.** −2.6 **23.** $3.\overline{3}$ **24.** $-2.\overline{54}$ **25.** $\dfrac{4}{3}$ **26.** −0.36 **27.** 8 **28.** $\dfrac{15}{28}$ **29.** $-\dfrac{1}{8}$ **30.** 0.0001 **31.** 2 **32.** 6 **33.** 9.1 **34.** −1 **35.** $\dfrac{5}{12}$ **36.** −0.375 **37.** 6 **38.** 20 **39.** −11 **40.** 1.3 **Estimates may vary for 41.–44. 41.** 10; 9.6 **42.** 18; 17.7 **43.** −2; −2.9 **44.** 2; 2.0 **45. a)** $412.50 **b)** $337.50 **46.** 1250

Using the Strategies p. 159

1. 126 cm **2.** 1, 5, 15, 30, 45, 51, 45, 30, 15, 5, 1; 1, 6, 21, 50, 90, 126, 141, 126, 90, 50, 21, 6, 1; 1, 7, 28, 77, 161, 266, 357, 393, 357, 266, 161, 77, 28, 7, 1 **3.** 2 cm **4.** Tuesday **6.** 47, 48, 49 **7. a)** 25 **b)** 51 **8.** Wednesday **9.** 63 **10.** 4 times **11. a)** 13 + 15 + 17 + 19 = 64 **b)** 21 + 23 + 25 + 27 + 29 = 125 **c)** 31 + 33 + 35 + 37 + 39 + 41 = 216 **d)** It is the mean of the numbers. **e)** 43 + 45 + 47 + 49 + 51 + 53 + 55 = 343 **12. a)** Ontario, Erie, Huron, Superior **b)** Erie

Chapter 4

Statistics p. 161

2. 3, 4, 5, and 6 years **3. a)** 400% **b)** 37.5% **4.** 1900 **5.** 750

Getting Started pp. 162–163

1 Bar Graphs 1. a) 45+, 35–44, 25–34, 15–24 **b)** 35–44 **c)** comparison is easier **2. b)** Asia; it has over twice the population for its percent of land. **c)** North America and South America; their populations are half their percent of land. **2 Circle Graphs 1. a)** 2150, 150 **b)** $\dfrac{23}{4}$, 5.75 **3 Pictographs 1.** Bahamas: 25; Canada: 60; France: 50; Japan: 45; Kuwait: 15; Lithuania: 20; Switzerland: 90; U.S.A.: 65 **b)** No; circle graph shows parts of a fixed total. **3. b)** A bar graph is easier to draw. **c)** No; circle graph shows parts of a fixed total. **Mental Math Percents 1.** 30% **2.** 7% **3.** 98% **4.** 42.5% **5.** 25% **6.** 30% **7.** 5% **8.** 12% **9.** 3 **10.** 8 **11.** 19 **12.** 48 **13.** 20 **14.** 3 **Adding a Column of Numbers 1.** 150 **2.** 221 **3.** 299 **4.** 422 **5.** 440 **6.–10.** Add the left column first, then add in the next column, then add in the next column, if any. **6.** 23.7 **7.** 31.3 **8.** 2390 **9.** 3010 **10.** 2255

Section 4.1 p. 167

Practice 1. census **2.** sample **3.** sample **4.** census **5.** sample **6.** secondary **7.** secondary **8.** primary **9.** primary **10.** secondary **11.** secondary **12.** primary **13.** primary **14.** secondary **Applications and Problem Solving 15. a)** secondary **b)** secondary **c)** primary **d)** either (You could sample or find the data somewhere else.) **16.–20.** Hypotheses will vary. Answers are available from various sources and may vary. **21.** 468 **22. a)** Answers will vary. **b)** 10%: 3, 20%: 7, 30%: 6, 40%: 8, 50%: 3, 60%: 2, 70%: 0, 80%: 1 **c)** No; data may be incorrect or incomplete. **d)** 40% **e)** Answers will vary. **23.–25.** Answers will vary.

Technology p. 168

1 Generating Random Numbers 1. There is no pattern to the list. The graphing calculator gave more digits but this is adjustable in the mode section of the graphing calculator. **2.** Answers will vary, depending on the calculator. **2 Random Sampling 1.** Answers will vary. Depends on the calculator. **2.** Ignore the second occurrence and generate another integer.

Section 4.2 pp.173–175

Practice **1–4.** No implication is clear, except young people in question 3. **5.** Variable: Relative popularity of movie stars; Population: Students in a school.
6. Variable: Hours spent using a computer. Population: Grade 9 students in the town or city.
7. Variable: Possession of a job; Population: Secondary students in Ontario. **8.** Variable: Liking of spinach; Population: People in Canada.
9–19. Answers will vary.

Applications and Problem Solving

20. a) convenience sampling **b)** convenience sampling **c)** simple random sampling **d)** stratified sampling **e)** convenience sampling **21. a)** convenience sampling **b)** People who shop at the mall **c)** Answers may vary.
22. a) convenience sampling **b)** Answers may vary. **23. a)** volunteer sampling **b)** Answers may vary.
24.–25. Answers may vary. **26. a)** Most early morning shoppers visit department stores. **b)** No; mix the sample with shoppers at various times throughout the entire day. **c)** Answers may vary. **27.–29.** Answers may vary. **30.** Yes. **b)** No; social activity preferences differ by gender. **31. a)** no **b)** yes **c)** no **d)** yes **e)** no
32.–35. Answers may vary.

Section 4.3 pp. 178–179

Practice **1.** selection bias **2.** non-response bias
3. response bias; The second question implies a positive response to the first question **4.** selection bias from working people only **5.** response bias
6. selection bias **7–13.** Answers may vary. **7.** Which tastes better, Cola A or Cola B? and reverse the colas occasionally. **8.** Remove the word "yappy."
9. Remove the first unrelated sentence. **10.** Must art be understandable by everyone? **11.** Delete the words "long" and "challenging." **12.** Delete the last 4 words. **13.** Is skiing Canada's favourite sport?

Applications and Problem Solving **14.** Answers may vary. **15.** Selection bias; magazine subscribers and home owners are over represented. Non-response bias; there is no incentive to complete the survey. **16. a)** By using a telephone survey, you get a response or phone someone else. **b)** Answers may vary. Restricting the survey to the town adds selection bias because they would be affected by the bypass. **c)** Answers may vary. **17.** Selection bias; only viewers of that station were polled. Non-response bias; those that are in total agreement or total disagreement might respond, but those in the middle may not respond. **18.** Selection bias; only those who use the Internet and see the question can respond.
19. Answers may vary. **20. a)** Yes; you may inflate your answers to feel better about yourself. **b)** Yes; the census is filled out by the head of the household. Asking factual questions reduces this selection bias. **c)** Yes; a few people may refuse to answer or answer incorrectly because they think the government is intruding into their lives. Laws stating you must fill in the census correctly help reduce this bias.
21–23. Answers may vary.

Section 4.4 p. 181

Applications and Problem Solving **1.** 06:10 **2.** $48
3. $100 **4.** 06:15 **5.** $40 **6.** 10:15 **7.** 80 h **8.** 15 **9.** 264
10. a) $32 000 **b)** $243 000 **11.** 3 500 000 **12.** Answers may vary.

Section 4.5 pp. 185–186

Practice **1.–6. Answers and reasons may vary. 1.** mode
2. median **3.** mode **4.** mean **5.** mean or median
6. mean **7.** 24.8, 25, 25, 6 **8.** 23, 23, no mode, 19
9. 18.3, 16, 8 and 16, 33 **10.** 51.3, 51, 80, 69
11. 2522, 2175, no mode, 3380

Applications and Problem Solving **12. a)** mean increases by 2 **b)** mean decreases by 2 **c)** mean doubles **13. a)** 21.8, 18, 20.5 **b)** Instead of adding repeated scores, multiply individual scores by their frequency, and then add. **14. a)** No; it is just a coincident that her two lowest scores are the same. **b)** Yes; it is more accurate than the mode, but it ignores her two low scores, which are much lower than the other scores.
15. a) $168 000, $147 000, $143 000 **b)** Answers may vary. Mean is usually better, but it is affected by the one very high number. Median might be better here.
16. a) 11.65%, 11.9%, 12.2% **b)** Answers may vary. Median is probably best. The mean ignores the population in each province. **17. a)** $100 000, $60 000, $40 000, $40 000, $40 000, $40 000, $30 000, $30 000 **b)** $47 500, $40 000, $40 000 **c)** All are ways of finding centre of the data and all have problems. Mean is skewed because of the one high salary. Mode is skewed because more of one type of worker is required. Median might be best here. **d)** $40 000, $40 000, $40 000 **e)** $50 000, $40 000, $40 000 **f)** mean **18.** Answers may vary.
19. Answers may vary from year to year. **20. a)** always **b)** sometimes **c)** sometimes **d)** sometimes **21.** 13
22. a) There is one longest bar. **b)** There are two equal bars that are the longest. **c)** All bars are of different lengths. **23.** Answers may vary. **a)** 11, 11, 12, 18, 23 **b)** 10, 10, 13, 17 **c)** 11, 15, 22, 23, 24, 25 **d)** 8, 16, 16, 16, 24

Career Connection p. 187
1 Volcanic Eruptions   1. CN Tower is 53 m higher
2. 1.68 cm
2 Numbers of Volcanoes   1. 20.1, 9, 9 and 6, 107
2. 4.8
3 Locating Information   1.–2. Answers may vary.

Investigating Math pp. 188–189
1 Space Shuttle Launches   1. Information is
represented by vertical bars. The length of the bars is
proportional to the number being represented. A
scale on the left gives the actual number.   **2.** The bars
represent sequential measurements rather than
isolated observations. The vertical scale is usually
numerical.   **3.** There will be a space if there are no
occurrences at some value, but since sequential
measurements are used, there is usually no space.
4. No; the data is only for a 2-year period.   **5.** 90
2 Precipitation   1. a) May **b)** 11   **2. a)** January and
February **b)** 4   **3.** The amount of rainfall on a June day
is higher on average than the amount of rainfall on a
July day.   **4. a)** 4, 4, 7, 10, 11, 9, 9, 10, 9, 10, 10 6;
mean 8.25, median 9, mode 10 **b)** Mean takes into
account the less rainy months.   **5.** Answers may vary.

Technology pp. 190–191
2 Comparing Graphs   The bar graph makes it easier
to compare types. The circle graph emphasizes that
we are comparing a fixed total. Both have their
advantages. The broken line graph is inappropriate
since there is no sequential connection among the
types of shoes.
3 Choosing Graphs   1. a) bar graph or broken-line
graph **b)** circle graph   **2.** Answers may vary.

Section 4.6 pp. 193–194
Applications and Problem Solving   1. b) 87
c) 133.5 km/h   **2. b)** Home 64; Away 57   **3. a)** 10 **b)** 31
c) No; 5 have this and 5 do not. **d)** 16 and 22   **4. a)** 3
b) 7 h to 56 h **c)** 18-year-olds tend to watch less
television **d)** Answers may vary.   **5.** You can transfer
the data directly to a stem-and-leaf plot in order.
6. b) mean 52.7, median 51, mode 69 **c)** mean or
mode   **7–9.** Answers may vary.

Section 4.7 pp. 197–198
Applications and Problem Solving   1. a) $\frac{1}{2}$ **b)** $\frac{1}{2}$
c) $\frac{3}{4}$ or 75%   **2.** 55th   **3. a)** 40, 54, 62, 76, 95 **b)** 37th
4. a) The range of Joanne's scores is greater. **b)** The
median is closer to the lower quartile. **c)** Melissa's
lowest score and lower quartile are equal.

d) Joanne's highest score is farther above the upper
quartile than her lowest score is below the lower
quartile. **e)** The mean is above the median because
scores above the median are farther away than the
scores below the median; means: Melissa 81.3, Joanne
80.9   **5. a)** $\frac{1}{2}$ **b)** Carlos; the middle 50% of his marks
cover a greater range. **c)** 25%   **6.–7.** Answers may
vary.   **8. a)** 13, 34, 45, 51, 56 **c)** Fredericton, Halifax,
Regina, Charlottetown **d)** Below; the lowest value is
much lower; mean 42.3 **e)** The mean is closer to the
centre of the box. **f)** Answers may vary.   **9. a)** 50% of
the entries are below the mean and 50% of the
entries are above the mean. **b)** 75% and 25%
10. 80% on a test means you did 80% of the work
correctly. This could be the best mark or the worst
mark on the test in the class, but not necessarily the
80th percentile.

Section 4.8 p. 201
Applications and Problem Solving   1. a) 1984 and
1988 **b)** 3.1 m **c)** Values between 0 and 63 are
omitted.   **2. b)** Scotia   **3. b)** Those with less than grade
9 is decreasing but the rate of decrease is slowing.
Those with University degrees is increasing and the
rate is increasing.   **4. b)** The average age is increasing.

Section 4.9 p. 203
Applications and Problem Solving   1. Drove from
8:00 to 8:50, stopped until 10:00, drove until 10:50,
stopped until 12:00, drove to gas station at 12:15 and
filled up. Left and drove until 12:30, stopped until
13:30, drove until 14:15, stopped until 16:00, drove
until 17:00.   **2.** A is more expensive; B is older; B is
faster; they are the same length.   **3. a)** A to B: driving
at 100km/h; B to C: stopped; C to D: driving at
50km/h; D to E: driving at 25km/h.   **4.–7.** Answers
may vary.

Section 4.10 pp. 206–208
**Applications and Problem Solving   Answers may
vary slightly, since they are estimates. 1. a)** 48 s
b) 11 times **c)** 140 s **d)** 1200 m   **2. a)** 2.6 m **b)** 0.9 m
c) 1.7 m **d)** As length increases, mass increases, but
not constantly. Mass relates to volume. Volume
relates to length cubed. Mass relates to length cubed.
3. b) Answers may vary.   **4. b)** Answers may vary.
5. a) Temperature decreases as latitude increases.
b) 12°C, 15°C **c)** yes **d)** 49°N **e)** 7°C, the sames as
49°S.   **6. b)** Answers may vary. The points show an
upward trend increasing in steepness. More countries
take part in the Olympics or there are more countries

in the world. **c)** 135, 165, 205 **d)** 92, 141, 197
e) Answers may vary. There were boycotts in 1976
and 1984. **7. a)** no pattern **b)** No; not all variables are
related. **8. a)** The points should be close to a line or a
curve. **b)** These suggest that mass varies
independently with length, or different kinds of bears
should not be compared. **9.** Answers may vary.

Section 4.11 p. 211
Applications and Problem Solving **Answers may
vary, as they are estimates. 1. b)** 2.00 m **c)** estimate was
high **d)** 2.57 m, 2.8 m **e)** Answers may vary. **f)** The
broken line graph shows the actual data exactly. It
does not show the underlying trend as well as the line
of best fit does. **2. b)** The number of rentals decreases
with time. **c)** The estimate is negative, so it does not
apply. **3. b)** Height increases as circumference
increases. **c)** 20 cm; 36 cm **d)** 3.2 m; negative, so it
does not apply **e)** height versus age; circumference
versus age **f)** Answers may vary. **4.** Answers may vary.
5. a) The values should be close to the values on
either side. **b)** Answers may vary. **6.** Answers may
vary.

Section 4.13 pp. 223–224
Applications and Problem Solving **1.** D **2.** 6889
3. 159 **4.** 25 **5.** 1 by 240, 3 by 80, 5 by 48, 15 by 16
(and 240 by 1, 80 by 3, 48 by 5, 16 by 15 optional)
6. a) 9 m by 8 m, 12 m by 6 m, 18 m by 4 m, 24 m by
3 m, 36 m by 2 m, 72 m by 1 m, 8 m by 9 m, 6 m by
12 m, 4 m by 18 m, 3 m by 24 m, 2 m by 36 m, 1 m
by 72 m **b)** 72 m by 1 m **c)** 9 m by 8 m **7. a)** 2
b) 4 **c)** 30 **8.** Aces: 3, 1, 1, 1, 3; Bears: 3, 1, 1, 1, 3;
Lions: 3, 2, 1, 0, 4; Pintos: 3, 0, 1, 2, 2 **9.** $26 **10.** 3
11. 4 **12.** 7 **13.** 36 **14.** 14 **15. a)** 6 km **b)** 36 min **16.** 8
h **17.** Answers may vary.

Computer Data Bank p. 225
1 Labour Force in Asia **2. a)** Divide the labour
force by the population, and multiply by 100.
4. 38%, both record 23 and record 24 are 38 **5.** 40%,
6 times **6.** 37% **8.** the labour force as a percent of
population for Canada; 12%
2 Educational Expenditure in Europe **2. a)** Divide
the educational expenditure percent by 100, and
multiply by the expenditure. **3.** median, 3.658; mode,
0.148; mean, 10.969. The most frequent just happens
to be a low value, and the mean is greater than the
median because the mean is affected by some very
high values.
3 Exports and Imports **2.** 16 or 17, depending on
rounding

4 Standard of Living United Arab Emirates is the
highest, Democratic Republic of Congo is the lowest,
and Canada is the 9th.

Section 4.14 p. 227
1. Number of Words: 16, 61, 64, 71, 29, 23, 14, 8, 6,
8, 4, 1, 2; Percent of Total: 6.2, 19.9, 20.8, 23.1, 9.4,
7.5, 4.6, 2.6, 2.0, 2.6, 1.3, 0.0, 0.1
2 Applying the Model Answers may vary.
3 Extending the Model Answers may vary.

Review pp. 228–229
1. secondary **2.** primary **3.** Answers may vary.
4. 12 days **5.** Population: high school students in
Ontario; Procedure: Answers may vary. Stratified
sampling **6.** Population: all Canadians; Procedure:
Stratified sampling, geographically **7.–10.** Answers
may vary. **11.** non-response bias, some selection bias
12. response bias **13.** selection bias, non-response bias
14. a) People who listen to the radio. **b)** selection bias;
restricted to those with listed phone numbers who are
at home on weekdays in May. **b)** Answers may vary.
15. a) mean 57.2, median 41, mode 37 **b)** mean
16. b) 51 km/h **18.** 58th **19. b)** The summer is warmer
in Alice Springs. The summer occurs in December,
January, February, and March. **20. c)** about 15 m
d) about 17 m; this is not reliable. The last two points
may be ignored or they may mean that there is a non-
linear relationship.

Exploring Math p. 229
1. b) 6 **2. b)** 3 **c)** 3 **4. a)** rounds: 1, 3, 3, 4, 4; games: 1,
3, 6, 10, 15 **b)** 11, 19, 49 **c)** 66, 171, 1225

Chapter Check p. 230
1. a) b) Answers may vary. **c)** secondary **2.** 144
3.–4. Answers may vary. **5.** response bias **6.** selection
bias **7.** mean 75.7, median 76, mode 72 and 80
8. 45th **9. c)** The number of new cars is decreasing
year-to-year, except for the last year. **d)** about 1125
e) A slight variation in the line will produce large
variations in the answer. The prediction is not valid.

Using the Strategies p. 231
1. a) 14, 16 **b)** $2n + 6$ **c)** 58 **d)** 43rd **2.** 84 **3.** 2, 1; 3, 4, 5;
7, 6 **4.** 05:55 **5.** Answers may vary. **6.** $277.\overline{7}$ h

7. Answers may vary. **a)** yes; 20, 9, 6, 6 **b)** yes; seven 6s
c) no **d)** yes; 20, four 6s **8.** 1125 m **9.** Answers may
vary. **10.** thirty-one or thirty-three **11.** 54.5 square
units **12.** All the time zones meet at the North
Pole. Any time you want. **13.** 1241 km

Cumulative Review, Chapters 1–4

pp. 232–233

Chapter 1 **1.** $300 + 800 + 100 = 1200$; 1221
2. $47 + 1 - 18 = 30$; 30.58 **3.** $50 \times 80 = 4000$; 4346
4. $5 \times 200 = 1000$; 1166 **5.** $2000 \div 40 = 50$; 52
6. $49 \div 7 = 7$; 6.5 **7. a)** 42 **b)** 66 **c)** 14 **d)** 15 **8. a)** 32.5
b) 38.5 **c)** 48 **9.** 39 **10.** 65 **11.** 4 **12.** 189 **13. a)** 25 **b)** 1
c) 27 **d)** 48 **14.** 3^9 **15.** 6^3 **16.** 4^9 **17.** x^8 **18.** x^3 **19.** x^{20} **20.** 6
21. -20 **22.** 19 **23.** 4 **24.** -72 **25.** 18 **26.** -4 **27.** 4
28. 9 **29.** -16 **30.** 64 **31.** 25 **32.** 16 **33.** 36 **34.** -50
35. 72 **36.** -29 **37.** 1 **38.** -14 **39.** 1 **40. a)** -24 **b)** 30
c) -2 **d)** -9 **e)** -19 **f)** -13

Chapter 2 **1.** 3.1 **2.** 1:4 **3.** 1:8 **4.** 3:1 **5.** 2:5 **6.** 9:4
7. 4 to 7; 4:7; $\dfrac{4}{7}$ **8.** 6 to 5; 6:5; $\dfrac{6}{5}$ **9.–11.** Answers will
vary. **9.** 10:4 **10.** 4:3 **11.** 8:15 **12.** yes **13.** no **14.** 2
15. 2.4 **16.** 0.3 **17.** 7.5 **18.** \$200 **19.** 200 s or
3 min 20 s **20. a)** 150 for \$9 **b)** 31 L for \$18.91
21. 34% **22.** 7% **23.** 165% **24.** 44% **25.** 65%
26. 125% **27.** 60% **28.** 70% **29.** 43.75% **30.** 0.13
31. 0.246 **32.** 0.046 **33.** 0.009 **34.** 2 **35.** 1.24 **36.** 25%
37. \$210 **38.** \$1200

Chapter 3 **1.** 3.4×10^5 **2.** 1.3×10^7 **3.** 6×10^{-6}
4. 5.6×10^{-4} **5.** 4 700 000 **6.** 0.000 000 78
7. 2.34×10^{-2} **8.** 2×10^2 **9.** 3^3 **10.** 5^4 **11.** 2^{-15} **12.** 4^4 **13.** 16
14. $\dfrac{1}{5}$ **15.** 16 **16.** 3 **17.** 6.6 **18.** -10.24 **19.** $\dfrac{-6}{5}$ **20.** $\dfrac{27}{8}$
21. -43 **22.** $1.37\overline{1\,428\,5}$ **23.** $\dfrac{2}{5}$ **24.** -2 **25.** $\dfrac{-13}{4}$
26. $\dfrac{42}{5}$ **27.** -8.5 **28.** -2.3 **29.** 200 **30.** 10 **31.** 0.21
32. $\dfrac{-28}{5}$ **33.** 81 **34.** 22.7 **35.** -48.6 **36.** 0.1
37. side 6.3 m, perimeter 25.3 m

Chapter 4 **1.** Answers will vary. **2.** Population: All
Canadian adults; Procedure: Answers will vary.
3. Selection bias, non-response bias **4.** mean 16,
median 14, mode 10, range 19 **6.** 79th **7. c)** 42%

Chapter 5

Linear and Non-Linear Relations p. 235

2. 80 m **3.** 8 s **4.** The shape is like a rainbow, and is
caused by the force of gravity. **5.** Answers may vary.

Getting Started pp. 236–237

2 Writing Statements **1.** Boat A is longer and faster
than boat B. **2.** Car D is more expensive and younger
than car C. **3.** Players E and F are the same

height. Player F has more points per game than
player E. **4.** Movies G and H cost the same to
make. Movie H is shorter than movie G. **5.** The
buildings in descending order of height are D, E, and
F. The buildings in descending order of age are E, F,
and D. **6.** Books T and R have the same number of
pages. Book S has fewer pages. Book S has the least
number of words, followed by book T and then book
R. **7.** Stamps W and Z have the same value. Stamp Y
is worth more. Stamp Y is the oldest, followed by
stamp Z and then stamp W. **8.** Trail mixes A and B
have the same mass. Trail mix C has a lower mass,
and the mass of trail mix D is the least. The trail
mixes in order of descending cost are D, B, C, and A.
Warm Up **1.** 20, 12, 5, 2 **2.** 1, -2, -7, -9 **3.** 35, 20, 0,
-30 **4.** 15, 9, -15, -27 **5.** $y = x$ **6.** $y = 2x$ **7.** $y = -3x$
8. $y = x + 1$ **9.** $y = x + 5$ **10.** $y = x - 3$ **11.** $y = 0.5x$
12. $y = -x$ **13.** $y = x^2$ **14.** $y = -x^3$
Mental Math
Equations and Expressions **1.** 3 **2.** 24 **3.** -12 **4.** -13
5. -9 **6.** 24 **7.** -10 **8.** 15 **9.** 6 **10.** -6 **11.** 12 **12.** -4
13. -8 **14.** 6 **15.** 12 **16.** 3 **17. a)** 10 **b)** 19 **c)** 6 **18. a)** 7
b) 9 **c)** -10
Multiplying in Two Steps **1.** 162 **2.** 136 **3.** 132 **4.** 195
5. 196 **6.** 240 **7.** 208 **8.** 700 **9.** 540 **10.** 408 **11.** 910
12. 729 **13.** Multiplication of numbers can be done in
any order. **14.** 23 and 37 cannot be factored because
they are prime numbers.

Investigating Math pp. 238–240
1 Polygons From 8 Squares **2.** Half the perimeter
plus the number of interior points is equal to the area
plus 1. **3.** $H = A - I + 1$ **4.** $P = 2(A - I + 1)$
2 Other Polygons **3.** Yes.
3 Using an Expression **1.** 24 **2.** 82 **3.** 400

Section 5.1 pp. 243–245
Practice **1. a)** The shadow starts out long, shortens
until noon, then lengthens until sunset. **b)** The
number varies, and is higher in months with holidays
such as Valentine's Day, Mother's Day, and
Christmas. **c)** You see more stars if your surroundings
are dark than if there is a lot of light. **2. a)** domain:
{2, 3, 5, 8}, range: {6, 9, 15, 24} **b)** Each element in the
range is 3 times the corresponding element in the
domain. **3. a)** domain: {9, 12, 18, 32}, range: {7, 10,
16, 30} **b)** Each element in the range is 2 less than the
corresponding element in the domain. **4. a)** domain:
{4, 5, 7, 21}, range: {9} **b)** For every element in the
domain, the corresponding element in the range is 9.
5. a) domain: {3}, range: {4, 7, 11, 30} **b)** For every
element in the range, the corresponding element in

the domain is 3. **6. a)** The sum of the *x*- and *y*-values is 4. **b)** 2, 3, 4, 5, 6 **c)** (2, 2), (1, 3), (0, 4), (−1, 5), (−2, 6) **d)** {2, 3, 4, 5, 6} **7. a)** The *x*-value minus the *y*-value is equal to 1. **b)** 2, 3, 4, 5, 6 **c)** (3, 2), (4, 3), (5, 4), (6, 5), (7, 6) **d)** {2, 3, 4, 5, 6} **8. a)** The sum of the *x*- and *y*-values is −2. **b)** −4, −3, −2, −1, 0 **c)** (2, −4), (1, −3), (0, −2), (−1, −1), (−2, 0) **d)** {−4, −3, −2, −1, 0} **9. a)** The *s*-value minus the *t*-value is 3. **b)** 1, 0, −1, −2, −3 **c)** (4, 1), (3, 0), (2, −1), (1, −2), (0, −3) **d)** {−3, −2, −1, 0, 1} **10. a)** The *y*-value is equal to 2 more than 4 times the *x*-value. **b)** 10, 6, 2, −2, −6 **c)** (2, 10), (1, 6), (0, 2), (−1, −2), (−2, −6) **d)** {10, 6, 2, −2, −6} **11. a)** The *y*-value is equal to 4 less than 3 times the *x*-value. **b)** 2, −1, −4, −7, −10 **c)** (2, 2), (1, −1), (0, −4), (−1, −7), (−2, −10) **d)** {2, −1, −4, −7, −10} **12. a)** The *y*-value is equal to 7 more than −2 times the *x*-value. **b)** 3, 5, 7, 9, 11 **c)** (2, 3), (1, 5), (0, 7), (−1, 9), (−2, 11) **d)** {3, 5, 7, 9, 11} **13. a)** The *y*-value is equal to 2 less than −1 times the *x*-value. **b)** 2, 1, 0, −1, −2 **c)** (−4, 2), (−3, 1), (−2, 0), (−1, −1), (0, −2) **d)** {−2, −1, 0, 1, 2} **14. a)** 7 **b)** 2 **c)** 13 **d)** 6 **e)** 10 **f)** 13 **15. a)** 3 **b)** 6 **c)** −5 **d)** 9 **e)** 2 **f)** −1
Answers may vary for 16.–19. 16. (0, 11), (1, 10), (2, 9), (3, 8), (4, 7) **17.** (7, 4), (6, 3), (5, 2), (4, 1), (3, 0) **18.** (0, 5), (1, 9), (2, 13), (3, 17), (4, 21) **19.** (−2, −11), (−1, −9), (0, −7), (1, −5), (2, −3) **20.** $x + y = 9$ **21.** $y = 3x$ **22.** $y = x − 2$ **23.** $y = −2x$
Applications and Problem Solving 24. (0, 1), (0, 2), (1, 0), (1, 1), (1, 2), (2, 0), (2, 1), (2, 2), (3, 0), (3, 1), (3, 2); no **25. a)** 80, 160, 240, 320 **b)** 400 km; 480 km **c)** Each distance is 80 km more than the one before. **d)** (1, 80), (2, 160), (3, 240), (4, 320) **e)** The distance in kilometres is 80 times the time in hours. **f)** $D = 80t$ **g)** 1040 km; 1680 km **26. a)** 5, 9, 14, 20, 27, 35, 44 **b)** The difference between consecutive entries increases by 1 each time. **c)** 54, 65 **d)** (4, 2), (5, 5), (6, 9), (7, 14), (8, 20), (9, 27), (10, 35), (11, 44) **e)** The number of diagonals is equal to half the sum of the square of the number of sides and −3 times the number of sides. **f)** $D = \dfrac{s^2 − 3s}{2}$ **g)** 170; 1175; 4850
27. a) 8, 16, 32, 64 **b)** Each number is twice the previous number. **c)** 128; 256 **d)** (1, 2), (2, 4), (3, 8), (4, 16), (5, 32), (6, 64) **e)** The number of regions is 2 raised to the exponent of the number of folds. **f)** $R = 2^n$ **g)** 1024; 4096 **28. a)** (140, 70), (150, 75), (160, 80), (170, 85), (180, 90) **b)** domain: {140, 150, 160, 170, 180}, range: {70, 75, 80, 85, 90} **c)** The length of the mirror is half the height of the person. **d)** $l = \dfrac{1}{2}h$ **29. a)** (7, 31), (8, 29), (5, 31), (5, 30),

(3, 31), (4, 30), (4, 31), (6, 31), (9, 30), (8, 30), (8, 31) (Note that January and October are represented by the same ordered pair.) **b)** domain: {3, 4, 5, 6, 7, 8, 9}, range: {29, 30, 31} **c)** No. **30. a)** name **b)** all the names of people with Social Insurance Numbers.

Section 5.2 pp. 248–249
Practice 1. J **2.** G **3.** N **4.** H **5.** P **6.** F **7.** M **8.** K **9.** L **10.** A **11.** D **12.** C **13.** B **14.** E **15.** I **16.** A(−6, 5), B(−5, 3), C(−2, 1), D(−4, −2), E(−1, −1), F(−6, −6), G(−2, −5), H(5, 6), I(0, 5), J(2, 2), K(4, 1), L(6, 0), M(5, −1), N(3, −2), P(5, −6), Q(4, −4) **32. a)** (−4, 4), (−3, 4), (−2, 4), (−1, 3), (0, 2), (1, 1), (2, 0) **b)** domain: {−4, −3, −2, −1, 0, 1, 2}, range: {0, 1, 2, 3, 4} **33. a)** (−4, −4), (−3, −3), (−2, −2), (−1, −1), (0, 0), (1, 1), (2, 2) **b)** domain: {−4, −3, −2, −1, 0, 1, 2}, range: {−4, −3, −2, −1, 0, 1, 2} **34. a)** (−4, 1), (−3, 2), (−2, 3), (0, 1), (2, 0), (2, 1), (2, 2), (2, 3) **b)** domain: {−4, −3, −2, 0, 2}, range: {0, 1, 2, 3} **35. a)** (−2, −1), (−2, 2), (1, 1), (2, 2), (3, 2), (3, −2) **b)** domain: {−2, 1, 2, 3}; range: {−2, −1, 1, 2}
Applications and Problem Solving 40. a) triangle; 10 square units **b)** rectangle; 18 square units **c)** parallelogram; 15 square units **d)** rectangle; 12 square units **e)** hexagon; 64 square units **41.** Answers may vary. C(−4, −6) **42.** F(1, 3), F(1, −1), F(3, 5), F(7, −3), F(9, −1), F(9, 3); 6 points with integer coordinates **43. b)** (4, 5), (6, −5), (−12, −3) **c)** 3 **46. a)** Sometimes true. (−1, 1) lies in the 4th quadrant, but (1, −1) lies in the 2nd quadrant. **b)** Always true unless the coordinates are (0, 0). **c)** Always true.

Section 5.3 pp. 252–253
Practice 1. (0, 0), (1, 1), (2, 2), (3, 3), (4, 4), (5, 5) **2.** (0, 25), (1, 20), (2, 15), (3, 10), (4, 5), (5, 0) **3.** 15, 20, 25 **4.** 18.00, 24.00, 30.00 **5.** 90, 120, 150 **6.** 180, 230, 280
Applications and Problem Solving 7. a) 40, 60, 80, 100 **b)** 2.4 h **9. b)** 3 mL **c)** 882 mL; 906 mL **d)** 819 mL **10. c)** No. **11. b)** No.

Section 5.4 pp. 257–258
1. −3, −2, −1, 0, 1 **2.** 0, 1, 2, 3, 4 **3.** 5, 4, 3, 2, 1 **4.** −2, 0, 2, 4, 6 **5.** range: {−1, 0, 1, 2, 3} **6.** range: {−4, −3, −2, −1, 0} **7.** range: {−3, −1, 1, 3, 5} **8.** range: {−5, −3, −1, 1, 3} **9.** range: {−2, 1, 4, 7, 10} **10.** range: {−8, −5, −2, 1, 4} **17.** $y = x + 2$ **18.** $y = −x$ **19.** $y = x − 4$ **20.** $y = 3x$ **21. a)** $y = x − 3$ **b)** domain: {−1, 0, 1, 2, 3} **22. a)** $y = −2x$ **b)** domain: {−2, −1, 0, 1, 2} **23. a)** $y = x + 5$ **b)** domain: all real numbers **24. a)** $y = 1.5x$ **b)** domain: all real numbers

Applications and Problem Solving **25. a)** 0, 1000, 2000, 3000, 4000, 5000, 6000 **c)** 5.5 min **d)** $d = 1000t$ **26. a)** 12, 24, 36, 48 **c)** $A = 6x$ **27. b)** 42 **28. b)** 9600 s; 2.7 h **30. a)** range: {3, 5, 7, 9, 11, 13} **b)** range: {−3, −1, 1, 3, 5, 7, 9} **c)** all real numbers **31.** continuous **32.** discrete

Section 5.5 pp. 265–267
Practice **1.** 9, 12, 15, 18 **2.** −6, −8, −12, −14 **3.** 1, 3, 4, 5 **4. a)** 3 **b)** $p = 3q$ **5. a)** 2.5 **b)** $a = 2.5b$ **6. a)** 0.6 **b)** $s = 0.6t$ **7. a)** $\frac{1}{3}$ **b)** $m = \frac{1}{3}n$ **8.** 56 **9.** 40 **10.** 32 **11.** 14 **12. b)** direct **13. b)** partial **14.** $y = x + 2$ **15.** $y = 3x + 1$ **16.** $y = x − 1$ **17.** $y = 2x − 2$
Applications and Problem Solving **18. a)** $A = 12t$ **b)** 22.5 h **19. a)** $d = 4t$ **c)** Yes. **d)** 22 m **e)** 6.25 min **20.** $247.50 **21. a)** $C = 400 + 200d$ **c)** 3 days; 10 days **22. a)** $E = 300 + 0.1s$ **c)** No. **d)** $950 **e)** $5250 **23. a)** 40; $E = 40t$ **b)** 140 kJ **c)** 8 min **24. b)** $12.00 **c)** $C = 12 + 1.5t$ **25. a)** $C = 500 + 0.15n$ **b)** $9500 **c)** 80 000 **26. a)** 23; 28 **c)** partial **d)** $A = 5n + 3$ **e)** 278 **27. b)** $60 **c)** $C = 60 + 50t$ **d)** $410 **e)** 5.5 h **28. a)** π **b)** 2π **29. b)** direct **c)** $W = 9.8m$ **d)** 735 N **e)** 55 kg **f)** No. **30. a)** $C = 300 + 10n$ **b)** $8 more per student **d)** $450 **31. b)** $y = −350x + 4200$ **c)** $4200 **d)** 12 months

Technology p. 268
1 Direct Variations **3. a)** $y = 2x$ **4.** $y = −0.5x$ **5. a)** $y = −4x$ **b)** $y = 0.3x$
2 Partial Variations **1.** $y = 2x − 2$ **2.** $y = 5 − 3x$ **3. a)** $y = 0.5x + 1$ **b)** $y = −2x + 1$
3 Problem Solving **1. a)** $y = 0.5x + 1.5$ **b)** Answers may vary. **2.** $m = 2.7V$ **3.** $d = 1 − 0.1t$

Section 5.6 pp. 271–274
Answers to all problems found using linear regression on a graphing calculator.
Practice **1. b)** 49.35; 116.9 **c)** 22.75; 38.29 **2. b)** −28.98; 44.73 **c)** 60.71; 20.01 **3. b)** Answers may vary. $y = x + 3.5$ **4. b)** Answers may vary. $y = x − 4$ **5. b)** Answers may vary. $y = −x$ **6. b)** Answers may vary. $y = 1.5x$
Applications and Problem Solving **7. b)** 110 m **c)** 148.5 m; 120.5 m **d)** It is equal to the speed minus approximately 40. **e)** It is equal to $\frac{3}{4}$ of the speed minus approximately 23. **f)** $y = x − 40$ **g)** $y = 0.75x − 23$ **8. b)** $p = 1.3n + 2.3$ **c)** 219 million **d)** No, because Portugal is not in South America. **9. b)** $y = 0.344x + 6.3$ **c)** $y = −0.648x + 24.58$ **e)** 1.9% **f)** 18.34% **g)** 1994 **h)** The x-coordinate of the

point of intersection is the year when they were equal. **j)** $y = −0.5x + 19$

Section 5.7 pp. 277–279
Applications and Problem Solving **5. a)** Area: 0, 1, 4, 9, 16, 25; Perimeter: 0, 4, 8, 12, 16, 20 **c)** 12.25 square units **d)** 17.89 units **6. a)** 27; 64 **c)** 3.375 cubic units; 15.625 cubic units **7. b)** 25 m; 42 m **c)** 107 km/h **8. a)** Area: 1, 4, 9, 16, 25; Volume: 2, 8, 18, 32, 50 **c)** 12.5 cm^3; 24.5 cm^3 **9. a)** 8, 16, 32, 64 **c)** 128; 256 **14. a)** $A = 2w^2$ **c)** 1st quadrant; A and w must be positive. **d)** 2.5 cm **15. b)** 2.7 s **c)** $d = 4.9t^2$ **d)** $y = 4.9x^2$ **16. a)** 4, 9, 16, 25 **b)** $b = (s − 2)^2$ **c)** 100; 2304 **d)** 25; 46 **e)** No, because 408 is not a perfect square.

Investigating Math pp. 280–281
1 Exploring Finite Differences **1. a)** y: 0, 2, 4, 6, 8; First Differences: 2, 2, 2, 2 **b)** y: 3, 4, 7, 12, 19; First Differences: 1, 3, 5, 7 **c)** y: −1, 2, 5, 8, 11; First Differences: 3, 3, 3, 3 **d)** y: 1, 2, 4, 8, 16; First Differences: 1, 2, 4, 8 **3.** $y = 2x, y = 3x − 1$ **4.** They are all the same. **5.** $y = x^2 + 3, y = 2^x$ **6.** They are all different. **7.** If the first differences for a relation are all equal, the relation is linear.
2 Using First Differences **1. a)** linear **b)** non-linear **c)** linear **d)** non-linear **e)** linear **f)** non-linear **g)** linear **h)** linear **i)** non-linear **2.** non-linear **3. a)** 14, 28, 42, 56, 70 **b)** linear **4. b)** linear **5. b)** non-linear **c)** linear **d)** No.

Section 5.8 pp. 283–285
Applications and Problem Solving **1. a)** Left the dock, fell, headed back toward the dock, went away from the dock, fell, then returned to the dock **3. a)** starting at school, travelling away at moderate speed, then stopping for some time **b)** staying at school for some time, then leaving at fairly slow speed **c)** leaving school at slow speed, then at a much faster speed **d)** starting away from school, going slowly farther away, then quickly to school **e)** starting some distance from school, going slowly toward school **f)** staying some distance away from school **4.** b and c **5. a)** A: went straight out, reversed direction and returned, B: went out (not as fast as a), stopped for awhile, continued out, stopped, started back, stopped, then returned very quickly; C: went out (slowest of the 3), stopped, then returned quite quickly **b)** B **c)** A **10.** Assuming they all stayed on the path: Erica was at the restaurant from 9:00 to 9:06, then walked to the waterfall, arriving at 9:12, meeting Steven on the way. Alicia was on the path 100 m past

the waterfall at 9:00, walked to the observatory, arriving at 9:09, and stayed there. She met Steven and then Lee. Lee was at the waterfall until 9:02, walked 100 m toward the observatory, meeting Steven, turned at 9:04 and walked 50 m past the waterfall, meeting Alicia and then passing Steven at the waterfall, turned back at 9:06, passing Steven at the waterfall at 9:07 and reaching the observatory at 9:12. Steven started at the observatory, walked to the waterfall passing Lee and Alicia, was at the waterfall from 9:05 to 9:07, where Lee passed him twice, the second time just as he left for the restaurant, where he arrived at 9:12.

Career Connection p. 286
1 Gold Mining **1. a)** 130 t **b)** 1.4 t **2. a)** 135 t **b)** 6.5 t

Computer Data Bank p. 287

1 Timed Events **1.** 61.19 s; 100-m Backstroke, Women **2.** 21.91 s; 50-m Freestyle, Men; 1992; Aleksandr Popov **3.** 9.84 s; 100-m Dash, Men; 1996; Donovan Bailey

2 Canadian Winners **1.** 9 **2.** $\frac{1}{5}$ **3.** 4 × 100-m Relay, Men and 100-m Dash, Men; Donovan Bailey (twice), Robert Esmie, Glenroy Gilbert, Bruny Surin **4.** 200-m Sprint, Men; 1908; Robert Kerr
3 World Records **2.** no, only 66 of 307 times

Section 5.9 pp. 288–289
Answers may vary.
1 Modelling the Flight of a Football Punted Nose First **1.** 43 m, 1.9 s; 52 m, 4.6 s **2.** 13°, 75°; 1.2 s, 5 s **3.** 35°, 59 m **4.** 45°, 3.7 s **5.** 90°, 0 m
2 Modelling the Flight of a Football Punted End-Over-End **1.** 34 m, 1.8 s; 36 m, 3.8 s **2.** 62°, 32 m **3.** 40°; 2.9 s **4.** 90°, 0 m
3 Comparing the Models **1.** Nose first is about 20 m longer than end-over-end. **2.** Nose first is about 1 s longer than end-over-end. **3. a)** 68% **b)** 78%

Review pp. 290–291
1. a) The sum of the *x*- and *y*-values is 8.
b) 10, 9, 8, 7, 6 **c)** (−2, 10), (−1, 9), (0, 8), (1, 7), (2, 6)
d) {6, 7, 8, 9, 10} **2. a)** The *x*- and *y*-values are equal. **b)** −2, −1, 0, 1, 2 **c)** (−2, −2), (−1, −1), (0, 0), (1, 1), (2, 2) **d)** {−2, −1, 0, 1, 2} **3. a)** The *y*-value is 2 more than the corresponding *x*-value. **b)** 0, 1, 2, 3, 4
c) (−2, 0), (−1, 1), (0, 2), (1, 3), (2, 4) **d)** {0, 1, 2, 3, 4}
4. a) The *y*-value is 5 more than 2 times the corresponding *x*-value. **b)** 1, 3, 5, 7, 9 **c)** (−2, 1), (−1, 3), (0, 5), (1, 7), (2, 9) **d)** {1, 3, 5, 7, 9} **Answers**

may vary for **5.–8.** **5.** (0, 6), (1, 5), (2, 4), (3, 3), (4, 2) **6.** (6, 2), (5, 1), (4, 0), (3, −1), (2, −2) **7.** (0, 3), (1, 2), (2, 1), (3, 0), (4, −1) **8.** (0, −3), (1, −1), (2, 1), (3, 3), (4, 5) **9.** $y = 2 - x$ **10.** $y = 4x$ **11. b)** (2, −2) **c)** 5 by 8
12. a) (−1, −3), (0, −2), (1, −1), (2, 0), (3, 1), (4, 2)
b) domain: {−1, 0, 1, 2, 3, 4}, range: {−3, −2, −1, 0, 1, 2} **13. a)** (2, −2), (2, −1), (2, 0), (2, 1), (2, 2), (2, 3) **b)** domain: {2}, range: {−2, −1, 0, 1, 2, 3} **14. a)** 0, 13, 26, 39, 52 **b)** 33.8 m; 62.4 m **15. a)** 2.5 m **b)** 17.5 m **17.** $y = x + 6$ **18.** $y = -3x$ **19. b)** partial **20. b)** direct **21.** 23.75 h **22. a)** 17; 21 **c)** $d = 4n + 1$ **d)** 401 **23. b)** $y = x + 4.6$ **24. b)** $y = 3x - 3$

Exploring Math p. 291
1. b) Answers may vary. **c)** Answers may vary.
2. Answers may vary.

Chapter Check p. 292
1. a) The sum of the *x*- and *y*-values is −2. **b)** 0, −1, −2, −3, −4 **c)** (−2, 0), (−1, −1), (0, −2), (1, −3), (2, −4) **d)** {−4, −3, −2, −1, 0} **2. a)** The *y*-value is 1 less than 2 times the *x*-value. **b)** −5, −3, −1, 1, 3 **c)** (−2, −5), (−1, −3), (0, −1), (1, 1), (2, 3) **d)** {−5, −3, −1, 1, 3}
3. Answers may vary. (−2, −2), (−1, 1), (0, 4), (1, 7), (2, 10) **4.** $y = x + 3$ **5.** $y = 5x$ **6. a)** isosceles triangle **b)** parallelogram **c)** rectangle **7. a)** (0, 4), (1, 3), (2, 2), (3, 1), (4, 0) **b)** domain: {0, 1, 2, 3, 4}, range: {0, 1, 2, 3, 4} **c)** The sum of the *x*- and *y*-values is 4. **d)** $x + y = 4$ **8. a)** (−2, −4), (−1, −2), (0, 0), (1, 2), (2, 4) **b)** domain: {−2, −1, 0, 1, 2}, range: {−4, −2, 0, 2, 4} **c)** The *y*-value is twice the corresponding *x*-value. **d)** $y = 2x$ **9. b)** partial **10. a)** 100 km **b)** 15 min **11. a)** 48; $w = 48t$ **b)** 576 **c)** 62.5 min **12. b)** $y = 320x$ **c)** 22 min; 31 min

Using the Strategies p. 293
1. 112 cm **2.** 11 **3.** 9 **6. a)** 6 **b)** 4 **c)** 2 **7.** $\frac{1}{24}$
9. February and March **10.** 78 **11.** 11, 12, 13, 15, 17, 19 **12.** 22:17

Chapter 6

Algebra p. 295
1. a) 53 580 **b)** 5875 **c)** 9.12 **2. a)** 2110 **b)** 1810
4. Answers may vary.

Getting Started pp. 296–297
1 Patterns in Tables **1.** 13, 8; 7; 14, 16, 17; 45, 48, 63, 91; The third number is the sum of the first two numbers. The fourth number is the product of the

first two numbers. **2.** 7, 5, 15; 18, 22, 10; 36, 44, 28, 60; 63, 77, 49, 35, 105; The second number is twice the first number. The third number is twice the second number. The fourth number is the sum of the first three numbers. **3.** 6, 2, 4; 10, 40, 16; 10, 8, 11; 8; The second number is the product of the third and fourth numbers. The third number is the sum of the first and fourth numbers. **4.** 24, 27; 4, 2; 9; 6, 5, 18; The first number is the product of the second and third numbers. The third number is the sum of the second and fourth numbers. **5.** 2; 20; 29, 26, 39, 35; 4, 5; The second number is the product of the first and fourth numbers. The third number is the sum of the other three numbers. **6.** 6, 8; 12, 24, 30; 13, 19, 31; 25, 37, 49, 61; The second number is 3 times the first number. The third number is 1 greater than the second number. The fourth number is the sum of the second and third numbers.

2 Stamp Patterns **1.** 6 **2.** 4 **3.** 8 **4.** Find all the pairs of numbers that have a product of 100; 9
3 Tile Patterns **1.** 1 grey, 8 orange **2.** 2 grey, 13 orange **3.** 4 grey, 21 orange **4.** 3 grey, 18 orange **5.** 6 grey, 29 orange **6.** 9 grey, 40 orange
Warm Up **1. a)** 10 **b)** -25 **c)** 0 **d)** -20 **2. a)** 1 **b)** 4 **c)** 16 **d)** -8 **3. a)** -3 **b)** 3 **c)** -11 **d)** 19 **4. a)** 1 **b)** -4 **c)** -10 **d)** 12 **5. a)** 1 **b)** -24 **c)** -6 **d)** 10 **6. a)** 7.5 **b)** 3 **c)** 0 **d)** 9.8 **e)** 1.9 **f)** 4.5 **g)** 0.25 **h)** -10.25 **7. a)** 29 **b)** 8 **c)** 13 **d)** 11 **e)** 36 **f)** -20 **8. a)** -2 **b)** -9 **c)** -1 **d)** -15 **e)** -18 **f)** -20 **9. a)** -0.6 **b)** -4.2 **c)** -12.8 **d)** -2.9 **e)** 8.4 **f)** 10.1 **g)** -12.0 **h)** 9.6
Mental Math
Order of Operations **1.** 10 **2.** -5 **3.** 0 **4.** 16 **5.** -6 **6.** 6 **7.** 8 **8.** -2 **9.** 32 **10.** 24 **11.** 3 **12.** -6 **13.** 30 **14.** 2 **15.** 4 **16.** -2
Multiplying Two Numbers That Differ by 2 **1.** 143 **2.** 168 **3.** 399 **4.** 899 **5.** 624 **6.** 1599 **7.** 9999 **8.** 3599 **9.** 999 999 **10.** 1.68 **11.** 1.95 **12.** 62 400 **13.** 89 900 **14.** 99.99 **15.** 14 300 **16.** 3599 **17.** 15.99 **18.** 24 990 **19.** 288 **20.** 80 990 **21.** 0.4899 **22.** Square their average and subtract 4. **a)** 165 **b)** 396 **c)** 221 **d)** 896 **e)** 621 **f)** 9996

Section 6.1 pp. 300–301
Practice **1.** 2 **2.** 3 **3.** 3 **4.** 2 **5.** 2; 1 **6.** 1; -4 **7.** 3, -2; 5 **8.** 1, -5; 3 **9.** $8x$ **10.** $6p$ **11.** $-9s$ **12.** $-23a$ **13.** $9r$ **14.** $2p$ **15.** $4w$ **16.** $-4a$ **17.** $-7q$ **18.** 0 **19.** $t + 5a$ **20.** $-3x - 7$ **21.** $5a - b$ **22.** $-10x + y$ **23.** $-p - 10q$ **24.** $-4j + 7k$ **25.** $3c$ **26.** $8p - 3q$ **27.** $-2j - k$ **28.** $2a - 5b$ **29.** $r - s$ **30.** $4y$ **31.** $2x + 5y + 11$ **32.** $4a - 5b - 5$ **33.** $-15t + 17r + 2$ **34.** $-19 - 9z + 9x$ **35.** $8r - 11q + 5p - 11$ **36.** $-13w + 4c - 8x$ **37.** $15j - 23d + 2c$ **38.** $-2q + 11n + 11p$

39. $2p + 4q + r + 1$ **40.** $2z - y - 13x$ **41.** $13q + 4s - 15r$ **42.** $-21 + 7a - 3c - d$ **43.** $3x^2 + 5x$ **44.** $4a^2 - 9a$ **45.** $3y^3 - 4y^2$ **46.** $3t^2 - 5t - 4$ **47.** $10a$; 20 **48.** $4t$; 12 **49.** $-14k$; 28 **50.** $-16y$; 48 **51.** $3 + 2x$; 4 **52.** $-8p - 5$; 7 **53.** $-x^2$; -16 **54.** $3n^2 - 2n$; 5 **55.** $-4m^2 + 2m$; 0 **56.** $2d^3 + 1.25$; 1
Applications and Problem Solving
57. a) $m + m + n$; $2m + n$ **b)** $z + z + z + z$; $4z$ **c)** $2a + a + 2a + a$; $6a$ **d)** $f + f + f + g + g + g$; $3f + 3g$ **e)** $x + y + y + x + y + y$; $2x + 4y$ **f)** $a + b + b + c + c$; $a + 2b + 2c$ **58. a)** $14c$ **b)** $a + 6c + d$ **c)** $4e + 8f$ **d)** $2p + 6r + 2s$ **59. a)** $-1, -1$ **b)** No. The terms are unlike. **60.** Unlike terms have been collected. **61.** $2p + 2q$

Investigating Math pp. 302–303
1 Representing Variables With Tiles **1. a)** $3x$; 6, -9 **b)** $-2x$; -4, 6 **c)** $2x^2 + 2x$; 12, 12 **d)** $-2x^2 + 3x$; -2, -27 **e)** $-3x + 4$; -2, 13 **f)** $x^2 - 2x - 4$; -4, 11 **g)** $-x^2 + 3x + 3$; 5, -15 **h)** $2x^2 - 4x - 2$; -2, 28
2 Representing Zero With Variables **1.** $-x + 1, -2$, 3; $-x^2 + 2x, -3, -8$; $x^2 - 2, 7, 2$; $-2x^2 + 4, -14, -4$
2. a) 2; two $-x$-tiles **b)** 3; three x^2-tiles **c)** 4; two x-tiles and two -1-tiles **d)** 4; three x^2-tiles and one x-tile **e)** 8; one $-x^2$-tile, three x-tiles, and four -1-tiles **f)** 4; one x^2-tile, two $-x$-tiles, and one 1-tile **g)** 3; one x-tile and two -1-tiles **h)** 7; two $-x^2$-tiles and five 1-tiles

Section 6.2 pp. 305–306
Practice **1.** monomial **2.** binomial **3.** trinomial **4.** binomial **5.** monomial **6.** trinomial **7.** 1 **8.** 4 **9.** 0 **10.** 5 **11.** 7 **12.** 6 **13.** 4 **14.** 1 **15.** 4 **16.** 8 **17.** 2 **18.** 6 **19.** 7 **20.** $x^5 + x^3 + x^2 + 1$ **21.** $-3x^3 + 2x + 5$ **22.** $-x^2 + 2xy + 5y^2$ **23.** $-4x^4 + 3x^3y^3 - 5x^2y + 25xy^2$ **24.** $7b^2x^4 - 3x^3 + 4abx^2 + 5ax$ **25.** $-2 + x + 3x^2 - 2x^3 + 5x^4$ **26.** $5 - x + x^2 - 3x^3 + 4x^4$ **27.** $4xy^2 - 2x^2y^2 + 2x^3y - 3x^4$ **28.** $-3 + 2xy^4z + 5x^2yz^2 + 3x^3y^4z^2$ **29.** $z - xy + x^2$ **30.** $16 - 2xy + x^2 - 3x^3$ **31.** $3xy + 2x^3y - x^5$ **32.** $-1 + xy + 3x^3y^2 + x^4y$
Applications and Problem Solving **33. a)** 3rd degree monomial **b)** 2nd degree binomial **c)** 1st degree monomial **34. a)** 50 cm², 100 cm², 200 cm², 50 cm², 100 cm², 200 cm² **b)** 700 cm² **c)** $2lw + 2lh + 2hw$ **35. a)** 1st degree binomial **b)** 1st degree binomial **c)** 1st degree trinomial **d)** 1st degree monomial **36.** 3822 cm³

Section 6.3 pp. 308–309
Practice **1.** $3x^2 + 6x + 3$ **2.** $-2x^2 - 2x - 3$ **3.** $x - 1$ **4.** $-x^2 - 2x + 1$ **5.** $2x$ and $5x$, $3y$ and $-2y$, $-4xy$ and $6xy$ **6.** $2a$ and $5a$, $-6b$ and $8b$, $-2c$ and $3c$ **7.** $3s^2$ and $7s^2$,

5s and s, −2 and −3 **8.** $7x - 1$ **9.** $4x^2 - 2x - 2$
10. $y^2 + 14y - 9$ **11.** $-2y^3 - 8y^2 + 2$ **12.** $6x + 9$
13. $7y^2 + 9y + 19$ **14.** $8x - 8y + 15$ **15.** $7x^2 - 8x - 5$
16. $9x^2 - x + 2$ **17.** $5y^2 - 6$ **18.** $-z^2 - 2z + 10$
19. $7x^2 + 5y^2 - 16$ **20.** $2x^4 + 2x^3 - 5x^2 + 7x - 4$
21. $9x^2 - x + 5$ **22.** $6y^2 + 3y + 1$ **23.** $m^3 + 9m^2 + 10$
24. $3x^2 - x - 6$ **25.** $3x^2 - 2xy + 5y^2$ **26.** $3y^2 - 2y + 1$
27. $4x^2y - 2xy + 5y^2$
Applications and Problem Solving **28. a)** $12x + 12$
b) 60 cm **29. a)** $10x + 4$ **b)** 74 cm **30. a)** triangle
b) 786 m **31.** $8x$ **32.** $4x^2 - 2x - 3$

Section 6.4 pp. 311–312
1. $-x^2 - 4x - 1$ **2.** $-x^2 + 2x + 3$ **3.** $-2x^2 - x + 5$
4. $3x^2 + 7x - 2$ **5.** $2x - 7$ **6.** $-2x + 6$ **7.** $2x + 7$ **8.** $2x - 9$
9. $3x^2 + 8x - 1$ **10.** $-5x^2 + 2x - 4$ **11.** $-x^2 - 8x + 11$
12. -5 **13.** $3x - 2$ **14.** $3x^3 - x^2 - x$ **15.** $-y - 11$
16. $7s^2 + 3$ **17.** $3y^2 - 12y - 2$ **18.** $-x^2 - 9x + 6$
19. $-7y^2 - 4y + 3$ **20.** $3t^2 - 2t + 7$ **21.** $-3n^2 - 8n - 5$
22. $1 - 3x + 6x^2$ **23.** $-4t^2 - 5$ **24.** $2x^2 + 12x - 8$
25. $4m^2 + 6m - 7$ **26.** $-2y^2 + 3y - 10$
Applications and Problem Solving **27.** $5x + 2$
28. $2x^2 + x + 1$ **29. a)** $4x - 8y - 3$ **b)** $2x^2 + 6x - 10$
c) $3x^2 - y^2$ **d)** $2t^2 + 5t + 8$ **30.** $3x^2 + 5x - 1$
31. a) $2x^2 + 50x + 5000$ **b)** 95 000 m² **32.** 0
33. a) No. $(x + y) + (2x + 2y) = 3x + 3y$;
$(2x + 2y) + (x + y) = 3x + 3y$
b) Yes. $(x + y) - (2x + 2y) = -x - y$;
$(2x + 2y) - (x + y) = x + y$

Section 6.5 pp. 314–315
Practice **1.** $5x + 5$ **2.** $3x - 6$ **3.** $4x + 8$ **4.** $2x - 6$
5. $7x - 7$ **6.** $5x + 15$ **7.** $2n + 12$ **8.** $4m - 20$ **9.** $7t + 21$
10. $3x - 12$ **11.** $10d + 20$ **12.** $9y - 27$ **13.** $0.5x + 1$
14. $4a - 2$ **15.** $6x + 4$ **16.** $9x + 3$ **17.** $10x + 5$
18. $8x + 12$ **19.** $12y - 6$ **20.** $15z - 10$ **21.** $14x + 7$
22. $18y + 12$ **23.** $-3x - 6$ **24.** $-8x - 4$ **25.** $-10y + 4$
26. $-9p + 6$ **27.** $-10x + 5$ **28.** $-10r + 6$ **29.** $-4x - 20$
30. $-2x + 1$ **31.** $-x - \dfrac{3}{2}$ **32.** $-0.6x + 1$ **33.** $-6x + 4y$
34. $-15x - 9y$ **35.** $-20a - 8b$ **36.** $-2x - y$ **37.** $5x - 5y$
38. $-7x + 21y$ **39.** $-6x - 14y$ **40.** $-8m + 4n$
41. $-8x - 12y - 4z$ **42.** $15x - 6y + 6$
43. $-6x + 18y + 24$ **44.** $-2c + 3d - 5$ **45.** $6y - 4$
46. $7x - 4$ **47.** $x + 26$ **48.** 6 **49.** $12g - 12$ **50.** $-10x + 10$
51. $-5x + 12y - 4$
Applications and Problem Solving
52. $5x^2 + 12x + 1$ **53.** $6x^2 + 18x - 18$ **54.** $7y^2 + 7y - 18$
55. $8x - 18y + 35$ **56.** $-3a + 2$ **57.** 11
58. $14x - 17y + 12$ **59.** $x + 6y - 15$ **60.** $-x^2 + 6y^2 + 7$
61. $2x^2 + 8x - 8y - 10$ **62.** $8y^2 + 23y - 12$
63. a) $x + 3, x$; $x^2 + 3x$ **b)** $2 + y, y$; $2y + y^2$

64. a) $3x - x^2$ **b)** $15x - 3x^2$ **65. a)** $P + Prt$ **b)** $330
66. a) $C = 2, D = -5$ **b)** $A = 1.5, B = 4$
c) $E = 1.5, F = 2.5$

Section 6.6 p. 317
Practice **1.** $8x^2$ **2.** $10y^2$ **3.** $8n^2$ **4.** $15xy$ **5.** $6mn$
6. $35st$ **7.** $24ab$ **8.** $6x^2y$ **9.** $20ab^2$ **10.** $12bc$ **11.** $6ab^2$
12. $18st$ **13.** $6xy$ **14.** $12ab$ **15.** $10x^2y^2$ **16.** $15abc$
17. $12xy$ **18.** $30xyz$ **19.** $6a^2b^2$ **20.** $9ab$ **21.** $35ab$
22. $-15x^2y^2$ **23.** $8at^3$ **24.** $-12abc^2$ **25.** $-24a^2y^2$ **26.** $25xyz$
27. $-48x^2y^2$ **28.** $14x^2y^2$ **29.** $10m^3n$ **30.** $-12s^3t^4$
31. $6a^3b^5xy$ **32.** $10s^6t^5$ **33.** $-20c^2x^5y^{10}$ **34.** $-15x^2y^2z^2$
35. $6cx^2y^2z^3$ **36.** $4x^2y^2z$ **37.** $-70x^2yz$ **38.** $-70xyz$
39. $90t^2xyz^2$ **40.** $-8a^2x^6y^2z^3$ **41.** $-6b^2x^2y^3z^3$ **42.** $10a^4b^5$
43. $-24a^3b^3c^3$ **44.** $4x^4y^4z^4$ **45.** $-24j^3k^3l^3$
Applications and Problem Solving **46. a)** $V = 27a^3$
b) $V = 42y^3$ **47. a)** $41x^2$ **b)** $28y^2$ **c)** $68c^2$ **d)** $16x^2$ **e)** $33x^2$
f) $20x^2$ **48. a)** The cost to make 24 hats. **b)** $36 **49.** $6x$

Section 6.7 p. 320
Practice **1.** x^2 **2.** a^3 **3.** p^5 **4.** n^4 **5.** t^6 **6.** $-y^6$ **7.** x^6 **8.** y^6
9. m^4 **10.** n^{12} **11.** x^9 **12.** y^6 **13.** z^{12} **14.** m^{20} **15.** p^{36}
16. s^{20} **17.** $-x^{31}$ **18.** 1 **19.** x^2y^2 **20.** a^3b^3 **21.** x^2y^2 **22.** m^4n^4
23. p^3q^3 **24.** $4x^2t^2$ **25.** $16x^2y^2$ **26.** $-8a^3x^3$ **27.** $-27r^3s^3$
28. x^6y^6 **29.** x^4y^6 **30.** a^6b^3 **31.** a^2b^6 **32.** m^3n^3 **33.** a^2b^4
34. c^6d^8 **35.** x^4y^2 **36.** -1 **37.** $8x^6$ **38.** $9y^6$ **39.** $16x^8$
40. $25y^4$ **41.** m^4 **42.** $-n^6$ **43.** $-8n^6$ **44.** $9y^4$ **45.** $9p^2q^2r^2$
46. $-27y^3z^3$ **47.** $-64x^6y^9$ **48.** $-9x^2$ **49.** $\dfrac{1}{8}a^3b^3c^3$
50. $\dfrac{1}{16}x^4y^8$ **51.** $4x^6y^7$ **52.** $-12x^3y^3$ **53.** $24x^5y^8$
54. $-540a^9b^8$ **55.** $-200a^4b^3c^3$ **56.** m^3n^4
Applications and Problem Solving **57. a)** $4x^2y^2$
b) $16x^4y^6$ **58. a)** $125y^6$ **b)** $27x^6y^3$ **59.** 157 464
60. a) No. The result is the same. **b)** Yes.

Section 6.8 p. 322
Practice **1.** $x^2 + 2x$ **2.** $x^2 - 3x$ **3.** $a^2 + a$ **4.** $t^2 - t$
5. $y^2 + 4y$ **6.** $m^2 + 5m$ **7.** $x^2 - 5x$ **8.** $y^2 - 7y$ **9.** $a^2 - 10a$
10. $3x^2 + 6x$ **11.** $4b^2 - 44b$ **12.** $5t^2 + 15t$ **13.** $6x + 2x^2$
14. $7y^2 - 35y$ **15.** $-2x^2 - 8x$ **16.** $-x^2 - 2x$ **17.** $-y^2 + 3y$
18. $5x$ **19.** $y + 2y^2$ **20.** $2m^2 - 2m$ **21.** $x^2 + 2$ **22.** $3y^2 - 7y$
23. $3a^2$ **24.** $-3x$ **25.** $5x^2 + 16x$ **26.** $x^2 - x$ **27.** $9x^2 + 5x$
28. $-3y^2 + 5y$ **29.** $5a^2$ **30.** $-x^2 + 2x$ **31.** $22x$
32. $x^3 + 2x^2 + 3x$ **33.** $3x^2 + 6x - 15$
34. $5x^3 + 10x^2 - 35x$ **35.** $-x^2 + 3x + 1$
36. $4m^3 - 20m^2 + 24m$ **37.** $6y^3 - 12y^2 + 9y$
38. $-9b^3 + 15b^2 - 3b$ **39.** $-5z^3 + 10z^2 + 25z$
Applications and Problem Solving
40. $2x^2 + 5x - 15$ **41.** $8x^2 + 13x - 35$ **42.** $2x^2 + 5x + 1$
43. $3x^3 - 3x^2 + 17x + 12$ **44.** $7m^2 - 26m + 24$
45. $y^2 - 7y + 9$ **46.** $x^2 - 8x$ **47. a)** $5y(7y - 4)$; $35y^2 - 20y$

b) $2x(4y + 7) + 3y(2x + 3)$; $14xy + 14x + 9y$
c) $(3x)(2x) + (4x)(8x)$; $38x^2$
d) $3x(3x + 2) - (2x)(x)$; $7x^2 + 6x$

Section 6.9 p. 324
Practice **1.** $2x$ **2.** $-3a$ **3.** $3y$ **4.** $4m$ **5.** $-5x$ **6.** $-5y$
7. 3 **8.** -6 **9.** 1 **10.** 32 **11.** -1 **12.** $4m$ **13.** $3z$ **14.** $-3b$
15. 3 **16.** $-9bc$ **17.** $4x$ **18.** $-5s$ **19.** 5 **20.** 2 **21.** 7 **22.** 9
23. $12t$ **24.** $3j$ **25.** $4qr$ **26.** $17df$ **27.** $5xy$ **28.** $-3a^2b^3$
29. $-2m^3n^7$ **30.** $-5x^3y^{14}$ **31.** $-a^2bc$ **32.** $4xy$ **33.** $2a^2b$
34. $3xy$ **35.** $-3m^3$ **36.** $2xyz^2$ **37.** $\dfrac{4}{3}$ **38.** $-\dfrac{3}{2}x^2y^2$ **39.** $2x^2y^4$
40. $-4a^2b^2$ **41.** $-4m$ **42.** $3x^9y$ **43.** $-\dfrac{4}{3}xy$ **44.** $\dfrac{9p^3q^{12}}{r^2}$

Applications and Problem Solving **45. a)** x **b)** p
c) $2x^2$ **d)** $3b^4$ **46. a)** 10 cm by 16 cm **b)** 20 cm by 8 cm
47. $\dfrac{x}{6}$ **48.** $B = 1$

Career Connection p. 325
1 Cardiorespiratory Assessment **1.** $\dfrac{50d}{s}$

2. a) 57.25; low average **b)** 82.19; good **c)** 76.92;
average
2 Burning Energy **1. a)** 579.4 kJ **b)** 895.0 kJ
c) 1849.8 kJ **2.** walking for 1 h by 3.15 kJ/kg

Section 6.10 p. 327
Practice **1.** $2 \times 2 \times 3$ **2.** $2 \times 2 \times 2 \times 2$ **3.** $2 \times 2 \times 7$
4. $3 \times 3 \times 7$ **5.** $2 \times 2 \times 2 \times 2 \times 3 \times 3$ **6.** $3 \times 3 \times 5 \times 5$
7. $2 \times 2 \times x \times y \times y$ **8.** $2 \times 3 \times 3 \times a \times a \times b \times b \times b$
9. $2 \times 2 \times 3 \times 3 \times x \times x \times y \times z \times z$ **10.** $2 \times 5 \times x \times x \times y$
11. $2 \times 3 \times 3 \times 3 \times x \times x \times x \times x \times x \times x$
12. $5 \times 5 \times 5 \times a \times a \times a \times a \times b \times b$ **13.** 5 **14.** 8 **15.** 9
16. 14 **17.** 24 **18.** 1 **19.** $2a$ **20.** x **21.** $2m^2$ **22.** $3abc$
23. 2 **24.** 7 **25.** $5x$ **26.** xy **27.** mn **28.** $2a^2$ **29.** $5bc$
30. $3xy$ **31.** 5 **32.** $2x$ **33.** $6a$ **34.** $5xy$ **35.** $4xy$ **36.** $4ab$
37. $7ab$ **38.** x^2y^2 **39.** $2x^2y$ **40.** $3xy^2$ **41.** $4ab^3$ **42.** $5s^3t^4$
Applications and Problem Solving **43.** 15 **44. a)** A:
Shirley, B: Gustav, C: Bob, D: Collette, E: Karin

Section 6.11 p. 329
Practice **1.** 6 **2.** x **3.** a **4.** $5x$ **5.** $4ab$
6. $3y^2 + 18y = 3y(y + 6)$ **7.** $14a - 12b = 2(7a - 6b)$
8. $4a^3 - 8a^2 = 4a^2(a - 2)$
9. $10x^3 - 5x^2 + 15x = 5x(2x^2 - x + 3)$
10. $33ab - 22b = 11b(3a - 2)$
11. $4a^3 - 10a^2 + 6a = 2a(2a^2 - 5a + 3)$
12. $27a^2b^2 - 18ab + 9b = 9b(3a^2b - 2a + 1)$
13. $6x^2y - 4xy^2 = 2xy(3x - 2y)$
14. $9a^3b - 12ab^4 = 3ab(3a^2 - 4b^3)$ **15.** $5(2x + 3)$
16. $14(2y - 1)$ **17.** $n(2m - 1)$ **18.** $5x(x + 2)$

19. $4x^2(2 + x)$ **20.** $3a^2b(3ab - 2)$ **21.** $2xy^2(2x - 3z^2)$
22. $7b^2(2a^2b^2 - 3c^2)$ **23.** $6xy^2z(xy + 2)$
24. $3b^4(5a^2b - 3c^5)$
Applications and Problem Solving
25. $3(3a - 2b + 1)$ **26.** $4(a - 2b + 4)$ **27.** $6x(2x^2 - x + 4)$
28. $5x(2x^2 - x + 3)$ **29.** $6x^2y(4x^2 - 3x + 2y)$
30. $8a(ab + 2b - 3)$ **31.** $5mn(5m^2 - 3mn + n^2)$
32. a) $2x + 2y = 2(x + y)$ **b)** $2(x + y)$
33. a) $5t(1 - t)$ **b)** 1.2 m

Technology p. 330
1 Adding and Subtracting Polynomials
1. $3x^2 - x + 6$ **2.** $3y^3 + 2y - 1$ **3.** $2a^2 - 8a - 2$
4. $2x^3 + 2x^2 + 2x + 3$
2 Multiplying and Dividing Monomials **1.** $12x^3y^4$
2. $-10a^4b^5$ **3.** $9x^4y^2z^2$ **4.** $-15.625m^6n^3$ **5.** $4p^3q$ **6.** $-4a^3b^3$
3 Expanding Expressions **1.** $6x^2 + 3x - 12$
2. $-2y^3 + 10y^2 - 6y$ **3.** $10a^2 - a - 8$ **4.** $-6x^2 - 4x - 14$
5. $z^2 + 4z - 6$ **6.** $-2x^2 + 21x$
4 Factoring Expressions **1.** $2 \times 2 \times 2 \times 5 \times 7$
2. $2 \times 2 \times 3 \times 3 \times 13$ **3.** $3(2x + 5y)$ **4.** $8t(4t - 5)$
5. $7mn^2(2mn + 7)$ **6.** $4ab^2(15a - 2)$
5 Evaluating Polynomials **1.** 117 **2.** 32 **3.** 230
4. -191 **5.** 34.25 **6.** -5.875

Section 6.12 pp. 331–333
1 Modelling Readability $G = 4.33$, $F = 84.90$

Review pp. 334–335
1. $3x + 7y + 11$ **2.** $3a - 4b - 5$ **3.** $2q - 7r + 1$ **4.** $x^2 - 4x$
5. $4y^2 + 2y - 4$ **6. a)** $t^2 + 6t - 1$ **b)** -9
7. $x + y + y + x + y + y$; $2x + 4y$ **8.** 3rd degree
monomial **9.** 5th degree monomial **10.** 3rd degree
binomial **11.** 2nd degree binomial **12.** 4th degree
trinomial **13.** 5th degree binomial **14.** 6th degree
trinomial **15.** 3rd degree trinomial **16.** 4th degree
binomial **17.** 5th degree trinomial **18.** $-5x^3 + x^2 + 3x$
19. $y^4 + 2y^2 - 3y + 5$ **20.** $-m^4 + 6m^3 - 3m^2 + 2m + 6$
21. $x^4 + x^3 + x^2 + x + 3$ **22.** $-2y^7 + 5y^6 + y^5 - 4y^2 + 3y$
23. $3m^2 - 2m + 2$ **24.** $4a^2 + 8a + 2$ **25.** $-b^2 - b + 6$
26. $2x^3 - 4x^2 + 8x$ **27.** $2x^2 - 8x + 2$ **28.** $a^2 + 2a - 4$
29. $9t^2 - 2t - 14$ **30.** $3a^2 - 6a - 1$ **31.** $-2m^2 + 3m + 2$
32. $2x^2 + x - 6$ **33.** $6x^2 - x - 2$ **34.** $-3x^2 + 2x + 2$
35. $5x^2 - 5x + 7$ **36.** $5x^2 - 3x - 8$ **37.** $9x + 14$
38. $7a + 14$ **39.** 10 **40.** $7y + 37$ **41.** $-x^2 - 17x - 11$
42. $-11y^2 + 2y - 23$ **43.** $40xy$ **44.** $-150xy^2$ **45.** $12abx^2$
46. $10a^2bp$ **47.** $-15x^2y^2$ **48.** $4a^3b$ **49.** $-8x^3y^2z$ **50.** $-3s^3t^5$
51. $5x^2$ **52.** x^6 **53.** y^{12} **54.** x^3y^3 **55.** $9y^6$ **56.** $x^4y^6z^2$
57. $-r^9s^{12}t^6$ **58.** $-8x^6y^9$ **59.** $25x^4y^4$ **60.** $2x^8y^7z^8$
61. $-27a^{12}b^4x^4$ **62.** $8k^{11}l^9m^9$ **63.** $-40a^9b^8$ **64.** $a^6b^7c^6$
65. $6y^2 - 19y - 10$ **66.** $-m^2 + m + 2$ **67.** $-2z^2 - 4z + 5$
68. $x^2 - 20x$ **69.** $-2y^3 + 6y^2 - 14y$ **70.** $-3t + 6t^2 + 3t^3$

71. $4m^3 + 8m^2 - 12m$ **72.** $-6x^3 + 12x^2 - 6x$ **73.** $4xy^2$
74. $9xy$ **75.** $5a^2b^2$ **76.** $-\dfrac{2ab^7}{c^2}$ **77.** $3mn$ **78. a)** 5 **b)** 7
c) 17 **d)** 24 **e)** $5a$ **f)** $4x$ **g)** $2ab$ **h)** $5xy$ **79. a)** $3xy$ **b)** 8
c) $9xy$ **80.** $5(x-3)$ **81.** $6x(x-3)$ **82.** $5a(b+2c)$
83. $7a^2(1+5a)$ **84.** $4bc(2a-3)$ **85.** $3(x^2+3y^2)$
86. $a(3a-6b+1)$ **87.** $2(x+3y-5z)$

Exploring Math p. 335
2. a) no **b)** 3, due to symmetry **3. a)** corner, middle side, middle **b)** between corner and middle side, between middle and corner, between middle and middle side **c)** 6 **4.** yes

Chapter Check p. 336
1. $y + 2$ **2.** $-5 + 6a - b - 10c$ **3.** $5y^2 - 8y - 11$
4. 2nd degree trinomial **5.** 3rd degree binomial
6. 3rd degree monomial **7.** $x^5 + x^4 + x^3 + 1$
8. $-yx^4 + 5x^3 + 2xy$ **9.** $-3x^4 + x^3y - 2x^2y + 10xy^2$
10. $-5b^2x^3 + 5abx^2 + 3ax - 1$ **11.** $6a^2 - 4$
12. $b^3 - b^2 + y + 7$ **13.** $5y^2 - 12x + 6$ **14.** $-t^2 - t - 5$
15. $-x^2 - 7x + 6$ **16.** $5y^2 + 14y + 1$ **17.** $8x^2 - 9x - 12$
18. $-2x^2 + 10x + 1$ **19.** $-50xy$ **20.** $45x^3y^3$ **21.** $-6b^2x^5yz$
22. $-15x^4y^2z^3$ **23.** $-27x^{12}y^9$ **24.** $-a^5b^{10}c^{10}$ **25.** x^5y^5z
26. $9x^8y^8$ **27.** $16y + 7$ **28.** $5x - 29$ **29.** $2x^2 - x + 9$
30. $-x^2 + 9x$ **31.** $-3x^3 + 6x^2 - 3x$ **32.** $4m^3 - 12m^2 - 20m$
33. $-2a^3b^2$ **34.** $3p^2qr^2$ **35. a)** 4 **b)** 6 **c)** $5ab$ **d)** xy
36. a) $5xy$ **b)** $4ab^2c$ **37.** $5(4x-1)$ **38.** $4t(t-3)$
39. $9a^2b(2b^2 + 3a - 1)$ **40.** $(3ab^2)^3 = 27a^3b^6$
41. $2x(2x+1) - x(x+1) = 3x^2 + x$

Using the Strategies p. 337
1. 7 **3.** $06{:}35$ **4.** 13 **5.** Saturday **6.** 3 nickels, 2 dimes, 5 quarters **8.** $1, 4, 9, 16, 25, 36, 49$ **9.** 32
11. Alberta and Saskatchewan; Alberta by 9290 km² **12.** 554 m

Chapter 7

Equations p. 339
1. 5 min, assuming a population of 30 million
2. 16 h 40 min, assuming a population of 6 billion
3. Answers may vary.

Getting Started pp. 340–341
Warm Up **1.** $7x$ **2.** $3x$ **3.** $9m$ **4.** $6t$ **5.** $-5a$ **6.** $-6n$
7. $2s$ **8.** y **9.** $x + 7y$ **10.** $-a + 3b$ **11.** $7x - 13$
12. $-s - 15t$ **13.** $-3x - 4y + 7$ **14.** $2a - 9b$
15. $-15x - 6y + 10$ **16.** $2x + 14$ **17.** $10x - 25$
18. $18x - 3$ **19.** $35x - 28$ **20.** $8a - 12b$ **21.** $12p - 6q$
22. $-6y + 14$ **23.** $-4x + 9$ **24.** $-10x + 15y + 20$

25. $-4x - 5y + 1$ **26.** 1 **27.** 7 **28.** -5 **29.** 5 **30.** 11
31. -12 **32.** -24 **33.** 29 **34.** 17 **35.** 15 **36.** -1 **37.** 29
38. 4 **39.** -11 **40.** -14 **41.** -2 **42.** -2 **43.** 21 **44.** 37
45. 0
Mental Math
Expressions and Equations **1.** -8 **2.** -1 **3.** 10 **4.** 14
5. -5 **6.** 6 **7.** 7 **8.** 14 **9.** 4 **10.** -5 **11.** 3 **12.** -1 **13.** 6
14. 11 **15.** 7 **16.** 7
Multiplying by Multiples of 9 **1.** 171 **2.** 252 **3.** 495
4. 792 **5.** 990 **6.** 1125 **7.** 40.5 **8.** 23.4 **9.** 51.3
10. 1170 **11.** 2430 **12.** 3690 **13.** $13\,500$ **14.** $33\,300$
15. $31\,500$ **16.** 441 **17.** 576 **18.** 945 **19.** 14.4
20. 34.2 **21.** 37.8 **22.** $9x = 10x - x$ **23.** To multiply a number by 11, first multiply the number by 10, then add the number itself. **24.** 396 **25.** 528 **26.** 58.3
27. 93.5 **28.** 2310 **29.** 7260

Section 7.1 pp. 344–345
Practice **1.** $x - 2 = 1; x = 3$ **2.** $x - 4 = 2; x = 6$
3. $x + 2 = 4; x = 2$ **4.** $x + 4 = 4; x = 0$ **5.** 3 **6.** 1 **7.** 7
8. 4 **9.** 10 **10.** 5 **11.** 6 **12.** 1 **13.** 2 **14.** 5 **15.** 3 **16.** 7
17. 1 **18.** 5 **19.** 4 **20.** -16 **21.** -8 **22.** 18 **23.** -6 **24.** 12
25. -12 **26.** -10
Applications and Problem Solving **27.** 2 **28.** 8
29. 6 **30.** 2.1 **31.** -3 **32.** 1 **33.** 0.8 **34.** 2.7 **35.** 5.8
36. 15.7 **37.** -7.7 **38.** -33.8 **39.** 25.12 **40.** -10.84
41. 5.688 **42.** 0.19 **43.** $x + 3 = 8; 5$ **44.** $x + 72 = 195;$
123 **45.** $x + 3.2 + 4.5 = 9.7; 2$ cm **46.** $\dfrac{1}{4}$ **47.** $\dfrac{6}{7}$ **48.** $-\dfrac{5}{8}$
49. $\dfrac{3}{4}$ **50.** $\dfrac{1}{12}$ **51.** $-\dfrac{1}{10}$ **52.** $5\dfrac{5}{6}$ **53.** $-1\dfrac{3}{8}$ **54.** 10
55. 7.1 km **56.** The equation stays the same.
57. a) $3, -3$ **b)** $8, -8$ **58.** Answers may vary.

Section 7.2 pp. 348–349
Practice **1.** $2x = 4; x = 2$ **2.** $3x = -6; x = -2$ **3.** 6 **4.** 2
5. 7 **6.** 11 **7.** 6 **8.** 9 **9.** 3 **10.** 2 **11.** 7 **12.** 5 **13.** 4 **14.** 6
15. 5 **16.** -6 **17.** -2 **18.** -3 **19.** 4 **20.** 4 **21.** 12 **22.** -5
23. 3 **24.** 4 **25.** -8 **26.** 21 **27.** -12 **28.** 32 **29.** -15
30. 50 **31.** -24 **32.** 44 **33.** 4.2 **34.** -2.1 **35.** 12 **36.** -3
37. 0.7 **38.** 3 **39.** 6 **40.** -42 **41.** -3
Applications and Problem Solving **42.** -1.44
43. -6.816 **44.** -98 **45.** -6328 **46.** $3x = 6; \$2$
47. $\dfrac{1}{3}x = 4.2; 12.6$ cm **48.** 360 cm **49.** 70 kg **50.** $0 = 0$
51. a) $x = 0$ **b)** Any real number y is a solution.
52. a) $6, -6$ **b)** $2, -2$ **53.** Answers may vary.

Section 7.3 p. 353
Practice **1.** Left side: Start, $5x + 2$, subtract 2, divide by 5, x, Stop; Right side: Start, 22, subtract 2, divide by 5, 4, Stop. **2.** Left side: Start, $2x + 5$, subtract 5,

divide by 2, *x*, Stop; Right side: Start, 25, subtract 5, divide by 2, 10, Stop. **3.** 4 **4.** 7 **5.** -2 **6.** 4 **7.** -3 **8.** -7 **9.** 5 **10.** -2 **11.** -2 **12.** -3 **13.** -4 **14.** 4 **15.** 3 **16.** -20 **17.** -10 **18.** 16 **19.** 18 **20.** 6 **21.** 6 **22.** -20 **23.** -33 **24.** -4 **25.** -2 **26.** 1 **27.** 2 **28.** -6 **29.** 1 **30.** 2 **31.** -4 **32.** -1 **33.** -4 **34.** -7 **35.** 4 **36.** -2 **37.** 1 **38.** -4 **39.** 7 **40.** -3 **41.** 3.2 **42.** 2.2 **43.** 5 **44.** 5 **45.** -2 **46.** -3.2 **47.** -5 **48.** 7.8 **49.** -1.1 **50.** 2.0 **51.** -1.7 **52.** 1.7 **Applications and Problem Solving** **53.** 36°, 54°, 90° **54.** 17, 8, 15 **55.** 6 years **56. a)** 3 **b)** Yes. **c)** Answers may vary. **57.** Answers may vary.

Section 7.4 p. 355
1. $3x = 2x + 4$; $x = 4$ **2.** $4x + 1 = 2x - 5$; $x = -3$ **3.** 7 **4.** 4 **5.** 2 **6.** -2 **7.** -2 **8.** 5 **9.** -1 **10.** 3 **11.** 10 **12.** 5 **13.** 3 **14.** -6 **15.** 0.05 **16.** 0.6 **17.** 1 **18.** 3 **19.** -4 **20.** 2 **21.** 4 **22.** 3 **23.** 2 **24.** -5 **25.** 1 **26.** 3 **27.** -2 **28.** 7 **29.** -1 **30.** -3 **31.** 4 **32.** 7 **33.** -4 **34.** 5 **35.** -3 **36.** -10 **37.** -2 **38.** 1 **39.** 4 **40.** 2 **41.** 6 **42.** -2 **Applications and Problem Solving** **43.** 20 **44.** 6 **45.** 14 km/h **46.** 6 **47. a)** $x = b + c + y - a$ **b)** $x = c - y - a + b$ **c)** $x = \dfrac{c - y - b}{a}$ **d)** $x = \dfrac{c - y}{a} + b$ **e)** $x = \dfrac{b + y + a}{c}$ **f)** $x = a(y - b - c)$ **48.** Answers may vary.

Section 7.5 p. 358
Practice **1.** 1 **2.** 4 **3.** 1 **4.** -6 **5.** -5 **6.** -7 **7.** 1 **8.** 3 **9.** 1 **10.** -2 **11.** -9 **12.** -3 **13.** 1 **14.** -1 **15.** 2 **16.** -2 **17.** 2 **18.** 3 **19.** 2 **20.** -30 **21.** 5 **22.** -1 **23.** 4 **24.** 5 **25.** 2 **26.** 2 **27.** 1 **28.** 5 **29.** -15 **30.** -3 **31.** 8 **Applications and Problem Solving** **32. a)** 3 **b)** 4 **33. a)** 3 **b)** 7 by 11 **34.** 24% **35.** Answers may vary.

Section 7.6 p. 361
Practice **1.** 0.6 **2.** 1.7 **3.** 0.3 **4.** -7.5 **5.** -3 **6.** -6.9 **7.** 1 **8.** -10 **9.** -3 **10.** 4 **11.** 2.4 **12.** -4 **13.** 0.4 **14.** -0.53 **15.** 1.09 **16.** -6 **17.** -11.8 **18.** 1 **19.** 2 **20.** 4 **21.** 4 **22.** -2 **23.** -3 **24.** -2 **25.** -6 **26.** 20 **27.** -1 **28.** 1 **29.** 15 **30.** -4 **31.** -2 **32.** 1 **33.** 14 **34.** 4 **35.** -9 **36.** -2 **37.** 5 **38.** -9 **39.** 2 **40.** 2 **Applications and Problem Solving** **41.** 34 kg **42.** 0.04 or 4% **43. a)** 9 **b)** 1.6 **c)** -8.2 **d)** 8

Section 7.7 p. 363
Practice **1.** $3x = 18$ **2.** $y - 6 = 4$ **3.** $x + 4 = 18$ **4.** $x - 4 = 10$ **5.** $\dfrac{m}{4} = 18$ **6.** $4x = 20$ **7.** $\dfrac{x}{2} = 5$ **8.** $x + 6 = 15$ **9.** $x + 5 = 12$ **10.** $x - 6 = 10$ **11.** $x - 4 = 7$ **12.** $x^2 = 25$ **13.** $10 - x = 2$ **14.** $x + 3 = 18$ **15.** $x - 5 = 9$

16. $x + 4 = 21$ **17.** $3x = 9$ **18.** $\dfrac{x}{5} = 10$ **19.** $x - 6 = -8$ **Applications and Problem Solving** **20.** $2b + 16 = 88$ **21.** $2p + 12 = 84$ **22.** $2a + 7 = 29$ **23.** $3a = 250\,000\,000$ **24.** $5.2c = 155\,000\,000$ **25. a)** $4x + 12 = 36$ **b)** $6x + 6 = 36$ **26. a)** $4x + 3 = 39$ **b)** $3x - 3 = 39$ **27. a)** Let *x* represent the number. Then $2x - 1 = 0$. **b)** Let *x* represent the number of dollars that Malia has. Then Leroy has $x - 1$ dollars. They have a total of \$9, so $x + x - 1 = 9$. The equation $2x - 1 = 9$ models the situation.

28. $\dfrac{2b + 2}{2} = 58$

Section 7.8 pp. 366–367
Practice **1.** $x, 35 - x$ **2.** $x, 50 - x$ **3.** $x, 125 - x$ **4.** $x, 36 - x$ **5.** $x, 32 - x$ **6.** $x, 738 - x$ **7.** $x, 468 - x$ **8.** $x, 246 - x$ **9.** 10 m, 12 m, 13 m **10.** 4 m, 5 m, 5 m **11.** 3 m by 6 m **12.** 5 m by 7 m **13.** 2 m by 6 m **14.** 5 m by 7 m **15.** 5.1 m **16.** 8.4 m **Applications and Problem Solving** **17.** 17, 29 **18.** St. Lawrence: 3058 km; Mackenzie: 4241 km **19.** 20 m by 25 m **20.** 34, 35, 36 **21.** 155 days **22.** 3 years **23. a)** 3 **b)** 38 **24.** 20 days **25.** 17 m, 17 m, 10 m **26.** \$0.75 **27.** 14 **28.** 7 nickels, 5 dimes **29.** 30 m **30.** 83 dimes, 57 nickels **31. a)** 16, 23 **b)** 16, 23 **c)** Answers may vary. **32.** 8, 3 **33. a)** 50 **b)** 50 **c)** Answers may vary. **34.** 21 large and 17 small **35.** 350 **36.** 109 m **37. a)** 20 cm **b)** 37 cm by 32 cm **38.** 3 m **39. a)** 2 cm **b)** 296 cm² **40.** Answers may vary.

Section 7.9 pp. 369–370
Practice **1. a)** 40 cm² **b)** 4 m **c)** 17 m **2. a)** 62.8 cm **b)** 100 cm **3. a)** 24 cm² **b)** 20 cm **c)** 6 m **4. a)** 30 m **b)** 14 m **c)** 36.7 m **5.** $w = \dfrac{A}{l}$ **6.** $b = \dfrac{2A}{h}$ **7.** $P = \dfrac{I}{rt}$

8. $r = \dfrac{C}{2\pi}$ **9.** $m = \dfrac{E}{c^2}$ **10.** $b = \dfrac{2A}{h} - a$ **Applications and Problem Solving** **11. a)** 480 000 km; 700 000 km **b)** 3.25 h **12. a)** 4.68 m **b)** Answers may vary. **c)** 2.4 m **13. a)** 160, 152, 144, 136, 128 **b)** 45, 55, 35 **14. a)** 10 250, 12 375, 15 250, 16 500, 20 875 **b)** 10°C **15.** Pablo

Section 7.10 p. 372
Practice **1.** 15, 18, 21; *b* is 3 times *a* **2.** 10, 12, 14; *n* is 3 more than *m* **3.** 21, 20, 19; *u* is 4 times *t* **4.** 160; $C = 40n$ **5.** 150; $w = 10.5h$ **6.** 120; $p = \dfrac{s}{5}$

Applications and Problem Solving **7.** $C = 3d + 100$
8. $C = 3 + 1.5d$ **9. a)** Regions = Roads − Towns + 1
b) Towns = Roads − Regions + 1
c) Roads = Regions + Towns − 1

Career Connection p. 373
1 Precipitation in Canada **1.** Answers may vary.
2. a) 1.98 trillion tonnes **b)** 0.002 mg
2 Greatest Precipitation **1.** 20.4 mm/h **2.** 38 h **3.** 6
days, assuming a height of about 3 m

Investigating Math pp. 374–375
1 No Points in the Interior **2.** Points: 3, 4, 6, 8, 6, 5,
7, 8, 4, 5, 9; Area: 0.5, 1, 2, 3, 2, 1.5, 2.5, 3, 1, 1.5, 3.5
3. equal **4.** 5 points, 1.5 square units; 6 points,
2 square units; 7 points, 2.5 square units; 8 points,
3 square units; 9 points, 3.5 square units
5. 4 square units **6.** $A = 0.5P − 1$ **8.** 48.5 square units
2 Points in the Interior **1.** 4 square units, 5 square
units, 6 square units, 7 square units, 8 square units,
9 square units, 10 square units **2.** Interior Points: 0,
1, 2, 3, 4, 5, 6; Area: 4, 5, 6, 7, 8, 9, 10 **3.** The area
increases by 1. **4.** 11 square units; 12 square units
5. $A = 0.5P + I − 1$ **7. a)** 17.5 square units
b) 29 square units **c)** 23 square units

Section 7.11 p. 377
Practice **1.** 180 km **2.** 170 km **3.** 45 km **4.** 45 km
5. 0.5 h **6.** 8 h **7.** 0.2 h **8.** 4.5 h **9.** 100 km/h
10. 80 km/h **11.** 90 km/h **12.** 80 km/h **13.** 4.5 h
14. 195 km **15.** 75 km/h **16.** $80x$ km **17.** $90x + 90$ km
18. $85x − 85$ km **19.** $\dfrac{200}{x}$ h **20.** $\dfrac{400}{x}$ km/h **21.** rt km

22. $\dfrac{D}{r}$ h **23.** $\dfrac{D}{t}$ km/h

Applications and Problem Solving **24.** 4 h
25. 3.75 h **26. a)** 7 h **b)** 7 h **c)** Answers may vary.
27. a) 1.5 h **b)** 10:15 **28.** 1 h **29.** Answers may vary.

Technology pp. 378–379
1 Solving Equations **1.** −11 **2.** −3 **3.** −3.4 **4.** 5.5
5. 26 **6.** −116
2 Solving Equations With Fractions **1. b)** 1.2
2. b) 9 **3.** 40 **4.** 48 **5.** −15 **6.** $−\dfrac{24}{7}$ **7.** 80 **8.** $\dfrac{23}{11}$ **9.** 5.4
10. −3 **11.** 2
3 Using the Solve Function **1.** 3 **2.** 1.75 **3.** −6 **4.** 6
5. 3.5 **6.** −8.5 **7.** −1.5 **8.** −2 **9.** 2.2 **10.** −12 **11.** 3
12. −1.4 **13.** −4 **14.** 0.4 **15.** −12 **16.** −17 **17.** −1 **18.** −2
4 Solving Formulas

1. $t = \dfrac{I}{Pr}$ **2.** $x = \dfrac{y − 1}{4}$ **3.** $c = b − \dfrac{a}{2}$ **4.** $y = \dfrac{w}{x + z}$
5 Problem Solving **1.** 245 000 km **2.** 4848 km²

Computer Data Bank pp. 380–381
1 Fat and Fibre **2.** 12 g **3. a)** 68 **c)** except for chili
con carne with beans and some nuts, the fibre content
is 0 g **4.** With a few exceptions like chili con carne
with beans and some nuts, the fat content is 0 g, 1 g,
or 2 g **5. a)** 7 g of fat, 0 g of fibre **6. a)** 114 g of fat,
0 g of fibre **b)** 0 g of fat, 1.6 g of fibre **c)** 5 g of fat, 0 g
of fibre **d)** 7 g of fat, 0 g of fibre
2 Energy From Fat **2.** Rounding errors caused by
the factor 38, the energy, and the mass of fat being
given to the ones place; if the factor 38 and the mass
of fat were rounded up, and the energy was rounded
down, a greater result occurs than would occur if they
were given to one or more decimal places; when the
Energy, kJ field value is 0.

Section 7.12 pp. 382–383
1 Modelling Fingerprints **4.** 608
2 Extending the Model **3.** 25

Review pp. 384–385
1. 5 **2.** 6 **3.** 4 **4.** −3 **5.** −7 **6.** −2 **7.** 0.6 **8.** −0.4 **9.** 10
10. −10 **11.** −9 **12.** 24 **13.** 10 **14.** 9 **15.** −1 **16.** −18
17. 24 **18.** 6 **19.** −16 **20.** −6 **21.** −4 **22.** 2 **23.** 3 **24.** −3
25. −7 **26.** 2 **27.** −2 **28.** 2 **29.** 3 **30.** −2 **31.** 2 **32.** 4
33. 13 **34.** −3 **35.** −2 **36.** −8 **37.** −25 **38.** 3 **39.** 7
40. −5 **41.** −3 **42.** −2 **43.** 2.8 **44.** −3.2 **45.** 2 **46.** −0.8
47. 3 **48.** 2 **49.** −3 **50.** 1 **51.** −1 **52.** −8 **53.** −4 **54.** $\dfrac{8}{3}$
55. −3 **56.** −1 **57.** −10 **58.** −5 **59.** 16 **60.** $x + 8 = 20$
61. $6x = 72$ **62.** $2c + 8 = 24$ **63.** $2p − 10 = 90$
64. $4t = 2400$ **65. a)** $3x + 4 = 64$ **b)** $2(2x + 2) = 64$
66. 8 m by 5 m **67.** 60, 61, 62 **68.** 29 **69.** 6.7 cm
70. a) 125 L; 50 L **b)** 13 min **71.** $l = \dfrac{P}{2} − w$
72. a) $E = 20 + 25t$ **b)** $95; $82.50 **73. a)** 45 min
b) 09:30 **74.** 5 h **75.** 4 h

Exploring Math p. 385
The lockers with square numbers on them: 1, 4, 9,
16, 25, 36, 49, 64, 81, 100, 121, 144, 169, 196, 225,
256, 289, 324, 361, 400, 441, 484, 529, 576, 625, 676,
729, 784, 841, 900, 961

Chapter Check p. 386
1. 8 **2.** −3 **3.** 6 **4.** −9 **5.** 8 **6.** 20 **7.** −9 **8.** 11 **9.** 35
10. 12 **11.** −3 **12.** −2 **13.** 5 **14.** −2 **15.** −5 **16.** −1
17. −0.4 **18.** −2.9 **19.** −9 **20.** −3 **21.** 1 **22.** 3 **23.** −4

24. 2 **25.** $2a + 4 = 36$ **26.** 81 **27.** length $= 26$ m, width $= 11$ m **28.** 33 m, 34 m, 35 m **29.** 75 **30.** 44 m
31. $h = \dfrac{2A}{b}$ **32.** 3 h **33. a)** $C = 50 + 40t$ **b)** $210
34. 2.5 h

Using the Strategies p. 387
1. 79, 80, 81, 82, 83 **2. a)** 14 **b)** $t = 2p + 2$ **3.** 37
4. 15:00 **5.** 4 quarters; 3 quarters, 5 nickels; 2 quarters, 10 nickels; 1 quarter, 15 nickels; 20 nickels
6. 27 **10. a)** $4 \times 5 - 12 = 8$ **b)** $3 + 14 - 7 = 10$
c) $6 + 7 + 8 \div 4 = 15$ **d)** $5 + 6 + 11 - 3 = 19$

Chapter 8

Analytic Geometry p. 389
1. about 24.2 cm/km **2.** about 7.6 cm/km **3.** about 11.8 cm/km **4.** about 2.5 cm/km **5.** Mississippi

Getting Started pp. 390–391
2 Describing Slope 1. a) steepness decreases
b) The ladder has a slope of 0. **c)** steepness increases
d) The ladder becomes too steep for numerical description.
Warm Up 1. -4 **2.** 2.5 **3.** -13.5 **4.** -2 **5.** -11.7 **6.** 0
7. -28 **8.** -33 **9.** 18.2 **10.** -3 **11.** -4 **12.** 4.1 **13.** 7
14. 2 **15.** -6 **16.** -10 **17.** 4.9 **18.** 2.5 **19.** $-9, -7, -5,$
$-3, -1$ **20.** $-\dfrac{1}{2}, 0, \dfrac{1}{2}, 1, \dfrac{3}{2}$ **21.** 3, 2, 1, 0, -1 **22.** $-5, -4,$
$-3, -2, -1$ **23.** $3x + 6$ **24.** $6x - 2$ **25.** $-20x + 8$
26. $4x + 5$ **27.** $-3x - 2$ **28.** -1 **29.** 8 **30.** 5 km/h
31. 8 pages/min **32.** $14/h **33.** $0.25/bagel
34. $0.62/min **35. a)** 0.154 **b)** 15.4% **36. a)** 22.5°/h
b) 540°/Earth day
Mental Math
Operations With Integers 1. 6 **2.** -3 **3.** -8 **4.** 15
5. -27 **6.** 16 **7.** 2 **8.** -2 **9.** -5 **10.** 2 **11.** -3 **12.** 1 **13.** 4
14. -3 **15.** 1
Adding Using Compatible Numbers 1. 81 **2.** 112
3. 112 **4.** 206 **5.** 281 **6.** 383 **7.** 4.1 **8.** 5.3 **9.** 12.3
10. 12.3 **11.** 19.1 **12.** 310 **13.** 420 **14.** 420 **15.** 1110
16. a) $10x + y + 10n + m$; $10x + y + 10n + m$ **b)** The first statement represents the original expression. The second statement represents writing the expression using compatible numbers. **c)** 10

Investigating Math pp. 392–393
1 Lengths on a Number Line 1. a) 6 **b)** 4 **c)** 5 **d)** 9
e) 7 **f)** 11 **2.** Subtract the smaller number from the larger number. **3. a)** 7 **b)** 12 **c)** 9 **d)** 14
2 Lengths of Horizontal Line Segments 1. AB: 6,
CD: 9, EF: 7, GH: 4 **2.** Subtract the smaller x-coordinate from the larger x-coordinate.
3. a) 6 **b)** 5 **c)** 3 **d)** 10
3 Lengths of Vertical Line Segments 1. AB: 5, CD: 8, EF: 7, GH: 6 **2.** Subtract the smaller y-coordinate from the larger y-coordinate.
3. a) 5 **b)** 6 **c)** 4 **d)** 3
4 Problem Solving 1. a) square; $P = 16$; $A = 16$
b) square; $P = 20$; $A = 25$ **c)** rectangle; $P = 22$; $A = 24$
d) rectangle; $P = 18$; $A = 18$ **2.** $Z(4, -1)$ **3.** $(2, 0)$ and $(2, -3)$ or $(-4, 0)$ and $(-4, -3)$ **4.** with integer coordinates: The coordinates for $S(x, y)$ are given. R has coordinates $(x, 0)$, T has coordinates $(0, y)$, and Q is the origin: $(1, 6), (6, 1), (2, 3), (3, 2), (-1, 6), (-6, 1),$ $(-3, 2), (-2, 3), (1, -6), (6, -1), (3, -2), (2, -3),$ $(-1, -6), (-6, -1), (-3, -2), (-2, -3)$

Section 8.1 pp. 399–401
Practice 1. AB: positive; CD: negative; EF: positive; GH: positive; IJ: negative; KL: negative **2.** MN: undefined; PQ: 0; RS: undefined; TV: 0; WX: undefined; YZ: 0 **3. a)** positive **b)** 3 **c)** 3 **d)** 1 **4. a)** 0
b) 0 **c)** 4 **d)** 0 **5. a)** negative **b)** -4 **c)** 5 **d)** $-\dfrac{4}{5}$

6. a) undefined **b)** 7 **c)** 0 **7. a)** positive **b)** 3 **c)** 6 **d)** $\dfrac{1}{2}$

8. a) negative **b)** -1 **c)** 5 **d)** $-\dfrac{1}{5}$ **9.** $\dfrac{3}{2}$ **10.** 2 **11.** 4 **12.** 0

13. $-\dfrac{3}{4}$ **14.** $-\dfrac{3}{2}$ **15.** -9 **16.** $\dfrac{3}{2}$ **17.** $\dfrac{5}{6}$ **18.** 1 **19.** undefined

20. $\dfrac{3}{2}$ **21.** 0.3 **22.** -7 **23.** 3 **24.** $-6\dfrac{2}{3}$ **25.** $1\dfrac{1}{5}$ **Answers**
may vary for 26.–29. 26. $(1, 1)$ and $(2, 2)$ **27.** $(1, 1)$ and $(3, 1)$ **28.** $(1, 1)$ and $(-1, 2)$ **29.** $(1, 1)$ and $(1, 4)$
Applications and Problem Solving 38. Answers may vary. **a)** $B(3, 3)$ **b)** $B(3, 1)$ **c)** $B(3, 4)$ **d)** $B(3, 0)$
e) $B(5, 2)$ **f)** $B(4, 3)$ **g)** $B(2, 5)$ **h)** $B(3, 9)$ **i)** $B(3, -2)$
j) $B(-1, 3)$ **k)** $B(4, 7)$ **39. a)** $(3, -3)$ **b)** $(2, 1)$ **c)** $(1, -5)$
d) $(0, -2)$ **e)** $(5, 0)$ **f)** $(-1, -2)$ **g)** $(5, 2)$ **h)** $(2, -11)$ **i)** $(2, 9)$
j) $(6, 4)$ **k)** $(-2, 5)$ **40.** Answers may vary. **a)** $(1, 3),$
$(2, 2)$ **b)** $(-2, 2), (-5, -2)$ **c)** $(-5, 2), (-2, -2)$ **d)** $(-2, -2),$
$(4, -3)$ **e)** $(-2, -3), (4, -2)$ **f)** $(2, -4), (-3, -4)$
g) $(-2, -2), (-5, 0)$ **h)** $(-2, -2), (5, 0)$ **i)** $(0, -5), (5, 0)$
j) $(0, 5), (5, 0)$ **k)** $(1, 3), (-3, 1)$ **l)** $(1, 3), (-3, 5)$
m) $(1, -1), (-2, -3)$ **n)** $(1, -3), (-2, -1)$ **o)** $(-5, -5),$
$(-1, 1)$ **p)** $(-5, -5), (-9, 1)$ **41.** Answers may vary.
a) $(1, 3), (2, 2); -1$ **b)** $(0, 2), (1, 3); 1$ **c)** $(0, -1), (2, 1); 1$
d) $(0, 5), (1, 3); -2$ **42.** $\dfrac{1}{10}, -\dfrac{1}{10}$ **43.** 90° **44.** Answers
may vary. $(1, 1), (2, 2), (3, 7)$ **45.** Answers may vary. $(0, 4), (1, 1), (2, 0), (1, 3)$ **46.** -5 **47.** 1

48. a) 27.5 km **b)** 1.5 h **c)** Danzel's speed **49. b)** AB: $\frac{2}{3}$;

PQ: $\frac{2}{3}$ **c)** The slopes are equal, so the lines are parallel. **50. c)** negative reciprocals **d)** yes, unless the lines are horizontal and perpendicular **51. a)** 698 m **b)** the longer ski slope **52. a)** yes **b)** no **c)** Answers may vary. $(-1, 3), (1, 1), (1, -3)$ **d)** 5 **53. a)** $(0, -10)$ **b)** $(0, 10)$ **c)** -2

Investigating Math p. 402
1 Comparing First Differences and Slope **1. a)** 2
b) 1 **c)** 2 **d)** Divide the first difference by the difference between consecutive x-coordinates.
2. a) -3 **b)** 1 **c)** -3 **d)** Divide the first difference by the difference between consecutive x-coordinates.
3. a) 1.5 **b)** 2 **c)** 3 **d)** Divide the first difference by the difference between consecutive x-coordinates. **4. a)** $\frac{2}{3}$
b) 3 **c)** 2 **d)** Divide the first difference by the difference between consecutive x-coordinates.
5. a) $-\frac{1}{2}$ **b)** 2 **c)** -1 **d)** Divide the first difference by the difference between consecutive x-coordinates.
6. Divide the first difference by the difference between consecutive x-coordinates.

2 Calculating Slopes **1.** 3 **2.** 2 **3.** -1 **4.** -4 **5.** $\frac{1}{2}$
6. $\frac{1}{3}$ **7.** $-\frac{3}{4}$ **8.** $-\frac{3}{5}$ **9.** $-\frac{1}{2}$ **10.** $\frac{5}{2}$

Computer Data Bank p. 403
1 Vertical Drop **3.** British Columbia
2 Finding Slope **6.** Mystic Ridge and Norquay

Section 8.2 pp. 407–408
Applications and Problem Solving **1.** $\frac{8}{7}$ m/month

2. -0.15 h/year **3.** $\frac{4200}{89}$ km/h **4. a)** 10 m/s **b)** speed of elephant **5. a)** -0.1 L/km **b)** rate of gas consumption
6. a) 2.05 m/min **b)** the number of metres to tape 1 min of film **c)** 1.025 m/min **d)** 0.68 m/min
7. 8500 students/year **8.** 3.2%/year
9. $-164\ 000\ 000$ passenger-kilometres/year
10. a) 2.8 million/year; -5.44 million/year; -1.32 million/year **b)** no **11. a)** 6.25 m/s **b)** no
12. a) 343 m/s **b)** the speed of sound **c)** 1270 m **d)** 7.3 s
13. a) 3% **b)** $\$480$ **c)** $\$609.75$
14. a) $\$7\ 090\ 800\ 000$/year **15. a)** 1.5 days/year **b)** yes
16. a) $208\ 000$/year **b)** 1949 **c)** 2093 **d)** Answers may vary. **17. a)** yes; yes; yes **b)** yes; yes; yes; no

Career Connection p. 409
1 Antarctic Ice **1.** 3 million km²
2. a) 18 million km² **b)** about twice the area of Canada
3. a) $100\ 000$ **b)** the increase in the area of ice per day **c)** 4167 km²/h; 69.4 km²/min **4.** It does not grow.
5. It melts back to an area of 3 million km²
6. a) $-200\ 000$ **b)** the decrease in the area of ice per day **c)** 8333 km²/h; 138.9 km²/min **7.** The slope is -2 times the slope in question 3.
2 Antarctic Krill **1.** $360\ 000\ 000$ tonnes, assuming a population of 6 billion and an average mass of 60 kg
2. The mass of krill is about 4 times the mass of humans.

Technology p. 410
1 Slope of a Line **2. a)** $1\frac{2}{3}$ **b)** -0.25 **c)** -2.25

2 Problem Solving **1.** Answers may vary. $(0, 3)$
2. a) 5 L/min **b)** 7200 L **3. a)** -2.1 beats/min/year
b) 83 beats/min **c)** 6 **d)** 117 beats/min **e)** no

Technology p. 411
1 Characteristics of Equations linear: 1, 3, 4, 8, 10, 12, 16, 17, 19 non-linear: 2, 5, 6, 7, 9, 11, 13, 14, 15, 18, 20
2 Selecting Linear Equations linear: 2, 3, 6, 7, 10, 11, 12, 16

Section 8.3 pp. 418–420
Practice **1.** $y - 2 = 5(x - 1)$ **2.** $y - 3 = 6(x - 4)$
3. $y - 1 = x + 4$ **4.** $y + 6 = -7(x - 5)$ **5.** $y + 2 = -7(x + 3)$
6. $y = 1 = 0$ **7.** $y + 3 = \frac{1}{2}(x - 2)$ **8.** $y - 8 = -\frac{3}{4}(x + 6)$
9. $2x - y + 8 = 0$ **10.** $5x + y + 2 = 0$ **11.** $3x + y - 26 = 0$
12. $4x - y + 2 = 0$ **13.** $x - 3y - 5 = 0$
14. $3x - 2y - 1 = 0$ **15.** $4x - y + 5 = 0$
16. $3x - y + 1 = 0$ **17.** $2x - y + 12 = 0$
18. $3x + y - 3 = 0$ **19.** $2x + y + 11 = 0$ **20.** $x + y - 7 = 0$
21. $5x - y + 30 = 0$ **22.** $y - 4 = 0$ **23.** $y + 3 = 0$
24. $x - 2 = 0$ **25.** $x - 2y + 11 = 0$ **26.** $2x + 4y + 21 = 0$
27. $4x - 3y + 16 = 0$ **28.** $3x + 2y + 4 = 0$ **Points may vary for 29.–32.** **29.** $x - y + 4 = 0$; $(0, 4), (-4, 0)$
30. $3x - y + 8 = 0$; $(0, 8), (1, 11)$ **31.** $x + y - 7 = 0$; $(0, 7), (7, 0)$ **32.** $4x + y - 11 = 0$; $(0, 11), (1, 7)$
33. $2x - y - 2 = 0$ **34.** $5x - y + 6 = 0$
35. $3x + y - 11 = 0$ **36.** $x - 2y - 11 = 0$
37. $x - 2y - 3 = 0$ **38.** $2x + 3y - 3 = 0$
39. $5x - 4y + 21 = 0$ **40.** $y + 7 = 0$ **41.** $4x - 5y + 20 = 0$
42. $x - 5 = 0$ **43.** $1.5x - y - 0.05 = 0$
44. $1.5x + y + 2.1 = 0$ **45.** $3x + 12y - 5 = 0$
Points may vary for 46.–49. **46.** $3x - y + 1 = 0$; $(0, 1), (1, 4)$ **47.** $x + y = 0$; $(1, -1), (2, -2)$ **48.** $4x + y = 0$;

(2, –8), (–1, 4) **49.** $x + 2y + 2 = 0$; (–2, 0), (–4, 1)
50. $2x – y + 1 = 0$ **51.** $x + y – 4 = 0$ **52.** $x – 2y – 2 = 0$
53. $x + 2y – 4 = 0$ **54.** $y + 3 = 0$ **55.** $x – 2 = 0$
Applications and Problem Solving **56. b)** Answers
may vary. $x – y + 3 = 0$ **57. b)** Answers may vary.
$10x + 7y – 9 = 0$ **58. b)** $a + 200t – 27\ 600 = 0$
c) 38 h; 8 h **59.** $bx + ay – ab = 0$ **60.** the coordinates of
a point on the line **61.** perpendicular lines that
intersect at (5, 5), $x = 5$ is vertical, $y = 5$ is horizontal
63. $y – 3 = 0$, $3x + y + 3 = 0$, $2x – y – 3 = 0$
64. KL: $10x – 3y – 8 = 0$; LN: $10x + 3y – 2 = 0$
65. a) 122 **b)** the increase in depth per minute
c) $122x – y = 0$ **d)** about 90 min **66. a)** (1, 0.98),
(2, 1.02), (3, 1.06), (4, 1.1) **b)** 0.04
c) the increase in mass of space debris per year
d) $0.04x – y + 0.94 = 0$ **e)** 1.62 million kg
67. b) $3.5x – y + 15 = 0$ **68. b)** Answers may vary.
$y = 5x + 16$ **c)** 91 years **69. a)** no **b)** $x – 1 = 0$
70. Calculator will give error message. **71.** 7 **72.** 1
73. a) (–4, –1) **b)** (0, 5) **74.** This does not represent a
line.

Technology pp. 421–423
1 Slope and Direction **2. a)** $y = 3x + 2$, $y = 0.5x – 4$
b) $y = –2x + 3$, $y = –0.9x + 5$ **3.** x-coefficient **4. a)** falls
b) rises **c)** falls **d)** rises
2 Steepness of Slopes **2.** $y = 6x – 7$ **3.** $y = 6x – 7$,
$y = 2x + 3$, $y = 0.5x + 1$ **5.** $y = –6x – 7$ **6.** $y = –6x – 7$,
$y = –2x + 3$, $y = –0.5x + 1$ **7.** x-coefficient **8. a)** same
steepness, opposite direction **b)** same steepness,
opposite direction **c)** same steepness, opposite
direction
3 Slope and y-Intercept **1. b)** –1 **c)** Answers may
vary. (1, 1) **d)** 2 **e)** slope: x-coefficient, y-intercept:
constant **2. a)** 2, 1 **b)** 0.5, 2 **c)** –1, –1
4 A Family of Lines **2. a)** 1 **b)** 0 **c)** –2 **3. a)** 0.5 **b)** 0.5
c) 0.5 **4.** They have the same slope and different
y-intercepts. **5.** Answers may vary. $y = 0.5x + 5$
5 A Different Family of Lines **2. a)** 1 **b)** 1 **c)** 1 **3. a)** 3
b) 1 **c)** –0.5 **4.** They have the same y-intercept and
different slopes. **5.** Answers may vary. $y = 9x + 1$
6 Related Lines
2. a) 3 **b)** 1 **c)** 0 **d)** –2 **3. a)** $\dfrac{3}{2}$ **b)** $\dfrac{3}{2}$ **c)** $\dfrac{3}{2}$ **d)** $\dfrac{3}{2}$ **4.** Yes: a
family with slope $\dfrac{3}{2}$. **5. b)** 90° **c)** $-\dfrac{2}{3}$ **d)** –1
6. b) perpendicular **c)** 2, $-\dfrac{1}{2}$ **d)** –1

Section 8.4 pp. 428–429
1. 3, 1 **2.** $\dfrac{1}{2}$, –2 **3.** –4, 3 **4.** –1, 5 **5.** –1, 7 **6.** 5, –4

7. 2, 0 **8.** 0, 3 **9.** –2, $\dfrac{3}{2}$ **10.** 1, –4 **11.** $-\dfrac{3}{2}$, –3 **12.** 0, –3
13. $\dfrac{1}{3}$, –3 **14.** $-\dfrac{5}{2}$, 5 **15.** –44, 2 **16.** $\dfrac{1}{2}$, –2 **17.** 8, 0
18. 4, –0.4 **19.** 1, 2 **20.** –1, 5 **21.** –1, –9 **22.** 2, 0
23. $\dfrac{3}{4}$, $-\dfrac{1}{2}$ **24.** $\dfrac{1}{2}$, $\dfrac{5}{2}$ **25.** $\dfrac{7}{4}$, $-\dfrac{3}{2}$ **26.** $-\dfrac{4}{3}$, $\dfrac{1}{3}$ **27.** $y = 2x + 3$,
$2x – y + 3 = 0$ **28.** $y = 3x – 2$, $3x – y – 2 = 0$
29. $y = –4x + 6$, $4x + y – 6 = 0$ **30.** $y = –5x – 7$,
$5x + y + 7 = 0$ **31.** $y = \dfrac{1}{2}x + 1$, $x – 2y + 2 = 0$
32. $y = \dfrac{2}{3}x – 2$, $2x – 3y – 6 = 0$ **33.** $y = –0.5x$, $x + 2y = 0$
34. $y = -\dfrac{2}{5}x – \dfrac{1}{3}$, $6x + 15y + 5 = 0$ **35.** $y = 4$
36. $x = 3$ **37.** $x = –1$ **38.** $y = –3$ **49.** 1, 1, $y = x + 1$
50. 2, –3, $y = 2x – 3$ **51.** $-\dfrac{1}{2}$, 2, $y = -\dfrac{1}{2}x + 2$ **52.** $-\dfrac{2}{3}$, –1,
$y = -\dfrac{2}{3}x – 1$
Applications and Problem Solving **53. a)** –6 **b)** 11
c) –10 **d)** –1 **54. a)** –1 **b)** $-\dfrac{1}{2}$ **c)** –2 **d)** 9 **55.** They have
the same y-intercept. **56. b)** 55 g **c)** 6 g **d)** 50
e) Answers may vary **57. b)** $250 **c)** $6.50
58. a) $d = 75t$ **b)** $d = 75t + 80$ **c)** 525 km; 605 km
59. b) $p = 10d + 100$ **c)** the increase in pressure per
metre of depth **d)** 100; the pressure at the surface of
the water **e)** 10 m **f)** 160 kPa **60. a)** slope: 0, y-
intercept: 7, no x-intercept, domain: R, range: {7}
b) slope: undefined, no y-intercept, x-intercept: –2,
domain: {–2}, range: R **c)** slope: 0, y-intercept: all
points, no x-intercept, domain: R, range: {0} **d)** slope:
undefined, no y-intercept, x-intercept: 5, domain: {5},
range: R **e)** slope: undefined, y-intercept: all points, x-
intercept: 0, domain: {0}, range: R **f)** slope: 0, y-
intercept: –4, no x-intercept, domain: R, range: {–4}
61. a) slope: undefined, no y-intercept, x-intercept: a,
range: R **b)** slope: 0, y-intercept: b, no x-intercept,
range: {b} **c)** slope: 1, y-intercept: 0, x-intercept: 0,
range: R
d) slope: m, y-intercept: b, x-intercept: $-\dfrac{b}{m}$, range: R
62. $p = 2$, $q = 6$ **63.** no **64.** yes, with y-intercept 0
65. a) $S = 180n – 360$ **b)** –360 **c)** no **d)** 3

Section 8.5 pp. 432–433
Practice **23.** $2x + 3y – 6 = 0$ **24.** $3x – 4y – 12 = 0$
25. $x + 3y + 6 = 0$ **26.** $y = 1$ **27.** $x – y + 4 = 0$ **28.** $x = 4$
Applications and Problem Solving **29.** Answers

may vary. $y = 2$ **30.** Answers may vary. $x = 3$
31. Answers may vary. $x + y = 4$ **32.** Answers may vary. $x - y = 0$ **33.** -1 **34. a)** 6600; the distance in kilometres from Rome to Montréal **b)** 8; the flying time in hours from Rome to Montréal **c)** -825; the speed of the plane in kilometres per hour **d)** 2310 km
e) 3.8 h **35. a)** $(0, 13\ 000\ 000)$, $(10, 15\ 500\ 000)$, $(20, 18\ 000\ 000)$ **c)** 250 000; the increase in telephone lines per year **d)** $n = 250\ 000t + 13\ 000\ 000$
e) 24 000 000 **f)** Answers may vary.
36. $bx + ay - ab = 0$ **37. b)** 0.2; the distance the car travels per kilometre per hour of speed **c)** $y = 0.2x$
d) 10 m; 20 m **e)** 0, 0 **38. a)** horizontal line with y-intercept $-\dfrac{C}{B}$ **b)** vertical line with x-intercept $-\dfrac{C}{A}$

c) line through the origin with slope $-\dfrac{A}{B}$

d) the x-axis **e)** the y-axis

Section 8.6 pp. 437–438
Practice **1.** neither **2.** parallel **3.** perpendicular
4. neither **5.** perpendicular **6.** neither **7.** parallel
8. neither **9.** perpendicular **10.** neither **11.** $-\dfrac{1}{3}$ **12.** $-\dfrac{4}{3}$
13. 8 **14.** $\dfrac{2}{5}$ **15.** $\dfrac{1}{6}$ **16.** 0 **17. a)** 2 **b)** $-\dfrac{1}{2}$ **18. a)** -1 **b)** 1
19. a) $\dfrac{1}{3}$ **b)** -3 **20. a)** $-\dfrac{2}{7}$ **b)** $\dfrac{7}{2}$ **21. a)** -4 **b)** $\dfrac{1}{4}$ **22. a)** -3 **b)** $\dfrac{1}{3}$
23. a) 2 **b)** $-\dfrac{1}{2}$ **24. a)** $\dfrac{5}{2}$ **b)** $-\dfrac{2}{5}$ **25. a)** $-\dfrac{2}{3}$ **b)** $\dfrac{3}{2}$ **26. a)** $\dfrac{3}{5}$
b) $-\dfrac{5}{3}$ **27.** perpendicular **28.** perpendicular
29. neither **30.** neither **31. a)** parallel **b)** neither
c) perpendicular **d)** neither **e)** perpendicular **f)** parallel
g) neither **h)** perpendicular **32.** $2x - 3y + 4 = 0$
33. $5x + y + 5 = 0$ **34.** $x + 6 = 0$ **35.** $x + 1 = 0$
36. $2x + 18y + 27 = 0$ **37.** $4x + y + 4 = 0$
38. $3x + 9y + 1 = 0$ **39. a)** $x + 4y - 17 = 0$
b) $x + 2y + 1 = 0$
Applications and Problem Solving **40.** -3 **41.** -12
42. 6 **43.** $\dfrac{3}{2}$ **44.** $\dfrac{6}{5}$ **45.** $-\dfrac{5}{2}$ **46.** -2 **47.** -4 **48.** 2 **49.** -6
50. 15 **51.** -18 **53.** trapezoid **54.** square
55. parallelogram **56.** rectangle **57.** square
58. $y + 2 = 0$ **59. b)** parallel **60. b)** Kate **61. a)** 9 **b)** -4
62. a) -4, 4 **b)** no **63. a)** $\dfrac{3}{2}, \dfrac{3}{2}$ **b)** No. They are coincident. **64. a)** yes **b)** no

Section 8.7 p. 441
Practice **1.** $(0, 1)$ **2.** $(-3, -2)$ **3.** $(0, 0)$ **4.** $(-1, -2)$

5. $y = x$, $y = -x$, $y = x - 1$, $y = 2x$ **6.** $(3, 6)$ **7.** $(2, 1)$
8. $(0, 3)$ **9.** $(2, 6)$ **10.** $(-2, 6)$ **11.** $(5, 7)$ **12.** $(\dfrac{1}{2}, -1)$
13. $(3, 2)$ **14.** $(-4, 5)$ **15.** $(3, 1)$ **16.** $(-1, 1)$
Applications and Problem Solving **17. b)** triangle
18. a) $y = 80 + 0.2x$, $y = 0.6x$ **c)** $(200, 120)$
d) For 200 km, both companies charge \$120. **e)** B; A
19. c) 15:00 **d)** 200 km **20. b)** They all pass through the same point. **21.** No. They are parallel.

Section 8.8 p. 443
1 Modelling Distances **1.** 10 000 cm **2.** 100 m
3. Answers may vary. 400 m **4.** 120 m **5.** 70 m, 30 m, 90 m **6. a)** 1500 m **b)** 1400 m **7. a)** 450 m **b)** 700 m
c) Answers may vary. **d)** Answers may vary.
2 Modelling Slopes **1. a)** $\dfrac{7}{13}$ **b)** $\dfrac{7}{33}$ **c)** $\dfrac{9}{35}$ **2.** climb
3. You cannot tell, since in this section of the map the stream does not cross any contours. **4.** No. There will be small ups, and downs, but the changes will always be less than 10 m. **5. a)** undefined

Review pp. 444–445
1. 2 **2.** $\dfrac{1}{7}$ **3.** -1 **4.** 3 **5.** -4.8 **6.** 0 **7.** undefined
13. 240 km/h **14. a)** 0.35%/year **b)** 2255 **c)** no
15. $2x - y - 3 = 0$ **16.** $3x + y = 0$ **17.** $x + y + 4 = 0$
18. $x - 2y - 2 = 0$ **19.** $0.2x + y + 0.6 = 0$ **20.** $y + 1 = 0$
21. $x - 5 = 0$ **22.** $2x - y + 1 = 0$ **23.** $3x + y - 1 = 0$
24. $x + 2y - 10 = 0$ **25.** $x - 3 = 0$ **26.** $3x - 4y - 27 = 0$
27. $y - 2 = 0$ **28.** $x - 4y - 12 = 0$ **29.** $5x - 2y + 3 = 0$
Points may vary for 30.–31. **30.** $4x - y - 3 = 0$; $(0, -3)$, $(1, 1)$ **31.** $x + y + 4 = 0$; $(0, -4)$, $(-4, 0)$ **32. b)** Answers may vary. $x - y = 0$ **33.** 4, 6 **34.** $-\dfrac{4}{5}$, 4 **35.** $\dfrac{1}{2}$, 2
36. $\dfrac{2}{3}$, -4 **37.** $5x - y + 2 = 0$ **38.** $4x + y + 3 = 0$
39. $4x - 3y = 0$ **40.** $x + 2y - 6 = 0$ **41.** 4, -9 **42.** -2, -2
43. b) \$480 **c)** 5% **d)** \$2400 **44.** $x - 2y - 4 = 0$
45. $3x + 2y - 6 = 0$ **50.** range: R, slope: 2, x-intercept: -2.5, y-intercept: 5 **51.** range: R, slope: -2, x-intercept: 1.25, y-intercept: 2.5 **52. a)** 5
b) $-\dfrac{1}{5}$ **53. a)** $\dfrac{1}{4}$ **b)** -4 **54. a)** $-\dfrac{3}{5}$ **b)** $\dfrac{5}{3}$ **55. a)** -2 **b)** $\dfrac{1}{2}$
56. a) $\dfrac{1}{3}$ **b)** -3 **57. a)** $-\dfrac{2}{3}$ **b)** $\dfrac{3}{2}$ **58.** $3x + 2y - 12 = 0$
59. $2x + y - 7 = 0$ **60. a)** $(0, 0)$ **b)** $(0, -2)$ **61.** $(-1, 6)$
62. $(1, -2)$ **63. a)** $(10, 12)$ **b)** The first number is the number of provinces in Cameroon. The second number is the number of provinces in Finland.

Exploring Math p. 445

1. 46, 47, 48, 49, 50; 246, 247, 248, 249, 250
2. a) $N = 5r - 4$ **b)** $N = 5r - 3$ **c)** $N = 5r - 2$
d) $N = 5r - 1$ **e)** $N = 5r$ **3. a)** Parallel: their slopes are
equal. **b)** No: the numbers are discrete. **4.** 1051,
1052, 1053, 1054, 1055; 2531, 2532, 2533, 2534,
2535 **5. a)** 1278 **b)** 1662 **6. a)** 471 **b)** 786 **7. a)** B **b)** C
8. Let the first number be in column A, row r_1. Let
the second number be in column B, row r_2. The sum
of the numbers is $5r_1 - 4 + 5r_2 - 3 = 5(r_1 + r_2) - 7$
$= 5(r_1 + r_2) - 5 - 2 = 5(r_1 + r_2 - 1) - 2$. Let
$R = r_1 + r_2 - 1$. Then the sum is $5R - 2$, which is a
number in column C. **9.** 58C **10.** Let the first
number be in column A, row r_1. Let the second
number be in column D, row r_2. The sum of the
numbers is $5r_1 - 4 + 5r_2 - 1 = 5(r_1 + r_2) - 5 =$
$5(r_1 + r_2 - 1)$. Let $R = r_1 + r_2 - 1$. Then the sum is $5R$,
which is a number in column E. **11.** 49E

Chapter Check p. 446

1. undefined **2.** $\dfrac{1}{2}$ **3.** $-\dfrac{5}{3}$ **4.** 0 **5.** $3x - y - 7 = 0$
6. $2x + 5y + 7 = 0$ **7.** $x - y + 3 = 0$ **8.** $x + 2y - 5 = 0$
9. $y + 3 = 0$ **10.** $x + 1 = 0$ **11.** 2, -3 **12.** $-\dfrac{1}{2}$, -4
13. perpendicular **14.** $2x - y - 1 = 0$ **15.** $x + 4y - 8 = 0$
16. $2x + y - 13 = 0$ **17.** slope: 4, x-intercept: $-\dfrac{3}{4}$,
y-intercept: 3 **18.** slope: $\dfrac{2}{5}$, x-intercept: -5,
y-intercept: 2 **19.** (2, 3) **20. a)** (0, 232), (700, 484)
c) 0.36 km/m **d)** the increase in distance per increase
in elevation **e)** $e = 0.36d + 232$ **f)** 322 m **g)** no
21. a) (4, 10) **b)** The first number is the number of
observatories in Ontario. The second number is the
number of observatories in other provinces.

Using the Strategies p. 447

1. 32 cm **2.** 1 unit: 17; 2 units: 6; 3 units: 3; 4 units: 1;
5 units: 1 **4.** yes **5.** 20 **6. a)** 180 **b)** 8 **c)** 44 **d)** 48
7. 212, 213 **8.** 14

Cumulative Review, Chapters 5–8
pp. 448–449

Chapter 5 **1. a)** The sum of the x- and y-values is 6.
b) 8, 7, 6, 5, 4 **c)** (−2, 8), (−1, 7), (0, 6), (1, 5), (2, 4)
d) {8, 7, 6, 5, 4} **2. a)** The y-value is 2 more than 3
times the x-value. **b)** −4, −1, 2, 5, 8 **c)** (−2, −4),
(−1, −1), (0, 2), (1, 5), (2, 8) **d)** {−4, −1, 2, 5, 8}
3. b) (2, −2) **c)** $P = 26$, $A = 42$ **4. a)** 0, 15, 30, 45, 60
c) 21 m; 54 m **6. b)** partial **7. b)** direct **8. c)** $y = -x - 2$
Chapter 6 **1.** $5x - 11y + 2$ **2.** $-9 - a - 5b + 4c$
3. $-x^2 - 2x + 1$ **4.** 2nd degree trinomial **5.** 4th degree

binomial **6.** 3rd degree monomial
7. $3x^5 - 6x^3 + x^2 - 4x + 2$ **8.** $5x^4 - 6x^3y^2 + 3x^2y - xy^2$
9. $3x^2 + x - 12$ **10.** $2y^2 - 4y - 15$ **11.** $-2m^2 + 2m + 5$
12. $-t^2 - 4t + 1$ **13.** $8x - 12y + 20$ **14.** $-x - 1$
15. $-7x + 25$ **16.** $-3x - 12$ **17.** $x^2 - 14x - 35$
18. $6y^2 - 10y + 10$ **19.** $22xy$ **20.** $10x^2y^3$ **21.** $12x^3y^3$
22. $10m^3n$ **23.** x^8 **24.** $81x^8y^4$ **25.** $-8x^9y^{12}$ **26.** $r^8s^{12}t^{16}$
27. $9x^2 - 14x$ **28.** $-8y^2 - 7y + 12$ **29.** $3x^3 - 12x^2 - 9x$
30. $-2x^3 + 7x^2 - x$ **31.** $-6x^3 - 2x^2 + 14x$ **32.** $3xy^2$
33. $-4y$ **34.** $5y(y - 3)$ **35.** $3ab(7ab - 1 + 2b)$
Chapter 7 **1.** 4 **2.** 15 **3.** 10 **4.** 4.5 **5.** -7 **6.** -12 **7.** 5
8. -4 **9.** -1 **10.** 2 **11.** 11 **12.** 2 **13.** -1 **14.** -12 **15.** 4
16. 4 **17.** -4 **18.** -2 **19.** -3 **20.** -1 **21.** 9 **22.** 3
23. 43 m, 44 m, 45 m **24. a)** 20, 30, 40, 50
b) $A = 5b$ **c)** 175 cm² **25. a)** 9 h **b)** 19:00
Chapter 8 **1.** 2 **2.** 1 **3.** 4 **4.** 0 **5. a)** 5% **b)** \$400
6. $5x - y - 31 = 0$ **7.** $x + 2y + 7 = 0$ **8.** $7x - y - 23 = 0$
9. $x - 2y + 13 = 0$ **10.** Points may vary. $x + 3y - 2 = 0$;
(−1, 1), (−4, 2) **11.** 3, 7 **12.** −2, 6 **13.** $\dfrac{1}{2}$, −4 **14.** $\dfrac{3}{4}$, −3
17. $3x + y - 2 = 0$ **18.** $x - 2y + 14 = 0$
19. $2x - 3y - 6 = 0$ **20.** (1, −1)

Chapter 9

Measurement p. 451

1. a) North Pole, South Pole **b)** 0° **c)** Both have a
radius of 0 m. **2. a)** They are equal, assuming the
Earth is a sphere. **b)** Same meridian; 180° in either
direction arrives at the same location. **c)** Answers may
vary.

Getting Started pp. 452–453

1 Polyominoes **1. b)** The shape with 4 in a square
and 1 attached to any side. **2. b)** square. **3. a)** 3 by 2
rectangle: It is closest to the square.
2 Areas of Irregular Figures **1.** The irregular
shapes can be broken down into smaller triangles or
half rectangles. The area of these is one-half times
base times height. Counting parts is shorter.
3 The Pythagorean Theorem **1.** 10 cm **2.** 12 m
3. 7 m **4.** 17 cm **5.** 8.6 cm **6.** 7.4 m **7.** 5.7 cm
8. 8.7 cm
Mental Math
Operations With Decimals **1.** 3140 **2.** 0.0314 **3.** 15
4. 3.1 **5.** 6 **6.** 5.5 **7-12.** Estimates may vary. **7.** 12
8. 75 **9.** 300 **10.** 18 **11.** 30 **12.** 210
Subtracting Using Compatible Numbers **1.** 36 **2.** 45
3. 41 **4.** 59 **5.** 39 **6.** 38 **7.** 3.5 **8.** 6.2 **9.** 2.9 **10.** 370
11. 810 **12.** 390 **13. c)** The number b or c should be
chosen so that either $m + b = 0$ or $m - c = 0$.

Investigating Math pp. 454–455
1 Finding the Perimeter **1.** 25.2 cm **2.** 23.4 cm
3. 30.8 cm **4.** 27.7 m **5.** 62.8 cm **6.** 20.6 cm
2 Finding the Area **1.** 13.5 cm^2 **2.** 73.9 m^2
3. 27.3 cm^2 **4.** 28.6 cm^2 **5.** 201.1 cm^2 **6.** 36.1 cm^2
7. 14.1 m^2 **8.** 16.6 m^2 **9.** 21.2 m^2
3 Finding the Perimeter and the Area
1. 24 m, 20 m^2 **2.** 38 cm, 75 cm^2 **3.** 52 cm, 144 cm^2
4. 60 m, 150 m^2 **5.** 60 cm, 150 cm^2 **6.** 38 m, 57 m^2

Section 9.1 pp. 457–459
Practice **1.** 46.1 cm^2 **2.** 58.8 m^2 **3.** 42.9 cm^2
4. 95.3 cm^2 **5.** 131 m^2 **6.** 98.8 m^2 **7.** 114.7 m^2
8. 220 m^2 **9.** 125 m^2 **10.** 41.1 cm^2 **11.** 40.5 m^2
12. 27 m^2
Applications and Problem Solving **13.** 61.2 m^2
14. 62.6 cm^2 **15.** 73.4 cm^2 **16.** 40.3 cm^2 **17.** 201.1 cm^2
18. 50 m^2 **19.** 57.8 m^2 **20. a)** 279 m^2 **b)** 24
21. 4000 cm^2 **22.** 430 cm^2 **23.** 1300 cm^2
24. a) 1005.3 cm^2 **b)** 20% **25.** 224 m^2
26. a) $200 - 50\pi$ **b)** 43 m^2 **27. a)** $4 - \pi$ **b)** 0.9 m^2

Investigating Math pp. 460–463
1 Fencing on Four Sides **1. b)** Width, Length,
Area: 1, 11, 11; 2, 10, 20; 3, 9, 27; 4, 8, 32; 5, 7, 35; 6,
6, 36 **c)** 6 m by 6 m **d)** 36 m^2 **2. b)** Width, Length,
Area: 1, 15, 15; 2, 14, 28; 3, 13, 39; 4, 12, 48; 5, 11,
55; 6, 10, 60; 7, 9, 63; 8, 8, 64 **c)** 8 m by 8 m **d)** 64 m^2
3. 56 m^2 **4.** square **5. a)** Square the perimeter and
divide by 16. **b)** 72.25 m^2, 47.61 m^2, 84.64 m^2
6. b) Width, Length, Perimeter: 1, 36, 74; 2, 18, 40; 3,
12, 30; 4, 9, 26; 6, 6, 24 **c)** 6 m by 6 m **d)** 24 m
7. b) Width, Length, Perimeter: 1, 16, 34; 2, 8, 20; 4,
4, 16 **c)** 4 m by 4 m **d)** 16 **8.** 22 m **9.** square
10. a) Take the square root of the area and multiply
by 4. **b)** 18 m, 20.8 m, 23.7 m
2 Fencing on Three Sides **1. b)** Width, Length,
Area: 1, 14, 14; 2, 12, 24; 3, 10, 30; 4, 8, 32; 5, 6, 30;
6, 4, 24; 7, 2, 14 **c)** 4 m by 8 m **d)** 32 m^2 **2. b)** Width,
Length, Area: 1, 26, 26; 2, 24, 48; 3, 22, 66; 4, 20, 80;
5, 18, 90; 6, 16, 96; 7, 14, 98; 8, 12, 96; 9, 10, 90; 10,
8, 80; 11, 6, 66; 12, 4, 48; 13, 2, 26 **c)** 7 m by 14 m
d) 98 m^2 **3.** 42.25 m^2 **4.** The length is twice the
width. **5. a)** Square the length of fence used and
divide by 8. **b)** 112.5 m^2, 59.4 m^2, 87.1 m^2
6. b) Width, Length, Fence Used: 1, 72, 74; 2, 36, 40;
3, 24, 30; 4, 18, 26; 6, 12, 24; 8, 9, 25; 9, 8, 26;
12, 6, 30; 18, 4, 40; 24, 3, 51; 36, 2, 74; 72, 1, 145
c) 6 m by 12 m **d)** 24 m **7. b)** Width, Length, Fence
Used: 1, 128, 130; 2, 64, 68; 4, 32, 40; 8, 16, 32; 16, 8,
40; 32, 4, 68; 64, 2, 130; 128, 1, 257 **c)** 8 m by 16 m
d) 32 m **8.** 22 m **9.** The length is twice the width.

10. a) Multiply the area by 8 and take the square
root. **b)** 20 m, 30 m, 23.7 m
3 Applications and Problem Solving **1. a)** square
b) It would reduce functionality. **2.** circle
3.–4. Answer may vary.

Investigating Math pp. 464–465
1 Modelling the Surface Area **1.** 126 cm^2
2. 108 cm^2 **3. a)** 442 cm^2 **b)** 408 cm^2 **c)** 312 cm^2
d) 150 cm^2
2 Modelling the Volume **1. a)** 60 **b)** 60 cm^3
c) 20 cm^2 **d)** 3 cm **e)** They are equal. **f)** $V = Bh$
2. a) 153 cm^3 **b)** 372 cm^3 **c)** 90 m^3 **3. a)** 168 m^3
b) 600 m^3 **c)** 648 cm^3 **d)** 343 m^3

Section 9.2 pp. 469–471
Practice **1.** rectangular prism **2.** triangular prism
3. cube **4.** triangular prism **5.** 3 **6.** 4 **7.** 300 m^2,
346 m^2 **8.** 34 cm^2, 43.6 cm^2 **9.** 150 cm^2 **10.** 958 m^2
11. 24 m^3, 24 m^3 **12.** 150 cm^3, 180 cm^3 **13.** 1000 cm^3,
1716 cm^3 **14.** 120 m^3, 108 m^3 **15.** 278 m^2, 198 m^3
16. 685 m^2, 850 m^3 **17.** 12 000 cm^2, 60 000 cm^3
18. 150 cm^2, 112 cm^3 **19.** 132 200 m^2, 3 036 000 m^3
20. 1637 m^2, 3300 m^3 **21.** 336 cm^2, 288 cm^3
22. 45.9 m^2, 12.15 m^3 **23.** 321 cm^2, 225 cm^3
24. 700 cm^2, 840 cm^3 **25.** 328 cm^2, 220 cm^3
26. 444 cm^2, 369 cm^3
Applications and Problem Solving **27.** 9 m^2
28. a) 94 m^2 **b)** 6; Assume the second coat uses as
much paint as the first coat. **29. a)** 4.6 m^2 **b)** $45.91
c) 27 227 **30. a)** 232 cm^2 **c)** rectangular prism
31. 5.44 m^3 **32.** 34 416 m^2 **33.** 6 cm on a side
34. a) 115 m^3 **b)** 6.4 h **35.** 211.7 m^2 **36.** 4 m by
2 m by 3 m **37.–38.** Answers may vary.

Investigating Math pp. 472–473
1 Modelling the Surface Area **1.** 18π cm^2
2. a) equal **b)** 5 cm **3. a)** equal **b)** 6π **c)** 6π cm
4. a) equal **b)** 30π cm^2 **c)** 30π cm^2 **5. a)** 48π cm^2
b) 151 cm^2 **6.** 192π cm^2 **7.** 280π cm^2 **8.** $2\pi r^2 + 2\pi rh$
9. 302 m^2
2 Modelling the Volume **7.** equal **8.** $V = Bh$
9. $V = \pi r^2 h$ **10. a)** 96π cm^3 **b)** 302 cm^3 **11. a)** 40π cm^3
b) 126 cm^3

Investigating Math pp. 474–475
1 Modelling the Surface Area **1.** 4π cm **2.** $\dfrac{1}{4}$
3. 64π cm^2 **4. b)** 16π cm^2 **5.** 4π cm^2 **6. a)** 20π cm^2
b) 63 cm^2 **7. a)** $2\pi r$ **b)** $\dfrac{2\pi r}{2\pi s}$ **c)** πs^2 **d)** $\dfrac{2\pi r}{2\pi s} \times \pi s^2$ or πrs
e) πrs **f)** πr^2 **g)** $\pi r^2 + \pi rs$

2 Modelling the Volume **1.** Answers may vary.

2. a) 3 **b)** Answers may vary. **3.** $\frac{1}{3}$ **4.** $V = \frac{1}{3}\pi r^2 h$

Section 9.3 pp. 479–480
Practice **1.** 641 cm^2 **2.** 144 cm^2 **3.** 201 cm^2
4. 109 cm^2 **5.** 150 m^3, 157 m^3 **6.** 480 cm^3, 687 cm^3
7. 1400 cm^3, 1466 cm^3 **8.** 36 m^3, 38 m^3 **9.** 792 cm^2
10. 264 cm^2 **11.** 327 m^2 **12.** 171 cm^2 **13.** 75 cm^2
14. 283 m^2 **15.** 101 m^2, 75 m^3 **16.** 302 cm^2, 302 cm^3
Applications and Problem Solving **17. a)** 6.7 cm
b) 63 cm^2 **18.** 213 628 cm^2 **19.** 13.8 m^2 **20.** 8 m^3
21. 2 L **22.** 2.5 m^3 **23.** 132 m^3 **24.–25.** Answers may
vary.

Investigating Math pp. 481–483
1 Volumes and Surface Areas of Prisms **1.** 6, 22;
48, 88; 162, 198 **2. a)** 2 **b)** 8 **c)** 4 **3. a)** 3 **b)** 27 **c)** 9
4. a) by a factor of 8 **b)** by a factor of 27 **5. a)** by a
factor of 4 **b)** by a factor of 9 **6. a)** by a factor of 64
b) by a factor of 1000 **7. a)** by a factor of 16 **b)** by a
factor of 100 **8. a)** 376 m^2, 480 m^3 **b)** 60 m^3 **c)** $\frac{1}{8}$

d) 94 m^2 **e)** $\frac{1}{4}$ **9.** When all the dimensions of a prism
are changed by a factor of k, the volume changes by a
factor of k^3. **10.** When all the dimensions of a prism
are changed by a factor of k, the surface area changes
by a factor of k^2.
2 Volumes and Surface Area of Cylinders
1. 3π cm, 8π cm^2; 24π cm, 32π cm^2; 81π cm, 72π cm^2
2. **2. a)** 2 **b)** 8 **c)** 4 **3. a)** 3 **b)** 27 **c)** 9
4. a) by a factor of 8 **b)** by a factor of 27
5. a) by a factor of 4 **b)** by a factor of 9
6. a) by a factor of 64 **b)** by a factor of 1000
7. a) by a factor of 16 **b)** by a factor of 100

8. a) 96π cm^3, 80π cm^2 **b)** 12π cm^3 **c)** $\frac{1}{8}$ **d)** 20π cm^2 **e)** $\frac{1}{4}$

9. When all the dimensions of a cylinder are changed
by a factor of k, the volume changes by a factor of k^3.
10. When all the dimensions of a cylinder are
changed by a factor of k, the surface area changes by a
factor of k^2. **11. a)** 9.4 cm^3 **b)** 75.4 cm; no **c)** They are
exact answers.
3 Changing Selected Dimensions of Prisms
1. a) 24 m^3 **b)** 52 m^2 **2. a)** 48 m^3 **b)** 72 m^3 **c)** 96 m^3
3. a) doubled, tripled, quadrupled **b)** yes; a direct
variation because the volume doubles when the
length doubles. **4. a)** 88 m^2 **b)** 124 m^2 **c)** 160 m^2
5. a) The surface area increases by the amount of
increase in the 2 bases and the 2 affected faces in each
case. The total area increases by a different amount in

each case. **b)** yes; partial variation **6. a)** 96 m^3
b) 216 m^3 **c)** 384 m^3 **7.** The volume increases by a
factor of 4, 9, and 16, respectively. **8. a)** 128 m^2
b) 288 m^2 **c)** 352 m^2 **9.** The lateral area increases by a
factor of 2, 3, and 4, and the area of the bases
increases by a factor of 4, 9, and 16, respectively. The
total area increases by a different amount in each
case.

Investigating Math pp. 484–485
1 Modelling the Surface Area **1.** 105 cm^2
2. 147 cm^2 **3. a)** 400 cm^2 **b)** 252.5 cm^2
2 Modelling the Volume **1.** Answers may vary.

2. a) 3 **b)** Answers may vary. **3.** $\frac{1}{3}$ **4.** $V = \frac{1}{3}Bh$

Investigating Math pp. 486–487
1 Modelling the Surface Area **1-7.** Answers may
vary. **8.** 4 **9.** πr^2 **10.** $4\pi r^2$ **11. a)** 804 cm^2 **b)** 1257 cm^2
c) 5027 cm^2
2 Modelling the Volume **1. a)** r **b)** $2r$ **2.** $V = 2\pi r^3$

3. $V = \frac{4}{5}\pi r^3$ **4. a)** 268 m^3 **b)** 524 m^3 **c)** 1437 m^3

5. Answers may vary.

Section 9.4 pp. 492–493
Practice **1.** 161 cm^2 **2.** 72 m^2 **3.** 50 cm^2 **4.** 113 cm^2
5. 50 cm^3, 50 cm^3 **6.** 15 m^3, 15 m^3 **7.** 375 m^3,
524 m^3 **8.** 192 cm^3, 268 cm^3 **9.** 360 m^2, 400 m^3
10. 132 m^2, 89 m^3
Applications and Problem Solving **11.** 170 m^2
12. 5027 mm^2 **13.** 339 m^2, 452 m^3 **14.** 288 m^2,
366 m^3 **15.** 236 cm^2, 283 cm^3 **16.** 4.5 cm **17.** 205 m^2

18. $\frac{32p}{3}$ **19. a)** 314 cm^2, 1256 cm^2 **b)** 4 **c)** no; rounding

off causes errors in the ratio. **d)** 100π, 400π **e)** 4 **f)** yes;
the answers are exact so the ratio is exact. **g)** There is
no loss of accuracy. **20. a)** The surface area increases
by a factor of 4, increases by a factor of 9, and

changes by a factor of $\frac{1}{4}$. **b)** The volume increases by a

factor of 8, increases by a factor of 27, and changes by

a factor of $\frac{1}{8}$. **21. a)** 100:1 **b)** 1000:1

22. a) 255 592 966 km^2 **b)** The Earth is spherical.

c) $\frac{1}{25}$ **23. a)** The volume is doubled. **b)** The volume

is tripled. **c)** The volume is doubled.
24. 9.08 billion km^3 **25.** 4608 cm^3 **26.** The height of
the pyramid is three times that of the prism.
27. The orange of diameter 9 cm has the greater
volume per penny.

Technology pp. 494–495
1 Designing Boxes   1. a) $2 \text{ cm} \times 2 \text{ cm} \times 3 \text{ cm}$
b) Answers may vary. **2. a)** $2 \text{ cm} \times 2 \text{ cm} \times 2 \text{ cm}$;
$1 \text{ cm} \times 1 \text{ cm} \times 12 \text{ cm}$ **b)** Answers may vary: Width,
Length, Height, Surface Area: 1, 1, 12, 25; 2, 1, 6, 20;
3, 2, 2, 16; 3, 1, 4, 19 **4. a)** $2 \text{ cm} \times 2 \text{ cm} \times 3 \text{ cm}$
b) $3 \text{ cm} \times 2 \text{ cm} \times 2 \text{ cm}$ **6. b)** The ratio increases.
7. Answers may vary. **8. a)** $2 \text{ m} \times 2 \text{ m} \times 2 \text{ m}$
b) $2 \text{ m} \times 2 \text{ m} \times 2 \text{ m}$ **9.** Answers may vary. The box
chosen is to be pleasing to the customer, not
functional.
2 Designing Cans   1. Answers may vary. **2.** Answers
may vary. Volume, Surface Area: 113, 232; 113, 138;
113, 132; 113, 264 **3. a)** 3 **4 - 5.** Answers may vary.
3 Heat Loss   1. a) cube **b)** $15\ 000 \text{ cm}^2$ **2. a)** sphere
b) It may roll around and can not be stacked without
holders. **3.** The cat rolls in a ball to prevent heat loss.

Career Connection pp. 496–497
1 Isometric and Orthographic Views   1. a) 9, 30,
3:10 **b)** 6, 26, 3:13 **c)** 9, 32, 9:32 **d)** 12, 42, 2:7

Technology p. 498
1 Using a Program   1. Title for the
program. Introduces the program; Allows you to
enter the numbers called radius R and slant height L;
The formula for surface area of a cone is assigned the
variable S. Prints S to the screen. **2.** The graphing
calculator can use the exact answers rather than an
approximate answer. **3.** 85.8 cm^2
2 Writing Programs
1. a) PROGRAM:SACYLINDER
:Prompt R,H
:$2\pi R^2 + 2\pi RH \rightarrow A$
:Disp A
b) PROGRAM:SASPHERE
:Prompt R
:$4\pi R^2 \rightarrow A$
:Disp A
c) PROGRAM:SAPYRAMID
:Prompt B,S
:$B^2 + 2BS \rightarrow A$
:Disp A
2. a) PROGRAM:VCYLINDER
:Prompt R,H
:$\pi R^2 H \rightarrow V$
:Disp V
b) PROGRAM:VSPHERE
:Prompt R
:$4\pi R^3/3 \rightarrow V$
:Disp V

c) PROGRAM:VCONE
:Prompt R,H
:$\pi R^2 H/3 \rightarrow V$
:Disp V
d) PROGRAM:VSBPYRAMID
:Prompt H,B
:$HB/3 \rightarrow V$
:Disp V
3. 294.1 cm^2 , 375.3 cm^3 **4.** 191.1 m^2 , 248.5 m^3
5. 17.5 m^3 **6.** 15.4 cm^2 , 3.1 cm^3

Section 9.5 p. 500
Practice   1. 5000 cm^3 **2.** $32\ 000 \text{ cm}^3$ **3.** 400 cm^3
4. $10\ 000\ 000 \text{ cm}^3$ **5.** 5 m^3 **6.** 0.045 m^3
7. $0.000\ 001 \text{ m}^3$ **8.** 25.2 m^3 **9.** 0.275 L **10.** 0.015 mL
11. 1500 L **12.** 100 L **13.** 7000 mL **14.** 250 mL
15. $1\ 000\ 000 \text{ mL}$ **16.** 45 mL **17.** $15\ 000 \text{ g}$ **18.** 4.5 g
19. 0.325 g **20.** 350 g **21.** 28 kg **22.** $15\ 000 \text{ kg}$
23. 0.54 kg **24.** 0.0001 kg **25.** 10 cm^3 **26.** 6100 cm^3
27. 0.0033 cm^3 **28.** 0.1 cm^3
Applications and Problem Solving   29. Answers
may vary. **30.** 50 kL **31.** 6 **32.** 1.42 L **33. a)** 4.5 m^3
b) 6 kL **c)** 7.5 min **34.** The inside dimensions could
be different. **35.** First find the mass of 1 L of
gasoline, then multiply by 4. **36. a)** 1 dm^3 **b)** no
c) Liquids are more commonly measured in litres.

Section 9.6 pp. 501–503
1 Modelling With Map Projections   1.–2. Answers
may vary.
2 Modelling Antipodal Points   1. They are equal in
degree; opposite in direction **2.** Their sum is $180°$;
opposite in direction **3.–5.** Answers may vary.
6. $12\ 756 \text{ km}$, the diameter of the Earth
3 Modelling the Area of the Earth
1. a) $514\ 718\ 540 \text{ km}^2$ **b)** $40\ 212 \text{ km}$ **c)** $20\ 106 \text{ km}$
d) $808\ 502\ 472 \text{ km}^2$ **2.** 1.6 **3.** The poles are most
distorted.
4 Extending the Model   1.–4. Answers may vary.

Review pp. 504-505
1. 544 m^2 **2.** 113 cm^2 **3.** 151 m^2 **4.** 173 cm^2
5. 376 cm^2 **6.** 31.5 m^2 **7.** rectangular prism
8. triangular prism **9.** 1734 m^2 **10.** 315.34 cm^2
11. 648 cm^3 **12.** $29\ 335.5 \text{ cm}^3$ **13.** 742 cm^2 , 876 cm^3
14. 3016 m^2 **15.** 1056 cm^2 **16.** 192 m^3 **17.** 707 m^3
18. 2.1 m^3 **19.** 7238 cm^2 **20.** 132 m^2 **21.** 864 cm^3
22. $33\ 510 \text{ m}^3$ **23.** 942 cm^2 , 2094 cm^3
24. The volume would increase by a factor of 27;
The surface area would increase by a factor of 9.
25. a) 1800 cm^3, 1.8 dm^3 **b)** 1.8 kg **c)** 1.8 L **26.** 1.62 L

Chapter Check p. 506

1. 112 m² **2.** 134 m² **3.** 220 cm² **4.** 2513 cm²
5. 384 m² **6.** 628 cm² **7.** 804 cm² **8.** 869 m² **9.** 101 m³
10. 1099 m³ **11.** 4189 cm³ **12.** 6 510 000 cm³
13. 938 cm², 1320 cm³ **14.** The volume would
increase by a factor of 8; The surface area would
increase by a factor of 4. **15.** 176 cm³, 188 cm²
16. a) 216 cm³ **b)** 180 mL **17.** 3 cm

Using the Strategies p. 507

1. 0, 4, or 8 **2.** A is 4, B is 2, C is 3, and D is 1

3. Answers may vary. **4.** 1 cm² **5.** $\frac{5}{2} + \frac{4}{3}$ **6.** 11, 12, 13

7. Answers may vary. **8.** 4624 **9.** 49 **10.** 20, 22, or 26
11. 7 cm **12.** 2 $5 bills, 1 $2 coin, 1 quarter, 1 dime,
1 nickel, and 3 pennies **13.** approximately 3 140 000

Chapter 10

Geometry p. 509

1. Answers may vary. **2.** The horse cannot see you
and you may startle the animal. **3.** For predators,
they wish to concentrate on their prey. For other
mammals, they need to see predators approaching.
4. Answers may vary. **5.** 140° horizontally on each
side, 60° upward and downward

Getting Started pp. 510–511

1 Length 1. The vertical appears longer. **2. a)** They
are the same length. **b)** Answers may vary.
2 Perspective 1. They appear bent. **2.** The circles
appear to bend the lines towards the centre.
3 Reversing Figures 2. The back face below the lid
becomes the open top of the box.
4 Impossible Figures 1. A figure with 3 prongs.
2. Not possible; as you move from right to left, the 2
top faces become 3 prongs.
5 More Illusions 1. The bottom figure appears
longer, but they are the same length. The tails
spreading out and the heads turning in distort the
lengths. **2.** The horizontal lines appear bent, but they
are all horizontal. The diagonal lines in different
directions cause distortion. **3. a)** There appears to be
a vertical tube and a horizontal tube. **b)** There
appears to be a pyramid with 1 block on top and
3 rows containing 1, 2, and 3 blocks. The second
pyramid has 2 blocks at the top left and three rows
containing 2, 3, and 2 blocks. **4. a)** You can not keep
going up the stairs and arrive at the spot you
started. **b)** You can not attach 3 pieces at right angles
and get back to the first piece. **5.** They appear to be

taller as you move to the right, but they are all the
same height. The lines behind the girls start out
parallel and move together as you move left. This
appears to indicate depth and the girls are farther
away. Since they are the same height, the tallest girl
appears to be farther away on the right.

Warm Up

1.–5. Answers may vary. 1. A, B, C, D, E; AB, DE,
GH, AG, BH **2.** AB, AC, AD, AE, BC **3.** ∠ABC,
∠CBD, ∠BDE, ∠EDG, ∠DGF **4. a)** R, S, T
b) NX,QY, MW **c)** ∠NRM, ∠QSW, ∠YTX, ∠MRT,
∠YTR, ∠RST **d)** SQ, SW, SY **e)** RT, TS, RS **5.** 6
6.–7. Answers may vary. AF, FE, EB, AB, BC, CD,
ED

Mental Math

Performing Operations and Solving Equations 1. 76
2. 51 **3.** 29 **4.** 136 **5.** 82 **6.** 43 **7.** 135 **8.** 59 **9.** 90
10. 74 **11.** 110 **12.** 46 **13.** 31 **14.** 65 **15.** 60 **16.** 45
17. 30 **18.** 90
Multiplying by Multiples of 12 1. 216 **2.** 252 **3.** 396
4. 576 **5.** 1560 **6.** 5400 **7.** 18 **8.** 31.2 **9.** 49.2
10. 1920 **11.** 3720 **12.** 26 400 **13.** 30 **14.** 38.4
15. 52.8 **16.** 12 = 10 + 2, First multiply by 10, then
multiply by 2 and add the answers. **17.** 22 = 2(10) + 2,
First multiply by 2, then multiply by 10 and add these
answers. **18.** 308 **19.** 484 **20.** 946

Investigating Math pp. 512–514

1 Angles 1. a) 30°, acute **b)** 65°, acute **c)** 86°, acute
d) 90°, acute **e)** 38°, acute **f)** 71°, acute **g)** 7°, acute
h) 90°, right **i)** 115°, obtuse **j)** 142°, obtuse
k) 173°, obtuse **l)** 180°, straight **2.** Answers may
vary. **2. a)** 90°, right angle **b)** 180°, straight angle
c) 45°, acute angle **d)** 110°, obtuse angle **e)** 80°, acute
angle **f)** 290°, reflex angle **g)** 120°, obtuse angle **h)** 60°,
acute angle **3. a)** 60° **b)** 48° **c)** 15° **d)** 81° **e)** 1° **f)** 24°
g) 75° **h)** 89° **4. a)** 140° **b)** 110° **c)** 95° **d)** 30° **e)** 55°
f) 172° **g)** 70° **h)** 1° **5. a)** 15° **b)** 45° **c)** 107° **d)** 63°
2 Intersecting Lines 1. a) $a = 131°$, $b = 49°$, $c = 131°$
b) $x = 14°$, $y = 166°$, $z = 14°$ **c)** $x = 40°$, $y = 80°$,
$z = 40°$, $t = 60°$ **d)** $a = 54°$, $b = 39°$, $c = 87°$, $d = 54°$
2. a) 124°, 56°, 124°, 56° **b)** 138°, 42°, 138°, 42°
c) 67.5°, 112.5°, 67.5°, 112.5° **d)** 64°, 116°, 64°, 116°
3 Triangles 1. a) isosceles, acute **b)** scalene, right
c) isosceles, obtuse **d)** scalene, obtuse **e)** equilateral,
acute **f)** isosceles, right **g)** scalene, acute **h)** isosceles,
acute **2. a)** scalene, right, equilateral, acute, scalene,
right **b)** isosceles, acute, isosceles, obtuse, isosceles,
acute, isosceles, obtuse **c)** scalene, obtuse, scalene,
obtuse, scalene, right **d)** scalene, right, scalene,
obtuse, scalene, obtuse, scalene, obtuse, scalene, right

Technology pp. 515–517
1 Interior Angles of a Triangle   1. Answers may vary. **1. d)** 180° **2. b)** 180° **3.** The sum to the measure of the 3 interior angles of a triangle is 180°.
4. a) The greatest angle is across from the longest side. **b)** The smallest angle is across from the shortest side. **c)** The greatest angle is across from the longest side and the smallest angle is across from shortest side. **5. b)** They are equal. **c)** They are equal.
6. The two numbers are equal. Angles across from the 2 equal sides of an isosceles triangle are equal.
7. b) They all equal 60°. **d)** They all equal 60°. **8.** The measure of each angle in an equilateral triangle is 60°.
2 Exterior Angles of a Triangle   1. e) The sum of the 2 interior angles that are opposite the exterior angle is the same as the exterior angle. **2. b)** They are equal. **3.** The sum of the 2 interior angles that are opposite the exterior angle is the same as the exterior angle.
3 Interior Angles of a Quadrilateral   1. c) 360°
2. b) 360° **3.** The sum of the measures of the 4 exterior angles of a quadrilateral is 360°.
4 Exterior Angles of a Quadrilateral   1. a) 360°
2. b) 360° **3.** The sum of the measures of the 4 exterior angles of a quadrilateral is 360°.

Section 10.1 pp. 522–524
Practice   1. 61° **2.** 24° **3.** $x = 62°, y = 79°$ **4.** $x = 61°$, $y = 119°$ **5.** $y = 55°, z = 70°$ **6.** $x = y = z = 60°$, $w = 120°$ **7.** $a = 46°, b = 61°, c = 73°$ **8.** $r = 54°$, $s = 35°, t = 91°$ **9.** $a = 45°, b = 83°$ **10.** $x = 50°, y = 25°$ **11.** $x = 53°, y = 37°$ **12.** $x = 64°, y = 64°, t = 78°$ **13.** 52° **14.** $b = 53°, a = 122°$ **15.** $a = 83°, b = 92°$, $c = 104°, d = 81°, e = 99°$ **16.** $x = 120°, y = 120°$, $z = 131°$
Applications and Problem Solving   17. a) $e = 133°$, $a = 71°, b = 19°, c = 62°, d = 90°$ **b)** $x = 27°, y = 19°$, $w = 90°, t = 117°$ **18.** $x = 113°, y = 113°$ **19. a)** 30°, 30°, 60°, 90° **b)** 60°, 60°, 95°, 25° **c)** 12°, 57°, 79°, 44° **d)** 7°, 90°, 53°, 37° **e)** 36°, 36°, 35°, 109°, 71° **f)** 74°, 79°, 71°, 30°, 150° **20. a)** 36°, 36°, 72°, 108°, 144° **b)** 60°, 60°, 60°, 120°, 120° **c)** 94°, 94°, 108° **d)** 91°, 86°, 95°, 81°, 98° **21.** quadrilateral; 135°, 45°, 135°, 45°; triangle; 45°, 45°, 90° **22.** $\angle C = \angle A$, $\angle B = 180° - 2\angle A$ **23.** $2\angle D$ **24. a)** 3 **b)** 1 **c)** 0 **25.** Yes; if it is an isosceles right triangle. **26.** 40°, 100° or 70°, 70° **27.** 20°, 20° **28. a)** never **b)** sometimes **c)** always **d)** sometimes **29.** 11.9 m **30.** Four triangles are formed. There are 360° in the angles formed at the chosen point. $4(180°) - (360°) = 360°$ **31. a)** no **b)** yes **c)** yes **d)** no **32. a)** They exist: A, B, C, D, E, G, H;

They do not exist: F, I **b)** In an equilateral triangle all angles are 60°. No 90° angle and no obtuse angle.

Technology pp. 525–526
1 Angle Bisectors of a Triangle   1. c) They all meet at a point. **3. b)** yes **c)** yes **d)** yes
2 Median of a Triangle   1. d) They all meet at a point. **2.** Each median splits the triangle in half. Each median meets at the centroid, which is the centre of gravity. **3. b)** yes **c)** yes **d)** yes
3 Altitudes of a Triangle   1. f) They all meet at a point. **2. b)** yes **c)** The orthocentre becomes the midpoint of the hypotenuse. **d)** It is outside the triangle. **e)** It is outside the triangle.
4 Making and Testing a Conjecture   1. The three perpendicular bisectors of the sides of a triangle meet a a point. **2.** They all meet at a point. **3.** The circumcentre of a triangle is the centre of the circle passing through the 3 vertices of the triangle. It is found as the perpendicular bisector of the 3 sides. The circumcircle passes through the 3 vertices of the triangle.

Investigating Math pp. 527–528
1. Place the compass point on vertex B of the angle. Draw an arc intersecting 2 arms of the angle at D and E. Place the compass point on D and draw an arc between the arms of the angle. Place the compass point on E and draw the same arc. The arcs meet at F. The ray BF bisects $\angle ABC$. **2.** Fold the paper so that the vertex of the angle lies on the crease and the two arms of the angle fall on top of one another.
3. Place the Mira so it passes through B and is between the arms of the angle. Move the other end of the Mira until the image in the Mira appears to lie on the back arm of the angle. **4.** 30°, 60°, 45°, 90°
2 Right Bisectors   1. Place the compass point on the point A. Draw an arc above and below the segment. Place the compass point on B and draw the same arc above and below the segment. The arcs meet at C and D. The line CD is the perpendicular bisector of AB. **2.** Fold the paper so that points A and B meet. **3.** Place the Mira between A and B. Adjust the Mira so that the line segment in the Mira is straight with the line segment behind the Mira. Move the Mira forward or backward until points A and B appear together and the line behind the Mira line up with the image.
3 Perpendicular Lines   1. Place the compass point at P and draw an arc intersecting the segment AB at C and D. Place the compass point at C and draw an arc

on the opposite side of AB from P. Place the compass point at D and draw the same arc. The arcs meet at Q. PQ is the line perpendicular to the segment. **2.** Fold the paper so that point P lies on the crease and a point C on the line segment AB lies on the crease and segments AC and BC fall on top of one another. PC is perpendicular to AB. **3.** Place the Mira through P and the segment AB. Move the Mira so that one ray through A or B lines up with the other ray. Draw the line along the Mira through P.

Investigating Math p. 529
1 Angle Bisectors of a Triangle   3. b) yes **c)** yes
2 Medians of a Triangle   2. The medians cut the triangle in half. The centroid is a point that is on the 3 medians. It is the centre of the triangle with equal halves on each of the 3 medians. It is the centre of gravity of the triangle. **3. b)** yes **c)** yes
3 Altitudes of a Triangle   2. at the vertex, which is the 90° angle **3.** It is outside the triangle.
4 Making and Testing a Conjecture   1.–2. Answers may vary. **3.** The circumcentre of a triangle is the centre of the circle passing through the three vertices of the triangle. It is found as the perpendicular bisector of the three sides. The circumcircle passes through the three vertices of the triangle.

Technology pp. 530–531
2 Alternate Angles   2. equal **3.** equal **4.** equal
5. equal **6.** When a transversal cuts parallel lines, pairs of alternate angles are equal.
3 Corresponding Angles   1. equal **2.** equal **3.** equal
4. equal **5.** When a transversal cuts parallel lines, pairs of corresponding angles are equal.
4 Co-Interior Angles   1. 180° **2.** 180° **3.** 180°
4. 180° **5.** When a transversal cuts parallel lines, pairs of co-interior angles are supplementary.

Section 10.2 pp. 535–536
1. $x = 75°$, $y = 105°$ **2.** $m = 98°$, $n = 82°$ **3.** $p = 70°$, $q = 110°$, $r = 110°$ **4.** $w = 88°$, $x = 92°$, $y = 88°$, $z = 92°$
5. $x = 87°$, $y = 103°$ **6.** 103° **7.** $t = 70°$, $x = 35°$, $y = 70°$
8. $m = 100°$, $x = 100°$, $y = 80°$ **9.** $m = 95°$, $t = 85°$, $x = 40°$ **10.** $x = 51°$, $y = 57°$ **11.** $t = 106°$, $x = 30°$, $y = 44°$ **12.** $a = 75°$, $b = 25°$, $c = 120°$, $d = 35°$, $e = 35°$, $f = 45°$, $g = 45°$ **13.** $x = 112°$, $y = 123°$, $z = 57°$
14. $x = 100°$, $y = 75°$ **15.** $v = 120°$, $w = 60°$, $x = 61°$, $y = 119°$, $z = 120°$ **16.** $x = 95°$, $y = 30°$, $z = 55°$
17. $p = 57°$, $q = 71°$, $r = 57°$ **18.** $x = 58°$, $y = 55°$, $z = 67°$
Applications and Problem Solving   19. $t = 82°$, $u = 98°$, $w = 98°$, $x = 98°$, $y = 105°$, $z = 82°$

20. $u = 46°$, $v = 81°$, $w = 81°$, $x = 46°$, $y = 46°$, $z = 99°$
21. $m = 57°$, $r = 123°$, $t = 123°$, $u = 57°$, $w = 33°$, $x = 147°$, $y = 33°$, $z = 147°$ **22.** $a = 85°$, $b = 54°$, $c = 95°$, $d = 52°$, $e = 74°$ **23. a)** $x = 9$; $a = 134°$, $b = 46°$, $c = 134°$, $d = 134°$, $e = 134°$ **b)** $x = 30$; $m = 47°$, $n = 133°$, $p = 133°$, $q = 47°$**24. a)** $x = 45$, $y = 60$; $a = 120°$, $b = 120°$ **b)** $x = 55$, $y = 125$; $m = 125°$, $n = 125°$ **c)** $x = 30$, $y = 12$; $a = 36°$, $b = 144°$ **d)** $x = 9$, $y = 25$; $q = 135°$, $p = 72°$ **25.** $\angle PAQ = 70°$, $\angle APQ = 55°$, $\angle AQP$ $55°$, $\angle QPB = 125°$, $\angle PQD = 55°$, $\angle DQC = 70°$, $\angle QCD = 55°$, $\angle QDB = 125°$, $\angle PBD = 55°$ **26.** $\angle 1 = x$, $\angle 2 = 90° - x$, $\angle 3 = 90° - x$, $\angle 4 = x$ **27.** $\angle XAB = \angle B$ alternate angles. $\angle BAC = \angle BAC$ same angle. $\angle YAC = \angle C$ alternate angles. Adding the left and right gives a straight line on the left or 180° and the three angles in the triangle on the right. **28.** They actually go around the world and join, so they are not lines. **29.** Skew lines are not parallel because they are in different directions. They are different. Both types of lines do not meet, so they are alike.
30.–31. Answers may vary.

Investigating Math pp. 538–539
1 Equilateral and Equiangular Polygons   1. a) not closed **b)** All sides are not lines. **c)** Starting at one vertex and going in one direction should bring you back to the first point only when you have gone around the entire polygon. **3.** A diamond shape called a rhombus. **4.** Rectangle
2 Diagonal Pattern   1. Polygon, Number of Diagonals; Quadrilateral, 2; Pentagon, 5; Hexagon, 9; Heptagon, 14 **2.** The number of diagonals increases by 3, then 4, then 5, etc. If n is the number of sides, then the number of diagonals is $\dfrac{n^2 - 3n}{2}$. **3. a)** 20
b) 27 **c)** 35
3 Angles and Regular Polygons   1. a) 360° **b)** 72°
c) isosceles, acute **d)** 54°, 54° **e)** 540° **f)** 108° **2. a)** 60°
b) equilateral **c)** 60° **d)** 720° **e)** 120° **3. a)** 45° **b)** 1080°
c) 135°

Technology pp. 540–543
1 Sides   1. a) If the midpoints of a quadrilateral are joined, a parallelogram is formed. **e)** Opposite sides are equal in length. **f)** Opposite interior angles are equal. **g)** Opposite sides are equal and opposite interior angles are equal. **h)** If the midpoints of a quadrilateral are joined, a parallelogram is formed.
2. a) If the midpoints of a parallelogram are joined, a rhombus is formed. **e)** All the sides are the same

length. **f)** Opposite interior angles are equal and adjacent interior angles are supplementary. **g)** All the sides are the same length. Opposite interior angles are equal and adjacent interior angles are supplementary. **h)** A rhombus is formed. **3. a)** If the midpoints of a rectangle are joined, a rhombus is formed. **e)** All the sides are the same length. **f)** Opposite interior angles are equal and adjacent interior angles are supplementary. All the sides are the same length. Opposite interior angles are equal and adjacent interior angles are supplementary. **h)** A rhombus is formed. **4. a)** If the midpoints of a rhombus are joined, a rectangle is formed. **e)** Opposite sides are the same length. **f)** All interior angles are 90°. **g)** Opposite sides are the same length. All interior angles are 90°. **h)** A rectangle is formed. **5. a)** If the midpoints of a square are joined, a square is formed. **e)** All sides are equal. **f)** All interior angles are 90°. **g)** All the sides are the same length. All interior angles are 90°. **h)** A square is formed. **6. a)** If the midpoints of a kite are joined, a rectangle is formed. **e)** Opposite sides are equal in length. **f)** All interior angles are 90°. **g)** Opposite sides are the same length. All interior angles are 90°. **h)** A rectangle is formed.

2 Diagonals **1. c)** They are not necessarily equal. **e)** The intersection point cuts the diagonals in half. **f)** They are equal in pairs. **g)** The point of intersection cuts each diagonal in half. **h)** In a parallelogram, the diagonals bisect and the intersection angles are not 90°. In a rhombus, the diagonals bisect and the intersection angles are 90°. In a rectangle, the diagonals bisect and the intersection angles are not 90°. In a square, the diagonals are equal and bisect. The intersection angles are 90°. **2. c)** The diagonals are equal. **e)** The point of intersection cuts each diagonal in half so all are equal in length. **f)** They are equal in pairs. **g)** The point of intersection cuts each diagonal in half so all are equal in length. The angles are equal in pairs. **h)** In a rectangle, the diagonals are equal and bisect. The intersection angles are not 90°. **3. c)** They are not equal. **e)** The intersection point cuts the diagonals in half. **f)** The intersection angles are 90°. **g)** The diagonals bisect and the intersection angles are 90°. **h)** In a rhombus, the diagonals are different lengths and they bisect. The intersection angles are 90°. **4. c)** The diagonals are equal in length. **e)** The intersection point cuts the diagonals in half. **f)** The intersection angles are 90°. **g)** The diagonals are equal and bisect. The intersection angles are 90°. **h)** In a square, the diagonals are equal and bisect. The

intersection angles are 90°. **5. c)** The diagonals are different lengths. **e)** The intersection point does not cut the diagonals in half. **f)** The intersection angles are equal in pairs and are not 90°. **g)** The point of intersection does cut one diagonal in half. The angles are equal in pairs. **h)** In a kite, the point of intersection cuts one diagonal in half. The angles are equal in pairs. **6. a)** rectangle and square **b)** parallelogram, rectangle, rhombus, and square **c)** rhombus, square, and kite **d)** rhombus and square **7. a)** A smaller regular pentagon is formed. **e)** Answers vary, but all are the same. **f)** All interior angles are 108°. **g)** The sides are all the same length and the angles are all 108°. **h)** The new pentagon is a regular pentagon. **8. b)** Answers may vary. **c)** 1.618

Investigating Math pp. 544–547
1 Sides **1. a)** If the midpoints of a square are joined, a square is formed. **c)** The lengths are all $4\sqrt{2}$. **d)** The angles are all 90°. **e)** Yes; a square was formed. **2. a)** If the midpoints of a rectangle are joined, a rhombus is formed. **c)** The lengths are all 5. **d)** $\angle KLM = \angle MNK = 74°$, $\angle LMN = \angle NKL = 106°$. They are different and supplementary. **e)** Yes; a rhombus was formed. **3. a)** If the midpoints of a quadrilateral are joined, a parallelogram is formed. **c)** The lengths are both 4.0. **d)** The lengths are both 4.6. **e)** $\angle SPQ = \angle QRS = 101°$, $\angle PQR = \angle RSP = 79°$; Opposite angles are equal. **f)** Yes; a parallelogram is formed. **4. a)** If the midpoints of a kite are joined, a rectangle is formed. **c)** HE = GF = 4, HG = EF = 5; $\angle HEF = \angle EFG = \angle FGH = \angle GHE = 90°$ **d)** Yes. A rectangle is formed. **5. a)** If the midpoints of a rhombus are joined, a rectangle is formed. **c)** WZ = XY = 4.5, WX = YZ = 8.9; $\angle WXY = \angle XYZ = \angle YZW = \angle ZWX = 90°$ **d)** Yes. A rectangle is formed.

2 Diagonals **1. b)** They are both 10. **c)** They are both 5. **d)** They are both 5. **e)** $\angle AED = \angle CEB = 74°$, $\angle DEC = \angle BEA = 106°$; They are equal in pairs. **f)** The diagonals of a rectangle are equal and bisected by each other. They do not intersect at 90°. **2. b)** DF is 8.5 and EG is 11.7. **c)** DH and FH are both 4.2. **d)** EH and GH are both 5.8. **e)** $\angle DHG = \angle FHE = 76°$, $\angle GHF = \angle EHD = 104°$. They are equal in pairs. **f)** The lengths of the diagonals are different but they do bisect each other. They do not meet at 90°. **3. b)** JL = 7 and MK = 6. They are different. **c)** JN = 2 and LN = 5. They are different. **d)** KN = 3 and MN = 3. They are equal.

e) $\angle$JNM = $\angle$ MNL = $\angle$LNK = $\angle$KNJ = 90°. They are all equal. f) The lengths of the diagonals are different and one diagonal is bisected.
4. b) RT is 4.5 and QS is 8.9. They are different.
c) RW = TW = 2.2. They are equal.
d) SW = QW = 4.4. They are equal.
e) $\angle$RWQ = $\angle$QWT = $\angle$TWS = $\angle$SWR = 90°. They are equal. f) The diagonals of a rhombus are different but they bisect each other. They also intersect at 90°.
5. b) WY = XZ = 11.3. They are equal.
c) WT = YT = 5.7. They are equal.
d) ZT = XT = 5.7. They are equal.
e) $\angle$WTZ = $\angle$ZTY = $\angle$YTX = $\angle$XTW = 90°. They are equal. f) The diagonals of a square are equal and they bisect. They meet at 90°. 6. a) rectangle, square
b) parallelogram, rectangle, rhombus, square
c) rhombus, square, kite d) rhombus , square
7. Lengths may vary. b) They are all equal.
c) All equal 108°. d) Yes. 8. Lengths may vary. c) 1.6

Career Connection p. 548
1 Designing With Triangles and Quadrilaterals
1. a) 60° b) 13 2. a) 30°, 75°, 75° b) 60°, 75°, 150°, 75°
3. a) 90°, 45°, 45° b) 16 4. a) 45°, 135°, 45°, 135° b) 8
5. Answers may vary.

Investigating Math pp. 550–551
1 Posing Questions Related to Triangles 1. The
sum of the lengths of 2 sides of a triangle is greater than the length of the third side. 2. When the midpoints D and E of 2 sides of a triangle are joined, this side DE is one-half the length of the side parallel to the joined side BC. 3. When the midpoints of the 3 sides of a triangle are joined to form a new triangle, the new triangle has sides one-half the length of the larger triangle and the angles are equal to the angles in the larger triangle. 4. a) Draw the 10 triangles that can be formed using three 6-cm, three 7-cm, and three 8-cm straws. b) Draw the 8 triangles that can be formed using three 4-cm, three 8-cm, and three 9-cm straws. c) Answers may vary.
2 Posing Questions Related to Parallel Lines
1. Are the exterior angles on the same side of the transversal supplementary? 2. a) Are the exterior angles on alternate sides of the transversal equal?
b) Are angles on the same side of the parallel lines but on opposite sides of the transversal supplementary?
3. Does the measure of $\angle$1 + the measure of $\angle$2 = x?
3 Posing Questions Related to Quadrilaterals
1. Is the sum of the interior angles of a concave quadrilateral 360°? 2. In an isosceles trapezoid, the

angles are equal in pairs. The top angles are equal and the bottom angles are equal. Are the top and bottom angles supplementary? 3. Are the lengths of the diagonals of a rectangle equal?

Section 10.3 pp. 553–554
Practice 1. Ontario shares a border with the United States. Newfoundland does not share a border with the United States. 2. Nova Scotia has a coastline. Saskatchewan does not have a coastline.
3. Toronto is south of 53°N latitude. Edmonton is north of 53°N latitude. 4. The square root of 4 is smaller than 4. The square root of 1 is not smaller than 1. 5. The x-coordinate of (3,2) is positive and the point is in the first quadrant. The x-coordinate of (3,–2) is positive and the point is not in the first quadrant. 6. The square of 6 is greater than 6. The square of 1 is not greater than 1. 7. 16 is a multiple of 4 and is divisible by 8. 12 is a multiple of 4 and is not divisible by 8. 8. The square root of 16 is a rational number. The square root of 2 is not a rational number. 9. A square has equal diagonals and it is not a rectangle. 10. If 2 angles of a quadrilateral are 45°, then the others add to 270° and are not supplementary. 11. A rhombus has 4 equal sides and is not a square. 12. True 13. One of the altitudes of an obtuse triangle lies outside the triangle. 14. The triangle with sides 3, $\sqrt{7}$, and 4 is a right triangle.
Applications and Problem Solving 15. False. In a 60°, 70°, 50° triangle, the smallest side is opposite the 50° angle. 16. False. 17. True. 18. False. A rhombus has perpendicular diagonals. 19. True. If three angles are 90°, to get a sum of 360°, the fourth angle would be 90°. 20. False. A quadrilateral with angles 90°, 120°, 60°, and 90° is not a rectangle. 21. True. 22. False. A quadrilateral with angles 90°, 120°, 60°, and 90° is not a rectangle. 23. True. 24. False. The angles must be equal to be a regular pentagon. 25. It may be obtuse, acute, right, or straight. 26. They may be perpendicular. Then B is not the midpoint. 27. False. 28. This happens in a kite and it is not a parallelogram.

Section 10.4 pp.555–557
Answers may vary.

Review pp. 558–559
1. 47° 2. 24° 3. $x = 65°$, $y = 48°$ 4. $x = 64°$, $y = 52°$
5. $w = 88°$, $x = 51°$, $y = 92°$, $z = 88°$ 6. 93° 7. $x = 82°$, $y = 115°$ 8. $u = 125°$, $w = 55°$, $x = 87°$, $y = 85°$, $z = 133°$ 9. $x = 65°$, $y = 65°$, $z = 76°$ 10. $x = 90°$,

$y = 16°$, $z = 32°$, $w = 106°$ **11.** $w = 90°$, $x = 60°$, $y = 120°$, $z = 30°$ **12.** $v = 64°$, $w = 26°$, $x = 52°$, $y = 77°$, $z = 64°$ **13.** 20; 40°, 60°, 80° **14.** 62; 62°, 99°, 19° **15.** 50.8; 48.8°, 56.8°, 74.4° **16.** 40; 40°, 80°, 120°, 120° **17.** 52; 70°, 142°, 107°, 41° **18.** 88; 90°, 81°, 93°, 96° **19.** $a = 115°$, $b = 65°$, $c = 115°$, $d = 115°$, $e = 65°$, $x = 65°$, $y = 115°$ **20.** $a = 100°$, $b = 80°$, $c = 100°$, $d = 80°$, $e = 100°$ **21.** $a = 47°$, $b = 62°$, $c = 71°$, $d = 109°$, $e = 109°$, $f = 118°$, $g = 118°$ **22.** $a = 34°$, $b = 87°$, $c = 34°$, $d = 59°$ **23.** $t = 83°$, $y = 51°$, $x = 46°$, $z = 83°$ **24.** $a = 65°$, $b = 105°$, $c = 115°$, $d = 115°$, $e = 105°$, $f = 75°$, $g = 65°$, $y = 75°$, $x = 40°$ **25.** $w = 106°$, $x = 56°$, $y = 50°$, $z = 74°$ **26.** $u = 132°$, $w = 48°$, $x = 76°$, $y = 76°$, $z = 48°$ **27.** 18; $a = 129°$, $b = 51°$, $c = 51°$, $d = 129°$ **28.** 10; $a = 119°$, $b = 119°$, $c = 61°$, $d = 61°$, $e = 61°$, $f = 61°$ **29.** 23; $a = 46°$, $b = 82°$, $c = 134°$, $d = 52°$ **30.** 14; $a = 28°$, $b = 82°$, $c = 70°$, $d = 110°$ **31.** 55° **32.** They do not intersect inside an obtuse triangle. **33.** A rectangle has equal diagonals. **34.** False. A rectangle has 4 equal angles. **35.** False. A kite has 2 pairs of equal angles and it is not a parallelogram. **36.** True; you would have a line. **37.** True.

Chapter Check p. 560
1. 58° **2.** $x = 28°$, $y = 152°$ **3.** $x = 82°$, $y = 49°$ **4.** 58° **5.** $x = 117°$, $y = 71°$ **6.** $u = 66°$, $w = 98°$, $x = 44°$, $y = 60°$, $z = 136°$ **7.** $x = 74°$, $y = 74°$, $z = 68°$ **8.** $x = 90°$, $y = 18°$, $z = 66°$ **9.** 36; 52°, 57°, 71° **10.** 68; 64°, 76°, 140° **11.** 46; 63°, 90°, 80°, 127° **12.** 83; 96°, 99°, 94°, 71° **13.** $a = 123°$, $b = 57°$, $c = 57°$, $d = 123°$, $e = 57°$, $f = 123°$, $g = 57°$ **14.** $a = 47°$, $b = 95°$, $c = 95°$, $d = 38°$ **15.** $a = 99°$, $b = 81°$, $c = 99°$ **16.** $a = 87°$, $b = 42°$, $c = 51°$, $d = 87°$ **17.** $a = 98°$, $b = 82°$, $c = 98°$, $d = 103°$, $e = 77°$ **18.** $a = 56°$, $b = 34°$, $c = 56°$, $d = 34°$, $e = 56°$ **19.** 20°; $a = 125°$, $b = 55°$, $c = 125°$, $d = 125°$ **20.** 23°, $m = 111°$, $n = 69°$ **21.** A triangle with angles 85°, 15° and 80° is scalene. **22.** The angles must also be equal. **23.** Only if it is an isosceles trapezoid. **24.** Only if the transversal is perpendicular to the parallel lines. **25.** A quadrilateral with interior angles of 95°, 95°, 100°, and 70° has three obtuse interior angles. **26.** True. **27.** True.

Using Strategies p. 561
2. $5\dfrac{9}{28}$ **3.** 4 **4.** Answers may vary. **5.** Spend $6.35,

$5.45, $8.15, $7.25, $3.65, $4.55, or $1.85 **6.** 35, 12, 23 **7.** 154, 42, or 126 **8. a)** 20, 30 **b)** $l^2 - 5l + 6$ **c)** 132, 1406 **9. a)** Lauryn wins by 1 m. **b)** Lauryn and Yolanda run at the same average speed as in the first race. **10.** $\dfrac{4}{20}$ or 20%

Cumulative Review, Chapters 9–10 p. 562
Chapter 9 1. 43 m² **2.** 78 m² **3.** 244 m² **4.** 679 m² **5.** 141 m² **6.** 1018 m² **7.** 213 cm³ **8.** 455 cm³ **9.** 1357 cm³ **10.** 38 cm³ **11. a)** 315 cm³ **b)** 315 mL
Chapter 10 1. 51° **2.** $x = 47°$, $y = 71°$ **3.** 121° **4.** $x = 57°$, $y = 121°$ **5.** 58°, 60°, 62° **6.** 46°, 83°, 135°, 96° **7.** $a = 113°$, $b = 67°$, $c = 67°$, $d = 113°$, $e = 67°$, $f = 113°$ **8.** $a = 102°$, $b = 36°$, $c = 102°$, $d = 42°$ **9.** 33; 110°, $b = 70°$, $c = 70°$, $d = 110°$, $e = 70°$, $f = 110°$ **10.** 23; $a = 95°$, $b = 95°$, $c = 85°$, **11.** The diagonals of a parallelogram bisect each other. **12.** A quadrilateral with angles of 50°, 120°, 50°, 160°. **13.** False. Any isoceles obtuse triangle has one acute exterior angle. **14.** False. A 90°, 45°, 90°, 135° quadrilateral has two 90° exterior angles.

Cumulative Review, Chapters 1–10
pp. 563–565
1. 211.7 **2.** 6.1 **3.** 598 **4.** 6.3 **5. a)** 30.6 **b)** 22.2 **c)** 35.4 **6. a)** 7 **b)** 1 **c)** 19 **7. a)** 2^8 **8.** 5^2 **9.** 7^{12} **10.** x^{11} **11.** x^5 **12.** x^{10} **13.** 2 **14.** −14 **15.** −56 **16.** 6 **17.** 16 **18.** −125 **19.** −10 **20.** −1 **21.** −15 **22.** −23 **23. a)** −2 **b)** 34 **c)** 20 **d)** 43 **24.** 3 to 4 **25.** 4:5 **26.** $\dfrac{2}{3}$ **27.** 5 **28.** $\dfrac{14}{3}$ **29.** 20 m **30.** $4.60 for 4 L **31.** 55% **32.** 9% **33.** 134% **34.** 0.24 **35.** 0.008 **36.** 1.43 **37.** $143 **38.** 1.23×10^7 **39.** 4.2×10^{-5} **40.** 320 000 000 **41.** 0.000 005 8 **42.** 4 **43.** 3 **44.** 5^{10} **45.** 9 **46.** $\dfrac{1}{16}$ **47.** 81 **48.** 22.1 **49.** −27.01 **50.** −54 **51.** 10.7 **52.** −3 **53.** $-9\dfrac{5}{8}$ **54.** $-\dfrac{10}{7}$ **55.** $-5\dfrac{2}{5}$ **56.** 2 **57.** 14.24 **58.** $6\dfrac{4}{5}$ **59.** 64 **60.** 23.0 **61.** 67.5 **62.** 0.9 **63.** 31.0 m **64.** Population: local secondary school students; stratified sampling **65.** 47%; 21% **66. c)** $54 billion **67. b)** perimeter 12 units; area 6 square units **68. c)** 7 m, 13 m **69.** partial variation **70.** direct variation **72.** $4x^2 + 4x - 1$ **73.** $-3y^2 + 2y - 15$ **74.** $12y - 1$ **75.** $5x + 1$ **76.** $-8x^2 + 15x - 10$ **77.** $9x^2 - 10x$ **78.** $12x^3y$ **79.** $-6d^3e^4$ **80.** $9x^4y^6$ **81.** $-8w^3x^9y^9$ **82.** $-5x^2y^3$ **83.** $7t^3$ **84.** $5x(3x - 2)$

85. $3xy(3xy - x + 2y)$ **86.** 8 **87.** −3 **88.** −6 **89.** −8
90. −4 **91.** 5 **92.** 1 **93.** −2 **94.** 1 **95.** Let x represent the area of Georgian Bay Islands National Park then use the second sentence to write the equation $x + (x - 10) = 40$. Solve the equation. The area of Georgian Bay Islands National Park is 25 km². The area of Point Pelee National Park is 15 km². **96.** 3
97. −2 **98.** 0 **99.** undefined **100.** $4x - y - 7 = 0$
101. $3x + 4y - 5 = 0$ **102.** $7x - y - 13 = 0$

103. $x - 3y - 11 = 0$ **104.** −3; 4 **105.** $\dfrac{5}{2}$; 5

108. $x - 3y + 17 = 0$ **109.** (1, 5) **110.** $y = 1.5x - 1.5$
111. 103.7 m² **112.** 100 m² **113.** 172 cm²; 112 cm³
114. 471 m²; 785 m³ **115.** 77 m²; 42 m³ **116.** 616 cm²; 1437 cm³ **117.** 256 cm²; 241 cm³ **118.** 292 m²; 276 m³
119. a) 157 cm³ **b)** 157 mL **120.** $x = 58°$, $y = 59°$
121. $x = 104°$, $y = 132°$ **122.** $a = 62°$, $b = 118°$, $c = 62°$, $d = 62°$, $e = 118°$, $f = 62°$, $g = 118°$ **123.** $a = 98°$, $b = 82°$, $c = 98°$ **124.** $x = 44°$; 56°, 61°, 63° **125.** $x = 6°$; $a = 127°$, $b = 53°$, $c = 127°$, $d = 127°$, $e = 53°$, $f = 127°$
127. The conjecture is not true. A counterexample is a rectangle.

GLOSSARY

A

acute angle   An angle whose measure is less than 90°.

acute triangle   A triangle in which each of the three interior angles is acute.

addition property of equality   Adding the same quantity to both sides of an equation produces an equivalent equation. For any numbers a, b, and c, if $a = b$, then $a + c = b + c$.

algebraic expression   An expression that includes at least one variable.

$2x + 5$, $4y$, $8 - 3w$ are all algebraic expressions.

algebraic modelling   The process of representing a relationship by an equation or a formula, or representing a pattern of numbers by an algebraic expression.

algorithm   A specific set of instructions for carrying out a procedure.

alternate angles   Two angles formed on opposite sides of a transversal.

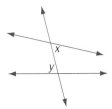

∠x and ∠y are alternate angles.

altitude   The height of a geometric figure. In a triangle, an altitude is the perpendicular distance from a vertex to the opposite side.

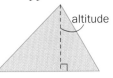

altitude

analytic geometry   The geometry that uses the xy-plane to determine equations that represent lines and curves.

angle bisector   A line that divides an angle into two equal parts.

application   The use of the concepts and skills of mathematics to solve real-world problems.

area   The number of square units contained in a region.

B

bar graph   A graph that uses bars to represent data.

base (of a power)   The number used as a factor for repeated multiplication. In 6^3, the base is 6.

BEDMAS   An acronym that lists the order of operations. BEDMAS stands for **B**rackets, **E**xponents, **D**ivision, **M**ultiplication, **A**ddition, **S**ubtraction.

binomial   An algebraic expression with two terms.

$3x - 4$ is a binomial.

box-and-whisker plot   A method of displaying numerical data to show the distribution of the data. A box is drawn between the upper and lower quartiles, and horizontal segments, the whiskers, extend from the box to the greatest and the least values.

broken-line graph   A graph showing data that relates two variables as ordered pairs, with consecutive points joined by line segments.

C

capacity   The greatest volume that a container can hold, usually measured in litres, millilitres, or kilolitres.

Cartesian coordinate system   The system developed by René Descartes for graphing points as ordered pairs on a grid made up of two perpendicular number lines.

census A survey in which data are collected from every member of the population.

centroid of a triangle The point of intersection of the three medians of a triangle. Also called the centre of gravity or balance point.

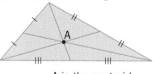

A is the centroid.

chord A line segment joining two points on a curve.

circle The set of all points in the plane that are equidistant from a fixed point called the centre.

circle graph A graph using sectors of a circle to represent data.

circumcentre of a triangle The point of intersection of the three perpendicular bisectors of the sides of a triangle.

circumcircle The circle with centre at the circumcentre, and passing through the three vertices of a triangle.

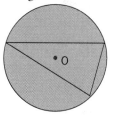

circumference The perimeter of a circle.

clustered sampling A method of choosing a sample, in which a random sample is chosen from one group within the population.

coefficient The factor by which a variable is multiplied. For example, in the term $8y$, the coefficient is 8; in the term ax, the coefficient is a.

co-interior angles Two angles between two lines and on the same side of a transversal.

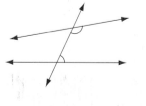

compatible numbers Groups of numbers that can be computed mentally.

complementary angles Angles whose sum is 90°.

composite figure A figure made up of two or more distinct figures.

concave polygon A polygon in which a line segment joining two points on the polygon can be drawn so that a part of the segment lies outside the polygon.

concurrent Two or more lines that have one point in common.

cone A three-dimensional object with a circular base and a curved lateral surface, which extends from the base to a point called the vertex.

congruence The property of being congruent. Two geometric figures are congruent if they are equal in all respects.

constant of variation In a direct variation, the ratio of corresponding values of the variables. For example, if d varies directly as t, then the constant of variation, k, is given by $\frac{d}{t} = k$ or $d = kt$.

constant rate of change A relationship between two variables illustrates a constant rate of change when equal intervals of the first variable are associated with equal intervals of the second variable. For example, if a car travels at 80 km/h, in the first hour it travels 80 km, in the second hour it travels 80 km, and so on.

constant term A term that does not include a variable.

continuous graph A graph that consists of an unbroken line or curve.

convenience sampling A type of non-probability sampling in which the sample is chosen in any convenient way.

convex polygon A polygon in which any line segment joining two points on the polygon has no part outside the polygon.

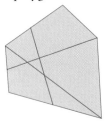

corresponding angles Four pairs of angles formed by two lines and a transversal. In the diagram, the pairs of corresponding angles are:

∠1 and ∠5

∠2 and ∠6

∠3 and ∠7

∠4 and ∠8

cross-product rule If $\dfrac{a}{b} = \dfrac{c}{d}$, then $ad = bc$.

counterexample An example that demonstrates that a conjecture is false.

cube A polyhedron with six congruent square faces.

curve of best fit The curve that best describes the distribution of points in a scatter plot.

cylinder A three-dimensional object with two bases, which are congruent circles, and a curved surface connecting the two bases.

D

decagon A polygon with ten sides.

degree of a polynomial in one variable The greatest exponent of the variable in any one term.

The degree of $n^3 + 2n^2 - 8n$ is 3.

degree of a polynomial in two or more variables The greatest sum of the exponents in any one term.

The degree of $2a^4b^2 + 3a^2b^2 - ab^4$ is 6.

denominator The number of equal parts in the whole or the group: $\dfrac{3}{4}$ has denominator 4.

diagonal A line segment joining two non-adjacent vertices of a polygon.

diameter of a circle A chord that passes through the centre of a circle.

difference of squares A technique of factoring applied to an expression of the form $a^2 - b^2$, which involves the subtraction of two perfect squares.

direct variation A relationship between two variables in which one variable is a constant multiple of the other.

discrete graph A graph that is made up of a series of separate points.

distributive property $a(b + c) = ab + ac$

division property of equality Dividing both sides of an equation by the same quantity produces an equivalent equation. For any numbers a, b, and c, where $c \neq 0$, if $a = b$, then $\dfrac{a}{c} = \dfrac{b}{c}$.

dodecagon A polygon with twelve sides.

domain The set of the first elements in a relation.

dynamic geometry software Computer software that allows the user to plot points on a coordinate system, measure line segments and angles, construct two-dimensional shapes, create two-dimensional representations of three-dimensional objects, and transform constructed figures by moving parts of them.

E

elements The individual members of a set.

equation An open sentence formed by two expressions related by an equal sign.

$2x - 7 = 3x + 2$ is an equation.

equilateral triangle A triangle with all sides equal.

equivalent equations Equations that have the same solution.

equivalent expressions Algebraic expressions that are equal for all values of the variable.

$7a - 4a$ and $3a$ are equivalent expressions.

equivalent fractions Fractions such as $\frac{1}{3}$, $\frac{2}{6}$, and $\frac{3}{9}$ that represent the same part of a whole or group.

equivalent ratios Ratios such as $1:3$, $2:6$, and $3:9$ that represent the same fractional number or amount.

evaluate To determine a value for.

exponent The use of a raised number to denote repeated multiplication of a base. In $3x^4$, the exponent is 4, and $3x^4$ means $3 \times x \times x \times x \times x$.

exponential form A shorthand method for writing numbers expressed as repeated multiplications.

3^4 is the exponential form for 81.

exponential notation The notation used by calculators to display numbers that are too large or too small to fit onto the screen of the calculator. For example, the number 135 000 000 000 might appear as "1.35 11" on a calculator screen. The digits 11 to the right of the expression indicate the number of places that the decimal point should be moved to express the number in standard form.

expression A mathematical phrase made up of numbers and variables, connected by operators.

exterior angle An angle contained between one side of a polygon and the extension of the adjacent side.

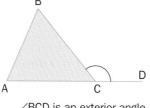

∠BCD is an exterior angle.

extrapolate Estimate values lying outside the range of given data. To extrapolate from a graph means to estimate coordinates of points beyond those that are plotted.

F

face A plane surface of a polyhedron.

factor To express a number as the product of two or more numbers, or an algebraic expression as the product of two or more other algebraic expressions. Also, the individual numbers or algebraic expressions in such a product.

family of lines Lines that share a common characteristic; the family may have the same slope or the same y-intercept.

finite differences Given a table of values in which the x-coordinates are evenly spaced, the first differences are calculated by subtracting consecutive y-coordinates. The second differences are calculated by subtracting consecutive first differences, and so on. In a linear function, the first differences are constant. For example:

x	y	First Difference	Second Difference
1	3		
2	5	5 − 3 = 2	
3	7	7 − 5 = 2	
4	9	9 − 7 = 2	
5	11	11 − 9 = 2	

first-degree equation An equation in which the variable has the exponent 1.

$3(2x + 1) + 5 = 7x - 6$ is a first degree equation.

first-degree inequality An inequality in which the variable has the exponent 1.

$3x + 5 \geq 2x - 4$ is a first degree inequality.

first degree polynomial A polynomial in which the variable has the exponent 1.

$6x + 5$ is a first degree polynomial.

five-number summary For a set of numerical data, these five measures are the least value, the greatest value, the median, the lower quartile, and the upper quartile.

frequency distribution table A table used to organize and collate data.

frustrum The part that remains after the top portion of a cone or pyramid has been cut off by a plane parallel to the base.

G

GST Goods and services tax.

generalize To determine a general rule or conclusion from examples. Specifically, to determine a general rule to represent a pattern or relationship between variables.

graphing calculator A hand-held device capable of a wide range of mathematical operations, including graphing from an equation, constructing a scatter plot, determining the equation of a curve of best fit for a scatter plot, making statistical calculations, and performing elementary symbolic manipulation. Many graphing calculators will attach to scientific probes that can be used to gather data involving physical measurements such as position, temperature, or force.

graphing software Computer software that provides features similar to those of a graphing calculator.

greatest common factor (GCF) The monomial, with the greatest numerical coefficient and greatest degree, that is a factor of two or more terms.

The GCF of $12ab$ and $8bc$ is $4b$.

H

heptagon A polygon with seven sides.

Heron's formula An equation that can be used to calculate the area, A, of a triangle based on the lengths of the sides a, b, and c, and half the perimeter, s. $A = \sqrt{s(s-a)(s-b)(s-c)}$

hexagon A polygon with six sides.

hexomino A polygon formed by joining six identical squares along whole sides.

histogram A graph, like a bar graph but with no space between the bars, used to show continuous data that can be organized into intervals.

hypotenuse The longest side of a right triangle.

hypothesis A possible generalization based on observations or data.

I

incentre The point at which the three angle bisectors of a triangle meet.

incircle A circle, drawn inside a triangle, with centre at the incentre and radius the perpendicular distance from the incentre to any side of the triangle.

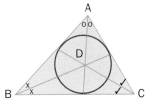

infer from data To make a conclusion based on a relationship identified between variables in a set of data.

inference A generalization based on data.

integer A number in the sequence ..., −3, −2, −1, 0, 1, 2, 3, ...

intercept The distance from the origin of the xy-plane to the point at which a line or curve crosses a given axis.

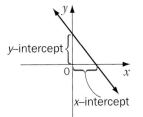

interior angle An angle that is inside a polygon.

interpolate To estimate values lying between elements of given data. To interpolate from a graph means to estimate coordinates of points between those that are plotted.

irrational number A number that cannot be written as the ratio of two integers.

$\sqrt{2}$, $\sqrt{3}$, and π are irrational numbers.

isometric view A two-dimensional representation, also called a corner view, of a three-dimensional object. It is often drawn on isometric dot paper. For example, a unit cube is shown.

isosceles trapezoid A trapezoid in which the two non-parallel sides are equal in length.

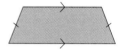

isosceles triangle A triangle with two equal sides.

K

kite A quadrilateral with two pairs of adjacent sides of equal lengths.

L

lateral area The sum of the areas of the lateral faces of a prism.

lateral edge The edge of a prism where two lateral faces meet.

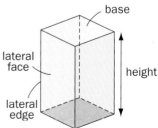

lateral faces The faces of a prism that are not the bases.

legs (of a right triangle) The two sides that form the right angle.

length of the period (of a decimal) The number of digits that repeat in a repeating decimal.

The length of the period of $0.\overline{27}$ is 2.

like terms Terms that have exactly the same variable(s) raised to exactly the same exponent(s).

$3x^2$, $-x^2$, and $2.5x^2$ are like terms.

line of best fit The straight line that best describes the distribution of points in a scatter plot.

line of symmetry A line such that a figure coincides with its reflection image over the line.

line segment The part of a line that joins two points.

linear equation An equation that relates two variables in such a way that orderd pairs that satisfy the equation would form a straight line pattern on a graph.

linear regression A method for determining the linear equation that fits the distribution of points on a scatter plot.

linear relation A relation between two variables that appears as a straight line when graphed on a coordinate system. May also be referred to as a linear function.

lower quartile In a set of numerical data, the number on or below which 25% of the data fall.

lowest common denominator (LCD) The least common multiple of the denominators of two or more rational expressions.

M

manipulate To apply operations, such as addition, multiplication, or factoring, on algebraic expressions.

mass A measure of the quantity of matter in an object, measured in milligrams, grams, kilograms, or tonnes.

mathematical model   A mathematical description of a real situation. The description may include a diagram, a graph, table of values, an equation, a formula, a physical model, or a computer model.

mathematical modelling   The process of describing a real situation in a mathematical form. See also mathematical model.

mean   Sometimes called the arithmetic average, calculated by finding the sum of the data and dividing that sum by the number of pieces of data.

measure of central tendency   A value that can represent a set of data, for example, the mean, the median, or the mode.

median (geometry)   A line segment that joins a vertex of a triangle to the midpoint of the opposite side.

median (statistics)   The middle value when data are arranged in numerical order. If there is an even number of pieces of data, then the median is the arithmetic average of the two middle values.

mixed number   A number that is part whole number and part fraction, such as $4\frac{2}{5}$.

mode   The number (or attribute) that occurs most frequently in a set of data. A set of data may have more than one mode or no mode.

monomial   An algebraic expression with one term.

$7x$ is a monomial.

multiple trials   A technique used in experimentation in which the same experiment is done several times and the results are combined through a measure such as averaging. The use of multiple trials smooths out some of the random occurrences that can affect the outcome of an individual trial of an experiment.

multiplication property of equality   Multiplying both sides of an equation by the same quantity produces an equivalent equation. For any numbers a, b, and c, if $a = b$, then $ac = bc$.

N

natural number   A number in the sequence 1, 2, 3, 4, ….

net   A pattern for constructing a three-dimensional object.

non-linear relation   A relationship between two variables that does not fit a straight line when graphed.

non-probability sampling   An arbitrary method, not based on random selection, of choosing a sample from a population.

non-response bias   Bias that occurs when a large number of the people selected for a sample do not complete the survey.

nonagon   A polygon with nine sides.

numerator   The number of equal parts being considered in the whole or the group: $\frac{5}{7}$ has numerator 5.

O

obtuse angle   An angle that measures more than 90° but less than 180°.

obtuse triangle   A triangle containing one obtuse angle.

octagon   A polygon with eight sides.

ordered pair   Pairs of values in which the second element is related to the first element by a given relation.

origin   The point of intersection of the x-axis and the y-axis on a coordinate grid.

orthocentre   The point of intersection of the three altitudes of a triangle.

orthographic view   A two-dimensional representation of a three-dimensional object showing how it appears from the top, front, and right side.

P

PST   Provincial sales tax.

palindrome   A number or word that reads the same forward and backward.

parallel lines   Lines in the same plane that do not intersect. Non-vertical lines are parallel if they have the same slope. All vertical lines, which have undefined slopes, are parallel.

$m_1 = m_2$

parallelogram   A quadrilateral with two pairs of opposite sides that are parallel.

partial variation   A relationship between two variables in which one variable is a constant multiple of the other, plus some constant. For example, if y varies partially as x, then $y = kx + c$, where k and c are real numbers and $c \neq 0$.

pentagon   A polygon with five sides.

pentomino   A polygon formed by joining five identical squares along whole sides.

percent   A fraction (or ratio) in which the denominator is 100.

percentile rank   If a number is in the nth percentile of a set of numerical data, then n percent of the data lie below that number.

perfect square   A number found by squaring an integer.

perimeter   The distance around a polygon.

period (of a decimal)   The digits that repeat in a repeating decimal. The period of $0.\overline{27}$ is 27.

Pick's formula   When a polygon is formed by joining lattice points, then the area, A, of the polygon can be determined using the equation $A = 0.5P + I - 1$, where P is the number of lattice points on the perimeter and I is the number of lattice points inside the polygon.

perpendicular lines   Two lines that intersect at 90°. Two lines that are not vertical or horizontal are perpendicular if the product of their slopes is −1. A vertical line is perpendicular to a horizontal line.

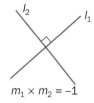

$m_1 \times m_2 = -1$

polygon   A two-dimensional closed figure whose sides are line segments.

point of intersection   The point that is common to two non-parallel lines.

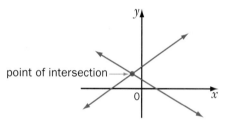

point-slope form of a linear equation   The equation for the line through (x_1, y_1) with slope m, is given by $y - y_1 = m(x - x_1)$.

polyhedron   A three-dimensional object with faces that are polygons.

polynomial expression   An algebraic expression of the form $a + bx + cx^2 + \ldots$, where a, b, and c are numbers.

polyomino   A polygon formed by joining identical squares along whole sides.

population   In statistics, the total number of individuals or items under consideration in a surveying or sampling activity.

power   A product obtained by using a base as a factor one or more times.

5^3 is a power.

primary data-gathering method   Use of a survey or an experiment to collect information.

principal square root The positive square root of a number.

prism A three-dimensional figure with two parallel, congruent polygonal bases. A prism is named by the shape of its bases, for example, rectangular prism, triangular prism.

probability sampling A method of selecting a sample that involves the random selection of units from a population.

proportion An equation that states that two ratios are equal.

proportional reasoning Reasoning or problem solving based on the examination of equal ratios.

pyramid A polyhedron with one base in the shape of a polygon and the same number of lateral triangular faces as there are sides in the base.

Pythagorean theorem The conclusion that, in a right triangle, the square of the length of the longest side is equal to the sum of the squares of the lengths of the other two sides.

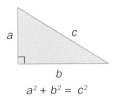

$$a^2 + b^2 = c^2$$

Q

quadrant One of the four regions formed by the intersection of the x-axis and the y-axis.

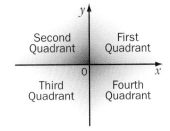

quadrilateral A polygon with four sides.

quotient The result of a division.

R

radical sign The symbol $\sqrt{}$.

random number A number chosen from a set of numbers in such a way that each number has an equally-likely chance of being selected.

random sample A sample in which every member of a population has an equal chance of being selected.

randomization A principle of data analysis that involves selecting a sample in such a way that each member of the population has an equally likely chance of being selected.

range The difference between the greatest and the least values in a set of data.

range of a relation The set of the second elements in a relation.

rate A comparison of two quantities expressed in different units.

$$\frac{9 \text{ m}}{2 \text{ s}} \text{ and } \$4/\text{kg are rates.}$$

ratio A comparison of two quantities with the same units.

rational number A number that can be expressed as the quotient of two integers where the divisor is not zero.

$$0.75, \frac{3}{8}, \text{ and } -2 \text{ are rational numbers.}$$

ray Part of a line extending in one direction without end.

real number A member of the set of all rational and irrational numbers.

rectangle A parallelogram in which each interior angle measures 90°.

rectangular solid A solid whose bases are congruent rectangles.

reflex angle An angle that measures more than 180° but less than 360°.

regression A method for determining the equation of a curve (not necessarily a straight line) that fits the distribution of points on a scatter plot.

regular polygon A polygon with all sides equal and all angles equal.

regular pyramid A polyhedron with a regular polygon as its base and lateral faces that are congruent triangles.

relation An identified relationship between variables that may be expressed as a table of values, a graph, or an equation.

repeating decimal A decimal in which one or more of the digits repeat without end.

representivity A principle of data analysis that involves selecting a sample that is typical of the characteristics of the population from which it is drawn.

response bias Bias that arises from the phrasing or construction of a survey question so that it tends to provoke a particular type of answer.

rhombus A parallelogram in which the lengths of all four sides are equal.

right angle An angle that measures 90°.

right bisector of a line segment A line that is perpendicular to a line segment and divides the line segment into two equal parts.

right cone A cone in which the line segment joining the centre of the base to the vertex is perpendicualr to the base.

right cylinder A cylinder in which the line segment joining the centres of the bases is perpendicular to the bases.

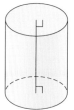

right prism A three-dimensional figure with two parallel, congruent polygonal bases and lateral faces that are perpendicular to the bases.

right triangle A triangle containing a 90° angle.

rise The vertical distance between two points.

run The horizontal distance between two points.

S

sample A small group chosen from a population and examined in order to make predictions about the population.

sampling error The difference between the results obtained by sampling and the truth about the whole population.

sampling technique A process for collecting a sample of data.

scalene triangle A triangle with no sides equal.

scatter plot A graph that attempts to show a relationship between two variables by means of points plotted on a coordinate grid. Also called a scatter diagram.

scientific notation A method of writing large or small numbers that contain many zeros. The number is expressed in the form $a \times 10^n$, where a is greater than or equal to 1 but less than 10, and n is an integer.

scientific probe A device that can be attached to a graphing calculator or to a computer in order to gather data involving measurement such as position, temperature, or force.

second-degree polynomial A polynomial in at least one term of which the variable has the exponent 2, and no term has the exponent of the variable greater than 2.

$x^2 + 5x + 7$ is a second-degree polynomial.

secondary data-gathering method Use of information collected by someone else.

sector A part of a circle bounded by two radii and an arc of the circumference.

selection bias Bias that occurs due to the type of sample selected.

sequence An ordered list of numbers.

simple random sampling Choosing members of a sample at random from the population, where each member has the same probability of being selected.

simplest form The form of a fraction whose numerator and denominator have no common factors other than 1.

simplest form of an algebraic expression An expression that has no like terms. For example, $2x + 7$ is in simplest form, $5x + 1 + 6 - 3x$ is not.

simulation A probability experiment to estimate the likelihood of an event. For example, tossing a coin is a simulation of whether the next person you meet will be male or female.

slant height (of a cone) The distance from the vertex to a point on the edge of the base.

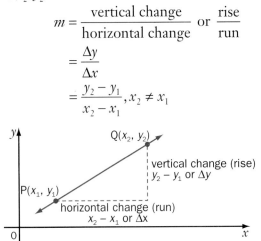

slant height, s

slant height (of a pyramid) The height of each triangular face.

slope A measure of the steepness of a line. The slope of a line, m, containing the points $P(x_1, y_1)$ and $Q(x_2, y_2)$ is

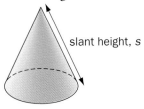

$$m = \frac{\text{vertical change}}{\text{horizontal change}} \text{ or } \frac{\text{rise}}{\text{run}}$$

$$= \frac{\Delta y}{\Delta x}$$

$$= \frac{y_2 - y_1}{x_2 - x_1}, x_2 \neq x_1$$

spreadsheet Computer software that allows the entry of formulas for repeated calculations.

square A rectangle in which the lengths of all four sides are equal.

square root A number that multiplies by itself to give another number.

standard form of a linear equation The equation of a line written in standard form is $Ax + By + C = 0$, where A, B, and C are integers, A and B are not both zero, and x and y represent real numbers.

statistics The science of collecting, organizing, and interpreting data.

stem-and-leaf plot A method of organizing numerical data by using the tens digits in the range of the data as the stems, and listing the units digits of the data beside the stems, in an evenly spaced way to form an instant bar graph.

straight angle An angle that measures 180°.

stratified sampling A method of choosing a sample in which the population is divided into groups, or strata, from which random samples are taken.

substitution Replacing a variable by a value.

subtraction property of equality Subtracting the same quantity from both sides of an equation produces an equivalent equation. For any numbers a, b, and c, if $a = b$, then $a - c = b - c$.

supplementary angles Angles whose sum is 180°.

surface area The number of square units needed to cover the surface of a three-dimensional object.

systematic sampling Choosing members of a sample from a list of the population using a selection interval, k. Every kth member on the list is sampled.

T

table of values   A table used to record the coordinates of points in a relation. For example,

$$y = 2x + 1$$

x	y
−1	−1
0	1
1	3
2	5

term   A number or a variable, or the product or quotient of numbers and variables.

The expression $x^2 + 5x$ has two terms: x^2 and $5x$.

terminating decimal   A decimal whose digits terminate.

tetromino   A polygon formed by joining three identical squares along whole sides.

transversal   A line that crosses or intersects two or more lines.

trapezoid   A quadrilateral with one pair of parallel sides.

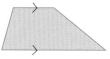

triangle   A polygon with three sides.

triangular pyramid   A polyhedron with a triangular base and three triangular lateral faces.

trinomial   A polynomial with three terms.

$$x^2 + 3x - 1 \text{ is a trinomial.}$$

U

unit price   The cost for one item, or for one unit of measurement.

unit rate   A comparison of two numbers in which the second term is 1, such as $\dfrac{3 \text{ m}}{1 \text{ s}}$ or 3 m/s.

unlike terms   Terms that have different variables, or the same variable but different exponents.

$3x$, $5y$, $-x^2$, and $2ab$ are unlike terms.

upper quartile   In a set of numerical data, the number on or above which 25% of the data fall.

V

variable   A letter or symbol, such as x, used to represent an unspecified number. For example, x and y are variables in the expression $2x + 3y$.

vertex   A point at which two sides of a polygon meet.

volume   The amount of space that an object occupies, measured in cubic units.

W

whole number   A number in the sequence 0, 1, 2, 3, 4, 5, ….

X

***x*-axis**   The horizontal number line in the Cartesian coordinate system.

***x*-coordinate**   The first number in the ordered pair describing a point on a Cartesian grid.

For the point P(4, 7), 4 is the x-coordinate.

***x*-intercept**   The x-coordinate of the point where a line or curve crosses the x-axis.

***xy*-plane**   A coordinate system based on the intersection of two straight lines called axes, which are usually perpendicular. The horizontal axis is the x-axis, and the vertical axis is the y-axis. The point of intersection of the axes is called the origin.

Y

***y*-axis**   The vertical number line in the Cartesian coordinate system.

***y*-coordinate**   The second number in the ordered pair describing a point on a Cartesian grid.

For the point A(5, −2), −2 is the y-coordinate.

***y*-intercept**   The y-coordinate of the point where a line or curve crosses the y-axis.

APPLICATIONS INDEX

Text Credits

xxi "Blizzard Hours" from Environment Canada, *Climates of Canada* by David Phillips, page 60. Reproduced with the permission of the Minister of Public Works and Government Services Canada, 1999; **41** Ian Crysler; **48** Based on map by Robbie Cooke-Voteary; **91** Ontario Ministry of Natural Resources; **96** Reprinted with permission from *The Globe and Mail*; **226** Excerpts from *Literary Lapses* by Stephen Leacock and published by McClelland and Stewart; **332** Excerpts from *Deadly Appearances* by Gail Bowen, © Gail Bowen 1990, published by Douglas & McIntyre. Reprinted by permission of the publisher.

Photo Credits

v Stephen J. Krasemann/VALAN PHOTOS; **vi** Canadian Olympic Association/Ted Grant; **x** COMSTOCK/H. A. Roberts; **xi** Ian Crysler; **xxviii** Stephen J. Krasemann/VALAN PHOTOS; **xx** Vancouver Public Library – Central Branch/Photo: Oi-Lun Kwan; **xxv left** Department of Tourism, Culture and Recreation, Government of Newfoundland and Labrador, right Mailbox provided courtesy of Canada Post Corporation; **xxvi** Mary Russel; **xxvii** John Fowler/VALAN PHOTOS; **xxxii–1** NASA; **4** Blank Archives/Archive Photos; **8–9** The Department of Tourism, Culture and Recreation, Government of Newfoundland and Labrador; **10** First Light; **12** Reproduced by permission of Royal Canadian Mint; **14** COMSTOCK/Russ Kinne; **17** Robert Lankinen/First Light; **19** Andre Gallant/Image Bank; **26** John Mitchell/VALAN PHOTOS; **30** Canapress Photo Service/Kevin Frayer; **32** Canapress Photo Service/David J. Phillip; **38** Darwin Wiggett/First Light; **41** Ian Crysler; **42–43** NASA; **48–49** Amy Knowlton, New England Aquarium; **52 centre** Tony Stone Images/M. De La Sabliere, **top right** COMSTOCK/Brian Thompson, **top left** Thomas Kitchin/First Light, **bottom** Tony Stone Images/Jan Kopec; **56** Ken Straiton/First Light; **59** V. Wilkinson/VALAN PHOTOS; **60** Fotos International/Archive Photos; **65** Canadian Olympic Association/Ted Grant; **70** Ken Straiton/First Light; **72** Tony Stone Images/Bob Thomas; **74** Birks; **79** Canapress Photo Service/Michael Illig; **85** Tony Stone Images/Dan Bosler; **88** Reproduced by permission of Royal Canadian Mint; **89** Canapress Photo Service/Paul Chiasson; **90–91** PhotoDisc; **96–97** Thomas Kitchin/First Light; **100** Ian Crysler; **101** Ian Crysler; **102** Reprinted by permission of *The Liberal*; **108** PhotoDisc; **113** R. Wahlstrom/ Image Bank; **116** Canapress Photo Service/Al Behrman; **118–119 top** COMSTOCK/George Hunter, **bottom** Sherman Hines/Masterfile; **124–125** Ian Crysler; **126** Courtesy Stock Market Place at the Toronto Stock Exchange; **130** National Currency Collection, Bank of Canada, photography James Zagon, Ottawa; **133** NASA; **134** Tony Stone Images/David Young Wolff; **136** Don Ford; **139** Ian Crysler; **140–141** Barros & Barros/Image Bank; **146** *The Gazette*, Montreal; **152** PhotoDisc; **160–161** Tony Stone Images/Don and Pat Valenti; **164–165** Doug MacLellan/Hockey Hall of Fame; **168** Ian Crysler; **169** COMSTOCK; **176** Warren Morgan/First Light; **180** COMSTOCK/H.A.R./Scholz; **182–183** W. Faidley/First Light; **187** CORBIS/Kevin Schafer; **188–189** NASA; **192** UPI/CORBIS-BETTMANN; **195 top left and right, centre left and right** National Archives of Canada / C-011415, **bottom left** Canapress Photo Service/Fred Chartrand, **bottom right** Canapress Photo Service/Tom Hanson; **199** Robert Lankinen/First Light; **204** Don Ford; **209** Tony Stone Images/Paul Kenward; **212** Tony Stone Images/Stewart Cohen, **inset top** Tony Stone Images/Richard Elliott, **inset bottom** T. Joyce/VALAN PHOTOS; **215** Ian Crysler; **216** Ian Crysler; **218, 220** Photos of CBL™ and CBR ™ courtesy of Texas Instruments; **222** © CIDA/ACDI photo: Benoit Aquin; **226** National Archives of Canada/PA110154; **234–235** Corel Corp./#230064; **238–239** Ian Crysler; **240** CORBIS/Roger Ressmeyer; **242** Photo courtesy of Gemini Observatory; **246** First Light; **250** James R. Page/VALAN PHOTOS; **254** NASA Dryden Teacher Resource Center; **259** Trevor Bonderud/First Light; **269** Library of Parliament; **275** First Light; **282** Canadian Olympic Association; **286** First Light; **287** Canadian Olympic Association; **288–289** John E. Sokolowski; **294–295** Ian

Crysler; **304** Canadian Olympic Association; **307** Royal Botanical Gardens; **310** CORBIS/Kevin R. Morris; **313** Canadian Olympic Association; **316** COMSTOCK/Hiroshi Higuchi; **318** Kennon Cooke/VALAN PHOTOS; **319** Masterfile/Damir Frkovic; **321** Canapress Photo Service; **323** Masterfile/J. A. Kraulis; **325** COMSTOCK; **326** Masterfile/Jim Craigmyle; **328** Jack Chow Insurance; **331** Ian Crysler; **332** Gail Bowen; **333** Ian Crysler; **338 top** Tony Stone Images/Andre Perlstein, **centre** Tony Stone Images/Jon Riley, **bottom left** Tony Stone Images/Tamara Reynolds, **bottom right** COMSTOCK; **339 right** Tony Stone Images/Lori Adamski Peek, **left** COMSTOCK; **342** Canadian Olympic Association; **346** Canadian Olympic Association; **350** PhotoDisc; **356–357** The National Archives of Canada, PA-34009; **359** Kennon Cooke/VALAN PHOTOS; **362** COMSTOCK/George Hunter; **364** Bombardier Aerospace; **368** COMSTOCK/Franklin Jay Viola; **371** Canapress Photo Service; **373** Canapress Photo Service/Robert Galbraith; **374** Ian Crysler; **376** Canapress Photo Service/Chuck Stoody; **382** PhotoDisc; **388–389** Kennon Cooke/VALAN PHOTOS; **390** Ian Crysler; **394** Tony Stone Images/Stephen Studd; **403** David Stoecklein/First Light; **404** Canadian Olympic Association; **409** Pat Morrow/First Light; **412–413** Tony Stone Images/Lonny Kalfus; **424** Copyright Air Canada. All rights reserved; **430** COMSTOCK/Jack Clark; **434** Tony Stone Images/Mark Wagner; **439** Ron Watts/First Light; **450–451** NASA; **456** COMSTOCK/Steve Vidler; **462–463** Don Ford; **466** COMSTOCK/H.A. Roberts; **473** Don Ford; **475** Ian Crysler; **476** Tom W. Parkin/VALAN PHOTOS; **481** Ian Crysler; **486** Ian Crysler; **487** Ian Crysler; **488** COMSTOCK/Hiroshi Higuchi; **494** COMSTOCK; **496** Habitat'67, The Safdie Archive, Canadian Architecture Collection, McGill University; **499** Hydro-Quebec; **502–503** Tony Stone Images/Peter Dazeley; **520** Royal Canadian Mint, Winnipeg Facility; **528** Ian Crysler; **532** Canadian Olympic Association/Claus Anderson; **549** COMSTOCK; **550–551** Ian Crysler; **555** Ian Crysler; **557 top** COMSTOCK, **bottom** Kennon Cooke/VALAN PHOTOS

Illustration Credits

vii Michael Herman; **xxvii** Bernadette Lau; **xxviii** Michael Herman; **36** Michael Herman; **45** Michael Herman; **48** Deborah Crowle; **86** Bernadette Lau; **96** Deborah Crowle; **105** Michael Herman; **108** Margo Davies Leclair/Visual Sense Illustration; **144** Michael Herman; **145** Michael Herman; **154–155** Michael Herman; **190** Margo Davies Leclair/Visual Sense Illustration; **225** Michael Herman; **296** Michael Herman; **298** Bernadette Lau; **305** Michael Herman; **390** Patrick Fitzgerald; **434** Peter Cook; **442** Peter Cook; **443** Michael Herman; **495** Jun Park; **501** Teco Rodrigues; **503** Teco Rodrigues; **508–509** Bernadette Lau; **537** Bernadette Lau; **552** Clarence Porter

Technical Art
Tom Dart, Bruce Krever, Alana Perez
First Folio Resource Group, Inc.